Associative Processing and Processors

Associative Processing and Processors

Anargyros Krikelis
Charles C. Weems

IEEE
COMPUTER
SOCIETY

Los Alamitos, California

Washington • Brussels • Tokyo

Library of Congress Cataloging-in-Publication Data

Associative processing and processors / Anargyros Krikelis, Charles C. Weems.
        p.   cm.
    Includes bibliographical references.
    ISBN 0-8186-7661-2
    1. Associative storage.   2. Parallel processing (Electronic computers)
3. Microprocessors.   4. Computer architecture.
I. Krikelis, Anargyros.   II. Weems, Charles C.
TK7895.M4A78   1997
004.5—dc21   97-5921
                                                            CIP

IEEE Computer Society Press Order Number BP07661
Library of Congress Number 97-5921
ISBN 0-8186-7661-2

Additional copies can be ordered from

IEEE Computer Society Press Customer Service Center 10662 Los Vaqueros Circle P.O. Box 3014 Los Alamitos, CA 90720-1314 Tel: (714) 821-8380 Fax: (714) 821-4641 Email: cs.books@computer.org	IEEE Service Center 445 Hoes Lane P.O. Box 1331 Piscataway, NJ 08855-1331 Tel: (908) 981-1393 Fax: (908) 981-9667 mis.custserv@computer.org	IEEE Computer Society 13, avenue de l'Aquilon B-1200 Brussels BELGIUM Tel: +32-2-770-2198 Fax: +32-2-770-8505 euro.ofc@computer.org	IEEE Computer Society Ooshima Building 2-19-1 Minami-Aoyama Minato-ku, Tokyo 107 JAPAN Tel: +81-3-3408-3118 Fax: +81-3-3408-3553 tokyo.ofc@computer.org

Publisher: Matt Loeb
Technical Editor: Jon Butler
Acquisitions Editor: Bill Sanders
Developmental Editor: Cheryl Smith
Advertising/Promotions: Tom Fink
Production Editor: Lisa O'Conner
Cover image Copyright © 1994, Archive Photos and Picture Network International, Ltd.
Cover design by Walzak Advertising & Design, Inc.

Printed in the United States of America by Braun-Brumfield, Inc.

Contents

Section III—Associative Processing Software

Section IV—Associative Processing Applications

Section V—Associative Processing and Neural Computation

Preface

This book appears at a time when associative processing re-emerges as one of the most interesting topics in computer science, both from theoretical and practical viewpoints. Existing computing models, especially supercomputing and parallel processing architectures, are too expensive and, sometimes, too narrow for the ever expanding user requirements. There is increasing evidence that the associative processing paradigm may be a better and more cost-effective alternative for a variety of applications. In addition, the nature of associative programming constitutes a natural bridge between the classical von Neumann computer architectures and newly emerging neural and genetic computational approaches. Although associative processors designs were initially proposed over thirty years ago, their semiconductor implementation was considered to be too costly in comparison to traditional memory and logic devices. However, progress in microelectronics has greatly reduced the implementation cost of practical associative systems, and they can now be viewed as an inexpensive alternative to complex and costly parallel processing arrays.

This book presents a collection of original papers together with selected papers from recent issues of *Computer* and *IEEE Micro* magazines. It is a cross-disciplinary presentation of the fundamentals, architectures, hardware, software, and applications of associative processing. The goal of this book is to offer a vertically integrated presentation of the capabilities of associative processing and processors which can be used as reference by post-graduate students, researchers, and engineers active in the areas of associative processing, massively parallel processing, and numerical and non-numerical applications of associative processing and processors. This goal is achieved by discussing the problems and solutions of practical implementations of associative processing and processors, highlighting strengths and weaknesses of associative processing models and architectural paradigms, and addressing associative processing software and applications.

The book is organized into five parts: Associative Processing, Associative Processing Architectures and Systems, Associative Processing Software, Associative Processing Applications and Associative Processing and Neural Computation.

Associative Processing

Associative processing is a totally different way of storing, manipulating, and retrieving data compared to traditional computational techniques. Its main feature is a more intelligent memory implementation, which can offload some of the data processing burden from the main processing unit and, furthermore, reduce the volume of data routinely passed between the execution unit and the storage unit. In this part, the contributed works review and discuss the principles of associative processing, the organization of simple associative processing structures, and basic algorithms and hardware features that are used to perform data search and selection. In addition, methods and implementation techniques are discussed which can simultaneously apply a number of dissimilar associative processing primitives (an approach known as multi-associative processing).

Associative Processing Architectures and Systems

There is a considerable amount of ongoing research activity associated with the definition, specification, implementation, demonstration, and evaluation of associative processing architectures and systems. This part of the book includes contributions from many of the leading efforts in this area. The applications targeted in such efforts are among the most computationally demanding, for example, computer vision, genetic computing, design rule checking of integrated circuit layouts, and so on. It is typical of associative processing systems to meet these demands with simple but massively-parallel processing structures, usually involving a bit-serial arithmetic unit and a few tens of bits of associative memory per processing element. Two of the contributions in this part also describe optoelectronic schemes for the implementation of associative processing systems, which offer potential advantages in storage, speed, and interconnection capabilities over traditional electronic implementations.

Associative Processing Software

Widespread use of associative computing techniques depends on the availability of programming paradigms, environments, and structures to facilitate efficient expression, implementation, and execution of associative processing. This part of the book presents activities that employ two-dimensional tables as a basic parallel data structure for use in both numerical and non-numerical computing. The tabular data structure provides a natural and understandable data organization for many computing applications, while the concept of processing an entire column/row of a table in parallel is easy to comprehend. The compiler optimization known as common sub-expression elimination is used to demonstrate the functionality and performance of associative computing models and techniques.

Associative Processing Applications

Associative processing holds promise for numerous application areas. In particular, associative processing is finding widespread utility in artificial intelligence. Two of the contributions to this part of the book describe such applications: a speech-to-speech translation system which has the potential to enable individuals speaking different languages to communicate in real-time using interpreting telephony, and a Prolog implementation using an associative processing system that achieves performance that is comparable with dedicated Prolog engines. Two other contributions to this part are concerned with the acceleration of three-dimensional graphics computations using associative processing systems. They describe the mapping of image rendering algorithms and the implementation of data structures for ray tracing on associative processing systems.

Associative Processing and Neural Computation

The field of neural computation has in recent years moved from a research curiosity to commercial fruition. In some ways, neural computation and associative processing are parallel fields of inquiry because a neural network, in terms of its computational capability, is essentially equivalent to an associative processor. This relationship is the subject of this last part of the book. These contributions describe the theoretical and functional similarities of neural networks and associative memories, the implementation of associative processing systems using neural associative memories as processing elements, and the mapping of neural computing onto more conventional associative processing systems.

Acknowledgments

Organizing the November 1994 issue of *Computer* Magazine and the publication of this book has been a very rewarding experience. The wealth of work described in both publications indicates that the interdisciplinary aspects of the field of associative processing and processors continue to be energetic and to expand. It has been a great pleasure to consider the work of such spirited colleagues for this book.

This book would not have been possible without the suggestion by Prof. Jon T. Butler, while he was Editor-in-Chief of *Computer*, who indicated the opportunity for such a publication emerging from the November 1994 issue. Indeed, Prof. Butler was instrumental in the publication of this book in his later capacity as Editor-in-Chief of IEEE Computer Society Press. We are grateful to the authors who contributed to this book for agreeing to have their work included and for persevering with our efforts to publish it. Finally, the production of this book has significantly benefited from the very capable staff of the IEEE Computer Society Press; we are especially grateful to Lisa O'Conner, our Production Editor, who so efficiently and with patience supervised the publication of the book.

Anargyros (Argy) Krikelis and Charles C. Weems
May 1997

Section I
Associative Processing

Associative Processing and Processors

Charles C. Weems
Department of Computer Science
University of Massachusetts, Amherst
Amherst, MA 01003
weems@cs.umass.edu

Anargyros Krikelis
Aspex Microsystems Ltd.
Brunel University
Uxbridge, UB8 3PH
United Kingdom
Argy.Krikelis@aspex.co.uk

Accordingly, therefore, when one wishes to recollect, this is what he will do: He will try to obtain a beginning of a movement whose sequel shall be the movement he desires to reawaken.

—Aristotle, *"On Memory and Reminiscence"*

Introduction

Since at least the time of Aristotle, people have recognized the associative nature of human memory—that one idea may trigger the recall of a different but related idea. For example, thinking of the word "blue" may trigger the recall of the word "sky," because sky has associated with it the attribute of being blue. Traditional computers, however, rely on a memory design that stores and retrieves data by its address rather than its content. Thus, to discover that "sky" is associated with "blue," the computer must either already know the address of the data associated with "sky" or search its memory, using "blue" as the key. In such a search, every accessed data word must travel individually between the processing unit and the memory.

The simplicity of this retrieval-by-address approach has ensured its success but has also produced some inherent disadvantages. One is the von Neumann bottleneck, where the memory-access path becomes the limiting factor for system performance. A related disadvantage is the inability to proportionally increase the size of a unit transfer between the memory and the processor as the size of the memory scales up. Associative memory, in contrast, provides a naturally parallel and scalable form of data retrieval for both structured data (for example, sets, arrays, tables, trees, and graphs) and unstructured data (raw text and digitized signals). As we show, an associative memory can be easily extended to process the retrieved data in place, thus becoming an associative processor. This extension is merely the capability for writing a value in parallel into selected cells.

A Brief History

Associative processing has its modern antecedent in a thought experiment proposed by Vannevar Bush [2] in 1945. Bush envisioned a database machine called MEMEX that would help people cope with the ever-growing body of general knowledge by storing textual information and retrieving it. His machine was to have three modes of access: sequential, successive selection of subclasses, and associative. In the last mode, the user would enter keywords or phrases, and all texts containing these words or phrases would be recalled. Twelve years later, Slade and McMahon [8] succeeded in taking the first step toward creating an electronic digital associative memory. In their system, called the Cryotron Catalog Memory, a pattern of bits was input in parallel to the memory, and an output line indicated whether a match was found. The Cryotron Catalog Memory could tell the user whether a pattern was found in memory but could not return associated information.

The golden age. In the sixties and seventies, interest in associative memory (sometimes called content-addressable memory, or CAM) grew rapidly with many machines being proposed and built [3, 4]. All of the designs in this period let users query the memory for an exact match to a broadcast value called the comparand. As an analogy, consider a classroom in which the teacher asks the students "Whose name begins with the letter A?" and those students who meet this criterion raise their hands. In an associative memory, the equivalent of hand-raising is setting a "responder" bit associated with each memory word whose value matches the comparand. By quickly looking at the class, the teacher can determine if any students have their hands up; similarly, the associative memory includes a circuit that returns the logical OR of the responder bits (usually called a Some/None response). With slightly more difficulty the teacher could count the number of raised hands, and indeed some associative memories also provide a responder-count circuit. The teacher could also ask one of the students to say his or her name; likewise an associative memory could select one of the responding words and read out its contents.

Implementing associative processing. In a typical design of this period, each word in the associative memory was quite long (say, 256 bits) to permit the storage of a record data structure. Although modern designs try to use shorter words, they retain many features of these earlier designs. A global mask register selects the fields of the records for matching, as shown in Figure 1. The mask register also supports queries based on inequalities to select all cells with a field in a certain range, or cells with the maximum value in a field. This process uses algorithms to manipulate the global mask to emulate a bit-serial processor, as shown by the algorithm in Figure 2.

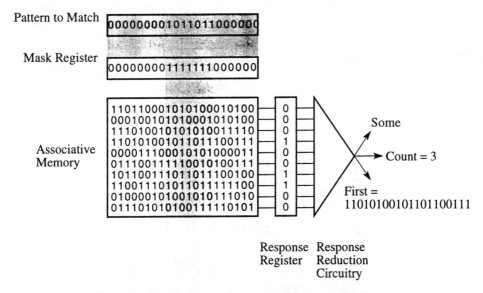

Figure 1. Typical associative memory organization.

```
SELECT ALL CELLS
Active := 1;
FOR Column := Highest to Lowest DO
        SELECT CELLS WITH Bit[Column] = 1 AND Active = 1
        IF Some Responders THEN
                SELECT CELLS WITH Bit[Column] = 0 AND Active = 1
                Active := 0
```

Figure 2. Bit-serial algorithm for selecting cells with the maximum value in a field.

Thus, a set of records can be identified by matching a key field, and an associated piece of information can be read from the first of these responders. We can turn off the response bit of the first responder and select another word for output. This operation can be repeated for all responders if we want to read out all information associated with the matches to the key. For example, we might select the first letter of the name field of all records, broadcast "A" as the comparand, and sequentially read out each name that begins with "A". However, sequentially reading values from the associative memory is time-consuming and fails to take advantage of the potential for parallel processing. For example, a teacher could subsequently say, "If you have your hand up, write down the following words." The *associative processor* is an associative memory that can write a value in parallel into the responding words. In many cases, this multiwrite capability makes it possible to perform the required data processing entirely within the associative processor rather than sending the data word by word to the CPU.

Simple associative processors

We divide associative processors into one of four major classes, based on how they access their memory words and bits, as follows.

Bit-serial, word-serial associative processors. This primitive associative processor structure, operating in a word sequential manner, is included here only for the sake of completeness. A single bit of the masked comparand is compared with a single bit from one word in each cycle. The words and bits can either be addressed or, as shown in Figure 3, be circulated serially through the comparator and back to memory.

Bit-serial, word-parallel associative processors. In this implementation, a single bit of the masked comparand is broadcast to a set of single-bit comparators, each of which is associated with one memory word. The bit columns of the memory structure can be selected by addressing or, as shown in Figure 4, each word can be circulated through its corresponding comparator. This approach is similar to that of bit-serial SIMD (single instruction, multiple data) processor arrays. Many modern associative processors employ this approach because it permits the use of low-cost standard memory cells and chips. Also, as noted previously, many associative processing operations such as inequality comparisons are implemented by accessing the data bit-serially through manipulation of the mask register.

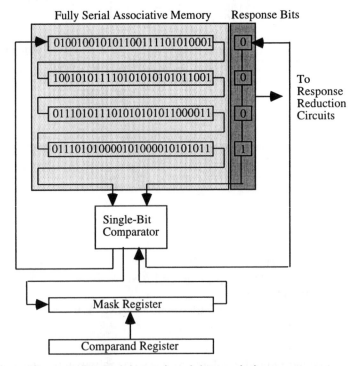

Figure 3. Bit-serial, word-serial associative processor.

4

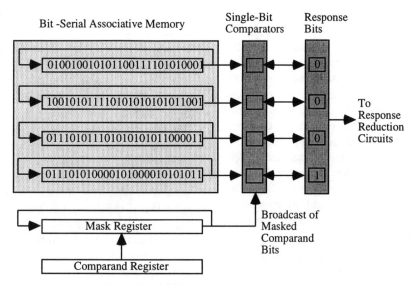

Figure 4. Bit-serial, word-parallel associative processor.

Bit-parallel, word-serial associative processors.
This structure operates in a word sequential manner.
Search operations are implemented by performing a
bit-parallel comparison between the masked comparand and one stored word in each cycle. Figure 5
shows an implementation in which the words circulate
through a word-wide comparator, but a conventional
addressed memory could also be used to fetch one
word at a time. A uniprocessor emulating an associative processor would take this approach. Low-cost
associative processors have been built along these
lines, using recirculating memory technologies such as
delay lines, in which all of the data automatically
flows past a processor as it is refreshed.

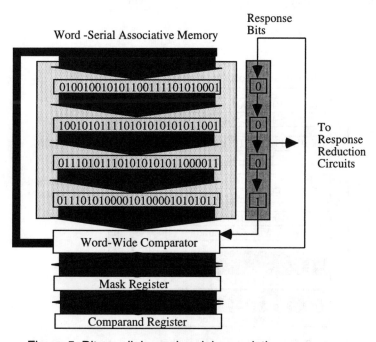

Figure 5. Bit-parallel, word-serial associative processor.

Bit-parallel, word-parallel associative processors. This structure represents the most powerful implementation of the generic associative processors. The fully parallel associative memory incorporates a word-wide comparator in every row of the associative memory, as shown in Figure 6. Often we implement it by constructing the memory so that every bit cell includes a comparison circuit. The match outputs of the bit-cells are wire-ANDed across each word and connected to the corresponding responder bit. Thus, for exact match operations, it is more than an order of magnitude faster than the bit-serial, word-parallel structure. One well-known application of this structure is in fully associative cache memories; another that is seeing wider use is in the storage of network router tables.

Low utilization. Associative architectures provide a tremendous quantity of potential parallelism—a simultaneous operation on every word of memory. However, in these simple designs, this potential is often highly underutilized because the number of responders to a query is often a small percentage of the data set. When processing is constrained to just the responders, the vast majority of the potential parallelism may sit idle. One argument that addresses this issue is that if parallelism becomes as inexpensive as memory, such underutilization is no more of a waste than the fact that large portions of memory in sequential computers are often empty and, even when memory is full, the sequential processor can utilize only one cell at a time. However, even if one ignores this argument, more modern designs are able to greatly increase the level of utilization for many tasks through techniques such as multiassociative processing, as described below.

Input, output, and oversized data sets. One significant problem that faces the developer of an associative processing application is the cost of input and output. While the simple associative processors address the bottleneck between the processor and memory, they do nothing to improve I/O bandwidth. Unless the data can remain in the associative processor and be used over and over again (as in the case of network router tables), performance may be no better than a sequential processor. To see the reason for this, consider that if the data set is loaded into the associative processor and a single search operation is executed, then the same search could be performed by a sequential processor as it inputs the data set into its normal memory. The parallelism of the associative processor must be applied many times to the data set before there is a significant benefit. Fortunately, such applications do exist, but even then another problem can arise that has a similar effect. If the data set is larger than the associative processor can hold, then it must be processed in pieces, with the pieces being input and output after each is processed. The effect of virtualizing a simple associative processor in this manner is to again reduce its performance to the level of a sequential processor unless a large number of operations can be executed on each piece of the data set before moving on to the next. Although there are applications with this nature, they are not commonplace. Fortunately, extensions to the traditional models address these problems.

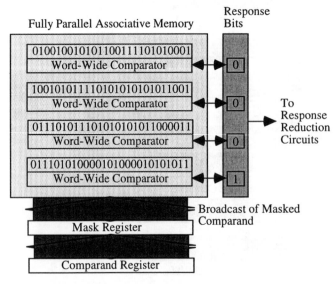

Figure 6. Bit-parallel word-parallel associative processor.

Extensions to the simple model

We can extend an associative processor with a processing unit (PU) for each word of memory to accelerate arithmetic and logical operations. With this extension, the associative processor begins to look like a traditional SIMD array. The major difference is that the memory words themselves contain the comparison logic that enables matching to be done in parallel with very wide data words. In some designs, the comparison logic is deleted from the memory in favor of standard memory, and the PUs fetch fields from memory, performing the comparison and setting a response tag. Such a processor can have a much larger memory built from standard RAM chips, and thus handle much larger data sets without having to virtualize the processors. The only factors that distinguish such a design from a SIMD array are

- the provision of logic in the central control unit to emulate the mask register of the CAM,
- support in the processors for one or more dedicated response tags, and
- (usually) a greater emphasis on rapid summary of results from the array (for example, a dedicated adder tree that counts the responders in one or more cycles.)

If we add a communication network to the associative processor, allowing data to move between cells, we can then implement searches based on the contents of neighboring or even distant locations. This capability is especially useful for applications associated with signal and image processing and data visualization.

Linear network. Most early associative processors employed a simple one-dimensional communication network that enabled data to be shifted along the length of the memory array in either of two directions. The linear network also allowed programmers to treat groups of smaller memory cells as one larger cell. Furthermore, a linear network also supports signal processing algorithms in which two digitized signals can be shifted with respect to each other. However, the network is a bottleneck for algorithms requiring more complex communication patterns.

Sorting and reconfigurable networks. The Goodyear STARAN associative processor [7] was the first commercially available system to address this limitation by including a sophisticated sorting network. Unfortunately, such networks are expensive additions to an associative processor, which otherwise is very low cost. One compensating advantage, however, is that these networks can greatly relieve the I/O bottleneck of traditional designs by providing highly parallel I/O channels. More recent designs have employed networks with simpler topologies, such as linear, comb, and mesh that can also reconfigure dynamically. In these networks, the cells can be partitioned into groups that are independent segments of the underlying network topology. Figure 7 shows this partitioning of a mesh network. The partitioning affects the responder summary circuitry as well as the transfer of data values among processors. Once partitions have been established, the central controller can select a master processor within each partition to broadcast values to the partition and receive the responder summaries. In effect, the associative processor can split itself into multiple smaller parallel processors, all of

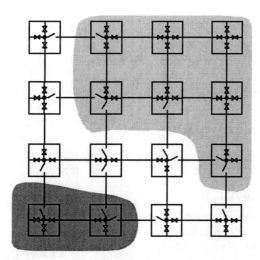

Figure 7. A reconfigurable mesh network connecting associative processing elements. Links between elements have opened at boundaries of regions in an image that is being processed.

which are directed by a single instruction stream while performing their own local searches.

Red cars. As an example of how this partitioning adds computational power, consider a search in a standard associative processor. Here, a query that requests a count of red cars for each state would require the central control to first select all red cars, then sequentially select each of the fifty states and count the responders. With a partitionable network, however, if the data is arranged properly, the central control directs the array to partition itself by state and has every partition select and count red cars. Effectively, the associative operation of the array is multiplied by the number of partitions. This mode of operation is therefore called multiassociative computation. It is exemplified in recent machines such as the Associative String Processor (ASP) [6] and the Content Addressable Array Parallel Processor (CAAPP) [9].

Reconfigurable networks have a wide range of applicability, and are especially useful in speech processing (linear networks) and image understanding (two-dimensional mesh networks) where they permit the data partitioning at feature boundaries such as phoneme breaks or regions of an image. These domains are particularly suited to multiassociative processing because the input data has a predetermined temporal or spatial organization that is easily mapped to a particular network topology. The data processing also can involve partitioning according to various feature measures, followed by further analysis of the partitions and their relationships to each other [5, 10]. For example, Figure 7 can be viewed as a mesh network that is partitioned along region boundaries in an image.

References

[1] J.I. Bear, "De memoria et reminiscentia," in *The Works of Aristotle,* W.D. Ross, Ed., Vol. 3, Oxford, Clarendon Press, 1931.

[2] V. Bush, "As We May Think," *Atlantic Monthly*, Vol. 176, July 1945, p. 101.

[3] R.H. Fuller, "Content-Addressable Memory Systems," Ph.D. Thesis, UCLA, June 1960.

[4] A.G. Hanlon, "Content-Addressable and Associative Memory Systems," *IEEE Trans. Electronic Computers*, Vol. EC-15, No. 4, Aug. 1966, pp. 509–521.

[5] A. Krikelis, "Computer Vision Applications with the Associative String Processor," *J. Parallel and Distributed Computing*, Vol. 13, No. 2, Oct. 1991, pp. 170–184.

[6] R.M. Lea, "ASP: A Cost-effective Parallel Microcomputer," *IEEE Micro*, Oct. 1988, pp. 10–29.

[7] J.A. Rudolph, "A Production Implementation of an Associative Array Processor: STARAN," *Proc. AFIPS 1972, Fall Joint Computer Conf.*, Vol. 41, Part 1, AFIPS Press, Montvale, N.J., 1972, pp. 229–241.

[8] A.E. Slade and H.O. McMahon, "A Cryotron Catalog Memory," *Proc. Eastern Joint Computer Conf.,* 1956.

[9] C.C. Weems and D. Rana, "Reconfiguration in the Low and Intermediate Levels of the Image Understanding Architecture," in *Reconfigurable SIMD Parallel Processors*, Hungwen Li and Quentin Stout, eds., Prentice Hall, Englewood Cliffs, N.J., 1991.

[10] C.C. Weems et al., "The DARPA Image Understanding Benchmark for Parallel Computers," *J. Parallel and Distributed Computing*, Vol. 11, No. 1, Jan. 1991, pp. 1–24.

Appendix I: Advantages of Associative Processors

Associative processors offer unique features that lead to cost-effective system solutions. Exploiting the current trend of microelectronics, the cost, density, and access time of associative memory approaches that of conventional memory designs while providing significantly more powerful functionality. In addition, associative processing systems offer distinctive advantages over other parallel processors such as:

- **Processor location address elimination.** Due to the associative nature of data selection and processing, there is no need to use addresses to access the processors in a system implementation; processors participate in an operation only on the basis of the data they hold.

- **Simplified system design.** The system backplane does not need a processor address bus; in its place equivalent backplane area can be used for system enhancements.

- **System scalability.** Because an associative processor is not bounded by the addressing range of the address bus, a system originally designed with a number of associative processors can scale up with advances in microelectronics. It is thus more independent of technology than conventional processors.

- **Fault-tolerance.** This is an especially important design element in massively parallel processing systems. Once a fault is detected, it is easily bypassed in associative processors because data to be processed can be distributed on 'good' processors without the need for program changes.

- **Low-power dissipation,** This is another increasingly significant design issue in large systems, especially for real-time applications. Associative processors can use their built-in selection capability to substantially reduce the system's power dissipation. Nonselected processors (that is, processors that do not participate in an operation) can automatically switch to low-power operation.

Appendix II: Additional Bibliography

Articles related to associative processing and processors have been widely published in books, journals and proceedings. In addition to the cited references, we recommend the following important and accessible works.

Books

C. Fernstrom, I. Kruzela, and B. Svensson, *LUCAS Associative Array Processor*, Springer-Verlag, Berlin, 1985.

C.C. Foster, *Content Addressable Parallel Processors*, Van Nostrand Reinhold, New York, 1976.

E. Hinton and J.A. Anderson, eds*., Parallel Models of Associative Memory*, Lawrence Erlbaum Associates, Hillsdale, N.J., 1989 (updated edition).

T. Kohonen, *Content Addressable Memories*, Springer-Verlag, Berlin, 1980.

T. Kohonen, *Self-organization and Associative Memory*, Springer Verlag, Berlin, 1984.

D. W. Lewin, "Introduction to Associative Processors", in *Computer Architecture*, A.K. Boulaye and D.W. Lewin, eds., D. Reidel, Amsterdam, 1977, pp. 217–234.

J.L. Potter, *Associative Computing—A Programming Paradigm for Massively Parallel Computers*, Plenum, New York, 1992.

Journals

K.E. Batcher, "Bit Serial Parallel Processing Systems", *IEEE Trans. Computers*, Vol. C-31, No. 5, May 1982, pp. 377–384.

C.A. Finnila and H.H. (Jr) Love, "The Associative Linear Array Processor," *IEEE Trans. Computers*, Vol. C-26, No. 2, Feb. 1977, pp. 112–125.

C.C. Foster and F.D. Stockton, "Counting Responders in an Associative Memory," *IEEE Trans. Computers*, Vol. C-31, No. 12, Dec. 1971, pp. 1580–1583.

IEEE Micro, Special Issue on Associative Memories and Processors—Parts 1 and 2, June and Dec. 1992.

R.M. Lea and I.P. Jalowiecki, "Associative Massively Parallel Processors," *Proc IEEE*, Vol. 79, No. 4, Apr. 1991, pp. 469–479.

J. Minker, "An Overview of Associative of Content Addressable Memory Systems and a KWIC Index to the Literature: 1956–1970, *ACM Computing Reviews*, Oct. 1971.

B. Parhami, "Associative Memories and Processors: An Overview and Selected Bibliography," *Proc. IEEE*, Vol. 61, No. 3, June 1973, pp. 722–730.

K.J. Thurber and L.D. Wald, "Associative and Parallel Processors," *Computing Surveys*, Vol. 7, No. 4, Dec. 1975, pp. 215–255.

S.S. Yau and H.S. Fung, "Associative Processor Architecture—A Survey," *Computing Surveys*, Vol. 9, No. 1, Mar. 1977, pp. 3–27.

Proceedings

R.H. Fuller, "Associative Parallel Processing," *Proc. Spring Joint Computer Conf.*, 1967, AFIPS.

Search and Data Selection Algorithms for Associative Processors

Behrooz Parhami
University of California
Department of Electrical and Computer Engineering
Santa Barbara, CA
parhami@ece.ucsb.edu

Abstract

Associative or content-addressable memories (AMs, CAMs) have been studied and used as mechanisms for speeding up time-consuming searches and for allowing access to data by name or partial content rather than by location or address. Also, more functional variants of such systems known as associative or content-addressable processors (APs, CAPs) have been the subjects of extensive research. Since AMs are essentially simple APs, we will use the term "AP" to refer to both AMs and APs. Many algorithms have been developed for performing search, retrieval, and arithmetic/logic operations on data stored in APs. In this paper, search and data selection algorithms for both fully parallel and bit-serial APs are reviewed and analyzed. Search and selection functions covered include exact-match, inexact-match (numerical or logical proximity), membership (multiple match), relational (<, ≤ >, ≥), interval (between limits), extrema (max, min, next higher, next lower), rank-based selection (kth or k largest/smallest), and ordered retrieval (sorting). Hardware features that facilitate or speed up these algorithms are also described. In addition to several algorithms being presented for the first time, discussions touch on two topics that have been inadequately covered in previous treatments: (1) Worst-case and average-case complexity analyses and (2) effects of hardware features and implementation details on the performance of search and data selection algorithms.

1   Introduction

Associative or content-addressable memories (AMs, CAMs) have been studied as mechanisms for speeding up time-consuming searches and for allowing access to data by name or partial content, rather than by location or address, since the advent of electronic digital computers. Also, more functional variants of such systems known as associative or content-addressable processors (APs, CAPs) have been the subjects of extensive research and development. Because AMs are essentially simple APs, we will use the term "AP" to refer to both AMs and APs.

Table 1 summarizes the events and advances of the past half century leading to modern APs of the 1990s. It also points to some key references for further study. The term "bit-ops" in the performance column stands for "bit operations per second."

Table 1. Entering the second half century of associative processing.

Decade	Events and Advances	Technology	Performance	Key References
1940s	Formulation of need and concept	Relays		[3], [37]
1950s	Emergence of cell technologies	Magnetic, Cryogenic	Megabit-ops	[33]
1960s	Introduction of basic architectures	Transistors		[10], [12]
1970s	Commercialization and applications	ICs	Gigabit-ops	[22], [36]
1980s	Focus on system/software issues	VLSI	Terabit-ops	[4], [17]
1990s	Scalable and flexible architectures	ULSI, WSI	Petabit-ops?	[11], [19]

Many algorithms have been developed for performing search, retrieval, and arithmetic/logic operations on data stored in APs. Such operations can be programmed using the basic masked exact-match search capability of simple AMs, but the provision of other types of hardware aids can have a significant effect on performance. Starting with the pioneering works of Falkoff [7] and Estrin and Fuller [6], research in AP algorithms and associated hardware speedup techniques has continued to the present [5], [8], [15], [16], [20], [32].

Even though bit-serial arithmetic operations can be programmed on virtually all APs, and special hardware features have been implemented or suggested in AP systems for facilitating or speeding up numerical computations, the primary focus of AP implementation efforts and research studies has been searching and other nonnumeric functions. In addition to simple exact-match search, many other search types have been implemented as primitives for data manipulation and retrieval functions. The basic search types are defined below:

- *Exact-match search*—locating data based on partial knowledge of contents.

- *Inexact-match searches*—finding numerically or logically proximate values.

- *Membership searches*—identifying all members of a particular set.

- *Relational searches*—determining values that are less than, less or equal, etc.

- *Interval searches*—marking items that are between limits or not between limits.

- *Extrema searches*—max- or min-finding, next higher, next lower.

- *Rank-based selection*—selecting kth or k largest/smallest elements.

- *Ordered retrieval*—repeated max- or min-finding with elimination (sorting).

In this paper, we illustrate hardware/software algorithms for such search functions along with the rich collection of techniques used for implementing them efficiently on both fully parallel and bit-serial AP architectures. More important, we show that despite the simplicity and intuitiveness of some of the algorithms, sophisticated optimization and analysis techniques are needed to achieve the best possible speedups with given hardware capabilities.

2   Background and assumptions

In its simplest form, an AP can be viewed as a hardware device consisting of N fixed-size cells, each being marked as empty or storing a W-bit data word or record (see Figure 1). The number of nonempty AP cells is denoted by n ($n \leq N$). Other notation is defined

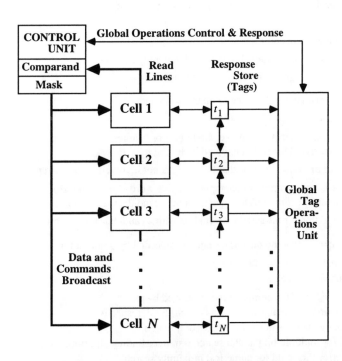

Figure 1. Functional view of an associative processor.

in subsection 2.2 and Table 2 following some needed background on AP architectures.

2.1   Architectural variations

Architecturally, associative processors come in four basic varieties depending on how they handle the processing of multiple words (records) and multiple bits in a word. These varieties, described in the following paragraphs are known as fully parallel, bit-serial, word-serial, and block-oriented [22].

Fully parallel (word-parallel, bit-parallel) APs have comparison logic associated with each bit of stored data. In simple exact-match searches, the logic associated with each bit generates a local match or mismatch signal. These local signals are then combined to produce the cell match or mismatch result. In more complicated searches, the bit logic typically receives partial search results from a neighboring bit position and generates partial results to be passed on to the next bit position. Although lookahead techniques can speed up the propagation of partial search results, they are seldom used in view of their high cost and marginal performance impact.

Bit-serial (word-parallel, bit-serial) systems process an entire bit slice of data, containing one bit of every word, simultaneously, but go through multiple bits of the search field sequentially. Bit-serial systems have been dominant in practice since they allow the most cost-effective implementations using low-cost, high-density, off-the-shelf RAM chips. However, fully parallel systems have also been implemented, particularly for applications that require high performance in the basic masked exact-match search capability.

Word-serial (word-serial, bit parallel) APs based on electronic circulating memories constitute hardware implementation of a programmed linear search. Even though several such systems were built in the 1960s, they are no longer cost-effective with today's technology.

Table 2. List of variables and symbols used in this paper.

Term	Definition or Meaning
'	Prime: Denotes logical complement (for example, c'_j is the logical complement of c_j)
b_{ij}	Strictly between-limits signal for cell i up to and including d_{ij}
c_j, C_j	Comparand's jth bit
d_{ij}	Bit j of the data word in cell i
e_{ij}, E_{ij}	Equal (exact-match) signal for cell i up to and including d_{ij}
g_{ij}, G_{ij}	Strictly greater-than signal for cell i up to and including d_{ij}
$g_{ij}^{(m)}$	Minimally greater-than signal for cell i up to and including d_{ij}
h_j	Hamming distance indicator for word j
k	Rank selection parameter (for example, kth largest or k largest)
l_{ij}, L_{ij}	Strictly less-than signal for cell i up to and including d_{ij}
m_j	Mask word's jth bit; $m_j = 0$ means that bit-slice j is not involved in the search
N, n	AP size in words and number of nonempty or active words (problem size)
S_{wrx}	Expected time for selecting the rth largest among x candidates in a w-bit field
T_{wx}	Expected search time for bit-serial max-finding with x candidates in a w-bit field
$T_{wx}^{(\gamma)}$	Same as T_{wx}, except that the bit-serial search is preceded by a search for the all-ones pattern in a subfield of length γ
t_i	Tag or response bit for cell i
v	The numerical value of the comparand c as masked by m
W, w	Width of AP word/record and width of a (search) field, respectively
x, y	Number of candidate cells in various stages of a search
γ	Group length for multiple-bit parallel searches in max-finding algorithms
ε	Comparison error threshold for numerical proximity search
ϕ	Masked bit position

Finally, *block-oriented* (block-parallel, word-serial, bit/byte-serial) systems represent a compromise between bit-serial and word-serial systems in an effort to make large systems practically realizable. Some block-oriented AP systems are based on augmenting the read/write logic associated with each head of a head-per-track disk so that it can search the track contents as they pass underneath. Such a mechanism can act as a filter between the database and a fast sequential computer or as a special-purpose database search engine.

Several instances of these four architecture classes are described in [36]. These four basic architectures, along with intermediate or hybrid schemes, provide AP designers with a vast design space and speed-cost trade-offs. Examples of the available cost-performance trade-offs in the design of a class of VLSI-based search processors can be found in [25].

2.2 Basics of AP search and arithmetic

Data stored in an AP cell may be numeric, nonnumeric (bit string), or a combination of both. Numeric values will be assumed to be unsigned integers or fixed-point values in much of our discussion. Modifications required for search and data selection with signed fixed-point and floating-point numbers will be briefly discussed in section 7.

When presented with a *comparand* (*search key*) c, a *mask m* specifying the relevant field(s) of the stored words, and possibly an *instruction* containing the type of search, a fully parallel AP responds by *marking* all the words that satisfy the search criteria. Marking is done by setting or resetting a *response bit* or *tag (bit) t* associated with the AP cell. A bit-serial AP performs its comparison by reading out an unmasked bit slice into a *bit-slice register*, comparing these bits to the corresponding bit of the comparand, and setting the tags accordingly. In addition, both fully parallel and bit-serial APs are usually capable of reading out bit slices into bit-slice registers and performing logical operations between these bit-slice registers. When bit-slice registers are used to indicate membership of cells in various subsets of the N AP cells, logical operations can be used to compute set union, intersection, and difference in a simple way.

The N response bits together form the AP's *response store*. A *response indicator* mechanism may provide information on the multiplicity of responders (zero, one, several) or an exact count of the number of responders (see subsection 2.3). The response indicator, multiple-response resolver, and several bit-slice registers are parts of the global tag operations unit shown in Figure 1. Other terminology and notation

will be introduced as needed. Table 2 contains a complete list of notation and symbols for reference.

Despite our focus on search algorithms, we need to understand how addition can be performed on multiple AP words for certain numerical search algorithms. Subtraction is the same as addition with the comparand negated. Bit-serial addition is straightforward and consists of repeated manipulation of bit slices, keeping the carries in a bit-slice register. If each AP cell is provided with a ripple-carry adder, then parallel addition is possible, provided that the carries are generated as the logical AND of actual carries and the mask bits (that is, carry should not propagate into or out of masked positions—those with $m_j = 0$). With parallel addition, the sum (difference) overwrites the current field contents, but since one operand is common to all operations, the original values can be restored by a final subtraction (addition) if desired.

2.3 Dealing with multiple responders

Each AP search operation yields a set of responding cells or candidates. When the set of responders is empty, the search has failed (not necessarily bad, as for example in searching for potentially hazardous situations) and the algorithm must follow an alternate branch. A unique responder usually means that the required data item has been identified and can be dealt with by reading it out or modifying it in place. With multiple responders, the appropriate course of action might be proceeding to further narrow down the set of candidates, simultaneously modifying all responders in place, or reading the responders out sequentially and dealing with each one individually. Hence, information might be needed both on the multiplicity of responders and on their physical locations in the AP array. Both of these are provided by the global tag operations unit depicted in Figure 1.

Response multiplicity indicators range from a simple binary "some/none" flag, obtained as the logical OR of all tag bits, at one extreme, to an exact count of responders, obtained by hardware in the form of parallel counter circuits [34], at the other. Intermediate solutions include the provision of a ternary "none/one/several" response indicator and counting or sorting the tags by way of high-speed shifting.

Response location information can be provided by a multiple-response resolver circuit [9]. The simplest (and slowest) implementation of a multiple-response resolver consists of cascaded OR gates producing an "inhibit" signal for cell i based on the logical OR of the tags for cells 0 through $i - 1$. This is essentially a priority circuit. Faster priority circuits have tree-structured designs. Many such designs are immediately derivable based on a parallel-prefix formulation [21] of the response resolution problem. It is also possible to obtain the address of the first responding cell through an N-input priority encoder.

3 Simple search algorithms

We cover the basic exact-match search in subsection 3.1. Inexact or approximate match can be defined in many different ways corresponding to various application-dependent notions of proximity. Our discussion will be limited to one-dimensional searches. Multidimensional searching, using Euclidean distance or other measures of proximity in higher-dimensional space, can be programmed by first computing the distances and then using the techniques discussed here. Two measures of proximity will be considered in subsections 3.2 and 3.3: Numerical proximity (approximate equality of numerical values with a comparison threshold ε) and logical proximity (closeness of bit strings measured by their Hamming distance).

3.1 Exact match search

Early APs were specifically designed to implement exact-match searches and very little else. As the name implies, in exact-match search, a data word must completely match the comparand in all unmasked bit positions in order to qualify as a responder.

In fully parallel architectures, the jth bit position within the ith cell produces the local match signal $m'_j + (c'_j \oplus d_{ij})$, with the cell then setting t_i to the logical AND of the match signals by implementing the recurrence

$$e_{ij} = e_{i,\, j\pm1}\, (m'_j + (c'_j \oplus d_{ij})), \text{ initially } 1 \qquad (1)$$

where the plus or minus sign in the $j \pm 1$ index represents right-to-left or left-to-right signal propagation and combining, respectively. The tag t_i is then set to e_{i0} or e_{iW}. It is also possible to find local mismatch signals $m_j(c_j \oplus d_{ij})$ and OR them to derive the cell mismatch result t'_i.

The use of wired logic can speed up the formation of the W-input AND (OR) function for reasonable values of the word width W. A tree-structured combining circuit can also be used, but such a circuit adds complexity to each cell and makes the cell structure less regular. Any such parallel combining scheme is represented by the logical expressions:

$$t_i = \prod_{j=0}^{W-1} (m'_j + (c'_j \oplus d_{ij}))$$

$$= (\sum_{j=0}^{W-1} m_j(c_j \oplus d_{ij}))' \qquad (2)$$

In the special case where $w = W$ (that is, the search field is as wide as an entire word), a dictionary lookup is performed whereby the presence or absence of a given word in the AP cells is determined. Design of VLSI-based dictionary machines, a subclass of APs, has received much attention since the early 1980s. For an overview and extensive references, see [23].

In bit-serial designs, exact-match search is implemented by sequentially reading out the unmasked bit slices, comparing each bit slice to the desired bit value, and keeping the logical AND of all bit-slice match indicators. Alternatively, mismatch signals may be produced for individual bit positions and ORed together to produce the word mismatch indicator. Either way, the scheme can implement both equality and inequality searches.

The worst-case and expected bit-serial exact-match search times are both $O(w)$ bit-slice search steps, where w is the width of the unmasked field(s). Note that we do not claim an $O(w)$ search *time*, as is commonly done in the literature, because the time needed for a bit-slice search increases with the AP size. Hence, a larger AP will take longer to carry out the same w-bit exact-match search (see subsection 7.3 on scalable APs).

3.2 Numerical proximity search

Numerical proximity searches are almost invariably programmed using a combination of other searches, since a direct implementation is not likely to be cost-effective. Let v be the value of the comparand c as masked by m. The objective is to mark words that have values in the interval $[v - \varepsilon, v + \varepsilon]$ in the corresponding field. This can be done through an interval search algorithm (see Subsection 4.3) or by subtraction, selective negation of negative differences (finding absolute values), and a relational "less-than" search (see subsection 4.1).

In either case, the search can be restricted in the intervals $[v, v + \varepsilon]$ or $[v - \varepsilon, v]$ to perform higher-within-threshold or lower-within-threshold search. When such one-sided numerical proximity searches are followed by min- and max-finding algorithms, respectively, the result is a next-higher-within-threshold or next-lower-within-threshold search. However,

14

transposing the order of the two operations—namely, finding the next higher or next lower (see subsection 5.2) and then checking if the difference is within the specified threshold—is more efficient since the proximity check can then be performed outside the AP system at higher speed.

3.3 Logical proximity search

The Hamming distance of two bit strings of equal length is defined as the number of bit positions in which they differ. If a fully parallel AP is implemented with only exact-match search capability, then determining all words that are a Hamming distance of 1 or less away from the masked comparand c requires $w + 1$ searches. This technique quickly becomes impractical for higher Hamming distances. For example, to find all words that are Hamming distance of 2 or less away would require $1 + w(w + 1)/2$ searches.

A fully parallel AP can be provided with a hardware mechanism to compute Hamming distances up to a maximum of h. For this, an $(h + 2)$-valued state must be passed between adjacent bit positions in a cell. This state would indicate partial Hamming distance from the left or the right end of the cell. The $h + 2$ states represent distances of 0, 1, 2, ... , h and $>h$. A masked-out or matching bit position would simply pass on the state as received from left (right) while a mismatch would update the state to the next higher one. For small values of h, clever encoding of the state can be found to minimize the logic complexity.

In a bit-serial AP, the state of the search for each cell must be stored in memory or in bit-slice registers within the processing elements. Feng [8] provides an algorithm and associated encoding for $h = 1$.

Once the Hamming distances are found, identifying all the words with distances of h or less is straightforward, particularly if the encoding was selected with this step in mind. One may also wish to follow this algorithm with a min-finding algorithm (see section 5) in order to identify the words that are closest to the comparand.

3.4 Membership search

A membership search identifies the words that match any member of a given set of comparands. One way to perform a membership search is to simply do a sequence of searches with each member of the set used as the comparand in turn. This way, both exact- and inexact-match searches can be handled but execution time may become unacceptable for large sets. In the following paragraphs, algorithmic speedup techniques

for the case of exact-match membership search are discussed.

Some membership searches can be converted to other searches. For example, to search for 0101, 0111, 1101, or 1111 in a 4-bit numerical field, one can perform exact-match search with the bit pattern $\phi1\phi1$, where ϕ represents a masked bit. Searching for 1101, 1110, or 1111 is equivalent to a >1100 or ≥1101 search (see section 4). In more general cases, special algorithms are needed as described below.

In a fully parallel AP, the problem of minimizing the number of search cycles for membership search can be solved in a way similar to two-level AND-OR logic circuit minimization: One needs to identify a minimal number of masked comparands or "prime implicants" that "cover" all input patterns. For example, to search for 0101, 0110, 0111, 1101, 1110, or 1111 in a 4-bit numerical field, two searches for the four-cubes $\phi1\phi1$ and $\phi11\phi$ will do.

The problem is even more interesting for bit-serial APs. Let us first look at the case of a set of size 2 [8], which we call "double-search" here. If the two words in the set are Hamming distance d apart, then $w + d$ bit-slice searches will identify the required words: $w - d$ searches to check for the $w - d$ bits that are equal and $2d$ searches to check for the complementary d bits. By taking one of the differing bit positions as a reference point and then comparing the other bits against this position using exclusive-OR operation between bit slices (XOR of any two bit slices among the complementary d bits must be the same), the number of bit-slice operations can be reduced to $w + d - 3$, which in the worst case of $d = w$ becomes $2w - 3$.

Feng [8] also suggests that for larger sets, the above procedure be applied to a number of pairs covering the entire set and having a minimal sum of pairwise Hamming distances. As an example, to search for members of the set {0101, 0110, 1001}, with pairwise Hamming distances of 2, 2, and 4, the two double-searches {0101, 0110} and {0101, 1001} will be conducted as above, leading to 7 bit-slice operations, including the final logical OR to combine the results of the two double-searches. This is about twice as fast as searching for each pattern separately and then ORing the search results.

4 Relational and interval searches

There are four relational searches: <, ≤, >, ≥. We consider the < and ≤ algorithms for fully parallel APs in detail, discussing briefly how the other two relational searches and bit-serial versions of the algorithms can be derived.

4.1   Less-than search

The fully parallel "less-than" search can be implemented based on signaling from left to right or from right to left. In the left-to-right version (msb to lsb), one needs a pair of logical variables per cell to keep track of numbers that are less than the comparand thus far (l_{ij}) and those that are equal to c thus far (e_{ij}). Updating rules and initial values for these variables are as follows:

$$e_{ij} = e_{i,j+1}(m'_j + (c'_j \oplus d_{ij})), \text{ initially } 1 \qquad (3)$$

$$l_{ij} = l_{i,j+1} + m_j e_{i,j+1} c_j d'_{ij}, \text{ initially } 0 \qquad (4)$$

At the end, l_{i0} indicates if the corresponding word i is less than the comparand.

Note that masked bit positions, corresponding to $m_j = 0$, do not affect the two variables and are effectively skipped. Thus, bit-serial versions of this and other algorithms in this section can be obtained by simply setting m_j to 1 in all equations and restricting the operations to unmasked bit-slices.

The right-to-left version of the "less-than" search is simpler in that only a single logical variable l_{ij} needs to be propagated as follows:

$$l_{ij} = m_j c_j d'_{ij} + l_{i,j-1}(m'_j + c_j + d'_{ij}),$$
$$\text{initially } 0 \qquad (5)$$

In the bit-serial implementation of this algorithm, we have the added advantage of being able to skip over trailing 0s in the comparand, since such trailing 0s will force l_{ij} to remain at its initial value of 0. For example, if the unmasked part of the comparand is 11001000, the search will skip the right-most three bit positions, leading to a reduction of 3 in the number of bit-slice searches and also in the associated logical operations of (5). Since the expected number of trailing 0s in a random string is about 1 (it is exactly 1 for an infinitely long string), the amount of savings is insignificant on the average.

4.2   Less-or-equal search

The left-to-right version of the "less-or-equal" ("not-greater-than") search can be performed by using (3) and (4) but setting the tag to $l_{i0} + e_{i0}$ instead of l_{i0}. Alternatively, the following recurrence equation for g'_{ij} ("not greater than" in cell i up to bit position j) can

be used along with (3) or its complementary version written in terms of e'_{ij}:

$$g'_{ij} = g'_{i,j+1}(m'_j + e'_{i,j+1} + c_j + d'_{ij}),$$
$$\text{initially } 1 \qquad (6)$$

Again, the right-to-left version is simpler and is defined by the single recurrence:

$$g'_{ij} = m_j c_j d'_{ij} + g'_{i,j-1}(m'_j + c_j + d'_{ij}),$$
$$\text{initially } 1 \qquad (7)$$

In the bit-serial implementation of this algorithm, trailing 1s in the comparand can be skipped in the same way as the skipping of trailing 0s discussed in connection with (5).

With more complex hardware in each cell of a fully parallel AP, the linear recurrences derived above can be computed by tree-structured parallel prefix circuits in much the same way as the carry-out signal of a carry-lookahead adder.

Clearly, when a string of γ consecutive 1s or 0s is encountered in the comparand, a single γ-bit search can be used to refine the candidate set or to identify the subset of the candidates that must be marked as "greater" in a fully parallel implementation. The speedup obtained here is modest as the expected length of strings of consecutive 1s or 0s in a random binary sequence is no more than $1/2 + 2/4 + 3/8 + 4/16 + \ldots + i/2^i + \ldots = 2$.

4.3   Interval searches

An interval (between-limits or not-between-limits) search can be implemented as a pair of relational searches as discussed in the previous subsections. However, there are opportunities for optimization in hardware or search speed if both relational searches are considered together rather than as two independent searches.

Consider searching in the closed interval $[c, C]$, where a responder d_i must satisfy $c \leq d_i \leq C$. Since we are assuming integer or fixed-point values, searches with open ($c < d_i < C$) or half-open ($c \leq d_i < C$, $c < d_i \leq C$) intervals can be easily converted to closed-interval searches by adjusting the endpoint(s) involved or can be handled by simple modifications to the following algorithms.

The left-to-right (msb to lsb) search algorithm needs two logical variables to keep track of equality with c and C (e_{ij} and E_{ij}) and one (b_{ij}) to indicate if d_i

is strictly between c and C up to this point. Recurrence (3) can be used for e_{ij}, and by changing e to E and c to C, for E_{ij}. The third recurrence is:

$$b_{ij} = b_{i,\,j+1} + e_{i,\,j+1} m_j\, c'_j\, d'_{ij} + E_{i,\,j+1} m_j\, C_j\, d'_{ij},$$
initially 0   (8)

In the bit-serial implementation of this procedure, an exact-match search can replace the above steps until the first occurrence of $c_j \_ C_j$. This saves a great deal of time in some of the cases where the interval of interest is relatively small. For example, to search for stored values between $90 = (1011010)_2$ and $92 = (1011100)_2$, inclusive, one first identifies all cells holding $1011\phi\phi\phi$ in the desired field and then uses the above algorithm to determine if the initially masked-out $\phi\phi\phi$ part is between $(010)_2$ and $(100)_2$. The same optimization can be applied to fully parallel AP algorithms that are not based on built-in interval search hardware in order to reduce the search time.

The right-to-left (lsb to msb) version of the interval search algorithm is again simpler since it is based on only two recurrences for the two searches $d_i \ge c$ and $d_i \le C$ instead of three for e_{ij}, E_{ij}, and b_{ij}.

$$l'_{ij} = m_j\, c'_j\, d_{ij} + l'_{i,\,j-1}(m'_j + c'_j + d_{ij}),$$
initially 1   (9)

$$g'_{ij} = m_j\, C_j\, d'_{ij} + g'_{i,\,j-1}(m'_j + C_j + d'_{ij}),$$
initially 1   (10)

The final result is $t_j = l'_{ij}\, g'_{ij}$. On the negative side, this algorithm does not lend itself to any optimization except ignoring or skipping of a number of right-most bit positions that simultaneously satisfy $c_j = 0$ and $C_j = 1$.

5   Extrema searches

There are four extrema searches: max, min, next-higher (minimum among greater values), and next-lower (maximum among lesser values). We will discuss only max-finding and next-higher search algorithms here as the others are similar. The analyses and optimizations presented in this section are original [29].

5.1   Max-finding search

The max-finding algorithm to be described next is essentially bit-sequential even when executed on a fully parallel AP with special max-finding hardware features such as those in [16]. Initially, at the msb position, all cells are candidates for holding the maximum value. At the start of a typical bit-slice step, a search is performed for the value of 1 in bit position j. Depending on the multiplicity of responders, the candidate set is modified as follows:

None:	Candidate set does not change.
One:	Stop; maximum already identified.
Several:	Candidate set is replaced by the set of responders.

At most, w bit-slice searches are required in the worst case. One can find the expected number of bit-slice searches based on the assumption of randomness of the stored bit patterns. Let T_{wx} denote the expected number of bit-slice searches for a field of width w when there are x candidate cells initially. Then:

$$T_{wx} = 1 + 2^{-x} T_{w-1,\,x} + 2^{-x} \sum_{y=2}^{x} \binom{x}{y} T_{w-1,\,y}$$

with $T_{0x} = T_{w1} = 0$ (11)

To justify the above recurrence, let y be the number of responders after searching for 1 in a particular bit slice and thus spending one search cycle. If $y = 0$ (no responder, probability of event $= 2^{-x}$), the search continues with the same number x of candidates in the remaining $w - 1$ bit positions. For $y = 1$, no further search is necessary. Finally, if there are $y \ge 2$ responders, an event having the probability $\binom{x}{y} 2^{-x}$ for each value of y, the search continues with y candidates in the remaining $w - 1$ bit positions. Figure 2 shows the variation of T_{wx} with the candidate set size x for several values of the field width w.

In a fully parallel AP, one can use the available multiple-bit parallel search capability to advantage for reducing the expected max-finding search time. Detailed analyses and algorithms are beyond the scope of this paper, but a simple example and a few charts can convey the extent of savings that can be achieved [29], [31].

Intuitively, when the number of candidates x is much larger than 2^w, it is very likely that the maxi-

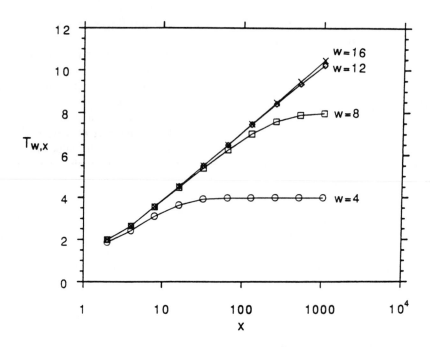

Figure 2. Expected number of cycles in a bit-serial max search as a function of the initial candidate set size x and field width w.

mum value is $2^w - 1$, represented by the all-ones bit pattern. Thus, in such a case, it makes sense to first search for the all-ones pattern and resort to a bit-serial max-finding algorithm only if the first search yields no match. Each word contains the all-ones pattern with probability 2^{-w}. Therefore, the probability that none of the given x words contains the all-ones pattern is $(1 - 2^{-w})^x$. Denoting the number of search steps with this strategy as $T_{wx}^{(w)}$, where the superscript designates the group length in the initial search, we have

$$T_{wx}^{(w)} = 1 + (1 - 2^{-w})^x\, T_{wx} \qquad (12)$$

where T_{wx} is the bit-serial search complexity given by (11). Plots of the value of $T_{wx}^{(w)}$ as a function of x for different values of w are given in Figure 3. Comparing Figures 2 and 3 reveals the advantages of this new strategy when x is larger than 2^w. For example, given $x = 1,000$ and $w = 8$, the initial search for the all-ones pattern reduces the expected search time from 8 (see Figure 2) to about 1.15 (see Figure 3), implying an average speedup of about 7.

Instead of searching the entire w-bit field for the all-ones pattern at once, one can proceed in smaller γ-bit groups. In other words, the w-bit search is divided into $\lceil w/\gamma \rceil$ phases, each involving a search for the γ-bit all-ones pattern followed by γ single-bit searches if the former is unsuccessful. The resulting search complexity $T_{wx}^{(\gamma)}$ is plotted in Figure 4 for $w = 12$. Figure 4 clearly shows how the optimal group size increases, from 2 to 3 to 4 for the data points shown, as the size x of the candidate set grows.

Finally, instead of using fixed-size groups, the length of the search subfield can be dynamically adjusted with the size x of the candidate set. Figure 4 also represents information on the optimal group size. Numerical experimentation has shown that the optimal length γ^{opt} of the search subfield grows roughly as $\log_2 x$.

5.2   Next-higher search

To find the next higher value relative to a masked comparand c, one can follow a relational $>$ or $\geq$ search (depending on how "next higher" is defined) with a min-finding algorithm. However, direct implementation can be more efficient.

Consider the next-higher ($>$) search algorithm as a bit-serial search proceeding from left to right (msb to lsb). Fully parallel implementation of the next-higher search is infeasible in view of the requirement for counting the set of candidates in intermediate bit-

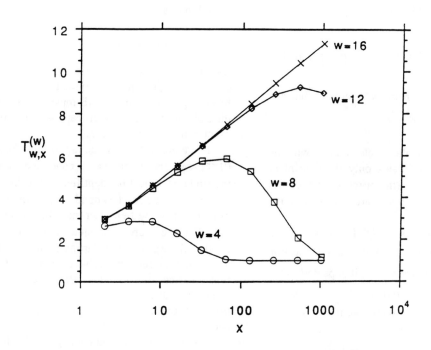

Figure 3. Expected number of cycles in a bit-serial max search with initial search for the all-ones pattern.

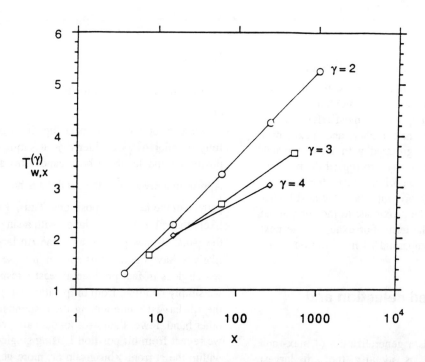

Figure 4. Expected number of cycles in max search in a field of width $w = 12$ with fixed group size γ.

19

slices, as will become evident shortly. Before inspecting bit-slice j, the present state of the search consists of two disjoint sets of candidates (maintained in two bit-slice registers).

Primary candidates: Equal to the comparand thus far (e_{ij})

Secondary candidates: Minimally greater than the comparand thus far ($g_{ij}^{(m)}$).

The required "next-higher" element(s) will be among the secondary candidates only if all primary candidates turn out to be $\leq c$ (the primary set becomes empty at some stage). If both sets are empty, then the search fails.

Updating of e_{ij} values is straightforward and can be done either bit-serially or in fully parallel fashion based on Equation (3). As for $g_{ij}^{(m)}$, it is passed to the next lower bit position unmodified if $c_j = 1$ and is changed according to the following rule if $c_j = 0$:

if $d_{ij} = 1$ for one or more primary candidates $\qquad$ (13)
then they become the set of secondary candidates
else $\quad$ **if** $d_{ij} = 0$ for one or more secondary
$\qquad$ candidates
$\qquad$ **then** they become the set of secondary
$\qquad$ candidates
$\qquad$ **else** there is no change
$\qquad$ **endif**
endif

Since the determination of $g_{i,j-1}^{(m)}$ from (13) requires two global responder operations, the algorithm is impractical for fully parallel implementation.

It is interesting to note that, in most references on associative processing, next-higher and next-lower searches are commonly grouped with inexact match searches. Here, we have chosen to regard them as extrema searches since the algorithms resemble those for max- and min-finding. More important, the next higher (lower) value need not be proximate to the comparand in the usual sense of the term. For example, the next higher value for the comparand 24 may turn out to be 106.

6 Rank-based selection and sorting

Rank-based selection is a generalization of max- and min-finding that lets us identify the kth largest (smallest) element in a set of n candidates. When $k =$

$\lfloor n/2 \rfloor$ or $\lceil n/2 \rceil$, the median value is obtained, which is useful in many application areas. The algorithms presented in this section are original [31].

6.1 *k*th-largest search

Like max-finding, the determination of the kth largest element is bit-sequential in nature. To execute the following algorithm, the AP must be equipped with a multiple response counter capable of providing the exact number of responders.

There are w steps in the algorithm. Consider step i ($0 \leq i < w$) that starts with x candidates among which the rth largest must be identified ($r \leq x$; initially, $x = n$, $r = k$). A search for 1 is conducted in the ith most significant bit of the field. Let there be y responders. If $y \geq r$, then the search continues among the responders for the rth largest value starting at the next bit slice. If $y < r$, then the required value must have a 0 in the current bit slice. The search continues among the nonresponding subset of the original set of candidates for the $(r - y)$th largest value, again starting at the next bit slice.

The average-case complexity of this algorithm can be analyzed in a manner similar to that of bit-sequential max-finding. The following recursive formulation of the expected number of steps for finding the rth largest among x values is directly derivable from the above description:

$$S_{wrx} = 1 + \sum_{y=r}^{x} \binom{x}{y} 2^{-x} S_{w-1, \, r, \, y} + \sum_{y=0}^{r-1} \binom{x}{y} 2^{-x}$$

$$S_{w-1, \, r-y, \, x-y} \qquad (14)$$

Boundary conditions for Equation (14) are $S_{w11} = S_{0rx} = 0$.

Here is one way to speed up the algorithm on a fully parallel AP. Consider a γ-bit subfield starting at position i and let there be x candidates at this point. Approximately $x/2^\gamma$ of the candidates have the all-ones pattern in the next γ bit positions. Thus, if $r < x/2^\gamma$, it is likely that γ bits can be relaxed with a single search for the γ-bit all-ones pattern since the rth largest value is likely to have the all-ones pattern in these γ bits. If the search does in fact produce at least r responders, then we simply continue from bit position $i + \gamma$, looking for the rth largest value among the responders. If, on the other hand, fewer than r responders are produced, then we repeat from bit position i, using single-bit searches within the current γ-bit group or, more generally, with a suitably chosen smaller group size. We can also select the search subfield size optimally in a manner similar to that of Subsection 5.1.

6.2 Finding the *k* largest elements

Another form of rank-based selection is to identify the set of *k* largest values (rather than just the *k*th largest values). This algorithm is quite similar to the previous one, except that if $y < r$, then all responders are marked as having been selected and the search continues for the $r - y$ largest values among the non-responders.

6.3 Ordered retrieval and sorting

Ordered retrieval is the sequential reading out of a selected subset of AP words in nondecreasing or nonincreasing order of keys contained in a given field. Ordered retrieval lets us pass on the results of various search and data selection functions to a conventional host computer in sorted order for further processing, archiving, or output.

The main component of most ordered retrieval schemes is a max- or min-finding algorithm. Simultaneous max- and min-finding can be used to effectively double the retrieval rate at the cost of some increase in hardware complexity [32]. It is also possible to mechanize the max-selection hardware in such a way that once the overall maximal element is identified, each successive maximum is identified and retrieved in one cycle [20], although this cycle is likely to be longer than a normal search cycle in view of the need for global communication (see subsection 7.3 on scalable APs). Ignoring these speedup techniques, the fundamental concept to be noted in ordered retrieval algorithms is a way to avoid spending the full *w* search cycles for identifying the next max or min element.

Consider ordered retrieval in nondecreasing order, requiring max-finding at each step. Once the overall maximum element(s) is (are) identified and retrieved, using the multiple response resolution mechanism if needed, the next largest value is likely to have many bits in common with the value just retrieved. Thus, it may be possible to avoid stepping through all *w* bit-slices for max-finding among the remaining elements.

This can be accomplished by a backtracking scheme. For example, if 1110 is identified as the overall maximum, we backtrack from the 0 to the preceding 1 and search for a 0 in that bit-slice, identifying all entries containing 110ϕ. We then move forward from the backtracking point, proceeding to search for 1101 and 1100 in turn.

The above algorithm is quite efficient when the number of elements to be retrieved is large

(comparable in magnitude to 2^w), since in such a case, the average amount of backtracking, in bit slices, is fairly small.

7 Extensions and generalizations

In this section we deal with several extensions to the algorithms presented thus far. Modifications required for searching with signed integers and floating-point numbers are discussed in subsections 7.1 and 7.2, respectively. Some ideas for extending these algorithms for use with certain scalable AP organizations and more general massively parallel architectures are presented in subsections 7.3 and 7.4.

7.1 Searching with signed numbers

Numerical fields were assumed to be unsigned in the main body of the paper to simplify the exposition of algorithms. Let us consider briefly the modifications that would be required to deal with signed integers represented in sign-and-magnitude or in two's-complement form for each search type.

Exact match. No change.

Inexact match. Numerical proximity search needs subtraction, computing of absolute values (through selective negation of negative differences), and min-finding. Alternatively, a more sophisticated min-absolute-value-finding algorithm can be developed directly that pursues separate search paths for nonnegative and negative values, but such an algorithm will not be more efficient than the simpler scheme already discussed due to overhead.

Relational searches. Values with one sign or the other can be ignored (the cells disabled) in relational searches. For example, when searching for values that are greater than a positive number, negative values can be removed from the candidate set in an initialization step.

Interval searches. Similar to relational searches.

Extrema searches. Consider max-finding (min-finding is similar). First, determine if there are nonnegative numbers in the initial candidate set. If so, remove all negative values from the set and perform unsigned max-finding on all bits excluding the sign bit. If not, then all the candidate numbers are negative. For sign-and-magnitude representation, perform unsigned min-finding. For two's complement representation, perform unsigned max-finding. This last statement is justified [18] by noting that the two's-complement number $x_{n-1} x_{n-2} \ldots x_1 x_0$ represents the value $-x_{n-1}2^{n-1} + (x_{n-2} \ldots x_1 x_0)_2$. Next-higher and next-lower numerical searches are programmed through in-place subtraction followed by min-finding.

General selection. Consider the problem of determining the kth largest value in a candidate set containing p nonnegative values. If $k \leq p$, then restrict the search to nonnegative values. On the other hand if $k > p$, then the $(k - p)$th largest value among the negative numbers must be found. Again with sign-and-magnitude representation, we must determine the $(k - p)$th smallest and with two's-complement representation, the $(k - p)$th largest value in the remaining bits.

Ordered retrieval. Handle nonnegative and negative values separately and in turn.

7.2   Searching with floating-point numbers

A floating-point number consists of a sign, an exponent (usually in biased format), and a significand. IEEE floating-point standard representation is assumed in the following [18], but the algorithms can easily be modified for other representations. For clarity, we will deal only with positive floating-point numbers. The sign can be handled by modifications similar to those discussed in subsection 7.1.

The relative numerical order and equality of two bit strings is the same whether they are viewed as binary fixed-point binary integers or floating-point representations with the exponent (in biased format) to the left of the significand. Thus, virtually all of the search and selection algorithms discussed in the previous sections of this paper apply, with no modification, to floating-point values. Note, however, that exact-match comparisons are usually avoided in floating-point arithmetic.

The only algorithm in need of special attention is that of *Inexact match*: In a vast majority of cases, numerical proximity search can be performed by simply limiting the search to values having the same exponent as the comparand. Exceptions occur when the comparand has a significand that is "very close," as determined by the comparison threshold ε and the comparand's exponent, to the lower and upper limit of its range (1 or 2 for the IEEE standard format). In such cases, the next higher or next lower exponent value must also be considered.

7.3   Searching on scalable APs

Recent advances in VLSI technology have made large APs and other massively parallel architectures practically realizable. Tens of thousands of processors or cells already appear in some commercially available systems and the use of one million processors is being contemplated. With such a large number of elements, optimization of processor design and scalability of processor interconnection mechanisms become major issues.

The above concerns have led to the formulation of the concept of systolic APs [24], which are built by interconnecting smaller building-block APs (BB-APs) and using them in a pipelined fashion [28]. Figure 5 shows a tree-structured systolic AP built of seven BB-APs, each containing 5 cells. Note that this small example is only for exposition. In practice, the number of cells per BB-AP would be much larger. The cells are numbered to facilitate communications between adjacent cells using the tree links. Instructions and associated data are given to the root and then move, in broadcast mode, to lower levels. Partial search results are combined in an upward sweep. Multiple instructions can be pipelined, provided they are scheduled to avoid data and control dependencies in a manner similar to the scheduling of instructions in a CPU instruction pipeline.

Some search algorithms work on such systolic architectures unmodified. Examples include less-than search (responding set is the union of the local sets) and max-finding (overall maximum is the largest of the local maxima). Others must be specifically designed with the particular systolic architecture in mind. For example, suppose that we want to search for the kth largest value in the AP of Figure 5 and that the BB-APs are bit-serial in architecture. The algorithm described in subsection 6.1 needs to know the number of responders in each bit slice to determine the set of candidates for the next step. Thus, the number or local responders must be summed in each step. Possible strategies for effective use of the hardware include interleaving of multiple independent searches (akin to exploiting multiple threads in some superpipelined microprocessors) and speculative execution of the more likely path or both branch paths by BB-APs pending the outcome of the tested condition.

7.4   APs as massively parallel processors

Associative processors constitute a prominent subclass of fine-grained, massively parallel SIMD (single-instruction-stream, multiple-data-stream) architectures [1], [14]. The validity and cost-effectiveness of the massively parallel processor (MPP) approach to high-performance computing and the relative merits of SIMD versus MIMD architectures have been the subjects of heated debates in recent years [30]. It is thus interesting to see where APs fit in the MPP world and how they are affected by these arguments.

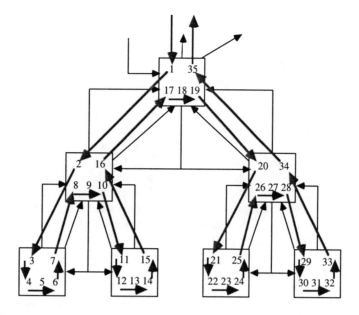

Figure 5. Tree-structured AP built of smaller building-block APs.

A bit-serial AP, with a shift capability for its response store as the only communication mechanism between the cells, can be viewed as a linear array architecture with a broadcast bus. Each processor or cell in this equivalent linear array receives instructions and data via the common bus and has adequate storage to keep an entire word of the original AP and to randomly access its bits.

Fully parallel APs in which comparand and mask are broadcast to each cell and the cell match signal propagates sequentially through all the cell bits before affecting the tag, are architecturally equivalent to 2D meshes with column buses, as shown in Figure 6(a). Obtaining the cell mismatch signal through wire-ORing the individual bit mismatch signals within a cell would be akin to providing row buses as well.

If tree-structured circuits are used for operand broadcasting within columns and combining of match signals within rows, then the architecture can be viewed as an augmented 2D mesh of trees [21] depicted with a few of its row/column trees in Figure 6(b).

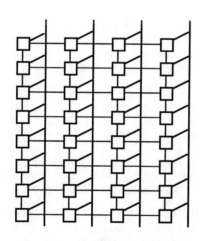

(a) 2-D mesh with column buses

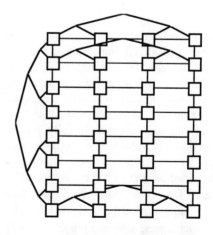

(b) 2-D mesh of trees (partially drawn)

Figure 6. APs form a special class of massively parallel processors.

However, both 2D meshes with row/column buses and mesh of trees architectures are usually envisaged to have considerably more general message-passing capabilities than APs. Whereas all the algorithms presented in this paper can be run, with minor adjustments, on these more flexible architectures, they would suffer from significant overhead compared to their execution on an AP with its highly specialized communications structure.

A fundamental trend in the design of massively parallel APs over the past decade has been the provision of more general capabilities for communication and collective computation [13]. Even though the entire spectrum of systems from bare-bone APs to general-purpose MPPs must be examined for any given application, no architectural "feature" comes for free, and simpler AP architectures remain the most cost-effective for certain application areas.

8 Conclusions

Search and data selection algorithms for both fully parallel and bit-serial APs were reviewed and analyzed. Search and data selection functions covered included exact-match, inexact-match (numerical or logical proximity), membership (multiple match), relational ($<, \leq, >, \geq$), interval (between-limits), extrema (max, min, next higher, next lower), rank-based selection (the kth or k largest/smallest), and ordered retrieval (sorting). Various hardware features that facilitate or speed up these algorithms were also described. In addition to several algorithms that were presented for the first time, discussions touched on two topics that have been inadequately covered in previous treatments: (1) Explicit analysis of search algorithm complexity, and (2) Effects of hardware features and implementation details on the performance of search and data selection algorithms.

Both worst-case and average-case complexities of the algorithms were considered. For example, average-case-optimal extrema search strategies for fully parallel APs were discussed. It was shown that significant speedup can be obtained when searching in a small field with a large number of initial candidates. Such optimizations are not only relevant to fully parallel systems but may find applications in bit-serial systems as well. Typically in such systems, multiple-bit searches are provided as part of the basic instruction set. An instruction for a γ-bit search is likely to execute much faster than a sequence of γ single-bit search instructions. In such cases, similar optimality results can be obtained, although optimal group sizes are likely to be much smaller compared to those of the fully parallel case.

This paper does not exhaust the discussion of AP search algorithms. Many interesting variations were left out in the interest of brevity. Other search algorithms can be devised and existing ones can be analyzed in greater detail (for example, modeling bit-slice reads/writes and logical operations separately, with allowance for various degrees of overlap between them in bit-serial APs) or with more realistic assumptions about the distribution of bit patterns in the stored data. Cost-effective hardware aids for speeding up fully parallel or bit-serial searches are also needed. There are numerous opportunities for further research.

Our search algorithms were described assuming conventional number representations. Other representations or codes such as the residue number systems [27], constant-weight codes [2], and order-preserving codes [26], proposed in connection with special applications, as well as set-based computations [35], would require their own search and selection algorithms. However, given the framework of this paper, such algorithms can be readily derived.

Acknowledgment

The research was supported in part by the US National Science Foundation, under Grant MIP-9001618.

References

[1] G.S. Almasi and A. Gottlieb, *Highly Parallel Computing*, Benjamin/Cummings, 1994.

[2] H.M. Alnuweiri, "Parallel Constant-Time Connectivity Algorithms on a Reconfigurable Network of Processors," *IEEE Trans. Parallel and Distributed Systems*, Vol. 6, No. 1, Jan. 1995, pp. 105–110.

[3] V. Bush, "As We May Think," Atlantic Monthly, Vol. 176, July 1945. Reprinted in *Computer Bulletin*, Vol. 4, Pt. 1, Mar. 1988, pp. 35–40. (Visionary in assessing the need for associative access to information and WWW-like bookmarks and trails).

[4] L. Chisvin and R.J. Duckworth, "Content-Addressable and Associative Memory: Alternatives to the Ubiquitous RAM," *Computer*, Vol. 22, No. 7, July 1989, pp. 51–64.

[5] W.A. Davis and D.-L. Lee, "Fast Search Algorithms for Associative Memories," *IEEE Trans. Computers*, Vol. 35, No. 5, May 1986, pp. 456–461.

[6] G. Estrin and R.H. Fuller, "Algorithms for Content-Addressable Memories," *Proc. IEEE Pacific Computer Conf.*, 1963, pp. 118–130.

[7] A.D. Falkoff, "Algorithms for Parallel Search Memories," *J. ACM*, Vol. 9, Oct. 1962, pp. 488–511.

[8] T.-Y. Feng, "Search Algorithms for Bis-Sequential Machines," *J. Parallel and Distributed Computing*, Vol. 8. No. 1, Jan. 1990, pp. 1–9.

[9] C. Foster, *Content Addressable Parallel Processors*, Van Nostrand Reinhold, New York, 1976, pp. 146-156.

[10] R.H. Fuller, "Associative Parallel Processing." *Proc. Spring Joint Computer Conf.*, 1967, pp. 471-475. See also Fuller's doctoral dissertation, EE Dept., Univ. of California, Los Angeles, 1960.

[11] K.E. Grosspietsch, (Guest Editor), Special Issue on Associative Processors and Memories (in 2 parts), *IEEE Micro*, Vol. 12, Nos. 6 and 12, June and Dec. 1992.

[12] A.G. Hanlon, "Content-Addressable and Associative Memory Systems: A Survey," *IEEE Trans. Electronic Computers*, Vol. EC-15, Aug. 1966, pp. 509–521.

[13] W.D. Hillis, *The Connection Machine*, MIT Press, Cambridge, Mass., 1985.

[14] R.M. Hord, *Parallel Supercomputing in SIMD Architectures*, CRC Press, Boca Raton, Fla., 1990.

[15] S.M.S. Jalaleddine and L.G. Johnson, "Associative IC Memories with Relational Search and Nearest Match Capabilities," *IEEE J. Solid-State Circuits*, Vol. 27, No. 6, June 1992, pp. 892–900.

[16] A. Kapralski, "The Maximum and Minimum Selector SELRAM and Its Application for Developing Fast Sorting Machines," *IEEE Trans. Computers*, Vol. 38, No. 11, Nov. 1989, pp. 1,572–1,577.

[17] T. Kohonen, *Content-Addressable Memories*, Springer-Verlag, Berlin, 2nd Edition, 1987.

[18] I. Koren, *Computer Arithmetic Algorithms*, Prentice-Hall, Englewood Cliffs, N.J., 1993, pp. 10–11.

[19] A. Krikelis and C.C. Weems (Guest Editors), Special Issue on Associative Processing and Processors, *Computer*, Vol. 27, No. 11, Nov. 1994, pp. 12–72.

[20] D.-L. Lee and W.A. Davis, "An $O(n + k)$ Algorithm for Ordered Retrieval from an Associative Memory," *IEEE Trans. Computers*, Vol. 37, No. 3, Mar. 1988, pp. 368–371.

[21] F.T. Leighton, *Introduction to Parallel Algorithms and Architectures: Arrays, Trees, Hypercubes*, Morgan Kaufmann, San Mateo, Calif., 1992, pp. 280–287.

[22] B. Parhami, "Associative Memories and Processors: An Overview and Selected Bibliography," *Proc. IEEE*, Vol. 61, No. 6, June 1973, pp. 722–730.

[23] B. Parhami, "Massively Parallel Search Processors: History and Modern Trends," *Proc. 4th Int'l Parallel Processing Symp.*, IEEE CS Press, Los Alamitos, Calif., 1990, pp. 91–104.

[24] B. Parhami, "Systolic Associative Memories," *Proc. Int'l Conf. Parallel Processing*, Vol. I, 1990, Penn State Press, University Park, Pa., pp. 545–548.

[25] B. Parhami, "The Mixed Serial/Parallel Approach to VLSI Search Processors," *Proc. Hawaii Int'l Conf. System Sciences*, Vol. I, IEEE CS Press, Los Alamitos, Calif., 1991, pp. 202–211.

[26] B. Parhami, "New Classes of Unidirectional Error-Detecting Codes," *Proc. Int'l Conf. Computer Design*, IEEE CS Press, Los Alamitos, Calif., 1991, pp. 574–577.

[27] B. Parhami, "Flexible Massively Parallel Arithmetic on Associative Processors," *Preprints of the 1st Associative Processing and Applications Workshop*, 1992.

[28] B. Parhami, "Architectural Tradeoffs in the Design of VLSI-Based Associative Memories," *Microprocessing and Microprogramming*, Vol. 36, 1992/93, pp. 27–41.

[29] B. Parhami, "Average-Case-Optimal Maximum and Minimum Finding on Fully Parallel Associative Memories," *Proc. 2nd Associative Processing and Applications Workshop*, 1993.

[30] B. Parhami, "SIMD Machines: Do They Have a Significant Future" (Report on a Panel Discussion at the 5th Symp. on the Frontiers of Massively Parallel Computation, McLean, VA, Feb. 1995), *Computer*, Vol. 28, No. 6, June 1995, pp. 89–91.

[31] B. Parhami, "Extreme-Value-Search and General Selection Algorithms for Bit-Serial and Fully Parallel Associative Processors," in preparation.

[32] C.V. Ramamoorthy, J.L. Turner, and B.W. Wah, "A Design of a Fast Cellular Associative Memory for Ordered Retrieval," *IEEE Trans. Computers*, Vol. 27, Sept. 1978, pp. 800–815.

[33] A. Slade and H.O. McMahon, "A Cryotron Catalog Memory System," *Proc. Eastern Joint Computer Conf.*, 1956, pp. 115–120.

[34] E. Swartzlander, "Parallel Counters," *IEEE Trans. Computers*, Vol. 22, Nov. 1973, pp. 1,021–1,024.

[35] D. Tavangarian, "Flag-Oriented Parallel Associative Architectures and Applications," *Computer*, Vol. 27, No. 11, Nov. 1994, pp. 41–52.

[36] S.S. Yau and H.S. Fung, "Associative Processor Architecture—A Survey," *Computing Surveys*, Vol. 9, No. 1, Mar. 1977, pp. 3–27.

[37] K. Zuse, *Der Computer-Mein Lebenswerk*, Springer-Verlag, Berlin, 1986 (Diagram on p. 77 shows an associative relay circuit sketched by Zuse in 1943).

Associative, Multiassociative, and Hybrid Processing

Martin C. Herbordt
Department of Electrical and Computer Engineering
University of Houston
Houston, TX 77204
herbordt@uh.edu

Charles C. Weems
Department of Computer Science
University of Massachusetts, Amherst
Amherst, MA 01003
weems@cs.umass.edu

Abstract

Multiassociative processing is the simultaneous associative processing of sets of elements. In the first part of this article, we define the associative and multiassociative processing models and evaluate their performance with respect to a class of generic, spatially mapped, functions. When compared with a conventional, realistic, parallel processing model, we find that multiassociative processing is superior in many cases and associative processing superior in the rest. Further analysis determines that a hybrid technique that combines associative and multiassociative processing is often superior to either one alone. Methods are presented for determining optimal partitions of these computations into associative and multiassociative phases.

In the second part, we describe how multiassociativity can be implemented on a reconfigurable broadcast mesh using a technique called coterie structures. The primary theoretical result is that techniques similar to those used in parallel access random memory (PRAM) graph contraction algorithms can be used to create an optimal algorithm for implementing a critical multiassociative primitive. We also derive basic properties of coterie structures and present algorithms for basic operations such as information exchange and symmetry breaking within and among structures.

The third part describes an application of the associative models to region segmentation, an important problem in image understanding. Using these techniques, a hybrid associative algorithm is developed

that reduces the number of communication instructions by more than an order of magnitude over previous algorithms.

1   Introduction

Multiassociativity is an additional level of parallelism: It is a flexible methodology for solving multiple problem instances simultaneously, each using parallel/associative processing. In its most general form, multiassociativity resembles nested parallelism [4] to depth 2. However, it has the advantage of being based solely on primitives that can be implemented efficiently (using available hardware with some software emulation), while yet being general enough to be useful as both an algorithmic and a programming paradigm.

Multiassociative processing was introduced in [12] and has already found a place in the spatially mapped phases of machine vision computation. The performance is especially good for classes of problems that are characterized by the need for processing nonuniform, but proximate, data sets. It is also likely that multiassociativity will find more applications within machine vision, in other machine perception domains, and in other tasks that use spatially mapped data.

We begin by defining the global and multiassociative paradigms using three different models: 1) in terms of their characteristic primitive operations, 2) by the types of queries they are suited to answer, and 3) through their virtual machine models (instruction sets). We then discuss a class of functions that subsumes many tasks in spatially mapped computation and compare the performance of the associative models with each other as well as with the standard serial and parallel computational models. We find the particular function instances for which the different models have superior performance, when hybrid algorithms are of use, and how this can be determined dynamically.

In section 3, we demonstrate an efficient implementation of multiassociativity on a reconfigurable broadcast mesh [18, 28, 20, 22]. The algorithms presented here use a different approach than those normally used on that network: they are based on the concept of the *coterie structure*, first introduced in [12]. Each data set, or region, is processed using only those PEs to which the pixels of the region have been mapped. Thus, although the underlying model is a reconfigurable mesh, the algorithms operate on arbitrary, connected subgraphs of the mesh. The basic method is to use knowledge that PEs can obtain about the network configuration in constant time to dynamically repartition the connected subgraphs into various coterie structures as appropriate for the algorithm. The primary result of this section is that PRAM symmetry breaking and graph contraction techniques can be applied to the coterie structures model to obtain an optimal randomized reduction algorithm (a critical multiassociative primitive) and near-optimal (within $O(\log * N)$) deterministic parallel prefix and reduction algorithms.

In section 4, we describe the application of associative processing to region segmentation, an important problem in image understanding. The critical computation is the characterization of region hypotheses. In previous work, Jenq and Sahni have published an $O(\log N)$ algorithm to compute simultaneously either the area or the perimeter of all components of an image using a reconfigurable mesh [15]. However, although their algorithm is asymptotically optimal, it requires 128 broadcast operations for each of the log N iterations. We present a hybrid associative reduction algorithm that runs in time equivalent to 7 log n communication operations for a large number of segmentations and with very small variance.

2 Characterizing associative models

2.1 Definitions

The prototypical associative memory operation consists of the controller broadcasting a key to the cell array and then performing some action on those cells where a match occurs. The actions typically consist of reading (or writing) some value from (or into) the cell; receiving a response in the form of a SOME/NONE (global OR of the response tag bits) or a COUNT (of tag bits); or selecting a single responder for further

processing. For example, the controller may execute the instruction, "How many cells have variable GREEN set to TRUE?" or "All elements with BROWN set to TRUE set SKY to FALSE." The basic associative operations are summarized below (after [9, 27]).

1. Global broadcast/local compare/activity control
2. Some/None of responders from array to controller
3. Count of responders from array to controller
4. Select a single responder

In multiassociative processing, we add the concept of a *set*, which we define as a collection of elements that share some property. Set properties are typically either an *a priori* distinguishing characteristic of the elements, say that GREEN = TRUE, or an attribute of the set itself, say, that it contains over 100 elements. The fundamental principle of multiassociativity is to replace some of the controller's function with a subset (often a single element) of the members of each set. The basic multiassociative operations are summarized below (after [12]).

1. Within each set: broadcast by a subset/local compare/activity control
2. Within each set: Some/None of responders to a subset
3. Within each set: Count of responders to a subset
4. Within each set: select a single responder
5. Split/Merge sets
6. Transfer data between sets

The first four operations are analogous to their globally associative counterparts, but are executed simultaneously in all selected sets. Of course, sets are only useful if elements can be added and removed with some efficiency. This is dealt with in the last two operations that together enable dynamic creation of sets and the implementation of divide-and-conquer algorithms.

As a consequence of the above definitions, algorithms that apply to globally associative arrays also apply to multiassociative processing, that is, to sets in parallel. For example, the well-known associative algorithm SelectSingleResponder [10, 7] can be performed simultaneously for each set using only a single global controller using the following code.

Algorithm SelectSingleResponder
{Beginning with the high-order bit, transmit ID}
{through the Response register. If any PE has a 1}
{in that bit, turn off activity in PEs with a 0 in that
bit.}
FOR BitNum := PEIdLength - 1 DOWN TO 0 DO
      Response := PEId[BitNum]
      IF (Response = Some)
         THEN Activity := Response

The following is a sample multiassociative instruction sequence:

1. Each set of elements with the same COLOR selects a single element to be the accumulator.
2. Each set of elements with the same COLOR send a count of the number of elements to their accumulator.

This sequence might be followed by a globally associative routine to obtain a histogram of the largest sets:

While Count (SetAccumulator = TRUE ∧ Count > 500 = 0
1. SelectFirst(SetAccumulator = TRUE)
   2. Read(Count)
   3. Read(Color)
   4. Write(FALSE → SetAccumulator)

In order to present a more formal description of global and multiassociativity, we define assembly-language–level machine models for associative and multiassociative memory processors. In both cases, the associative memory cells consist of bits that are not distinguished in terms of function: That is, any cell location can be referenced in any cell operand. The associative instruction consists of five fields as shown below:

1. OPCODE —Operations are: Compare, Read, Write, Count, SelectFirst
2. OPERAND 1 —Controller operand
3. OPERAND 2 —Cell operand
4. ACTIVITY —Indicates cells taking part in the computation
5. RESULT —I/O for some instructions

Field 2 is a value generated by the controller and broadcast to the array. Fields 3-5 are cell locations. As an example, the Compare instruction compares the data broadcast by the controller as indicated by OPERAND 1 with the data given by OPERAND 2 in each cell whose bit pointed to by ACTIVITY is on. If the data match, then the cell location in the RESULT field is set to TRUE. The multiassociative instruction word consists of seven fields:

1. OPCODE —Operations are: Compare, Read, Write, Count, SelectFirst
2. PARTITION —Partitions multiassociative memory
3. OPERAND 1 —Cell operand 1
4. OPERAND 2 —Cell operand 2
5. ACTIVITY 1 —Indicates cells taking part in the computation as operand 1
6. ACTIVITY 2 —Indicates cells taking part in the computation as operand 2
7. RESULT —I/O for some instructions

In this case, all fields besides the OPCODE are cell locations. The PARTITION field divides the memory into sets: Cells with identical values are members of the same set. Two activity fields are needed: one to indicate which cells are senders and one for the receivers. As an example, the Compare instruction is now applied in parallel to each set as given by the PARTITION location. Within each set, cells with ACTIVITY 1 turned on distribute the values at location OPERAND 1 to cells with ACTIVITY 2 turned on. If there are multiple writers, then the value becomes the bitwise logical OR of the send values. The readers compare the received value with their own value at OPERAND 2 and set RESULT according to whether there is a match.

Multiassociative processing extends the concept of multiassociative memory in the same way that associative processing extends associative memory. Additional computing capability is added to each cell to enable the generation of symbolic tags to constrain further processing. Rather than forcing an operand to be an existing value, it can be the result of a complex computation. A simple example of associative processing is "All elements with $G > 128$ and $R < 128$ and $B < 128$ set GREEN to TRUE." An example of a more complex multiassociative routine is "All elements with the same color that are contiguous form connected components."

2.2 A generic function template

In order to discuss a real implementation of a subset of multiassociative processing, we restrict our attention to a generic function of the type that frequently arises in spatially mapped vision computation. This function will be used to compare global and multiassociative processing with each other and with the familiar serial and parallel processing paradigms.

Pixels are mapped to PEs. Those that are contiguous and have certain values in common are formed into regions. These regions are then processed using some number each of three basic operators: SelectSubset, Characterize (often a Count of PEs within a component that have a certain property), and UpdateSet. Depending on the task and the processing model, some preprocessing might be helpful to set up communication paths. Examples of tasks that use the generic-function template are region-parallel versions of Count, Histogram, FindMedian, FindMean, SelectConvexHull, and many others from computational geometry.

2.3   Performance of basic operators

In this section, we use big-O notation to make broad comparisons. For the parallel and multiassociative cases, it is assumed that there is at least one set (region) with $O(N)$ elements, a likely occurrence in practice. The results are summarized in Table 1.

Serial processing model. In the serial model, processing time depends not on the size of the sets but on the number of elements in the entire array that are involved in each computation. SelectSubset requires $O(|$total elements selected$|)$ operations, while the other two operators require that all elements be examined and so have $O(N)$ complexity.

Parallel processing model. In the parallel model, we assume a controller, PE array with N processors, and a global OR circuit. The best possible performance for combining routing networks with a nontrivial number of processors is $O(\log N)$ We assume that all sets are processed simultaneously. The best way to execute the generic function is to select a PE per set to be the accumulator. Once this has been done, Count takes one combining communication operation, or $O(\log N)$. A region-parallel Update uses a similar propagation method as a connected-components labeling algorithm: It requires $O(\log N)$ communication

operations for a total complexity of $O(\log^2 N)$ [19]. Select uses Update $\log N$ times (using the algorithm in [7] and so has $(\log^3 N)$ complexity.

Global associative model. In this model, sets are necessarily processed serially. The basic operations have the following complexity *per set*: Select is $O(\log N)$, Count and Update are $O(1)$. If $|S|$ is the number of sets, the total complexities are then $O(|S| \log N)$, $O(|S|)$, and $O(|S|)$, respectively. The complexities are derived in [27].

Multiassociative model. Here, as in the parallel model, sets are processed simultaneously. The Count and Select operations are each $O(\log N)$ while the update operation is $O(1)$. These values are justified by results in [15, 12].

2.4   Performance of the generic function

If we are to assume bounded-size arrays, the big-O results of the previous section cannot be taken entirely at face value. But when taken together with empirical results (see Section 4), two general conclusions can be made. The first is that multiassociative processing is faster than parallel processing as long as set characterization operations do not dominate. The second is that global associative processing is superior to both parallel and multiassociative processing when $|S|$ is small but inferior when $|S|$ is large.

To compare global and multiassociative models in greater detail, we must determine the constants within the big-O and examine their performance as several parameters are varied. These are the proportion of Counts, Updates, and Selects in the generic function instantiation; the input image (on which the number of sets depends); and the choice of multiassociative Count algorithm. The choice is significant because several algorithms exist that are not asymptotically optimal but are fast in practice.

Table 1. Big-O complexities of basic operators on various computational models. $|S|$ denotes the number of sets into which the array has been partitioned. It is assumed that at least one set has O(N) elements, which is the worst case for the parallel and multiassociative models.

Model	Complexities of Basic Operators		
	Count	**Update**	**Select**
Serial	$O(N)$	$O(N)$	$O(|$total number selected$|)$
Parallel	$O(\log N)$	$O(\log^2 N)$	$O(\log^3 N)$
Associative	$O(|S|)$	$O(|S|)$	$O(|S| \log N)$
Multiassociative	$O(\log N)$	$O(1)$	$O(\log N)$

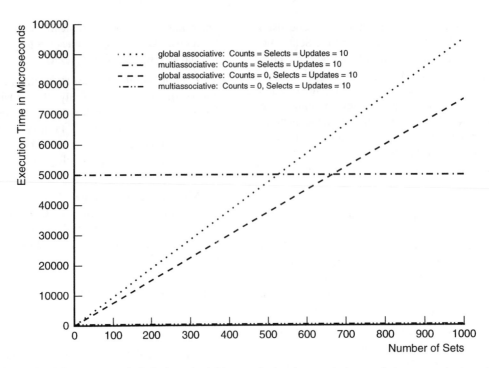

Figure 1. Plot of performance of global and multiassociative instantiations of the generic function versus the number of sets in the image. Times from Table 2 are assumed. For reference, during the early stages of region-merging segmentation algorithms, there are commonly several thousand regions (sets) to be processed.

The following results give a flavor for the relative performance of the models. Timings for the basic operators on a 256×256 content addressable array parallel processor (CAAPP) are given in Table 2. Graphs giving the behavior of functions with different proportions of operators are given in Figure 2. The multiassociative Count procedure used is a largely data-independent implementation of the general communication operation [12] and thus gives consistent, though suboptimal, performance.

2.5 Hybrid associative algorithms

The generic function we have been examining computes a function F for each of a number of sets s_i in an array. We make the following observations:

- If we apply the resources of the entire array, including those of the controller, to compute F for *any particular set* s_i of S, then a result will almost certainly be obtained more quickly than if F is computed using only those PEs to which si is mapped.
- In the case where F is calculated multiassociatively for all si of S, there is often a wide variation in elapsed time for the different si's. Such a distribution is shown in Figure 2.

From these observations, it follows that there may be some function/partition combinations for which a hybrid of a globally associative algorithm A_G and a multiassociative algorithm A_M may be preferable to either by itself.

Table 2. Estimated times in tens of cycles for basic template function operations on a 256×256 CAAPP. $|S|$ is the number of sets in the array. Multiassociative algorithms represented are data independent.

Model	Timing of Basic Operators		
	Count	Update	Select
Associative	$5|S|$ overhead, $2|S|$ per Count	$5|S|$	$2|S|$
Multiassociative	5,000	20	20

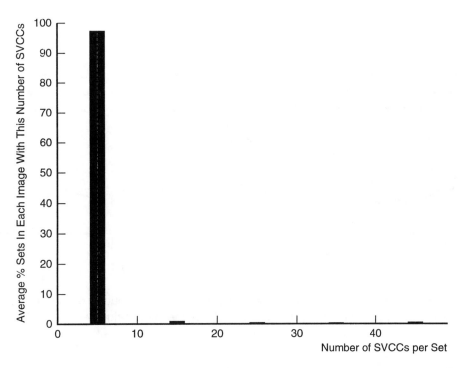

Figure 2. This histogram, taken from work on a multiassociative count algorithm, shows the fraction of sets that fall within given intervals of singly vertically connected component (SVCC) counts. The significance is that the performance of the algorithm in a set is proportional to the number of SVCCs in that set. The histogram shows that most sets tend to be well behaved, but a significant fraction are not.

Algorithm Hybrid-GENERIC
DO an optimal number (O) TIMES
   1.   Execute an iteration of A_M.
DO UNTIL F is done for all sets
   2.   Use GlobalSelectSingleResponder to select a set *si* from S, the set of sets for which A_M did not run to completion.
   3.   Use A_G to process *si*.
   4.   Remove *si* from S.

We refer to the execution of the first loop as local removal and the second as global removal. To get some intuition as to what O should be and how it can be determined dynamically, we show graphically what happens to the distribution of the remaining sets during local and global removal (see Figure 3). Global removal is roughly equivalent to reducing the area under the graph by one unit per iteration; the graph of the expected new distribution is generated by reducing the height of the graph at each point by a constant fraction of the height at that point. Local removal is equivalent to moving the Y-axis to the right one unit per iteration.

The optimal value for O minimizes the following expression:

$$K * O + \int_O^\infty dist(t)dt,$$

where K is the ratio of local to global removal execution times and $dist(t)$ is the distribution of the number of sets that require a certain number of iterations of local removal to run to completion. The integral is the number of sets remaining after the local elimination phase has been completed.

If the distribution is known *a priori*, then O can be found using the following procedure. Find the minimum point t between 0 and T (where T is the maximum nonzero value in the distribution) such that the following condition holds:

$$\forall(t')(t < t' < T)\left[\int_t^{t'} dist(t)dt > K(t'-t)\right].$$

The fact that $dist(t)$ is usually not known *a priori*, plus the complexity of the algorithm, make it impractical for dynamic use, however. But if the distribution decreases monotonically, as has proved to be the case in practice, then the procedure can be simplified substantially: The only t' between t and T that needs to be checked is t itself.

31

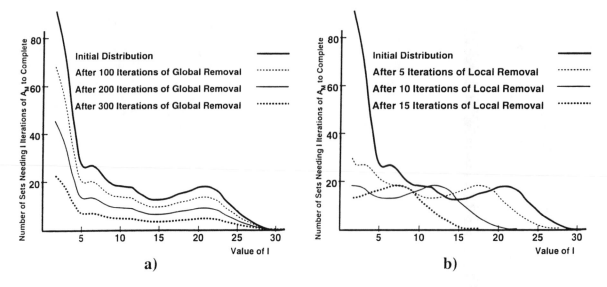

Figure 3. Local and global removal have very different effects on the distribution of the number of sets with certain values of I. I is the number of iterations of A_M left for the processing of a particular set to be completed.

There are two methods for determining O in practice. O can be computed off line for a data set known to be similar to that being processed. If the variance turns out to be small, as has often proved to be the case, then O can be fixed *a priori*, at least for that domain. Alternatively, we can use the monotonicity assumption: Determining whether the local removal phase should be terminated reduces to obtaining $|S|$ after every (perhaps ith) iteration. This can be done efficiently by using global count on the remaining set accumulators.

3 Implementation of multiassociativity

Here we describe the implementation of a multiassociative capability on the coterie network (also known as the reconfigurable broadcast mesh or RMESH).

3.1 Coterie network

The coterie network [28] is related to other reconfigurable broadcast networks. Members of this family of networks have two characteristics: They are describable using hypergraphs [1], and they are dynamic. In particular, the *time-t $n \times n$ Coterie Network graph $C_n^{(t)}$* ($t = 0,1,\ldots$) has node-set Z_n^2. Each node of $C_n^{(2)}$ is incident to precisely one *coterie-hyperedge*: The coterie-hyperedge incident to node (i, j) of $C_n^{(2)}$ is a subset S of Z_2^n that (1) contains node (i, j) and (2) is connected in the sense that the induced subgraph of the $n \times n$ mesh on the set S is a connected graph. Note that

at each time t, the coterie-hyperedges partition the node-set Z_n^2 of $C_n^{(t)}$. The coterie-hyperedges of $C_n^{(t)}$ do not depend in any way on the coterie-hyperedges of $C_n^{(t-1)}$.

The coterie network processor array is built on the coterie network graph. Each PE has an input and output port connecting it to precisely one *coterie*: that is, a (possibly irregularly shaped) bus—PEs (i, j) and (k, l) of the coterie network array are connected at time t to the same coterie (bus) just when nodes (i, j) and (k, l) of the coterie network graph $C_n^{(t)}$ are incident to the same coterie-hyperedge. A coterie is a bus in the sense that, at any time, a single incident PE can "talk" while all other incident PEs "listen." The coterie network has the additional feature that if multiple PEs "talk," the listeners receive the bitwise logical OR of those messages. For more on hypergraphs and coteries, see [23].

In the physical implementation, each PE controls four switches—N, S, E, W—enabling the creation of coteries. These switches are set by loading the corresponding bits of the mesh control register, which is viewed as local storage within each PE. Thus, coterie configurations can be loaded from memory or set from local data-dependent calculations. See Figure 4.

We also assume that nearest-neighbor mesh connections are available for local communication. These connections are not strictly necessary, either for algorithmic correctness or for asymptotic complexity. However, they are useful conceptually and relatively inexpensive from a hardware point of view once the wires of the coterie network are in place.

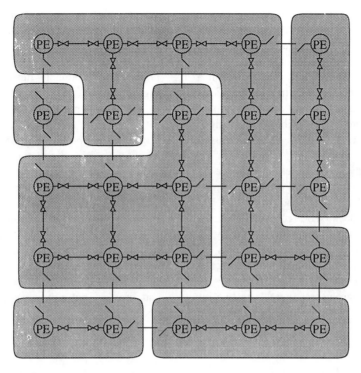

Figure 4. A 5 × 5 coterie network with switches shown in "arbitrary" settings. Shaded areas denote coteries (the sets of PEs sharing the same circuit).

3.2 Coterie structures

Advantages of the coterie network are support of one-to-many communication within coteries, reconfigurability of the coteries, and propagation of information over long distances at electrical speeds. Disadvantages are that a circuit can carry only one datum per communication step, and that partitions of the network are constrained by the underlying geometry.

The fundamental strategy in using the coterie network is to orchestrate the partitioning of the array (or some previously determined subsets) into coteries such that the maximum number of PEs needing to exchange information on any algorithm step can do so. To do this efficiently in data-dependent algorithms, each PE must determine in a small constant number of time-steps what role it is to play in the next phase or operation of the algorithm: whether it is a sender, receiver, or off; and how the section of the network controlled by that PE should be configured. The key is using the information available locally to each PE, for example: (1) the row and column ID, (2) the tag and the tags of the nearest neighbors, and (3) the OR of some bit of information in a given memory location of coterie members.

Note that there are significant differences between the coterie-structures model and other models (for example, the PRAM and the data-parallel model de-

scribed by Hillis and Steele [13]. In particular, pointer jumping is not a viable algorithmic paradigm as the model does not support unit-time random access operations on nonlocal memory.

3.2.1 Node classification

In coterie-structure algorithms, it is often convenient to classify PEs by whether a PE is an interior or a perimeter point and how the switches are set. A PE has different capabilities in controlling the flow of information through the network depending on its number of connections to its nearest neighbors. We call a PE with 0 connections *unconnected*, 1 an *endpoint*, 2 a *through-point*, 3 a *T-junction*, and 4 a *cross*.

We introduce some other terms here. A closed switch that connects a PE to a coterie (implying that the opposing PE has its switch closed as well) is a *link*. A PE is a *node* if it is taking an active part in a computation, that is, if it holds data and controls links. It is a *null node* if it takes part in a computation only for algorithmic convenience; that is, the node itself is only carrying the identity element. And finally, it is sometimes useful for a PE to carry no data but to control links; we refer to these as *helper nodes*.

3.2.2 Coterie classification

It is also useful to classify entire coteries into categories (we call these *coterie structures*). As is the case with data structures, certain algorithms are either available only on some coterie structures, or have different complexity depending on the structure. As we shall see later, an effective strategy is to partition a coterie that does not meet an algorithmic specification into a number of coteries that do, and then to combine the results. Before describing such algorithms, we first introduce the coterie structures used in our discussions.

Coteries have already been defined; see Figure 5d for examples. *Horizontal* (or *vertical*) *lines* are defined to be coteries where all the North and South (or East and West) switches are open; see Figure 5e. A coterie is a *chain* if it comprises two endpoints joined by an arbitrary number of (0 or more) through-points. A *boundary component* is always defined with respect to a coterie: It is the subset of PEs having the property that at least one of its eight nearest neighbors (we include diagonals here) is not a member of the same

coterie. Not all connections among those PEs are closed, however. In order for two PEs to have a link, they must be mutually adjacent to at least one PE common from outside the region. Figure 5f contains boundary components derived from the coteries in Figure 5d.

PEs are members of the same level of a coterie if they are in the same row (column). PEs in the same level need not be in the same line. *Singly monodimensionally connected components* (SMCC) come in two varieties, vertical and horizontal. An SVCC is a coterie where at most one PE in each level has an uplink and one PE has a downlink (the same PE may have both). See Figure 5g for examples.

A *spanning tree* of a coterie contains all PEs in the original structure, but where links have been opened to remove all cycles. See Figure 5h for examples.

A coterie is a *C-graph* if all endpoints, T-junctions, and crosses, but not necessarily through-points, are nodes.

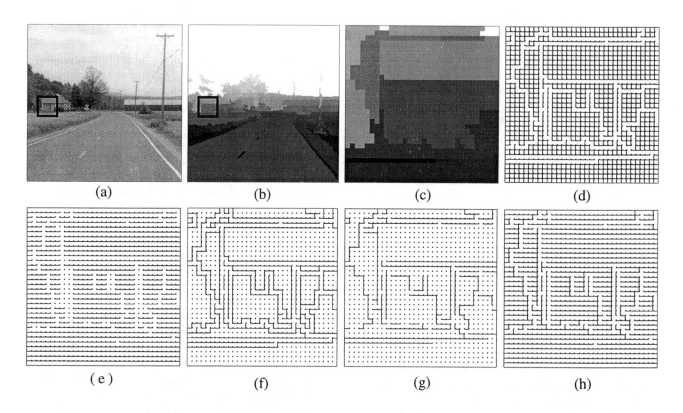

(a) (b) (c) (d)

(e) (f) (g) (h)

Figure 5. (a) Image of a road scene; (b) segmentation of the image; (c) 32 × 32 subimage of segmentation. (d) through (h) represent coterie structures derived from subimage: (d) coteries corresponding to regions; (e) horizontal lines; (f) boundary contours; (g) singly vertically connected contours; (h) spanning trees.

3.3 Parallel prefix on simple coterie structures

The literature describing the properties, algorithms, and applications of parallel prefix (also known as scan) is vast; for a sample see [14, 17, 16, 3]. The definition is: Given a set $[x_1, \ldots, x_i]$ of n elements with each element assigned to a different processor and a binary associative operator $*$, compute the n S_i's, where $S_i = x_1 * x_2 * \ldots x_i$, leaving the ith prefix sum in the ith processor. Besides usefulness in its own right, parallel-prefix algorithms are usually also the best way of computing reductions, that is, operations identical to parallel prefix but where the partial sums need not be saved. The parallel-prefix operation requires $2 \log n$ communication steps on a tree-connected parallel processor, but only $\log n$ are required for a reconfigurable bus. Refer to Figure 6 for an illustration.

The parallel-prefix algorithm for an $n \times m$ rectangle is also well known and follows almost immediately from the line algorithm. It has three phases.

Algorithm Parallel-Prefix Rectangle

1. Partition the rectangle into m horizontal lines. Run parallel prefix on the lines.

2. Create a vertical line from the m right endpoints. Run parallel prefix on that line.

3. The endpoints update the lines beneath them.

Parallel prefix for a rectangle requires $\log n + \log m + 1$ communication and arithmetic operations.

Somewhat surprisingly, parallel prefix on an SMCC is no more complex and only slightly more complicated than parallel prefix on a rectangle. Again, begin by partitioning the structure into lines and computing parallel prefix. The second phase is slightly more complex because the right endpoints are not neatly aligned and therefore cannot be simply merged into a vertical line. Instead, we have up to three different PEs in each row perform the functions performed by the right endpoint PE in the rectangle algorithm. The right PE endpoint holds and processes the information as before, but two possibly different PEs control the links to the rows above and below respectively (up- and downlinks). Recall from the definition of SMCC that (except for the top and bottom rows), exactly one PE in each row controls the uplink and one PE controls the downlink. These PEs recognize this fact in unit time by looking at their mesh control registers. See Figure 7 for an SMCC with those PEs labeled.

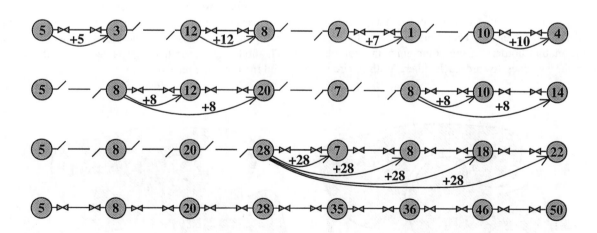

Figure 6. Three iterations and final result of parallel prefix on a line using the + operator. The arrows represent the broadcast operation to elements of the coteries formed when the switches are closed as indicated.

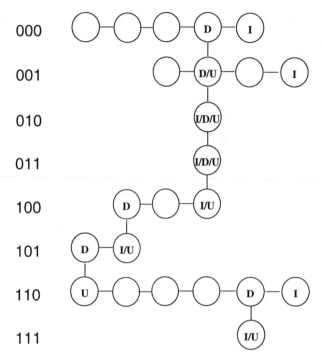

Figure 7. A single vertically connected component (SVCC) with information-carrying, up- and downlink PEs indicated.

3.4   Basic coterie structure algorithms

The algorithms presented here will be used as primitives later. The complexity is assumed to be $O(1)$ unless otherwise indicated.

3.4.1   Communication and symmetry breaking

Task. Transfer of data between two adjacent coteries.

Algorithm. Assume that a protocol has been decided upon between two neighbors. The PEs that are on the mutual borders of the communicating coteries close the switches toward each other. With a circuit comprising both coteries thus formed, the PEs of the sending coterie broadcast while the PEs of the receiving coterie listen. See Figure 8.

Task. Symmetry breaking (establishing precedence) between a pair of nodes in a coterie.

Randomized algorithm. The nodes simultaneously broadcast a sequence of independently generated random bits and their complements until the bit-one node broadcasts is the complement of the bit the other node broadcast. Nodes can tell this has occurred by comparing the broadcast results (the two ORs of the two pairs of signals) with the bits they just broadcast. The node that generated the 1 is designated the sender and the other the receiver.

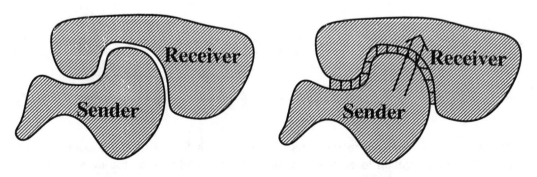

Figure 8. Coteries close mutual switches to communicate.

Deterministic algorithm. Nodes broadcast their *ID*s and $\overline{IDs}$. After reading the two bitwise ORs and comparing them with the values they broadcast, each obtains its opposite's *ID*. The node with the higher *ID* becomes the sender and the other the receiver.

Task. Two nodes within a coterie exchange information.

Algorithm. Precedence is established by using one of the symmetry-breaking algorithms immediately above. The task is completed with a pair of broadcasts.

Task. Each node in a C-graph exchanges information with all its neighbors.

Deterministic algorithm. Recall that nodes are separated by chains of null nodes of arbitrary length and that, therefore, all nodes have links either to other nodes, or to chains of PEs that have a node at the other end. The basic idea is to use the neighbor connections to break the symmetry; otherwise it would be impossible to tell deterministically which pair of nodes should communicate when. The cases where the length of the intermediate chain is 0, 1, and > 1 are handled separately (see Figure 9). In all three cases, the algorithm starts with the nodes using the nearest-neighbor connections to transfer copies of their information to all the PEs toward which a link is established.

Case 1. Chain length = 0. The nearest-neighbor move has already completed the transfer.

Case 2. Chain length = 1. The intermediate PE swaps the data from the two adjacent nodes and transfers them to their destinations.

Case 3. Chain length > 1. The two-node swap algorithm is used to transfer the data between the two endpoints of the chain. Neighbor transfers complete the exchange.

Randomized algorithm. We use a variation of the randomized symmetry-breaking procedure presented above. It is assumed that nodes have a list of links to their neighboring nodes. Nodes randomly close switches in the direction of one of the links, opening those in all the other directions. Nodes then use one of the symmetry-breaking procedures to check whether the opposite node has done the same. The nodes that did not form a correspondence with a neighbor again randomly select a link for another try. This continues for a constant number of iterations during which a constant fraction of the nodes in the C-graph will have established correspondence. Corresponding nodes exchange information and temporarily remove each other from their adjacency lists. This procedure continues until all nodes have completed the information exchange with all their neighbors.

Task. $O(1)$ coloring a chain.

Algorithm. When using the standard PRAM $O(1)$ coloring algorithm [11] for constant degree graphs, the number of colors is small when operating on an ordered structure, say a list or rooted tree (see, for example, [6]), but exponential in the degree of the graph when not. The idea is to use information available locally to nodes on the chain to create such an ordering. Nodes obtain their neighbors' *ID*s, which are compared with their own. Nodes label themselves ↖↗, ↗↖, ↖, or ↗, depending on whether the *ID* "slope" is up or down in each direction. Nodes exchange slope labels with their neighbors. The neighbor on each link can have one of two possible labels: Either the slope continues in the current direction (for example, ↗ goes to ↗), or it can go to a local maximum or minimum (for example, ↗ goes to ↗↖). Nodes that are ↖↗ and ↗↖ cannot be adjacent to other nodes that have that same slope label and so simply color themselves ↖↗ and ↗↖. The remaining nodes form monotonic *ID* sequences. These sequences, which now have direction information, can be colored using the previously mentioned 6-color algorithm and then spliced together with the ↖↗ and ↗↖ nodes to form an 8-colored chain. To reduce the number of colors to 6, the ↖↗ and ↗↖ nodes examine their neighbors' colors and choose any of those remaining to be their own. The 6-color PRAM list algorithm has $O(\log * N)$ complexity, as does the 6-color coterie chain algorithm.

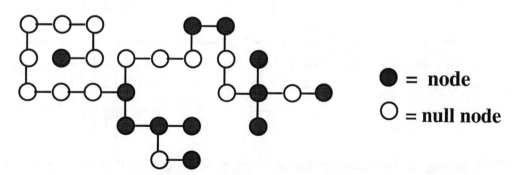

Figure 9. C-graph with nodes separated by chains of null nodes of varying length.

● = node

○ = null node

Task. Create maximal independent set of nodes in a C-graph.

Deterministic algorithm. Use the information exchange algorithm above to implement the $O(\log * N)$ complexity MIS algorithm found in [11].

3.4.2 Minimum partition of coteries into SVCCs

Here we prove the somewhat surprising result that a minimum partition of a coterie into SVCCs can be constructed in constant time. (A simple algorithm for a nonminimum but useful partition is presented in [12].) Besides the inherent usefulness of this result (see section 5), the significance is that the algorithm performs a complex function using only information that can be determined locally by each PE in constant time.

A requirement of an $O(1)$ partitioning algorithm is to determine (as yet unspecified) properties independently of distances. We have such a tool in the F-G algorithm (see below). In particular, the following question can be answered in constant time: "For any PE P with property F on a line, is there a PE Q with property G between P and either the next PE with property F (to either the left or right) or the end of the line?" We define such a PE Q to be *adjacent* to PE P. If two adjacent PEs become members of the same coterie by closing switches toward each other and opening switches away, then those PEs are said to be *merged*.

Algorithm F-G
{For all PEs with property F, find out whether there}
{is a PE with property G between it and the next PE}
{to the left with property F, or the end of the line.}
SaveCoterieSettings()
Coterie[N,S] := OPEN
If (Tag = F) Coterie[E] := Open
If (Tag = G) Broadcast(TRUE)
If (Tag = F) G-AdjacentLeft := CoterieInput
RestoreCoterieSettings()

We start by observing that a greedy algorithm produces the desired partition: Starting at the top level, draw circles around each downlink. Then level by level, expand each circle to include links at the lower levels while not letting the circles intersect. See Figure 10 for an example.

Lemma 1 *The cardinality of the minimal set of SVCCs |S| in a coterie is equal to the number of SVCCs that must be added with the addition of each new level.*

Proof. Assume that a coterie partition contains fewer SVCCs than the number that must be added at every level. Then, one of the levels of the coterie would be partitioned into fewer SVCCs than by the above method. But that would either leave vertical links unaccounted for, or an SVCC with multiple vertical links. Both of these are contradictions.

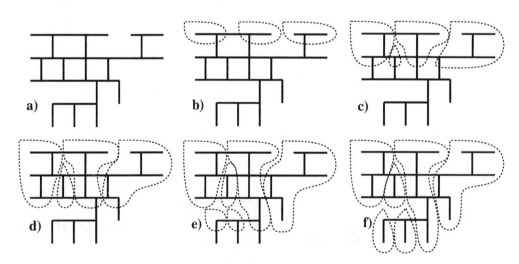

Figure 10. A coterie can be partitioned into a minimum set of SVCCs through a serial level-by-level growth algorithm.

Lemma 2 *To create a minimal set of SVCCs within a coterie, it suffices to create a maximal matching between adjacent up- and downlinks and merge them together.*

Proof. The maximal matching leaves the fewest possible leftover vertical links, requiring that the fewest possible new SVCCs need to be created at that level.

We now present the SVCC construction algorithm. First, label the PEs with up- and downlinks as *U* and *D*. All other PEs are ignored. Next, partition the coterie into lines. Within each line, create a maximal matching between adjacent *U* and *D* PEs, a sufficient condition for creating a minimal partition of a coterie into SVCCs. This is a multistep process:

1. Each *U* (*D*) determines whether there are adjacent *D* (*U*) PEs to the left and/or right using the *F-G* algorithm.

2. Each *U* (*D*) PE labels itself with a 0, 1, or 2 depending on the number of adjacent *D* (*U*) PEs. We call those numbers the incidences of each PE.

3. The *U* (*D*) PEs send the number of incidences to their adjacent *D* (*U*) PEs, if any.

4. Each PE is labeled with an ordered triple composed of the number of incidences of the left adjacent PE, its own incidences, and the incidences of the right adjacent PE.

5. The value of the ordered triple is sufficient to determine whether each PE should open or close its East and West switches to create the

optimal partition for all but the (2,2,2) case. PEs with (-,0,-) do nothing, with (*,1,*) merge with their one adjacent PE, with (1,2,1) arbitrarily merge with either left of right adjacent PE, and with (2,2,1) or (1,2,2) merge with the adjacent PE with one incidence.

6. PEs with (2,2,2) merge with adjacent PEs according to the procedure described below.

See Figure 11 for an illustration of the labeling of a single line. Before presenting the (2,2,2) case, we show the correctness of what we have described so far.

Lemma 3 *A U(D) PE can only form an SVCC with a single, adjacent, D (U) PE.*

Proof. Assume not. Then either two or more *D* PEs must be in the SVCC at that level. If the *D* PE is not adjacent, the line must be open circuited. Both are contradictions.

Lemma 4 *The U-D merges effected by the SVCC construction algorithm are correct for the cases shown in step 5 (not the (2,2,2) case).*

Proof. From Lemma 4, we know we need only ensure that each PE merges with the correct, adjacent PE. Cases (-,0,-), (*,1,*), and (1,2,1) are trivial. In the first case, nothing can be done; in the second, there is no choice; and in the third, the choice does not matter. In the cases (2,2,1) and (1,2,2), the PE should merge with the PE with one incidence: It is possible for the PE with two incidences to find another PE with which to merge, while the PE with one incidence has only this opportunity.

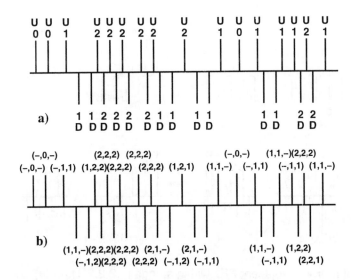

Figure 11. A line of one level of a coterie with (a) uplinks, downlinks, and incidences labeled, and (b) ordered triples of incidences of own and neighboring PEs.

39

The (2,2,2) case is critical: If the merger is not done correctly, the complexity of our parallel-prefix algorithm increases from $O(\log N + |S|)$ to $O(N)$. We formalize this fact in the following lemma.

Lemma 5 *If a PE P with label (2,2,2) is not guaranteed to merge with the correct PE, then it is possible for an adversary to force the creation of an SVCC partition where |S| is O(N) greater than optimal.*

Proof. As previously, we are concerned only with U and D PEs. The neighborhood of the line around P necessarily has the following form: a PE with one incidence, followed by a series of PEs with two incidences, followed by a PE with one incidence (1,2, ..., 2,1). The series of two-incidence PEs can have either an even or an odd number elements. If odd, and all the (2,2,2) PEs merge arbitrarily with either their right or left neighbors, then exactly one PE is left over, the best possible result. In the even case, however, such a uniform merging strategy leads to there being either zero or two leftover PEs. If no method existed to make the correct decision, it would thus be possible for an adversary to create $O(N)$ strings of constant length, which after partitioning would each leave two unmatched links.

We now solve the (2,2,2) case. From Lemma 6 we know that we need worry only about the case where the series of PEs with two incidences is of even length. There are two possibilities: The (2,2,1) PE at the right end of the 2, ..., 2 series is either a U or a D; the

(1,2,2) PE at the left end is always the opposite. In the first case, all (2,2,2) PEs that are U should merge left, in the second case they should merge right.

A procedure for handling the (2,2,2) case follows. PEs that are (2,2,1) open their East switches and PEs that are (1,2,2) open their West switches to form lines with the pattern (1,2, ..., 2,1). The PE that are (2,2,1) and U broadcast a one, those that are (2,2,1) and D broadcast a zero. The procedure is repeated for the (1,2,2) PEs. The (2,2,2) PEs read these values and have four cases: (0,0), (0,1), (1,0), and (1,1). In the (0,0) and (1,1) cases, there are an odd number of U (D) PEs: These can thus merge arbitrarily (but uniformly) with their left or right (right or left) adjacent D (U) PE. In the (0,1) case the D (U) PEs merge right (left) and in the (1,0) case the D (U) PEs merge left (right). See Figure 12 for an illustration of the four cases with the merges done correctly.

Lemma 6 *The U-D merges effected by the SVCC construction algorithm are correct for the cases where all elements of the triple are 2's.*

Proof. Follows from previous two paragraphs.

Theorem 1 *The SVCC construction algorithm partitions any coterie into a minimal set of SVCCs in constant time.*

Proof. That the time is constant is immediate: There are no loops and no dependencies on the number of PEs. The correctness follows from the preceding lemmas.

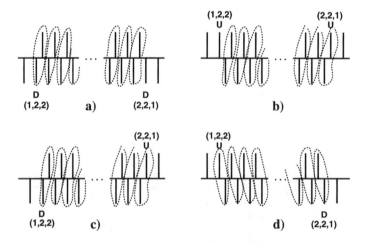

Figure 12. Four cases of merging adjacent PEs within strings (1,2,2,2,1). In (a) and (b), there are an odd number of (2,2,2) PEs and either the (1,2,2) or the (2,2,1) PE always remains unmerged. In (c) and (d), there are an even number of (2,2,2) PEs. The merges must all go in the correct direction or both (1,2,2) and (2,2,1) PEs will remain unmerged.

3.5   Algorithms based on graph contraction

In this section we again show how techniques used in other models can be applied to coterie structures. In particular, the communication and symmetry-breaking algorithms of the previous section are integrated with PRAM contraction techniques (see [21, 24]) to produce an $O(\log N)$ randomized-reduction algorithm and $O(\log * N \log N)$ deterministic parallel-prefix and reduction algorithms. Since the prefix algorithm follows almost immediately from the reduction algorithm, only the latter is presented.

Algorithm REDUCE
While |nodes| > 1 **do in parallel**
> Use MERGE to merge legal pairs
> of adjacent nodes such that the resulting
> vertices have degree $\leq d_{max}$.

Phillips shows that, for bounded-degree planar graphs, there is always a constant fraction of nodes eligible for merger as long as $d_{max}. \geq$ the degree of the graph [24]. That a constant fraction of nodes eligible for merger does so follows by arguments similar to those used in the previous section. The **While** loop thus executes $O(\log N)$ times.

The MERGE procedure is more complicated when applied to coterie structures than the equivalent PRAM algorithm. The reason is that in a distributed memory model, nodes cannot simply be eliminated once their data have been combined: The wires associated with the underlying PEs may still be needed to transmit information between the nodes remaining in the computation. Since these leftover PEs are always through-PEs, MERGE operates on a C-graph.

The constraint that no node ever have degree > 4 creates a relatively small constant number of merge cases that can be handled separately. This number is decreased by imposing the convention that the node with smaller degree always transfer its data to the node with larger degree. We examine five cases (see Figure 13); the others are analogous.

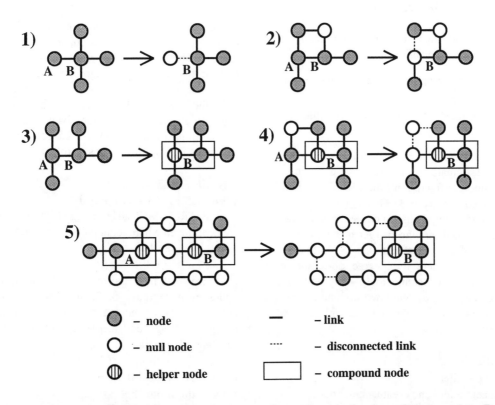

⬤ – node	—	– link
⭘ – null node	....	– disconnected link
⦶ – helper node	▭	– compound node

Figure 13. Five cases of nodes merging on C-graphs. In all cases, **A** merges into **B.**

1. An arbitrary node merges with a node with degree 1 or 2. If the lower degree node is d_1, the higher degree node eliminates the link to that node. If it is d_2, then the links remain intact, although that node is removed.

2. A d_3 node merges with another d_3 node with which it has one common neighbor. One node is selected to send data, the other to receive. The receiver retains its link to the common-neighbor node while the sender removes it.

3. A d_3 node merges with another d_3 node with which it has no common neighbors. The resulting node has degree 4, but its functionality must be distributed over the two original nodes. One node holds the data and controls two links, while the other, which has now become a helper node, controls the other two links.

4. A d_4 node with a helper node merges with a d_3 node with which it has one common neighbor. The d_3 node is turned off, and the link from the d_3 node to the common neighbor is eliminated.

5. Two d_4 nodes with helpers and two common neighbors merge. One of the nodes (and its helper) are turned off, and its links to the common neighbors are removed.

For this list to be exhaustive (including analogous cases), the following propositions must be true:

Proposition 1: Only nodes of degree 4 can ever need a helper PE.

Proposition 2: No node ever needs more than one helper PE.

The truth of these propositions follows from the fact that for nodes created using the above procedures, the only possible configuration where a helper node can be introduced is in case 3. That is because compound nodes (nodes with helpers) can only be created when the node formed through merger has greater degree than either of the two constituents. We observe that after a merger where the degree does not increase—between any node and a d_2, a d_3 with one common neighbor, or a d_4 with two common neighbors—the merged node is a through-PE with no need to control information flow.

Procedure MERGE

$\forall$ nodes **do in parallel**
1. Find adjacent nodes and create a neighbor list.
2. Exchange neighbor lists with all neighbors.
3. $\forall$ neighbor lists **do sequentially**

    Eliminate duplicates, determine neighbors with which merger is legal.
4. Execute either the random or deterministic version of SELECT-MATCH-PAIRS.
5. Combine nodes according to the cases presented above.

Since all the nodes are guaranteed to have bounded degree, steps 1, 2, 3, and 5 are $O(1)$.

Procedure DETERMINISTIC-SELECT-MATCH-PAIRS
1. Run the COTERIE-MIS algorithm from section 3.1.
2. Members of the MIS that are members of a legal merge pair choose a merge partner. The partner breaks ties if it is multiply selected.

The complexity of COTERIE-MIS is $O(\log * N)$, which is also the complexity of the algorithm.

Procedure RANDOMIZED-SELECT-MATCH-PAIRS
While nodes in match pairs are unmatched and have an unmatched partner Nodes in match pairs randomly select a match partner. If the nodes agree, they declare themselves matched.

Since nodes have a constant probability of being matched during every iteration, the expected time of the algorithm is $O(1)$. Therefore, step 4 of MERGE is $O(1)$ if the randomized algorithm match-select algorithm is used, and $O(\log * N)$ in the deterministic case. Thus the overall REDUCE complexities are $O(\log N)$ and $O(\log * N \log N)$, respectively. The complexity constant improves drastically if the coterie is known to be a tree. The algorithm runs as follows:

Algorithm TREE-REDUCE
While |nodes| > 1 **do in parallel**
    Use TREE-MERGE to merge legal pairs of adjacent nodes where legal pairs have at least one node with degree 1 or 2.

Since trees have the property that at least half the nodes have degree 1 or 2, the **While** loop executes $O(\log N)$ times. The fraction of nodes available for merger in the general merge algorithm is likely to be substantially smaller.

Procedure TREE-MERGE
$\forall$ nodes **do in parallel**
1. Find adjacent nodes and compute degree.
2. Exchange degree information with all neighbors.

3. Execute either the random or deterministic version of TREE-SELECT-MATCH-PAIRS.
4. Combine nodes according to case 1 presented above.

The tree version of the randomized match-pair selection algorithm is identical to the nontree version. In the deterministic case, however, we need only run chain MIS, rather than the coterie version.

Procedure TREE-DETERMINISTIC-SELECT-MATCH-PAIRS
1. Nodes adjacent to d_1 nodes select one of them for merger.
2. Nodes with degree 3 or 4 adjacent to d_2 nodes choose one for merger with the d_2 node breaking ties.
3. Form chains of the contiguous remaining d_2 nodes. Members of the MIS choose merger partners, with chosen nodes breaking ties.

The advantages of TREE-MERGE are that no neighbor lists need to be created, exchanged, or searched for duplicates; that symmetry breaking is much easier on a chain than on a bounded-degree planar graph; and that only case 1 of the actual node combining needs to be executed. However, since we are not aware of any algorithm to create a spanning tree out of arbitrary coteries that is itself not $O(\log N)$, TREE-REDUCE will likely only be useful if multiple reductions on a coterie partition are to be computed.

4 Practical algorithms and experimental results

Now we investigate the performance of reduction algorithms in a working image-segmentation system. This system has been used extensively in image interpretation research in various image domains. We find that a hybrid global/multiassociative technique yields the best performance in practice.

4.1 A segmentation system

Many segmentation systems use a region-merging paradigm based on the extraction of local region properties and the constraint of global criteria [5, 8, 26, 2]. Region merging begins by characterizing each region by the means and standard deviations of various spectral quantities, by its size, and by the lengths of its common borders with adjacent regions. Based on these values, merge scores are calculated with respect to the adjacent regions. Region pairs are merged if their merge score is both a local maximum and surpasses a global threshold. The process is repeated until no merge scores surpass the global threshold.

The bulk of the computation occurs during the original region characterization; thereafter, characterizations are computed from the attributes of the constituent regions. The critical problem is therefore the efficient reduction of the regions of the oversegmented image.

The data set consists of 28 256×256 intensity images of which 13 are road scenes and 15 are house scenes. Figure 14 shows a sample image from the road scene domain, the phase 1 output (oversegmented image), and the final segmentation. See [2] for more examples. The oversegmented images have an average of 1900 regions with a standard deviation of 788. See Figure 15 for details.

4.2 Multiassociative reduction algorithms

We now present an SVCC-based multiassociative reduction algorithm for arbitrary coteries that is the basis for our practical algorithm. The parallel-prefix algorithm follows as before with little added complexity.

Algorithm Local REDUCE
1. Partition the coterie into horizontal lines.
2. Reduce lines and leave the result in the right endpoint.
3. Partition the coterie into SVCCs.
4. Reduce SVCCs leaving the result in the bottom endpoint. The bottom endpoints of the SVCCs in each region form a set S with cardinality $|S|$.

DO UNTIL $|S| = 0$ for all coteries
5. Use SelectSingleResponder to select an element s from S.
6. s broadcasts its partial sum to the elements in S which combine that value with their own.
7. s removes itself from S.

Steps 1 and 3 are constant time operations, while 2 and 4 require $\log n$ communication and arithmetic operations. (From here on, the algorithm used in step 3 is assumed to be the one in [12].) In the DO loop (a phase we refer to as *local removal*), Step 5 uses an $O(\log N)$ algorithm (although with a small constant), while Steps 6 and 7 are again constant time operations. The overall complexity is therefore proportional to $\log N$ and depends on the number of SVCCs $|S|$ into which the worst-behaved coterie has in the image been partitioned. Since it is relatively easy to construct a coterie where $|S| = O(N)$, we are left with an $O(N \log N)$ algorithm.

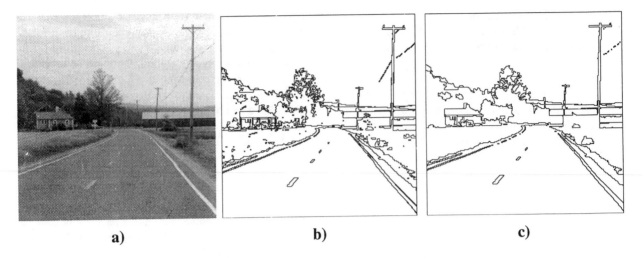

a)   b)   c)

Figure 14. (a) Sample image is road scene 16; (b) oversegmentation of image; (c) image after region merge.

Image Type	Average number of regions	Average number of SVCCs	Average SVCCs per reg.	Max SVCCs per reg.	Average count of regions with this # SVCCs				
					1–10	11–20	21–30	31–40	41+
road	1824.6	2871.5	1.60	216.5	1810.2	7.1	2.6	1.5	3.3
house	1965.3	2717.5	1.38	98.3	1952.8	6.7	2.5	0.9	2.4
average all	1900.0	2789.0	1.48	153.1	1887.6	6.9	2.5	1.2	2.8

Figure 15. Image statistics for the data set after completion of the oversegmentation phase. For reference, the average number of regions per image is substantially greater than *n*, and the average number of regions per image with more than 10 SVCCs is 13.4.

Since we are investigating practical algorithms in this section, a quantity more important than the worst case of $|S|$ is its size during real applications. Results are presented in Figure 15. In summary, it is common for at least one region per image to be so badly behaved as to make the above algorithm impractical: The DO loop would have to be executed an average of 153 times and a value of 300 would not be unlikely. However, the number of badly behaved regions per image is small (with an average of only 13 regions per image having more than 10 SVCCs), signaling the possibility of large performance gains with a relatively small amount of additional work.

One possibility is to add one or more SMCC reduction steps, that is, to repeat steps 3 and 4 alternating between the vertical and the horizontal dimension. After all, if SVCC reduction of endpoints eliminates a large fraction of the horizontal line accumulators, it seems likely that SHCC reduction of SVCC accumulators could also be helpful.

Algorithm SMCC REDUCE
1. Partition the coterie into horizontal lines.

2. Reduce lines and leave the result in the right endpoint.
DO I TIMES
3. Partition the coterie into SVCCs.
4. Reduce the SVCCs leaving the result in the bottom endpoint.
5. Partition the coterie into SHCCs.
6. Reduce the SHCCs leaving the result in the right-most endpoint.
DO UNTIL $|S| = 0$ for all coteries
7. Use SelectSingleResponder to select an element *s* from *S*.
8. *s* broadcasts its partial sum to the elements in *S* which combine that value with their own.
9. *s* removes itself from *S*.

The distribution of $|S|$ as a function of *I* (see Figure 16) shows that the return diminishes rapidly. What happens is that some regions have a large number of SVCC-SHCC pairs that contain each other's accumulators. No progress was ever made after *I* reached 20.

A more promising alternative is the hybrid algorithm in the following section.

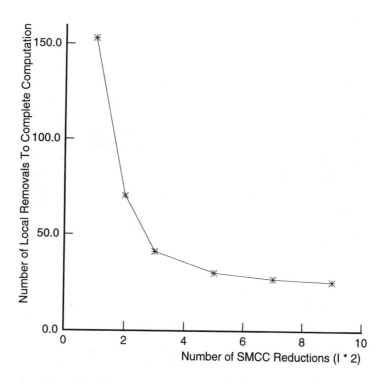

Figure 16. Graph of Max(|S|) versus *I*. The reduction in the number of times local removal must be executed levels off after *I* = 2 (number of reductions = 4).

4.3   A hybrid reduction algorithm

For any particular region *r* from the set of regions *R*, it is usually faster to execute reduction/prefix algorithms by applying the resources of the entire array to that problem instance than it is to use only those PEs to which the region is mapped. There follows a simple reduction algorithm based on array reduction procedures (which we call *global removal*).

Algorithm Global REDUCE
DO UNTIL |R| = 0
  1.   Use GlobalSelectSingleResponder to select an arbitrary region *r* from *R*.
  2.   Use the resources of the array to reduce *r*.
  3.   Remove *r* from *R*.

Depending on the operation being used during the reduction, the complexity of step 2 can range from $O(\log N)$ in the general case, down to $O(1)$ when executing the CountSelectedResponders operation with appropriate hardware support [25]. Similarly, step 1 can also have complexity from $O(1)$ using hardware described in [9] to $O(\log N)$ if only a global OR circuit is available. In any case, the algorithm is efficient if

and only if |R| is small. We have seen, however, that the number of regions in an oversegmentation can be huge: in the case where regions are relatively small, |R| = $O(N)$.

The idea behind hybrid reduction is to combine the global algorithm with the local removal operation used in the SMCC-based algorithm. After two reduction passes (steps 1-4), an as-yet-undetermined number of local removals is executed. Global removals are then used to finish the reduction.

Algorithm Hybrid-REDUCE
  1.   Partition the coterie into horizontal lines.
  2.   Reduce lines and leave the result in the right endpoint.
  3.   Partition the coterie into SVCCs.
  4.   Reduce SVCCs leaving the result in the bottom endpoint. The bottom endpoints of the SVCCs in each region form a set *S* with cardinality |S|.
DO an optimal number (*O*) TIMES
  5.   Use SelectSingleResponder to select an element *e* from *S*.
  6.   *e* broadcasts its partial sum to the elements in *S* which combine that value with their own.
  7.   *e* removes itself from *S*.

45

DO UNTIL |R| = 0

    8.   Use GlobalSelectSingleResponder to select a region r from R.

    9.   Use a global reduction algorithm to reduce r.

    10. Host broadcasts result back to r.

    11. r removes itself from R.

Recall from Section 2.5 and Figure 3 the rationale behind hybrid algorithms: The first loop moves the curve to the left until only the long, flat tail remains; the second loop processes the tail in a number of steps equal to its maximum height. The optimal number of iterations for the first loop (O) can be approximated using either of the two methods previously described. In particular, we see in Figure 17 that for each ratio of global to local removal time, O has a relatively small variance. This indicates that O can be fixed *a priori*, with only a small cost in compute time.

4.4   Performance and comparison

Now we examine how the Hybrid-REDUCE algorithm is likely to perform using existing technology, and how its relative performance is likely to change with technological advances. Throughout this subsection the operation is assumed to be CountSelected PEs, the data to be 32-bit integers, and the array to consist of a 256×256 grid of PEs.

The relative performance of primitive operations on existing technology was obtained by using results from the CAAPP prototype, a 64×64 array of bit-serial processing elements, and through hardware simulation of the full-size array. The instruction durations in machine cycles are as follows: coterie communication instructions $t_{Cot} = 10$, GlobalCount $t_{GC} = 20$, and all other instruction, including ALU broadcast and PE arithmetic instructions, $t_{PE} = 1$. Since a single iteration of local and global removal take about 100 and 580 cycles respectively, the ratio $K = 6$. We have used average case values for the local and global loop counts from Figure 17: $O = 4$ and $R = 17$. These are justified because of the small variance of O. Bookkeeping added up to fewer than 100 cycles and was ignored.

Significant is that the local and global removal phases—the parts of the computation that are not asymptotically optimal—take a similar number of cycles as the reductions executed during the first phase. This means that executing extra reductions as in the SMCC-Reduce algorithm is not likely to improve performance.

	Ratio of Local to Global Removal Execution Times (K)									
	1	2	3	4	5	6	7	8	9	10
average of O	13.3	9.7	8.2	6.6	6.2	5.7	5.3	5.2	5.0	4.8
Sigma of O	4.0	2.8	2.4	1.7	1.6	1.6	1.2	1.2	1.1	1.2
average of R	9.3	13.4	16.7	21.7	23.6	25.8	28.4	29.2	30.9	32.2
Sigma of R	3.6	4.7	4.9	6.2	7.1	6.9	7.6	7.2	8.0	8.6

Figure 17. Average optimal values over the entire data set for local and global removal operations (O and R) and their standard deviations for different ratios of local to global removal execution times (K).

$$FirstTwoReductions \Rightarrow 2 * \log n * (32 * t_{Cot} + 64 * t_{PE}) = 2624 \; cycles$$

$$LocalRemoval \Rightarrow O * \begin{cases} SelectSingleResponder \Rightarrow \log N * (t_{Cot} + 2 * t_{PE}) \\ BroadcastPartialSum \Rightarrow 32 * t_{Cot} \\ CombinePartialSum \Rightarrow 64 * t_{PE} \end{cases} \quad = 3480 \; cycles$$

$$GlobalRemoval \Rightarrow R * \begin{cases} GlobalSelectSingleResponder \Rightarrow 3 * \log N * t_{PE} \\ GlobalCount \Rightarrow t_{GC} \\ BroadcastResult \Rightarrow 32 * t_{PE} \end{cases} \quad = 2652 \; cycles$$

Two likely changes in hardware performance will alter the relative performance of the algorithms: the latency of the coterie network broadcast, and the path width of the coterie network bus. The expression

$$cycles = \frac{512}{w}(t_{Cot} + 2) + O(\frac{32}{w} + 16)$$

$$(t_{Cot} + 2) + R(70 + \frac{32}{w})$$

relates the performance of Hybrid-REDUCE to the two parameters, width = w and coterie communication latency = t_{Cot}. The loop counter values O and R are again obtained empirically from Figure 17 where K is determined as follows:

$$K = \frac{(\frac{32}{w} + 16)(2 + t_{Cot})}{70 + \frac{32}{w}}$$

The resultant changes in performance of the hybrid algorithm are illustrated in Figure 18. The improvement due to increasing path width levels off because SelectSingleResponder is inherently bit-serial.

The range of coterie latency to PE instruction ratios was selected with the following scenarios in mind. The current ratio is about 10. An increase is likely as the VLSI process improves, while the basic packaging configuration remains as it is. We estimate a factor of 3 maximum relative speedup here over the short term as the design improves, but no greater since clock distribution problems for massively parallel arrays are significant. A decrease in the ratio is likely in future-generation machines when the entire array will fit on a wafer (or chip). However, it is very unlikely that the coterie latency will ever be less than the global signal propagation, bounding the minimum of the ratio at 1.

5   Conclusion

We have presented new associative computational models, shown that they can be implemented efficiently on reconfigurable broadcast networks, and that they are effective in the domain of spatially mapped applications.

The method we use to implement multiassociative processing involves coterie structures. This model can compensate for the absence of an efficient, general, distributed-memory access capability (available only in idealized models) through the orchestrated partitioning of the subgraphs induced by the data. In this way, certain PRAM results were shown to hold for arbitrary, connected components of the reconfigurable mesh as well. We have also shown how to take advantage of coterie broadcast to break symmetries and to obtain information independent of distance.

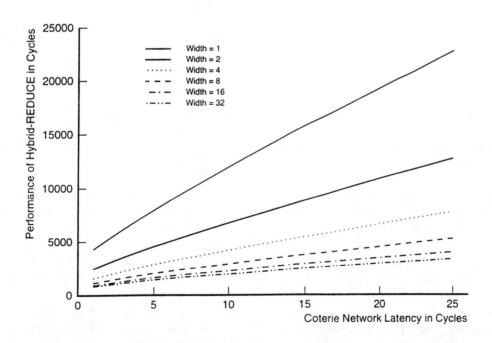

Figure 18. Expected performance of Hybrid-REDUCE given changes in network latency and path width.

The algorithms presented are significant from both a theoretical and a practical point of view—the former because they show the richness of this computational model, the latter because they are likely to be the fastest available. In fact, Hybrid-REDUCE runs more than an order of magnitude faster than previous methods. Another significant result, however, is that we have shown it is possible to create efficient algorithms "without leaving the coterie;" that irregular graphs need not preclude good solutions for problems on reconfigurable broadcast networks.

We assume that the definitions, basic algorithms, and methodology will be useful in solving many other multiassociative problems. Especially promising is the use of coterie structures to solve problems in computational geometry. Of longer term interest is the problem of creating a system that efficiently responds to general multiassociative queries.

Acknowledgment

We thank Seth Malitz for many useful conversations and for his encouragement in this project. This work was supported in part by the Defense Advanced Research Projects Agency under Contract DACA76-89-C-0016, monitored by the US Army Engineer Topographic Laboratory; under Contract DAAL02-91-K-0047, monitored by the US Army Harry Diamond Laboratory; and by a CII grant from the National Science Foundation (CDA-8922572). Martin Herbordt was supported in part by an IBM fellowship.

References

[1] C. Berge, *Graphs and Hypergraphs*, North-Holland, Amsterdam, 1973.

[2] J.R. Beveridge et al., "Segmenting Images Using Localized Histograms and Region Merging," *Int'l J. Computer Vision*, Vol. 2, No. 3, 1989, pp. 311–347.

[3] G.E. Blelloch, "Scans as Primitive Parallel Operations," *IEEE Trans. Computers*, Vol. C-38, No. 11, 1989.

[4] G.E. Belloch and G.W. Sabot, "Compiling Collection-Oriented Languages onto Massively Parallel Computers," *J. Parallel and Distributed Computing*, Vol. 8, 1990, pp. 119–134.

[5] C. R. Brice and C. L. Fennema, "Scene Analysis Using Regions," *Artificial Intelligence*, Vol. 1, 1970, pp. 205–226.

[6] T.H. Cormen, C. Leiserson, and R.L. Rivest, *Introduction to Algorithms*, MIT Press, Cambridge, Mass., 1990.

[7] A.D. Falkoff, "Algorithms for Parallel Search Memories," *J. ACM*, Vol. 9, No. 4, 1962, pp. 488–511.

[8] J.A. Feldman and Y. Yakimovsky, "Decision Theory and Artificial Intelligence I: A Semantics-Based Region Analyzer, *Artificial Intelligence*, Vol. 5, 1974, pp. 349–371.

[9] C.C. Foster, *Content Addressable Parallel Processors*, Van Nostrand Reinhold, New York, N.Y., 1986.

[10] E.J. Gauss, "Locating the Largest Word in a File Using a Modified Memory," *J. ACM*, Vol. 8, 1961, pp. 418–425.

[11] A.V. Goldberg and S.A. Plotkin, "Parallel ($\delta + 1$) Coloring of Constant Degree Graphs," *Information Processing Letters*, Vol. 25, No. 4, 1987, pp. 241–245.

[12] M.C. Herbordt, C.C. Weems, and M.J. Scudder, "Nonuniform Region Processing on SIMD Arrays Using the Coterie Network," *Machine Vision and Applications*, Vol. 5, No. 2, 1992, pp. 105–125.

[13] W.D. Hillis and G.L. Steele Jr., "Data Parallel Algorithms," *Comm. ACM*, Vol. 29, No. 12, 1986, pp. 1,170–1,183.

[14] K.E. Iverson, *A Programming Language*, John Wiley and Sons, New York, N.Y., 1962.

[15] J.F. Jenq and S. Sahni, "Reconfigurable Mesh Algorithms for the Area and Perimeter of Image Components," *Proc. 1991 Int'l Conf. Parallel Processing*, CRC Press, Boca Raton, Fla., pp. 280–281.

[16] R.M. Karp and V. Ramachandran, "A Survey of Parallel Algorithms for Shared-Memory Machines," in *Handbook of Theoretical Computer Science*, North-Holland, Amsterdam, 1988.

[17] R.E. Ladner and M.J. Fisher, "Parallel Prefix Computation," *J. ACM*, Vol. 27, No. 4, 1980, pp. 831–838.

[18] H. Li and M. Maresca, "Polymorphic Torus Network," *IEEE Trans. Computers*, Vol. C-38, No. 9, 1989, pp. 1,345–1,351.

[19] J.J. Little, G.E. Blelloch, and T.A. Cass, "Algorithmic Techniques for Computer Vision on a Fine-Grained Parallel Machine," *IEEE Trans. Pattern Analysis and Machine Intelligence*, Vol. 11, No. 3, 1989, pp. 244–257.

[20] M. Maresca, "Polymorphic Processor Arrays," *IEEE Trans. Parallel and Distributed Systems*, Vol. 4, 1993, pp. 490–506.

[21] G.L. Miller and J.H. Reif, "Parallel Tree Contraction and its Applications," *Proc. 28th IEEE Symp. Foundations of Computer Sci.*, IEEE CS Press, Los Alamitos, Calif., 1985, pp. 478–489.

[22] R. Miller et al., "Parallel Computations on Reconfigurable Meshes," *IEEE Trans. Computers*, Vol. 42, No. 6, 1993, pp. 678–692.

[23] B. Obrenic et al., "Using Emulations to Construct High-Performance Virtual Parallel Architectures," Tech. Rep. TR91-40, Dept. of Computer Sci., Univ. of Massachusetts, 1991.

[24] C.A. Phillips, "Parallel Graph Contraction," *Proc. 1st ACM Symp. Parallel Algorithms and Architectures*, ACM Press, New York, N.Y., 1989, pp. 148–157.

[25] D. Rana and C.C. Weems, "The iua Feedback Concentrator," *Proc. Int'l Conf. Pattern Recognition*, IEEE CS Press, Los Alamitos, Calif., 1990, pp. 540–544.

[26] J.M. Tenenbaum and H.G. Barrow, "Experiments in Interpretation Guided Segmentation," *Artificial Intelligence*, Vol. 8, 1976, pp. 241–274.

[27] C.C. Weems, "Image Processing on a Content Addressable Array Parallel Processor," doctoral dissertation, Univ. of Massachusetts, Dept. of Computer and Information Sci., Univ. of Massachusetts, Amherst, 1984.

[28] C.C. Weems et al., "The Image Understanding Architecture," *Int'l J. Computer Vision*, Vol. 2, No. 3, 1989.

Section II
Associative Processing
Architectures and Systems

ASP: A Cost-effective Parallel Microcomputer

Highly versatile, this densely packed parallel processor exploits advanced micro-electronic trends.

R. M. Lea
Aspex Microsystems Ltd.
Brunel University

Associative String Processor microcomputers provide highly versatile components for the low-cost implementation of high-performance information processing systems. By mapping application data structures to a string representation and supporting content addressing and parallel processing, ASP achieves both application flexibility and a step-function improvement in cost-performance figures. This improvement occurs without the loss of computational efficiency usually suffered by general-purpose parallel processors.

The ASP architecture offers cost-effective support of a particularly wide range of both numerical and nonnumerical computing applications while exploiting state-of-the-art microelectronic technology. This technology achieves processor packing densities that are more usually associated with memory components. In fact, we designed ASP to benefit from the inevitable VLSI-to-ULSI-to-WSI (very large, ultra large, and wafer-scale integration) technological trend, with a fully integrated, simply scalable, and defect/fault-tolerant processor interconnection strategy.

Here, I discuss the architectural philosophy, structural organization, operational principles, and VLSI/ULSI/WSI implementation of ASP and indicate its cost-performance potential. ASP microcomputers have the potential to achieve cost-performance targets in the range of 100 to 1,000 MOPS/$1,000 (million operations per second). This gives ASPs an advantage of two to three orders of magnitude over current parallel computer architectures.

The ASP architecture is based on a fully programmable and reconfigurable, homogeneous computational structure emerging from research at Brunel University and being developed by Aspex Microsystems. ASP[1-4] offers particularly flexible (see the box on "Associative Processing") support for structured data processing as indicated by the examples in Table 1.

The breadth of this application range indicates a large potential market for ASP within the aerospace, telecommunications, automobile, and manufacturing industries as well as the commercial, defense, and research sectors. It also demonstrates the importance of application flexibility and architectural extensibility (scaling processing power to match application requirements) as ASP design requirements.

While ASP exploits the opportunities presented by the latest advances in the VLSI-to-ULSI-to-WSI technological trend, it also makes use of the continually improving high-density system assembly techniques (multichip,

Reprinted from *IEEE Micro*, Vol. 8, No. 5, Oct. 1988, pp. 10–29.

52

Associative Processing

Many information processing applications require users to reference a set of data elements, associated with a common key, by the value of an associated key (rather than by their physical locations within some storage structure). Examples of data elements might include the selection of those Rover cars sold after 1987 with air-conditioning or those graduate software engineers with two years of experience in Ada programming or those pixels corresponding to a particular intensity value in a computer vision system or those facts and rules that are related to a particular query in a knowledge-based artificial intelligence system.

With traditional von Neumann computers, such data access requires repeated (sequential) navigation through some tree-structured (possibly complex) indirect-addressing mechanism to unique storage locations (where the sought data may or may not exist). This access method results in loss of accessing efficiency and much redundant processing.

In contrast, with associative processing users access the set of data elements in parallel by content addressing and simple association linking. The addresses of such data have no logical significance and only relevant data can be accessed. Moreover, associative processing avoids the additional overheads of sequentially transferring data to an external processor by (parallel) in-situ processing.

Associative processing involves a particularly flexible and naturally parallel form of symbolic representation and manipulation of structured data (sets, arrays, tables, trees, and graphs) processing. Potential benefits include simplicity of expression, storage capacity, and speed of execution over a wide variety of nonnumerical and numerical information processing applications.

Table 1.
ASP information processing applications.

Special-purpose applications

Nonnumerical information processing
  Text processing, database management, office systems, information management
  Information (document) retrieval for information, legal and patents services
  Intelligent knowledge-based, or expert, systems (medical, automotive systems)
Numerical information processing
  Digital signal processing in aerospace, military, telecommunications systems
  Speech recognition in military, business, automotive systems
  Image-related processing
    Computerized tomography for medical, industrial, geophysical image reconstruction
  Image clarification, scene analysis, pattern recognition in support of remote sensing (for satellites and surveillance), artificial vision (for robotics, automation)
  Computerized image generation for graphic arts and special television effects and CAD/CAM (3D image generation, associated database management)

General-purpose applications

Vector processing for research modeling and design simulation
Symbolic processing for compilation, translation, theorem proving
Artificial intelligence processing for fifth-generation (declarative) support of programming languages such as functional (LISP) and logic-based (Prolog)

---

multilayer thin-film ceramic, and silicon-on-silicon superhybrids). ASP remains independent of technology, so it can benefit from the inevitable improvement in microelectronics technology without architectural modification.

ASP system architecture

As indicated in Figure 1, an ASP system comprises a dynamically reconfigurable parallel processing structure of communicating ASP substrings, each supported with an ASP data buffer (ADB), a controller, and a data communications network.

ASP substrings. Each ASP substring comprises a string of identical APEs (associative processing elements), as shown in Figure 2. Each APE connects to an inter-APE communications network (which runs in parallel with the APE string). All APEs share common bit-parallel data, activity, and control buses, and one feedback line called Match Reply, or MR. An external controller maintains the buses, feedback line, and Link

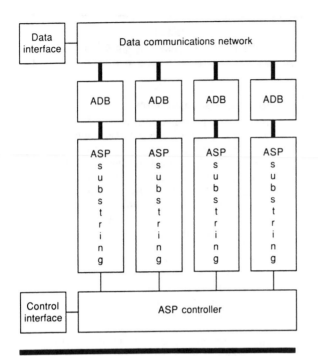

Figure 1. Activation of matching/mismatching APEs: before (1) and after (2).

Left and Link Right ports (LKL and LKR) of the inter-APE communications network.[2-4]

In contrast to more traditional parallel computer architectures, ASP uses content-matching rather than location-addressing techniques. Thus, ASP selects APEs for subsequent parallel processing by comparing their data and activity content with the states of the corresponding data and activity buses. Moreover, the lack of location addressing also simplifies system configuration and extension, implementation, and especially fault tolerance.

In operation, each ASP substring supports a form of set processing in which the subset of active APEs (those which match broadcast data and activity values) support scalar-vector and vector-vector operations. ASP either directly activates matching APEs or uses source inter-APE communications to indirectly activate other APEs (see the accompanying box). The match reply line indicates whether or not any APEs match. The controller either directly broadcasts scalar data or receives it via the bit-parallel data bus.

Similarly, ASP can also exchange input-output vector data (output dumped and input loaded in a single step) sequentially in APEs via the data bus with the bit-parallel primary data exchanger (PDX). As shown in Figure 2, the bit-parallel primary data exchanger

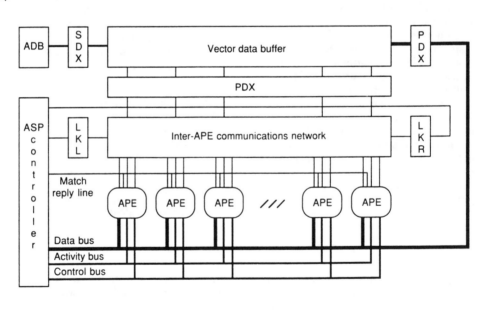

SDX = Secondary data exchanger
PDX = Primary data exchanger
LKL = Link left port
LKR = Link right port
APE = Associative processing element

Figure 2. ASP substring.

APE Activation Options

Associative processing elements may be activated for read or write operations by one of the following activation options.

Matching and mismatching APEs

Assuming the state of an ASP substring shown in Figure A1, where M represents matching APEs, activation A of matching and mismatching APEs appears as seen in Figure A2.

Asynchronous communication

For each of the five activation examples shown in Figure B, the first ASP substring state indicates matching M APEs. The second and third states indicate activations A following asynchronous signal transmission (to the left and right respectively) from LKL, LKR, or source S matching APEs to destination D previously matched APEs. The examples assume inter-APE communication within a single ASP segment, such that all block links are closed. As an option of the fourth and fifth activations, the first source APE may also be included in the set of activated APEs.

Figure A. Activation of matching/mismatching APEs: before (1) and after (2).

Figure B. Activations with asynchronous communication: an isolated matching APE (1); neighbors of matching APEs (2); remote APEs linked with matching APEs (3); substrings between matching APEs (4); and all APEs between matching APEs and one end of the string (5).

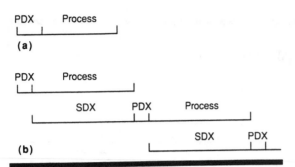

Figure 3. Example of unacceptable loss of efficiency (a); minimal loss of efficiency (b).

exchanges data. However, ASP loses the parallel processing advantage during sequential vector data exchange. Thus, depending on the time required to process the loaded vector data, the exchange could incur an unacceptable loss of parallel processing efficiency, as indicated in Figure 3a. In such cases, a vector data buffer supports a much faster APE-parallel exchange facility, in which a bit-serial PDX performs the task at a very high data rate. Thus we minimize the loss of parallel processing efficiency (Figure 3b).

Similarly, but at a lower data rate, the secondary data exchanger (SDX) provides a bit-parallel vector data exchange between the vector data buffer and the external ADB. The SDX overlaps parallel processing and, therefore, does not present a sequential processing overhead. Consequently, whereas the bit-parallel PDX is a fundamental feature of a substring, the vector data buffer and its support bit-serial PDX and SDX are optional components of ASP. They are incorporated only for those applications requiring relatively short parallel processing periods.

Associative processing element. Each APE incorporates an n-bit data register and an a-bit activity register, an $(n+a)$-bit parallel comparator in which the values of n and a are 32 to 128 bits and 4 to 8 bits, depending on the application class for which ASP is optimized. Moreover, an APE includes a single-bit full-adder and four status flags (C to represent arithmetic carry, M and D to tag matching and destination APEs, and A to activate selected APEs). An APE also includes control logic for local processing and communication with other APEs. See Figure 4.

Data modes and activity bits. ASP hardware supports three modes of data representation (word, byte, and bit) within the n-bit data register (DR), as defined (in Pascal) in the following example (for $n = 32$ bits).

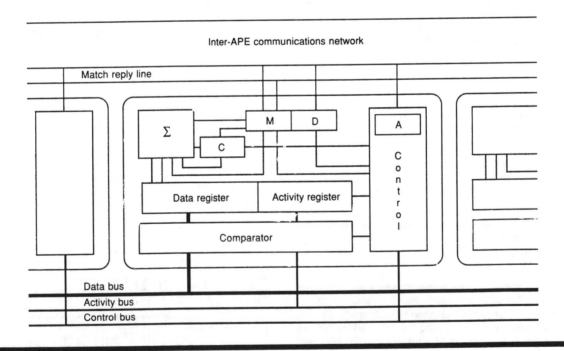

Figure 4. Associative processing element, or APE.

```
DR = record
    case data_mode of
        word_mode : (word : array [0..31] of 0..1);
        byte_mode : (byte : array [0..3,0..7] of 0..1);
        bit_mode  : (sf_1 : array [3..13] of 0..1;
                     sf_2 : array [14..22] of 0..1;
                     sf_3 : array [25..31] of 0..1)
    end
```

In word mode the data register provides storage for (and supports bit-parallel processing of) an n-bit binary word, as shown in Figure 5a. Alternatively, in byte mode the data register stores 8-bit byte fields, as shown in Figure 5b, and supports bit-parallel processing of a selected byte field. In bit mode the data register can store variable-length binary fields for bit-serial processing (Figure 5c). Users can declare one, two, or three such serial fields for unary, binary, or ternary bit-serial operations. Moreover, data representation is not limited by the n-bits of a single data register, since, in all three data modes, a contiguous string of APEs can be allocated for operand storage.

In contrast, the a-bit activity register provides storage for an a-element ordered set defined in Figure 5d (for 5 activity bits) as a Pascal-set type. Sets are stored such that the inclusion or exclusion of aB is represented by the state (1 or 0 respectively) of the Bth activity bit in the activity register.

Data and activity masking. To support data and activity masking, without the processing overheads normally incurred with specific mask registers, both the data bus and the activity bus support ternary data. The data bus incorporates a mask field, such that, for each bit of the data register, the data bus can support a 2-bit ternary digit representing one of three values (dX, d0, and d1).

The digits of the data bus in selected byte fields and those corresponding to the indexed bits of selected serial fields (in byte and bit modes) may be set to any of

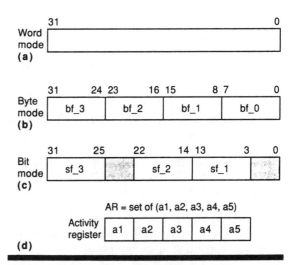

Figure 5. Data representation modes in the data register: word (a), byte (b), and bit (c). Activity register storage (d).

the three values. And, all digits in nonselected byte fields and serial fields, plus those digits corresponding to the nonindexed bits of selected serial fields, automatically assume the dX value. However, to economize on ASP chip input ports, designers chose not to allow the dX value in word mode.

Similarly, the activity bus supports 2-bit ternary digits such that its Bth activity digit can represent the presence or absence of aB or a masked aB in the activity register.

Basic APE operations. APEs support four basic operations, match, add, read, and write. Examples of each in pseudo-Pascal statements appear in the accompanying box. In a match operation the M and D tags become true in matching APEs and false in mismatching APEs. In an add operation the M tag and the C flag (in all APEs matching the specified activity bits) repre-

Basic APE Operations

Match: the M and D tags become true in matching APEs and false in mismatching
          APEs, as suggested by the following pseudo-Pascal statements

```
forall APEs do                       {simultaneously in each APE}
    if DR_match and AR_match
    then case tagoption of
        M         :   the M tag becomes true;
        MandD     :   both the M and D tags become true;
        DaltM     :   for each ASP segment, the D and M
                      tags become true starting (from the left
                      end of the segment) with D
    end
```

sent the sum and carry of a bit-serial addition (or subtraction) operation. During read, ASP updates each digit of the data bus DB[j] to the state of the wire-AND (0's are "stronger" than 1's) of the corresponding DR[j] bits of all activated APEs and their activity registers can be updated. During a write operation ASP updates the data register and the activity register in activated APEs according to the states of the data bus and the activity bus.

Inter-APE communications network. As indicated in Figure 2, each substring supports two styles of inter-APE communication,

• bit-parallel, single-APE communication via the shared data bus and
• bit-serial, multiple-APE communication via the inter-APE communications network.

Although the former can be used to advantage on many occasions, we discuss the latter here.

The inter-APE communications network implements a globally controlled and dynamically reconfigurable, tightly coupled APE interconnection strategy. This strategy supports cost-effective emulation of common network topologies (see box on p. 18). Most significantly, the APE interconnection strategy supports simple modular network extension, to enable tailoring of parallel processing power to match user requirements.

In contrast to the networks adopted by other parallel computer architectures, we did not design the inter-APE communications network primarily for the transfer of actual data between APEs. Instead, and much more simply, we restricted communication to the high-speed transfer of activity signals (or M-tag patterns) between neighboring or selected remote APEs (those matching the selection criteria). Since APEs can easily be activated by content addressing and their data content processed in situ, we reduce the time-consuming movement of data to an absolute minimum.

```
        else case tagoption of
            M              :    the M tag becomes false;
            MandD, DaltM   :    both the M and D tags become false
        end
```

where DR__match and AR__match are defined as follows.

For each APE, assuming DR__match has been initialized as true

```
    forall j in [1..n] do                      {simultaneously for each digit}
      if DB[j] < > dX
        then DR__match := DR__match and (DB[j] = DR[j]);
      AR__match := ([included AB bits] < = AR) and      {set inclusion test}
                   (AR < = ([a1,a2,a3,a4,a5] − [excluded AB bits]))
```

If any M tag becomes true, as a result of the match operation, then the global Match Reply also becomes true, otherwise MR becomes false.

Add: in all APEs matching the specified activity bits, the M tag and C flag represent the sum and carry of a bit-serial addition (or subtraction) operation, as suggested by the following pseudo-Pascal statements, assuming C has been initialized as '0'

```
    forall APEs do                             {simultaneously in each APE}
      if AR__match
        then begin
              M := not M0 < > (M1 < > (C = 1));
              if not M0 and (M1 or (C = 1)) or (M1 and (C = 1))
                then C := 1
                else C := 0
        end
```

where, M0 and M1 are derived in each APE, for the bits (indexed by j and k) of selected serial-fields, as follows

```
    case addend of
        scalar   : M0 := DB(J) = DR[z];        { scalar addend}
        vector   : M0 := DR(j) = 0;            {vector addend}
        M__tag   : M0 := not M                 {vector addend}
    end;
        M1 := DR[k] = 1                         {vector augend}
```

58

In fact, the APE interconnection strategy supports two modes of inter-APE communication:

• **Circuit-switching**. Asynchronous, bidirectional, single-bit communication occurs via multiple signal paths, dynamically configured (programmer transparent) to connect APE sources and corresponding APE destinations of high-speed activation signals. Circuit-switching implements a fully connected permutation and broadcast network for APE selection and inter-APE routing functions.

• **Packet-switching**. Synchronous, bidirectional, multibit communication via a high-speed bit-serial shift register, routing M-tag patterns along each APE substring for data/message transfer.

To preserve continuity at the two ends of the inter-APE communications network, the LKL and LKR ports (shown in Figure 2) allow activation or M-bit signals to be injected and sensed by the external ASP controller. They also act as the left and right neighbors of the leftmost and rightmost APEs in the associative string processor.

APE block bypassing. Each substring is partitioned into equal-length APE blocks, separated by block links, as indicated in Figure 6 on p. 19. At an abstract level, and assuming a programmable connection between the LKL and LKR ports, the inter-APE communications network can be considered as a hierarchical chordal-ring structure, with the chords bypassing APE blocks (and groups of APE blocks). The network:

• *Accelerates inter-APE communication signals.* APE blocks, not including destination APEs are automatically bypassed for both circuit-switched and (if required) packet-switched modes of inter-APE communication and, if appropriate for the former mode, activated in a single step.

---

where DR(z) indexes a single-bit serial-field of 0's, and for subtraction (i.e., 2's complement addition), C is initialized as '1' and M0 is not complemented.

Read: each digit of the data bus DB[j] is updated to the state of the wire-AND (i.e., 0's are "stronger" than 1's) of the corresponding DR[j] bits of all activated APEs, as suggested by the pseudo-Pascal statements

```
forall j in [1..n] do                    {simultaneously for each bit}
  if DR[j]_test
    then DB[j] := d0
    else  DB[j] := d1
```

where DR[j]_test, assuming it has been initialized as false, is derived as follows

```
forall APEs do                           {simultaneously in each APE}
  if A
    then DR[j]_test := DR[j]_test or (DR[j] = 0)
```

and the Activity Register AR is updated as for write operations.

Clearly, it is sensible to activate only one APE per ASP substring for read operations.

Write: the Data Register (DR) and Activity Register (AR) are updated in activated APEs according to the states of the data bus and the activity bus as suggested by the following pseudo-Pascal statements

```
forall APEs do                           {simultaneously in each APE}
  if A
    then begin
         forall j in [1..n] do           {simultaneously for each bit}
           if DB[j] < > dX
             then DR[j] := DB[j];
         AR := AR + [included AB bits] − [excluded AB bits]
    end                                  {set union and difference}
```

ASP Support of Structured Data

We specifically designed the reconfigurable inter-APE communications network of the ASP substring to support any data structure with cost-effective emulation of common network topologies. Examples of these topologies appear in Figures C through F.

Arrays

For vectors, data registers store consecutive elements j in consecutive APEs within a segment, with an activity bit or L's, providing local origins for element j indexing. See Figure C1.

For matrices, concatenated vectors (segments) separated with an activity bit or L's represent consecutive matrix rows i. L's provide local origins for column j indexing, as indicated in Figure C2.

For cubes, hyperspace structures can be represented in a similar manner to that shown for the matrix. For example, the binary n-cube (where $n = 3$) structure could be represented as shown in Figure C3 and navigated with exchange mappings (see address permutations).

Tables

The fields F, each being allocated one or more consecutive APEs, are ordered and delimited with an activity bit (for example, a1). Similarly, entries can be separated with another activity bit or with L's, if each entry is allocated a segment (see Figure D).

Trees

An n-ary tree can be represented in list form, with the head of each sublist being a parent node and the tail comprising the n-child nodes. One or more consecutive APEs represent each node. Sublists may be delimited with an activity bit or with parentheses as:

$$(A(BCD)(EF(GHI)))$$

With this representation many subtrees can be navigated and reduced in parallel.

Graphs

Semantic networks may be represented in list form, as indicated earlier for trees. However, for large complex networks, APE data registers can be allocated to nodes, which comprise in-links (lowercase letters), data (uppercase letters), and out-links (see Figure E). Users navigate the semantic network by searching for an in-link that has been read from the out-links of the previously matching node.

In general, for address permutation networks we try to avoid the actual movement of data between

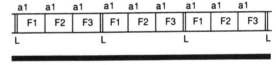

Figure D. Table example.

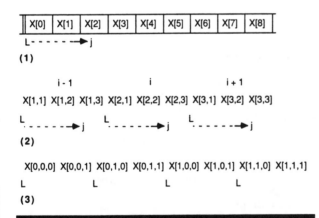

Figure C. Array examples for vector (1); matrix (2); and cube (3).

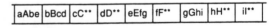

Figure E. Tree example.

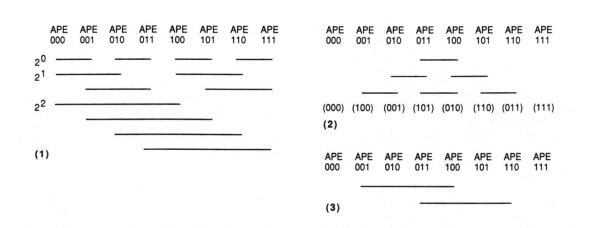

Figure F. Moving data between APEs by exchange (1), shuffle (2), and butterfly (3) techniques.

physically addressed APEs in favor of content addressing and activation alternatives. Modifying logical addresses assigned to a field of APE data registers effectively achieves data transfer, for those algorithms requiring association of data with processor location. However, if data movement between physically addressed APEs is definitely required, we accomplish it with one or more of the following techniques.

• **Exchange.** We achieve a specified mapping with a single shift in each direction along the substring

for a distance that is an appropriate power of 2, as indicated in Figure F1's three examples.

• **Shuffle.** For N APEs, we achieve the perfect shuffle in $\log_2 N$ steps by pyramidal neighbor exchange, as shown in Figure F2.

• **Butterfly.** For N APEs, a single exchange, as indicated in Figure F3, achieves this address permutation.

• **Shifting.** As its name suggests, we achieve this address permutation by synchronously shifting (left or right) M-tag patterns between selected APEs.

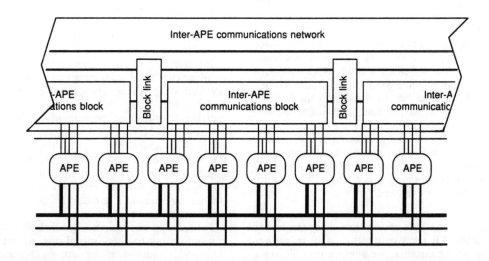

Figure 6. APE block bypassing.

• *Provides APE block defect/fault tolerance.* APE blocks failing a test routine, either in manufacture or service, switch out of the string, such that defective or faulty blocks are simply bypassed.

To provide cost-effective improvement of inter-APE communication speed and defect/fault tolerance, APE block bypassing depends on the implementation. For example, a VLSI ASP may support bypassing of 8-, 64-, and 256-APE block groups and entire ASP substrings. ULSI/WSI ASPs bypassing block groups of 4 and 64 APEs and entire branches (ASP substrings) may be specified as design criteria.

To avoid loss of computational efficiency, designers chose to make hardware features of the APE blocks, block links, and block bypassing transparent to the ASP programmer.

ASP segments and segment links. Each substring may be partitioned into programmer-defined segments, separated by segment links, in support of structured data. See box entitled "ASP Support of Structured data." APE block links incorporate bistables, which can be toggled to convert the block links into programmable segment links. The segment links can be opened or closed to prevent or allow the transmission of inter-APE communication signals between adjacent segments. Thus, each segment comprises a span of contiguous APE blocks, with internal block links closed and end block links converted to segment links.

Users can create variable-length segments by writing segment links corresponding to the M_tags at the ends of APE blocks. Alternatively, they can create equal-length segments, comprising power-of-2 APEs, with a special command.

ASP data buffer. Each ADB module provides data block storage immediately before and after processing within its local substring as shown in Figure 1. In addition to data storage each ADB module incorporates bit-parallel primary and secondary data exchangers (PDX and SDX) similar to those shown for the vector data buffer in Figure 2. In operation the PDX of each ADB module complements the SDX of its ASP substring. The corresponding SDX in each ADB module complements the data interface (DI) and the SDX of other ADB modules via the data communication network.

Consequently, in contrast to inter-APE communication within each substring, the ADB modules allow data communication between substrings to be fully overlapped with substring processing. This feature avoids data transfer overheads.

ASP controller. With appropriate management of the LKL and LKR ports of multiple ASP substrings within the ASP controller, we achieve two different configurations:

• multiple substrings, under the control of one controller, to form a SIMSIMD (single-instruction control of multiple SIMD modules) configuration, and

• multiple substrings, each under the control of an independent controller, to form a MIMSIMD (multiple-instruction control of multiple SIMD modules) configuration.

Moreover, by feeding LKL and LKR ports to a programmable router (within the ASP controller), users could also construct reconfigurable ASP structures that could adapt dynamically to the changing needs of complex computational tasks. The reconfigurable structures would provide flexible coverage of the wide range of information processing applications already outlined.

In operation, the ASP controller executes a sequence of procedures (stored as microprograms) called by an application program running in the host machine. All APEs in a substring receive microinstructions that are broadcast on the control bus. In addition to the microprogram unit, the ASP controller also incorporates a scalar data buffer and a scalar processor.

In common with typical high-speed microprogram-controllers, users could implement a general-purpose controller with standard bit-slice microprocessor components on two double-extended Eurocards. This approach could be reduced to one board for simpler controllers. Indeed, in cases where eventual production volume justifies the extra development cost, semicustom VLSI implementation could reduce the controller to a small chip set. Moreover, for some application-specific ASPs, dedicated control logic could be incorporated on the VLSI ASP substring chip.

ASP data communications network. The interprocessor communication network usually dominates parallel computer cost and performance. Consequently, the integration of a cost-effective APE interconnection strategy was a major design goal for the ASP system architecture.

Investigation of the interprocessor communication requirements for a wide range of parallel algorithms revealed a Zipf-curve relationship between frequency and distance. Short-distance communication is common and long-distance communication is rare. Consequently, the hierarchical interconnection strategy adopted for ASP supports a high degree of parallelism for local communication (within the inter-APE communications network) and progressively lower degrees of parallelism for longer distance communication (within the inter-APE communications and data communications networks).

Thus, we do not restrict SIMSIMD and MIMSIMD configurations to the chordal-ring structure of the inter-APE communications network. For example, we could configure the data communications network

ASP Operations

In operation, the ASP controller dynamically formats the data bus and, consequently, the data registers of all APEs to support appropriate operand fields (see Figures G1 and G2).

ASP performs parallel operations on selected APE subsets, as indicated by the statements (ASP software) shown in Figure H. Such operations support both bit-serial and bit-parallel operations.

Bit-serial/word-parallel

Assuming the data register format shown here, ASP supports bit-serial/word-parallel, scalar-vector (S-V) and vector-vector (V-V) arithmetic, relational, and logical operations (o) as seen in Figure I.

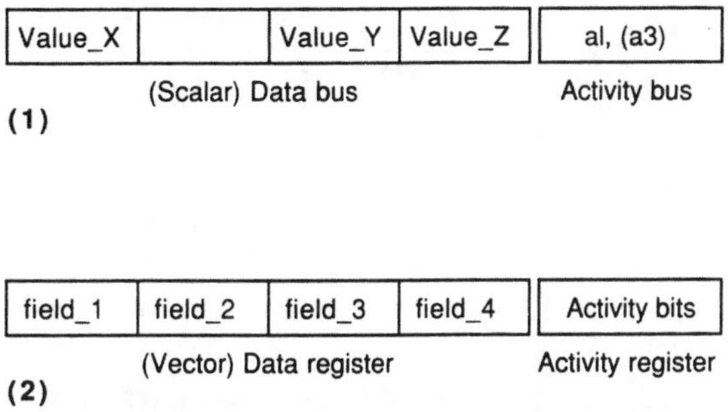

Value_X		Value_Y	Value_Z		al, (a3)

(1)   (Scalar) Data bus   Activity bus

field_1	field_2	field_3	field_4		Activity bits

(2)   (Vector) Data register   Activity register

Figure G. Operation examples: scalar data bus (1); vector data register (2).

```
where <scalar-vector match condition> tag <tag option>;
activate <activation option> do
  <scalar-vector or vector-vector operation>
```

Figure H. ASP operation statement.

```
e.g.  for j := ls_bit to ms_bit do
        begin
          where (DR.field_1 = Value_X) and
                (a1 in AR) and not (a3 in AR) tag M;
          activate M_tagged_APEs do
            begin
              DR.field_4[j] := Value_Y[j] o DR.field_3[j];    {S-V}
              DR.field_3[j] := DR.field_1[j] o DR.field_2[j]  {V-V}
            end
        end
```

Figure I. Bit-serial/word-parallel operations.

shown in Figure 1 to implement an alternative network topology (cross-bar, mesh, torus, shuffle, exchange, butterfly, or binary n-cube).

In summary, to optimize cost-effectiveness and application flexibility, ASP incorporates two levels of interprocessor communication. The lower level provides low-cost implementation of large-scale, fine-grain parallelism, and the upper level minimizes (what would have been a high) implementation cost with small-scale, medium-grain parallelism. In addition, a particular performance advantage of this two-level interconnection strategy is that upper-level communications can be fully overlapped with substring processing. To illustrate the functionality of the architecture we've just described, see ASP operations box.

ASP software

The degree of programmability and associated software complexity are key issues for general-purpose parallel computer design. Unfortunately, the history of parallel algorithm development reveals a profoundly steep learning curve, with much evidence of poor exploitation of natural parallelism and cost-ineffective use of applied parallelism. The height of the learning

```
                  where DR.field_1 = value_X tag M;              {byte mode only}
                  activate M_tagged_APEs do
                     begin
                        DR.field_4 := Value_Z;                    {byte mode only}
                        AR := AR + [a1] - [a3]           {set union and difference}
         (1)       end



         e.g.  for bit-parallel vector-vector addition of APEs  marked with
               activity bit a4, assuming the prior execution of

                  where a4 in AR tag M;
                  activate M_tagged_APEs do C := 0

                  where (DR[j] = 0) and (DR[k] = 0)
                       and (a4 in AR) tag MandD;
                  where (DR[j] = 1) and (DR[k] = 1) and (a4 in AR) tag M;
                  activate left_substrings_of_M_tagged_APEs do C := 1;
                  where a4 in AR tag M;
                  activate M_tagged_APEs do DR[r] := DR[j] + DR[k]

         (2)      where the variables r, j and k support word-indexing.
```

Figure J. Scalar-vector matching and assignment operations (1); vector-vector arithmetic, relational and logical operations (2).

Bit-parallel/word-parallel

ASP executes scalar-vector and vector-vector operations in bit-parallel modes, as outlined in Figures J1 and J2. Assuming our data register format, ASP supports bit-parallel/word-parallel, scalar-vector matching and assignment operations of the type seen in Figure J1.

Assuming that R-bit data registers of a group of P contiguous APEs are allocated to store R P-bit data words, ASP also supports bit-parallel/word-parallel vector-vector arithmetic, relational, and logical operations. See Figure J2. Note that in this operating mode we configure an N-APE ASP as N/P P-bit processors, each supported by R P-bit registers. For example, the 256-APE VLSI chip shown in Figure 9 could support 32 8-bit (or sixteen 16-bit or eight 32-bit or four 64-bit) microprocessors, each with 32 general-purpose registers in this mode.

curve may span as much as two to three orders of magnitude in performance.

The solution to this problem should be found in a high-level parallel programming language that offers simple expression of natural parallelism and flexible control of applied parallelism. But, as yet, no widely accepted such parallel programming language exists.

Experimenting with existing declarative languages and extending existing procedural languages with parallel processing constructs are unlikely to promote efficient parallel algorithms. Worse still, these languages do not encourage programmers to climb the learning curve and improve parallel processing performance. Indeed, algorithm performance benchmarks, published by parallel computer vendors offering such language extensions, are normally based on assembly-level coding.

Moreover, programmers are very reluctant to change their working environments. Indeed, the cultural change to parallel processing is traumatic enough, without complicating the issue by enforcing adoption of an alien programming language and (possibly) an unfamiliar operating system, not to mention the concomitant loss of access to existing software. Consequently, the pragmatic approach adopted for ASP accepts that parallel computer users are best served with their familiar (sequential) software development systems.

Users can write ASP application programs entirely in a familiar block-structured, high-level language (Pascal, Modula-2, C, or Ada) under a familiar operating system (Unix, VMS, or MS-DOS). Such programs include calls to external precompiled ASP algorithms and procedures, written and progressively refined (in the same language) by experts, with an intimate knowledge of the ASP architecture, using a set of built-in function and procedure primitives. Thus, the average ASP application programmer/user does not face the full complexity of parallel algorithm development. The user has the much less-demanding task of selecting and interfacing appropriate code from the hierarchically organized ASP algorithm and procedure library. Only occasionally must programmers resort to the creation of such code.

Nevertheless, we are actively investigating parallel constructs for ASP programming. I offer the syntax definitions in Figure 7, written in EBNF (extended Backus-Naur formalism) and the example procedures in Figure 8 in an attempt to explain the nature of ASP programs.

ASP procedure examples. The first example of an ASP procedure marks the maximum and minimum values in the data field [ls_bit...ms_bit] of a subset of positive (binary) integers (already marked with activity bit a4) with activity bits a1 and a2. See Figure 8a.

The second example procedure in Figure 8b marks the first and last characters of all words (text strings delimited at both ends with spaces) that match an *n*-character word with activity bits a1 and a2 respectively.

Development program

As mentioned earlier, the ASP concept is particularly well matched to the exciting opportunities and exacting constraints of VLSI chip fabrication. Reasons include the high APE packing density, the highly compact inter-APE communications network, and, especially, the independence of I/O requirement from string length. (Compare the linear ASP with a two-dimensional array in which the I/O requirement grows as the square root of the array size.)

Moreover, ASP is highly amenable to defect/fault tolerance, owing to its construction from a large number of identical APEs, lack of location-dependent addressing and simple inter-APE interconnection. Consequently, as reducing feature sizes and increasing chip sizes drive VLSI chip fabrication technology toward the prospect of ULSI chips and WSI devices, the ASP architecture offers consistency and becomes increasingly more cost-effective.

Pioneering investigations. In the early seventies Brunel University developed two experimental ASP prototypes. The first (funded by the United Kingdom Department of Industry) was based on LSI associative memory chips, designed by the author and fabricated by GEC-Marconi. We based the second (funded by the UK Science and Engineering Research Council) on a TTL (transistor-transistor logic) emulation of an LSI ASP chip design. Both prototypes demonstrated the architectural principles and low-level software and stimulated interest in the application potential of ASP.

The ASP chip development program at Brunel University from 1976 until 1981 included the design at the university and the fabrication at Plessey of two LSI ASP test chips. The project demonstrated the feasibility of microelectronic implementation of the architecture.

In addition, a series of research contracts, funded by British Aerospace in 1978 strongly influenced ASP systems and software development. The projects investigated the application of ASP to real-time image processing tasks.

VLSI ASP chips. Since 1981 a three-phase program to develop VLSI ASP chips has been running at Brunel University.

Phase 1, experimental prototyping. Complementary SCAPE and Script projects ran from 1981 to 1987. Their objectives were to develop VLSI ASP chips that

```
statement = Pascal_statement ¦ ASP_construct.

ASP_construct = tag_statement ";" {activation_statement}.

tag_statement = ifany_statement ¦ where_statement.

ifany_statement = "ifany" tag_function "then" statement
                   ["else" statement].

where_statement = "where" tag_function.

tag_function = match_condition "tag" tag_option.

activation_statement = "activate" activation_option "do" APE_operation.
```

Figure 7. Syntax definition in ASP parallel constructs.

```
type nrange = 1..n;

ASP_procedure MAXMIN (ls_bit,ms_bit:nrange);
var j : integer;
begin {MAXMIN}
  where a4 in AR tag M;
  activate M_tagged_APES do AR := AR + [a1,a2];                  {set union}
  for j := ms_bit downto ls_bit do
    begin
      ifany (DR[j] = 1) and (a1 in AR) tag M
        then begin
               where (DR[j] = 0) and (a1 in AR) tag M;
               activate M_tagged_APES do AR := AR - [a1]   {set difference}
             end
      ifany (DR[j] = 0) and (a2 in AR) tag M
        then begin
               where (DR[j] = 1) and (a2 in AR) tag M;
               activate M_tagged_APEs do AR := AR - [a2]   {set difference}
             end
    end
end {MAXMIN}
```

(a)

```
ASP_procedure FIND_WORDS (n:integer;word:string);
var i : integer;
    match : boolean;
begin {FIND_WORDS}
  i := 1; match := true;
  where [] <= AR tag M;
  activate M_tagged_APEs do AR := [];
  where DR = ' ' tag MandD;
  activate right_neighbours_of_M_tagged_APEs do
    AR := AR + [a1,a2];                                          {set union}
  while (i <= n) and match do
    begin
      ifany (DR = word[i]) and (a2 in AR) tag M
        then begin
               activate all_APEs do AR := AR - [a2];        {set difference}
               activate right_neighbours_of_M_tagged_APEs do
                 AR := AR + [a2]                                {set union}
             end
        else match := false;
      i := i + 1
    end;
  if match
    then begin
           where (DR = ' ') and (a2 in AR) tag M;
           activate left_substrings_of_M_tagged_APEs do
             AR := AR + [a3];                                   {set union}
           where (DR = word[1]) and ([a1,a3] in AR) tag M;
           activate all_APEs do AR := AR - [a1,a3];        {set difference}
           activate M_tagged_APEs do AR := AR + [a1]          {set union}
           where a2 in AR tag M;
           activate all_APEs do AR := AR - [a2];           {set difference}
           activate left_neighbours_of_M_tagged_APEs do
             AR := AR + [a2]                                   {set union}
         end
    else write ('match fails')
end {FIND_WORDS}
```

(b)

Figure 8. Example ASP procedures: marking the maximum and minimum values in the data field (a); marking the first and last characters of all matching words (b).

66

Plans call for construction of application-specific and general-purpose chips for research and commercial exploitation.

would demonstrate the applicability of the ASP architecture to numerical (image processing) and nonnumerical (text-based symbolic processing) applications and assess their cost-effectiveness.

In 1986 Plessey fabricated the first samples of the 68-pin SCAPE (single-chip array processing element) chip. The chip is a 256-APE (32-bit data and five activity bits) VLSI ASP (funded by the UK Ministry of Defence from December 1982) in a 2μm complementary metal-oxide semiconductor (CMOS) process with two-layer metal.[4-7] The SCAPE chip appears in Figure 9.

A two-year research contract funded by UK's Alvey (Man Machine Interface) initiative involved collaboration with Quantel UK and the University of Bristol to investigate the design and evaluation of SCAPE-based image processing equipment.

Another two-year Alvey VLSI contract, starting November 1984 and involving Plessey, detailed a design requirement analysis and architectural specification for the Script chip. We based the chip on design and performance data derived from the SCAPE project.

Presently, Brunel University is investigating the design and evaluation of Script-based systems as part of the Scantrax (a back-end processor for relational database management and information retrieval) project.[1]

Phase 2, design consolidation. Since 1987 we based ASP implementation activity on the development of a cell-based design methodology. The methodology allows the VLSI chip designer to select fully engineered, exactly butting, CMOS layout cells from the ASP cell library and compose specific layout blocks for full-custom VLSI chips.

Both Brunel University and Aspex Microsystems staffs pursue such design consolidation in complementary tasks. The former activity investigates new cells and cell variants in research projects, and the latter provides the engineering development required to enable commercial VLSI ASP chips to be based on library cells.

To date, Phase 2 has involved the development of four VLSI ASP test chips, fabricated through the silicon foundry services of the UK's MCE Company

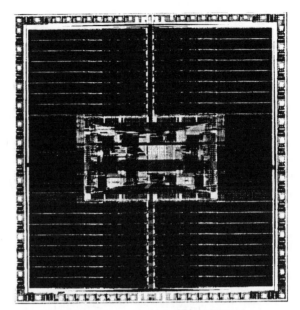

Figure 9. Photomicrograph of the VLSI ASP (SCAPE) chip.

and a 64-APE (32-bit data and five activity bits) VLSI chip. Currently, Plessey is fabricating the latter (in 2μm CMOS with two-layer metal). Based on new cells and incorporating design improvements, this SCAPE-like VLSI chip is intended for ASP demonstrator construction.

Phase 3, product development. Following establishment of a comprehensive cell library, plans call for phase 3 to develop both application-specific and general-purpose VLSI chips for ASP construction for both university research and commercial exploitation. Prominent among such chips are 256-APE and 1,024-APE VLSI chips being developed by Aspex Microsystems for fabrication in 1989 and 1990.

ULSI and WSI devices. Since the cost-performance potential of the ASP architecture improves with increasing string length, demonstration of the advantages of SCAPE-based image processing modules stimulated us to further research leading toward more improvements in cost-effectiveness. Moreover, since the ASP is so highly amenable to defect tolerance that chip area ceases to be a limiting factor, ULSI and WSI ASP devices become natural targets.

An important advantage gained by significantly increasing chip size is that we can also integrate much of the ASP controller and data communications network on the same chip. Indeed, in contrast to VLSI building blocks for the implementation of substrings (see Figures 2 and 9), ULSI and WSI devices implement an entire ASP system, as shown in Figure 1, on a single

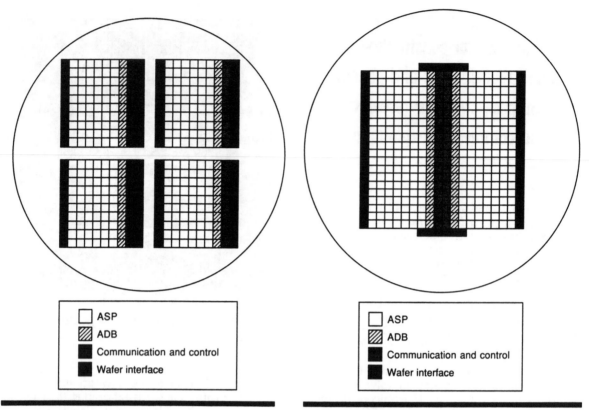

ASP
ADB
Communication and control
Wafer interface

ASP
ADB
Communication and control
Wafer interface

Figure 10. ULSI ASP chips.

Figure 11. WSI ASP device.

silicon die. A single die offers major savings in size, weight, and cost together with increased reliability and ease of maintenance. ULSI and WSI devices, comprising 2,048 and 8,192 APEs, as shown in Figures 10 and 11, are being investigated in the WASP (WSI Associative String Processor) project at Brunel University.[8] The project includes the fabrication and evaluation of defect/fault-tolerant test chips and ULSI/WSI ASP technology demonstrators. It has been funded since 1985 under a UK Alvey (VLSI) contract and involves Plessey, GEC, ICL, and Middlesex Polytechnic.

In a separate project, Aspex Microsystems under a US Office of Naval Research contract is developing a WASP application demonstrator for iconic to symbolic image processing for fabrication in 1990.

ASP performance forecasts

To provide a simple indication of ASP performance, we designed VLSI/ULSI/WSI ASP chips (with 2μm CMOS fabrication technology) to allow each step of bit-serial and bit-parallel operations to be completed in 100 nanoseconds. Consequently, we can estimate the

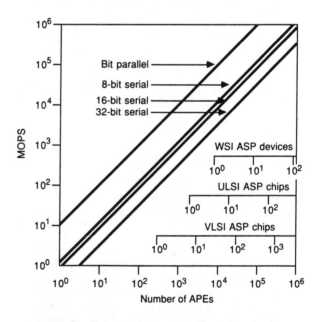

Figure 12. ASP performance estimation. MOPS = million operations per second.

limit of performance of an *N*-APE ASP approximately as follows:

$$\text{Performance} = \frac{10 \times N}{\text{No. steps per operation}} \text{MOPS}$$

Based on this expression, Figure 12 displays the potential performance of VLSI/ULSI ASP chips and WSI ASP devices.

The Associative String Processor is a highly versatile, parallel processing, computational architecture with the potential to achieve step functions in cost-performance over a wide range of information processing tasks. Indeed, ASP hardware and software modules provide the core technology for the construction of cost-effective, general-purpose and application-specific computer workstations designed for the end user.

Having described its architectural philosophy, structural organization, operational principles, and microelectronic implementation, I review the ASP in terms of the desirable features for fifth-generation computer systems shown in Table 2.

In terms of cost-effectiveness, application studies and benchmark evaluations demonstrate that ASP can match and often improve on the performance figures of contemporary parallel computers. And, consequently, the competitive edge becomes that of implementation cost.

Table 2.
ASP features applicable to fifth-generation computing systems.

Feature	Description
Application flexibility	As a fully programmable parallel processor with a reconfigurable interprocessor communication network, ASP provides flexible support for structured data processing thereby amortizing procurement costs over a wide range of both numerical and nonnumerical information processing applications.
Operational simplicity	By mapping all data to intermediate string-processing form, which can be accessed associatively and is supported by a reconfigurable interprocessor communication network, ASP provides simple support of data-level application parallelism (concurrency occurring naturally in structured data and in the algorithmic requirement) and simple control of process and instruction-level parallelism.
Computational efficiency	By enabling close matching between the applied parallelism of its architecture and the natural parallelism of applications with the interprocessor communication network, and by reducing sequential processing overheads with elimination of redundant processing, processor addressing, and unnecessary data movement, ASP maximizes computational efficiency with content addressing and in-situ processing.
Architectural extensibility	As a homogeneous parallel computer, ASP allows scaling of processing power with simple modular adjustment of string length to match user performance requirements.
Size and weight	By exploiting the latest advances in the VLSI-to-ULSI-to-WSI technological trend and high-density system assembly techniques, users can implement ASP in a very compact form.
Power requirement	Since only active processors dissipate and redundant processing has been eliminated, state-of-the-art microelectronic implementation allows ASP to be designed for low power consumption.
System reliability	As a fault-tolerant parallel architecture exploiting microelectronics technology, ASP offers high reliability and ease of maintenance.
Technology independence	Owing to its simple homogeneous string structure, ASP benefits from the inevitable improvement in microelectronics technology (increasing chip size and reducing feature size) without architectural or software modification.

In contrast to its contemporaries, we specifically developed ASP as a silicon-efficient parallel architecture. We achieved cost reductions by maximizing processor packing density, incorporating the interprocessor communications network on chip, and using defect/tolerant circuit design.

With 9,472 bits of content-addressable storage on a VLSI chip (with a $2\mu m$ feature size), Figure 9 demonstrates that the processor packing density ASP achieves is not too far behind that achievable with static RAM chips. Since system designers seem not to be concerned that all (but one) RAM storage locations are idle at any given instant, whereas many (if not all) ASP processors can be simultaneously active, it can be claimed that ASP has achieved the goal of compensating for inevitable processor redundancy with implementation cost reduction.

The curves of Figure 12 indicate potential ASP cost-performance. Assume that VLSI chips could be produced (in volume) for less than $100 each, that the chips dominate system implementation costs (an unlikely event, but prediction of system implementation costs are beyond the scope of this article). Allow (therefore) an arbitrary factor of 10 for a contingency/profit margin. Also estimate an order-of-magnitude improvement with WSI ASP devices. With these assumptions the comparative cost-performance curves in Figure 13 indicate the potential of 100 MOPS/$1,000 and 1,000 MOPS/$1,000 for VLSI- and WSI-based ASPs. For a more objective assessment of ASP

cost-effectiveness, consider the following comparison of ASP with Thinking Machine's CM-1 (the Connection Machine).[9]

The 16-processor-element CM-1 processor chip and the 256-APE SCAPE chip share a common 68-pin package. Therefore, it seems reasonable to assume that a CM-1 printed circuit board (accommodating 32 processor chips, supporting RAM, and "glue" logic) could implement 8,192 APEs, supporting ASP data buffer and glue logic. Moreover, our detailed design studies show that a SIMSIMD ASP controller and data communications network for an ASP system, as shown in Figure 1, would only require one such board. The CM-1 requires at least an additional 12 boards (assumed, since the processor boards account for more than 90 percent of CM-1 circuitry[9]) for interprocessor communication, control, and input-output interfacing.

In summary, a 64K-APE VLSI ASP system would require only nine boards and an equivalent WSI ASP would require only eight wafers. Compare this with the 140 boards required for the 64K-processor CM-1. Moreover, with a one-square-centimeter area, the CM-1 chip costs approximately twice as much as the 75-square-millimeter SCAPE chip,[5,6] for typical VLSI foundry fabrication defect densities. For a 32-bit addition, the peak performance of a 64K-APE ASP would be around 20 gigaoperations per second, compared with only one GOPS for the CM-1. The CM-1 dissipates 12 kW of power; the VLSI and WSI ASPs would dissipate less than 300W and 100W. ▓

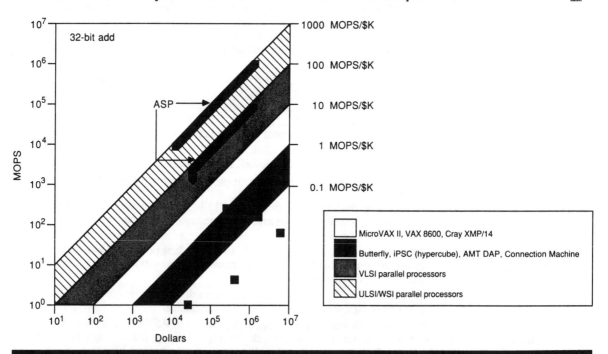

Figure 13. ASP cost-effectiveness. MOPS = million operations per second.

Acknowledgments

I gratefully acknowledge the enthusiastic contributions to ASP-based projects from past and present members of the Computer Architecture Group and Aspex Microsystems Ltd. at Brunel University, the support of the UK Alvey initiative, and US Office of Naval Research funding.

References

1. R.M. Lea, "Associative Processing," *Advanced Digital Information Systems*, I. Aleksander, ed., Prentice-Hall, New York, 1985, pp. 531-575.

2. R.M. Lea, "VLSI and WSI Associative String Processors for Cost-effective Parallel Processing," *The Computer Journal,* Vol. 29, No. 6, 1986, pp. 486-494.

3. R.M. Lea, "VLSI and WSI Associative String Processors for Structured Data Processing," *IEE Proc. Comput. and Digital Tech.,* London, Vol. 133, Pt. E3, 1986, pp. 153-162.

4. R.M. Lea, "The ASP, a Fault-Tolerant VLSI/ULSI/ WSI Associative String Processor for Cost-Effective Systolic Processing," *Proc. IEEE Int'l. Conf. Systolic Arrays*, K. Bromley, S.Y. Kung, and E. Swartzlander, eds., CS Press, Los Alamitos, Calif., 1988, pp. 515-524.

5. R.M. Lea, "SCAPE: a Single-Chip Array Processing Element for Signal and Image Processing," *IEE Proc.,* Vol. 133, Pt. E3, 1986, pp. 145-151.

6. I.P. Jalowiecki and R.M. Lea, "A 256-Element Associative Parallel Processor," ISSCC, 1987, pp. 196-197.

7. S.R. Jones et al., "A 9Kbit Associative Memory for Parallel Processing Applications," *IEEE JSSC,* Vol. 23, No. 2, 1988, pp. 543-548.

8. R.M. Lea, "A WSI Image Processing Module, Wafer Scale Integration," G. Saucier and J. Trilhe, eds., Elsevier Science Publishers B.V. (North-Holland), 1986, pp. 43-58.

9. D. Hillis, *The Connection Machine,* MIT Press, Cambridge, Mass., 1986.

Questions concerning this article can be addressed to R. M. Lea, Brunel University, Uxbridge, Middlesex UB8 3PH, United Kingdom.

The Associative Processor System CAPRA : Architecture and Applications

Associative processor systems are of growing interest in certain application fields. The innovative features of the novel architecture that we propose for such a system include intelligent memory cells (they directly include processing logic), a maskable memory decoder supporting multiaccess operations on the array, and integration of optical sensor elements. We describe the basic features of our content-addressable processor/register array (CAPRA) and discuss its potential for applications in database support, basic numerical tasks, and image processing.

Karl E. Grosspietsch

German National Research Center for Computer Science

Ralf Reetz

University of Karlsruhe

Advanced hardware integration techniques like very large scale integration (VLSI) or wafer scale integration (WSI) imply the potential to efficiently implement new architectures formerly unrealized because of technological restrictions, such as pin limitations or too-small bit capacities. In this context, approaches that eliminate the bottleneck between processor and data appear especially interesting.

In conventional von Neumann machines, data must be fetched from memory and transferred to the processor every time it is manipulated. The result is then stored into memory. So, for many of these operations, data transfers account for most of the execution time.

One solution to the processor/memory bottleneck is to integrate more logic directly into the memory structure—that is, to make the memory more intelligent. Such intelligent-memory architecture especially applies to nonnumerical data processing fields like database management, logic programming, pattern recognition, image processing, and CAD graphics.

Because they are a step toward smarter memories, systems for associative (meant here as a synonym for content-addressable) data processing can again become important.[1] For the first time, hardware integration promises the implementation of such systems with a reasonable size and cost/bit ratio.

The architectural approach

Several interesting approaches for content-addressable processor systems have been reported in the last few years. The June issue contains a comprehensive survey.[1] We base our approach mainly on the ideas of Lea,[2] extending that solution to achieve the following objectives:

- increase the flexibility of logic elements,
- combine processor cell arrays with ordinary content-addressable memory (CAM) and RAM parts, and
- modify the resulting architecture for testability and fault tolerance features.

The latter implies not only structural redundancy (by spare components) but also functional redundancy, in the sense that a more complex component's function can be stepwise degraded to less comfortable functionality.[3]

Basic principles and requirements. We achieve our goals by including a CAM segment in an existing RAM structure. As shown in Figure 1, a RAM, a CAM, and a content-addressable processor/register array (CAPRA) together form a kind of storage hierarchy where the main part consists

Reprinted from *IEEE Micro*, Vol. 12, No. 6, Dec. 1992, pp. 58–67.

of an ordinary RAM. The "smarter" components are included as additional memory segments within one uniform physical memory space; we can thereby arbitrarily tailor their individual storage capacities to the application's specific needs.

Compatibility between the steps of a hierarchy is achieved in the sense that smarter parts also provide the full functionality of simpler parts. So, the CAM parts are also made operable as RAMs, and some functional extension of the CAM architecture implements the CAPRA.

For the introduction of more flexible logic, the following architectural properties appear promising:

- *Extension of the conventional simple-bit mechanisms of present CAM architectures—equivalence between data, potentially modified by some kind of masking—to solutions that also allow more sophisticated bit evaluation for pattern matching.* (For example, we can use a threshold number of identical bits in the search pattern and compared data to decide about hit, or use other similarity metrics between the search pattern and data in storage.)
- *Extension, with relatively low hardware effort, of the usual comparison logic of a CAM cell to provide an entire set of 1-bit Boolean operations.*
- *Modification of arithmetic logic units from sequential 1-bit adder elements per word cell to at least 4-bit adder elements.* Each of these ALUs has a data path to neighbor ALUs in the two nearest word cells. So, in addition to parallel processing of data, the architecture provides parallel exchange of data between word cells of the CAPRA segment. Apart from requirements to restrict additional area size if possible, we chose a four-bit ALU length to support the processing of pixels with 16 gray levels in image processing.
- *Implementation of features for multiaccess write operations[1,4] and parallel evaluation of test outcomes in word cells using extended logic[5] to support test of the architecture.*

We can easily integrate the proposed architecture into a conventional system because, unlike other unorthodox architectural approaches, our features comply with the von Neumann machine's usual control-flow programming paradigm. We therefore planned our architecture to work as a coprocessor of a conventional main processor; the coprocessor's instructions are modularly added to those of the processor.

The resulting hardware architecture. The following architectural features fulfill our requirements:

- The CAM has an additional RAM access mode so that it can, for example, be loaded or read like ordinary RAM cells.

Frequently used symbolic abbreviations

f	Gray-level intensity
i, j, l, x, y	Index variables
k	Number of pixels stored in a word cell
L_A, L_B	Bit length of records of relations A,B
m	Dimension of vector
M	Dimension of neighborhood matrix
n	Memory word length
N	Dimension of pixel array
N_A, N_B	Cardinalities of relations A,B
P_A, P_B	Smallest power of $2 \geq N_A, N_B$
r	Pixel resolution
w	Word capacity of the CAPRA segment
z	Number of pixel rows stored in CAPRA

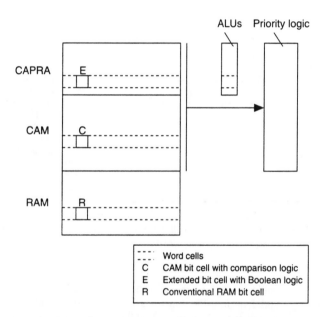

Figure 1. The architecture combines a RAM structure, a CAM segment, and a CAPRA.

- In the CAPRA architecture, illustrated in Figure 2, next page, RAM bit cells again serve as base cells. Moreover, a simple logic block is associated to every bit cell, which enables Boolean 1-bit operations between two 1-bit operands. This allows bit-parallel and word-parallel execution of a Boolean operation on all words of the CAPRA segment.
- In addition, in the CAPRA word cells the classical CAM

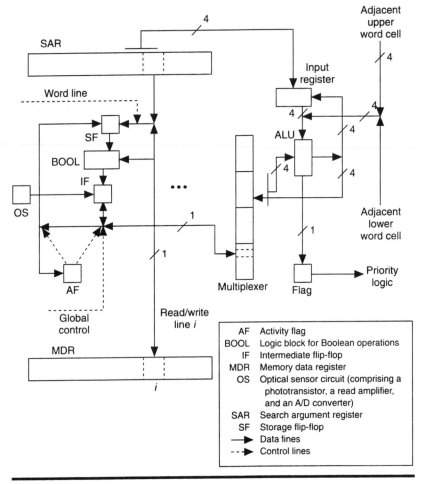

Figure 2. Schematic of the CAPRA architecture showing one extended bit cell *i*
(*i*=0, ..., *n*–1) of a word cell, together with the ALU and the optical-sensor element associated to that word cell.

of this register to 1, an arbitrary part of the address bits can be declared don't-care bits. Thus we can implement concurrent access to word cells that have common address bit subpatterns (the survey article contains a detailed description).

Figure 3 shows CAPRA's operation. Data can be written into a word cell—controlled by the corresponding word line emanating from the memory decoder—via the memory data register and read/write lines. We can combine the contents of every bit of a word cell, contained in the storage flip-flop (SF), with the contents of the read/write line by a Boolean operation in the functional block BOOL. The result of this operation is latched in the intermediate flip-flop (IF). From there it can be propagated further (indicated by control line TRANSFER), either to the adjacent ALU (line LOCAL/GLOBAL = 1) or to be memorized in the SF (LOCAL/GLOBAL = 0). These transfers take place either unconditionally (control line UNCOND=1) or conditionally (line UNCOND=0), depending on the status of the cell memorized in the activity flag (AF). (Signal line COND equals 1 if AF stores a 1.) As a third sink for the bit transfer from the IF, setting of the AF is possible (control line SET FLAG). This is performed either unconditionally (control line UNCOND = 1) or dependent on the present status of the AF (control line COND' = 1). In the latter case, the AF can be set only if it has not yet been set—that is, if the AF is storing a 0. (COND' then equals 1.)

The intermediate flip-flop can receive a data bit not only from the functional block BOOL, but, alternatively, from the adjacent ALU (control line REC = 1).

Sensor integration. For image processing applications, we plan to integrate optical sensors with our intelligent bit cell array on one piece of silicon. One sensor element is associated to each word cell of the CAPRA segment. The sensor element comprises a phototransistor, a read amplifier, and a programmable analog-to-digital converter (refer back to Figure 2).

The phototransistor was implemented as a PMOS transistor with floating bulk,[5] an efficient way to integrate it into a CMOS process without process modifications.[6] The

equivalence check operation is possible, realized by three additional transistor functions (refer to the survey article[1]).

- To every word cell in the CAPRA, we assign a simple 4-bit adder/shifter unit; so, for example, with a classical word length of *n*=32 bits, an arithmetic operation can be performed on all words of the CAPRA segment in parallel in about eight cycles.

- An additional flag bit is associated to each bit cell of the CAPRA, which enables us to flexibly define arbitrary "activity patterns" for the array cells. We therefore can process data not only on all processor elements but also on a previously defined, arbitrary subpattern of processing elements.

- An additional mask register provides a simple extension of the memory decoder[4] for RAM access. By setting bits

Legend inside the figure:

AF	Activity flag
BOOL	Logic block for Boolean operations
IF	Intermediate flip-flop
MDR	Memory data register
OS	Optical sensor circuit (comprising a phototransistor, a read amplifier, and an A/D converter)
SAR	Search argument register
SF	Storage flip-flop

→ Data lines
--→ Control lines

phototransistor's sensitivity depends on its operating point and on the incident light's wavelength.

The converter transforms the incoming analog signal into a digital bit pattern in a number of iterations. The accuracy of the conversion—the bit length of the digitized signal pattern—depends on the number of conversion cycles, so this resolution is easily programmable. We have selected a resolution of $r=4$ bits for our planned applications. The resulting bits are stored in r consecutive bit cells of the corresponding memory word, starting from a previously determined bit position.

Nearly all approaches for such sensors have been based on analog solutions. But most of these analog converters are not compatible with standard digital CMOS processes—they depend on special complicated fabrication steps that cannot be integrated into the production of standard CMOS structures. As an alternative, we use a sensor element that is fully realized in CMOS technology.[6] Thus we can integrate all the components on a single chip or wafer by one standard CMOS fabrication process.

To realize an A/D converter of programmable resolution, we used the so-called cyclic conversion technique.[7] The converter performs an r-bit conversion in $3r$ clock cycles. This cyclic converter's operation is based on recirculating the input voltage, thus precisely doubling the voltage.[8] For example, a conversion time of 20 μs is necessary for the chosen resolution of 4 bits.

CAPRA's basic instruction set. We have defined the following set of operations for the described memory structure:

- WRITE, ADR; / normal RAM write access (executable in all system parts)
- READ, ADR; / normal RAM read access
- MWRITE, ADR, MASK; / masked RAM write access: multiple access to a set of word cells in memory that have some address subpattern in common
- ASSOCOMP; / word-parallel and bit-parallel comparison of the contents of word cells with a predefined search pattern in the search argument register (executable in the CAPRA and in the CAM part)
- BOOLOP; / Boolean operation combining the bits of all memory words with an external operand's bits. (This operation name is a placeholder for the 16 different Bool-

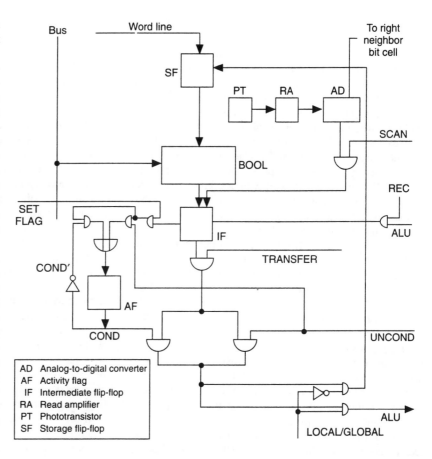

Figure 3. Gate structure of the extended bit cell.

ean operations of two 1-bit operands.)

- STORE, COND (UNCOND); / stores in the bit cells of the CAPRA part the result of the Boolean operation either unconditionally (for all bit cells in the CAPRA) or conditionally (depending on the local activity flags of each cell)
- SET AF, COND (UNCOND); / transfers the contents of the intermediate flip-flop into the AF either unconditionally or conditionally (only for those bit cells where AF=FALSE)
- SCAN(j); / transfers digitized sensor input with a 4-bit resolution from the sensor elements to the IFs of bit slice j, $j+1$, $j+2$, $j+3$.

We can group CAPRA's ALU operations into unconditional and conditional operations. Unconditional operations are executed in all ALUs. Second-class operations correspond exactly in their structure to those of the first class, except they execute in a local ALU only if it has a flag set to TRUE.

Unconditional operations have the structure ALU OP, BUFFER(j), REGISTER, DESTINATION;. The first operand BUFFER(j) is always a 4-bit segment of all memory words; the index j gives its position. As the second operand REGISTER, we may use the registers REGA, REGB, REGC, or SAR. REGA is the 4-bit input register belonging to each ALU in the CAPRA segment. REGB and REGC just represent the REGA register of the upper (lower) neighbor ALU. As an alternative, we can use the least significant 4 bits of the SAR to provide one global 4-bit operand to all the ALUs of the CAPRA. So, by selecting the second operand, we can combine an operand held in a memory word with local data residing in either the corresponding ALU or one of its neighbors (thus enabling communication between neighbors). Or we can combine the operand with a global operand provided from outside. The sink DESTINATION of the operation is either again BUFFER(j) or the register REGA.

The ALU operations are either unconditionally executed on all CAPRA word cells or conditionally controlled by local ALU flags. The setting of these flags depends either on the outcome of certain ALU operations (as is usual in conventional ALUs) or on an explicit instruction from outside. For the latter purpose we have the operation SET, ADR, MASK, which provides—analogously to the masked write operation MWRITE—access to one or several ALUs in one cycle.

This short list omits instructions that deal with handling priority operations and with data transfers between the memory and the main processor.

State of the system implementation. The entire architecture has been specified with the VHDL hardware description language. Not only does this description cover the register transfer level, but we also defined our own abstract data types to exactly model the behavior of our circuits' basic transistor functions at switch level. This level models transistor functions as digital switches. It coarsens the more detailed physical characteristics of the transistor such as delay times, switching speed, and analysis of transient behavior. On the other hand, it provides more refined information about the transistor than the usual gate-level models used to study the steady-state behavior of circuits.[9]

We based our circuit model on a six-valued logic that comprises two different low-impedance states, three high-impedance states, and one undefined/unknown state. Apart from contributing somewhat to the emerging VHDL design technique, the detailed switch level model of our architecture is especially useful for fault simulation and derivation of test patterns.

Together with the simulation environment of VHDL, our description also provides an exact runtime simulator of the specified architecture. In addition to measurements made at the switch level, we aggregated the fine-grain routines of this simulation to higher units at the register transfer level. This allows us to measure performance in units of machine cycles

with considerably reduced computing time.

Correspondingly, for the machine language introduced earlier, we wrote an assembler to enable the development of symbolic programs for the described architecture. The assembler transforms symbolic instructions into binary machine words that the simulator interprets. In addition, we implemented a simulator environment that can combine CAPRA machine language procedures with high-level language main programs (to be executed on a main processor) written in Modula. Based on the translator and its environment, a number of application examples currently are being studied and demonstration software implemented.

At the level of the basic hardware circuits, we exhaustively simulated central components (the intelligent bit cell, the ALU part) using the transistor simulator SPICE. Corresponding layouts were generated and partially transformed into silicon.[8]

In the future, we plan to integrate the different developed cell layouts on a common chip.

Database applications

Associative processing is especially useful for applications where data is structured in sets or arrays. Because database applications involve set-like data organization, this field always has been one of the principal applications of associative processing.[10] We illustrate the merits of our CAPRA approach by considering some classical operations in relational databases: selection, intersection, product, semi-join, and join. As a comparison, we refer to an investigation by Fernstrom, Kruzela, and Svensson at the University of Lund, Sweden.[11]

We consider the basic elements of the database, the data records—that is, ordered tuples of data items. Each subfield of a record stores one item. Sets of such records (often called relations) are represented by tables of such records. The relational operations we mentioned work on either one or two tables as input operands, producing a third table as the result. Let us call the source relations A and B. Without loss of generality, we assume that the number of data records in A is the same as or more than those in B. For the cardinalities N_A and N_B of A and B, we thus have the condition $N_A \geq N_B$. Correspondingly, L_A and L_B denote the bit lengths of the records of relations A and B.

In our CAPRA approach, a record is stored in a number of consecutive words in memory (that is, if the record contains more than the n bits fitting into one memory word). Correspondingly, search patterns ranging over the entire bit length of the record must be split up into a number of search words (each of n bits), which subsequently are used for search operations. So, associative checking of the records of relations A or B can be performed in $\lceil L_A/n \rceil$ or $\lceil L_B/n \rceil$ cycles, respectively (with $\lceil x \rceil$ denoting the smallest integer $\geq x$). It is not necessary to store a table—that is, a set of records—in a segment of consecutive data words. Instead, in an associative system, it is possible to characterize the members of the set by some common properties, namely, values of some items or a common mark bit.

The selection operation. The simplest relational database operation, the selection, selects a subset of the given set A of tuples. This subset comprises records that obey certain search criteria for one or several tuple items. In CAPRA this operation can be carried out by a number of simple associative checks that consecutively compare the values of some tuple fields of the records with search patterns in the SAR; hits are memorized by setting a new mark bit in the data record. Thus, the entire select operation can be carried out by at most $\lceil L_A/n \rceil$ associative search operations; then in one cycle, a mark bit is written into all records found. If no ordering of items with regard to one fixed property is possible, so that hashing techniques cannot be applied, the same search procedure on a von Neumann machine takes the order $O(N_A \cdot \lceil L_A/n \rceil)$.

The intersection operation. This operation has two source relations as inputs and, as a result, produces a common subset of both relations. The CAPRA system carries out this operation by sequentially reading the contents of the smaller relation B. The records of relation A are compared with one record of relation B by $\lceil L_A/n \rceil$ associative search operations. So, processing the entire intersection operation on CAPRA takes the order $O(\lceil L_A/n \rceil \cdot N_B)$, compared with $O(N_A \cdot N_B \cdot \lceil L_A/n \rceil)$ on a von Neumann machine. Analogous time complexities also turn out for the union operation.

The product operation. The Cartesian product operation applied to relations A and B generates all pairs of records. One record of the pair belongs to relation A, the other to relation B. This operation has a time complexity of $O(N_A N_B)$ on a sequential von Neumann architecture as well as in the bit-sequential, word-parallel LUCAS (Lund University Content-Addressable System) approach of Fernstrom, Kruzela, and Svensson. The CAPRA approach can considerably reduce this time complexity, at the expense of increasing the set cardinalities to the smallest powers of 2 that are $\geq N_A$ ($\geq N_B$); let us call them P_A and P_B. Then, the concatenated pairs of data records can be produced very efficiently in time complexity $O(\lceil L_B/n \rceil \cdot P_A + \lceil L_A/n \rceil \cdot P_B)$. Figure 4 shows that, in one cycle, a masked write access produces P_B copies of a data word of the first relation. These masked write operations are performed for all members of the first relation.

Then, with a changed mask, P_A copies of all the second relation's members are produced in $P_A \cdot \lceil L_B/n \rceil$ masked write operations. Thus, compared to the other mentioned computer architectures, time complexity is reduced by a factor of about N_B at the expense of a memory space capacity of the order $O(P_A \cdot P_B)$. But this seems justified because memory costs are falling drastically.

The semi-join operation. As a characteristic example of this operation, the study by Fernstrom, Kruzela, and Svensson considers two relations, one with attributes g and b, the other with attribute b. The result is a subset of the first relation,

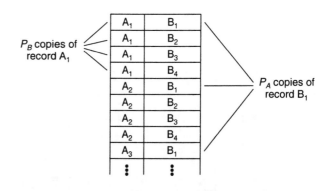

Figure 4. Generation of the two Cartesian product relations A and B using masked write operations. (A_1, A_2, ..., are records of relation A; B_1, B_2, ..., are records of relation B.)

consisting of tuples where the value of attribute b is the same as some value of attribute b in the second relation. This can be produced by sequentially taking members of relation B and associatively checking them against relation A. This takes a time complexity of $O(\lceil L_A/n \rceil \cdot N_B)$.

The join operation. This operation is similar to the semi-join, but matching tuples are concatenated, thereby removing the joining attribute. With CAPRA, we carry out this operation by first sequentially scanning the N_B tuples of relation B. Now relation B is marked, showing where a match occurs in the tuples of relation A. Subsequently, the Cartesian product of the tuples of relations A and B is formed by $\lceil L_B/n \rceil \cdot P_A + \lceil L_A/n \rceil \cdot P_B$ masked write operations. Tuples not marked as matching are logically removed by setting an invalid bit. In the remaining tuples, we remove the attribute to be erased by simply setting another invalid bit in the subfield containing that attribute.

In an analogous way, we can use multiaccess operations to speed up the join operation. Because several (slightly different) versions of this operation have been proposed in the literature,[10] we shall not discuss these modifications here.

In general, CAPRA's parallel search features reduce the time complexity of relational database operations by the order of the cardinality of the larger of the two input relations—that is, by $O(N_A)$ in our example. The CAPRA approach has further advantages if data need not only be found but also updated in some regular way (for example, incrementing or decrementing a subfield in all records found).

Basic numerical operations

We did not specifically intend for our architecture to efficiently support operations of scientific and numerical computing such as matrix-oriented operations (matrix-vector multiplication, matrix-matrix multiplication, fast Fourier transform). But it turned out that the architecture does have some

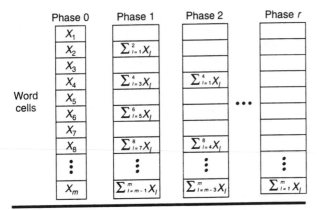

Figure 5. Parallel summing up of the components of an *m*-dimensional vector.

interesting features in this area.

As a simple example, we use the summing up of the components of a vector of dimension *m*. A single processor system must sequentially carry out this task in *m*–1 steps. Our architecture yields a much better result because of the parallelism of computing elements, even though only a simple shift-register-like interconnection joins them.

Consider the vector components to be stored in consecutive word cells, as shown in Figure 5. The first summing-up phase is carried out by transferring each odd-indexed component to its next lower word cell and adding its value to that of the neighbor's cell. So, half the computations necessary for summing up can be executed in parallel, independently of the vector's dimension (provided that this dimension is less than the number of word cells in the CAPRA segment). In the next phase, all the odd-indexed partial results are moved down two word cells to meet the next corresponding partial result. This can be performed in two machine cycles. So, again the partial results have decreased by half in number, while their distances within the CAPRA segment have doubled.

If this strategy is always used, the need to move partial sums over increasing distances sometimes will win over the advantage of being able to sum up partial results in parallel. So, after the described strategy is used for an optimal number of phases, the few remaining partial results (now situated within the CAPRA segment very far away from each other) are then simply read and added sequentially. Reetz shows in detail that if one switches strategy at the optimal point, the entire summing up can be carried out in $O(\sqrt{m})$ steps.[12] For larger values of *m*, this result is significantly better than the $O(m)$ steps necessary in the case of a single processor. The optimal value for summing up *m* numbers is of order $O(\log m)$; however, a binary adder tree is necessary for summing up the different values. So, whereas this optimal solution needs complex extra hardware, our architecture just as a by-product performs close to the optimal value for many values of *m* used in practice.

Reetz[12] shows that, based on this effect, the multiplication of an $m \times m$ matrix with an *m*-dimensional vector can be performed in order $O(m)$ steps, a result comparable to other special architectures laid out for numerical computing, such as certain systolic arrays.[13]

Picture-processing applications

The most interesting application of associative processor systems in the area of array-oriented data organization is picture processing. A digital picture is usually given by an array of pixels (x,y), where *x* and *y* denote the coordinates of the pixel within the image. For the dimensions of the two-dimensional pixel array, we shall confine our discussion to a typical square image of *N* rows and columns. Each pixel has certain gray-level intensities $f(x,y)$ (typically used are 16 gray levels represented by 4 bits or 256 gray levels represented by 8 bits).

The picture is processed at several levels:

- image compression (incoming pixel data is reduced),
- noise reduction and image enhancement (relevant pixels are enhanced),
- feature extraction,
- classification of patterns, and
- analysis of geometric objects.

We can group the used algorithms into three general classes: frequency-oriented algorithms, space-oriented algorithms, and statistical algorithms.[14,15]

Frequency-oriented algorithms consider a picture as a wave pattern—that is, an infinite series of sine and cosine functions represent a picture. The frequencies of these harmonic oscillations give the individual characteristics of the picture.

Space-oriented algorithms interpret a picture as a geometric structure of objects. These objects are characterized by the size, shape, distance to neighbor objects, and the gray-level intensities of their pixels. Space-oriented algorithms comprise operations on local environments of each pixel. Usually, these environments consist of the pixel's four or eight nearest neighbors (see Figure 6).

Statistical algorithms consider a picture as a distribution of gray levels. A histogram usually represents such a discrete distribution. From the distribution, the algorithms derive global transformations of the pixels.

On-line picture-processing architectures comprise peripheral devices from which data enters the system (cameras, integrated sensors); large memory segments (RAM or background devices) to intermediately store the image to be processed; and a processing part to carry out transformations of the picture.

Usually, the data size of an image causes some thread for

the data lines to transfer the picture. For example, a digital image of typical size 512×512 pixels, each pixel with 256 gray levels, comprises 2 Mbits of data that the data lines must transfer. This causes considerable loading times if the image has to be loaded into memory sequentially in units of, for example, 32 bits. We can now circumvent these data path limitations by transferring optical data directly to memory via arrays of optical sensors integrated into the memory array, as discussed earlier.

Operations on local environments enable massive parallelism because each pixel needs information only from its local neighbor pixels to compute its new value. Local operations can be performed for a large set of pixels simultaneously, if a suitable number of appropriate processing elements is available.

Segments of CAPRA word cells can efficiently carry out these parallel processing tasks: The storage flip-flops of the word cells store the pixel data, and the BOOL units and ALU parts of each word cell work as processing elements.

Input data is scanned into the array through either a row-oriented or a column-oriented method. As most output devices are row-oriented, we shall consider this strategy for the input as well.

Two approaches are possible for memorizing a picture in a CAPRA segment. In the row approach, the image is read in row by row. To process an eight-neighborhood of the pixels of one row for a space-oriented algorithm, it is sufficient to store three rows (the actual one and its upper and lower neighbor rows). For each pixel point of these three rows, r bits in a memory word are used. Figure 7 shows the storage scheme of this approach.

In the so-called block approach, the entire picture is read into a larger CAPRA part. Because an entire row of pixels usually does not fit into one CAPRA word cell, a number of word cells interleavingly store its data, as Figure 8 shows. Each memory word stores $k = n/r$ pixels. The N pixels belonging to one row of the image are stored in the same bit positions of N consecutive memory words, so the corresponding ALUs can analogously process them.

Of course, the block approach necessitates a CAPRA capacity about $N/3$ times as large as that of the row approach. Usually, as an intermediate way between the row approach and the block approach, the CAPRA segment can store a number of $z = w \cdot k / N$ rows of pixels for a given word capacity w of the segment.

These two storage schemes offer to exploit the potential to process the pixels in parallel, as well as to carry out concurrent search operations on them. Thus our architecture appears especially interesting in regard to supporting statistical and space-oriented algorithms.

Many space-oriented algorithms are based on considering each pixel point's corresponding neighborhood. As an example, Figure 9a, next page, shows some approximations for

$$\begin{bmatrix} & f(x,y-1) & \\ f(x-1,y) & f(x,y) & f(x+1,y) \\ & f(x,y+1) & \end{bmatrix} \begin{bmatrix} f(x-1,y-1) & f(x,y-1) & f(x+1,y-1) \\ f(x-1,y) & f(x,y) & f(x+1,y) \\ f(x-1,y+1) & f(x,y+1) & f(x+1,y+1) \end{bmatrix}$$

Figure 6. A local environment of four or eight nearest neighbors for the gray-level value of a pixel point (x, y).

Word cells	$f(i-1,0)$	$f(i,0)$	$f(i+1,0)$
	$f(i-1,1)$	$f(i,1)$	$f(i+1,1)$
		$\vdots$	
	$f(i-1,N-1)$	$f(i,N-1)$	$f(i+1,N-1)$

Figure 7. Scheme of the row approach for memorizing pictures. N consecutive CAPRA words store three rows of the image.

Word cells	$f(0,0)$	$f(1,0)$	•••	$f(k-1,0)$
	$f(0,1)$	$f(1,1)$	•••	$f(k-1,1)$
		$\vdots$		
	$f(0,N-1)$	$f(1,N-1)$	•••	$f(k-1,N-1)$
	$f(k,0)$	$f(k+1,0)$	•••	$f(2k+1,0)$
	$f(k,1)$	$f(k+1,1)$	•••	$f(2k-1,1)$
		$\vdots$		
	$f(k,N-1)$	$f(k+1,N-1)$	•••	$f(2k-1,N-1)$
		$\vdots$		
	$f(N-k,0)$	$f(N-k+1,0)$	•••	$f(N-1,0)$
	$f(N-k,1)$	$f(N-k+1,1)$	•••	$f(N-1,1)$
		$\vdots$		
	$f(N-k,N-1)$	$f(N-k+1,N-1)$	•••	$f(N-1,N-1)$

Figure 8. Scheme of the block approach. The shaded area represents one complete row (row $2k-1$) of the image.

the gray-level gradient using the Prewitt operator, the Sobel operator, and the Roberts gradient. These image operators estimate the value of a given pixel's gray-level gradient using weighted differences of the neighbor points' gray levels.[14,15] Figure 9b shows that matrices of $M=3$ rows and columns also can formally represent the weights.

Because of the different weights, adding up the weighted sum under one instruction stream takes an order of $O(M^2)$ subsequent operations. However, with z rows of a pixel stored in the CAPRA segment, $z \cdot k$ neighborhoods can be processed concurrently. So, compared with the von Neumann architecture, processing speeds up by a factor of $O(z \cdot k)$. Here, spe-

- $\partial f/\partial x\ f(x,y) \approx f(x,y) - f(x+1,y)$

$\partial f/\partial y\ f(x,y) \approx f(x,y) - f(x,y+1)$

- Prewitt operator

$\partial f/\partial x\ f(x,y) \approx [f(x+1,y-1) + f(x+1,y) + f(x+1,y+1)]$
$\qquad - [f(x-1,y-1) + f(x-1,y) + f(x-1,y+1)]$

$\partial f/\partial y\ f(x,y) \approx [f(x-1,y-1) + f(x,y-1) + f(x+1,y-1)]$
$\qquad - [f(x-1,y+1) + f(x,y+1) + f(x+1,y+1)]$

- Roberts gradient

$\partial f/\partial x\ f(x,y) \approx f(x,y) - f(x+1,y+1)$

$\partial f/\partial y\ f(x,y) \approx f(x+1,y) - f(x,y+1)$

- Sobel operator

$\partial f/\partial x\ f(x,y) \approx [f(x-1,y+1) + 2 \cdot f(x,y+1) + f(x+1,y+1)]$
$\qquad - [f(x-1,y-1) + 2 \cdot f(x,y-1) + f(x+1,y-1)]$

$\partial f/\partial y\ f(x,y) \approx [f(x+1,y-1) + 2 \cdot f(x+1,y) + f(x+1,y+1)]$
$\qquad - [f(x-1,y-1) + 2 \cdot f(x-1,y) + f(x-y,y+1)]$

(a)

$$\frac{\partial f}{\partial x}f(x,y): \begin{bmatrix} 0 & 0 & 0 \\ 0 & 1 & -1 \\ 0 & 0 & 0 \end{bmatrix} \qquad \frac{\partial f}{\partial y}f(x,y): \begin{bmatrix} 0 & 0 & 0 \\ 0 & 1 & 0 \\ 0 & -1 & 0 \end{bmatrix}$$

$$\frac{\partial f}{\partial x}f(x,y): \begin{bmatrix} -1 & 0 & 1 \\ -1 & 0 & 1 \\ -1 & 0 & 1 \end{bmatrix} \qquad \frac{\partial f}{\partial y}f(x,y): \begin{bmatrix} 1 & 1 & 1 \\ 0 & 0 & 0 \\ -1 & -1 & -1 \end{bmatrix}$$

$$\frac{\partial f}{\partial x}f(x,y): \begin{bmatrix} 0 & 0 & 0 \\ 0 & 1 & 0 \\ 0 & 0 & -1 \end{bmatrix} \qquad \frac{\partial f}{\partial y}f(x,y): \begin{bmatrix} 0 & 0 & 0 \\ 0 & 0 & 1 \\ 0 & -1 & 0 \end{bmatrix}$$

$$\frac{\partial f}{\partial x}f(x,y): \begin{bmatrix} -1 & -2 & -1 \\ 0 & 0 & 0 \\ 1 & 2 & 1 \end{bmatrix} \qquad \frac{\partial f}{\partial y}f(x,y): \begin{bmatrix} -1 & 0 & 1 \\ -2 & 0 & 2 \\ -1 & 0 & 1 \end{bmatrix}$$

(b)

Figure 9. Approximations for the gray-level gradient at pixel (x,y) of a picture (a), and corresponding 3×3 matrices (b).

cial approximations usually are chosen for the nonexisting neighbor points of the picture's edge points. For instance, these points are assumed to have either some constant, predefined value or to have the same value as the corresponding edge points. Several authors present detailed discussions.[12,14,15]

As one numerical example, the evaluation of the Roberts gradient for an image of 512×512 pixels (each with 256 gray levels) takes 0.74 ms using the row approach for a CAPRA segment of 1,024 words of 32 bits. Comparative operations on LUCAS take 3.64 ms, and a conventional VAX computer needs 218 ms.

Whereas the space-oriented algorithms usually operate on very regularly structured subgrids of pixel neighborhood points, statistical algorithms demand evaluation of data properties in very irregularly shaped pixel patterns. The associative operations of the CAPRA architecture very efficiently support the necessary search operations.

To evaluate statistical results, we finally must sum up the hits of these search operations, carried out over the pixel array. This is equivalent to summing up the components of a vector, as discussed earlier. So, for example, in the block approach this phase has a time complexity $O(\sqrt{N^2}) = O(N)$ for a matrix of N^2 pixel elements; on a single processor system it would be of the order $O(N^2)$. Thus, a performance improvement of $O(N)$ results for the CAPRA architecture. Reetz discusses these aspects in more detail.[12]

CAPRA, a new experimental architecture for associative processor systems, comprises several innovative features. They are inclusion of logic elements directly within the word cells or bit cells of memory; use of a maskable decoder to enable multiaccess to the memory and computing devices of the array; activity flags within the cells of the array to enable flexible definition of activity patterns; and integration of sensor elements for the direct parallel input of optical data. This architecture supports database and picture-processing applications. Related application fields like hardware support of neural networks and fuzzy systems already have been investigated by others.[5,13] The CAPRA architecture is an interesting candidate for demonstrating the flexibility and comfort of associative algorithms.

In the future, we plan to complete the hardware realization and to study the described applications, especially under the requirements of real-time systems. ▯

References

1. K.E. Grosspietsch, "Associative Processors and Memories: A Survey," *IEEE Micro*, Vol. 12, No. 3, June 1992, pp. 12-19.

2. R.M. Lea, "ASP: A Cost-Effective Parallel Microcomputer," *IEEE Micro*, Vol. 8, No. 5, Oct. 1988, pp. 10-29.

3. K.E. Grosspietsch, "Architectures for Testability and Fault Tolerance in Content-Addressable Systems," *IEEE Proc.*, Vol.136, Part E, No. 5, Sept. 1989, pp. 366-373.

4. D. Tavangarian, "Ortsadressierbarer Assoziativspeicher" ["Location-Addressable Associative Memory"], *Elektronische Rechenanlagen* [*Electronic Computing Systems*], Vol. 25, No. 5, Oct. 1985, pp. 264-278.

5. J. Bueddefeld et al., "An Intelligent Sensor Integrated Preprocessing Facility for Neural Networks," *Microprocessing and Microprogramming*, Vol. 32, 1991, pp. 335-342.

6. S.D. Kirkish et al., "Optical Characteristics of CMOS-Fabricated MOSFETs," *IEEE J. Solid-State Circuits*, Vol. 22, No. 2, Apr. 1987, pp. 299-301.

7. H. Onodera, T. Tateishi, and K. Tamaru, "A Cyclic A/D Converter That Does Not Require Ratio-Matched Components," *IEEE J. Solid-State Circuits*, Vol. 23, No. 1, Feb. 1988, pp. 152-158.

8. R. Klinke et al., "Eine Photodetektor-Matrix in Standard-CMOS-Technologie" ["A Photodetector Matrix in Standard CMOS Technology"], *Proc. GME Conf. Mikroelektronik*, VDE/VDI: Gesellschaft Mikroelektronik (GME), Berlin, 1991, pp. 175-180.

9. K.E. Grosspietsch, U. Schaefer, and M. Kohn, "A VHDL Model for the Specification and Simulation of Complex VLSI Architectures," *Proc. Int'l. Workshop Euro-VHDL*, Vol. 276, Swedish Institute of Microelectronics, Kista, Sweden, 1991, pp. 46-52.

10. P. Mishra and M.H. Eich, "Join Processing in Relational Databases," *ACM Computing Surveys*, Vol. 24, No. 1, Mar. 1992, pp. 63-113.

11. C. Fernstrom, I. Kruzela, and B. Svensson, "LUCAS Associative Array Processor," *Lecture Notes in Computer Science*, Vol. 216, Springer-Verlag, Berlin, 1986.

12. R. Reetz, "Parallele Algorithmen und Anwendungen fuer das assoziative Prozessorsystem CAPRA" ["Parallel Algorithms and Applications for the Associative Processor System CAPRA"], *GMD-Studien*, No. 207, Gesellschaft fuer Mathematik und Datenverarbeitung, St. Augustin, Germany, 1992.

13. C. Mead and L. Conway, *Introduction to VLSI Systems*, Addison-Wesley, Reading, Mass., 1980.

14. W.K. Pratt, *Digital Image Processing*, John Wiley & Sons, New York, 1978.

15. R.C. Gonzalez and P. Wintz, *Digital Image Processing*, Addison-Wesley, 1987.

Direct questions or comments about this article to Karl E. Grosspietsch, German National Research Center for Computer Science, P.O. Box 1316, D-5205 St. Augustin, Germany; or email at grossp@gmdzi.uucp.

ADARC
Associative Processors and Processing

Justin Strohschneider, Bernd Klauer, Stefan Zickenheiner, Frank Henritzi, and Klaus Waldschmidt

J.W. Goethe-University
Technische Informatik
P.O. Box 11 19 32
D-60054 Frankfurt, Germany
jstrohs@germany.synopsys.com

Abstract

Dataflow computers are an approach to exploit fine-grain parallelism at the instruction level. The dataflow principle is based on a data-driven execution of instructions. Unfortunately, the data-driven program execution requires complex control mechanisms. The performance of dataflow computers depends strongly on the efficient implementation of those control mechanisms and on a high communication bandwidth between the processing elements. An approach to implement the dataflow control mechanisms efficiently is the use of associative memories, and this approach has already been pursued in some dataflow computers. But there still remains some potential for further improvements because conventional associative memories show an input/output bottleneck that restricts the performance significantly.

In this article, the associative dataflow architecture (ADARC) is presented. This architecture demonstrates the efficient use of associativity to accelerate the dataflow control mechanisms. It consists of a set of processors to compute dyadic instructions and a non-blocking communication network to route the operands between them. The network is controlled by a distributed associative memory unit avoiding the input/output bottleneck of conventional associative memories. Each memory word controls a switch due to the latest result of a match operation, so each word-cell gains the functionality of a switch controller. Associativity is used to change the communication structure dynamically according to the current requirements. In that way, ADARC is able to exploit the complete inherent parallelism of algorithms without being limited by any system bottlenecks.

After simulating the architecture and validating the correctness of its behavior, a prototype hardware of ADARC has been implemented. For the implementation of the associative communication network, an application-specific VLSI circuit (ASIC) has been designed and fabricated. Together with the hardware prototype, a programming environment for ADARC has been developed and implemented. First performance evaluations based on the computation of artificial neural nets have been carried out. All work was carried out at J.W. Goethe-University Technische Informatik.

1 Dataflow architectures

Dataflow computers, proposed in the early seventies by J.B. Dennis, are an approach to exploit fine-grain parallelism at the instruction level [Den74, DaM75]. They take full advantage of all implicit parallelism of algorithms by executing instructions whenever their input operands are available. Parallelism is restricted only by the data dependencies between instructions.

The operational principle of dataflow computers can be described by dataflow graphs, which are their base language. Dataflow graphs are directed and—in the classic approach—acyclic graphs. The nodes of dataflow graphs represent program instructions. They are connected by arcs representing the flow of data and which denote the data dependencies between the instructions. Tokens carrying the operands are passed along the arcs from instruction to instruction. The computer executes an instruction as soon as tokens are available on each input arc, then consumes the input tokens and generates an output token carrying the instruction's result.

This procedure is called node firing. In the dataflow computation scheme, based on the single assignment principle, values are assigned to a specific variable only once within a single computation cycle. Besides the graphical representation of dataflow programs, they can be described as a collection of activity templates which is closer to a machine language representation [Den79]. Each activity template corresponds to a node in a dataflow graph. An activity template is shown in Figure 1. The opcode describes the node's operation. The receiver fields store incoming operands while the destination fields point to the node's successors. Since processing elements typically perform dyadic instructions, the number of receiver fields may be limited to two. The number of destination fields depends on the maximum output degree of the nodes in a dataflow graph.

1.1 Organizational aspects of dataflow architectures

Several dataflow architectures have been proposed previously [ABU91]. They classified as static or dy-namic, based on how they synchronize instructions. According to the synchronization method, different methods to determine executable instructions are applied. In static dataflow architectures, operands are stored in the instruction's receiver fields as soon as they are available. This method is called token storage [TBH82] and is illustrated in Figure 2. A data token consists of an operand value and the address of the destination instruction. The computer updates memory by storing the operand values into the instructions specified by the memory addresses then, after an updating cycle, checks the instruction for executability. The addresses of executable instructions are transferred to the fetch unit, which loads them and transfers them to the processing unit for execution.

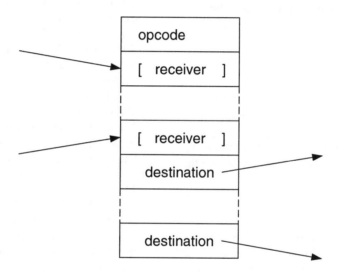

Figure 1. Activity template of a node.

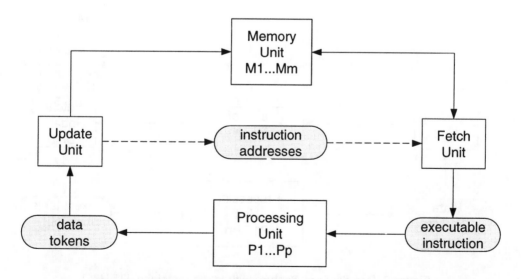

Figure 2. Dataflow architecture with token storage [TBH82].

In dynamic dataflow architectures, operands are not stored in the instruction words. Figure 3 shows the organization of a dataflow architecture performing token matching. Data tokens are buffered in a matching unit until all operands for a specific instruction are available. As soon as the set of tokens required for an instruction is complete, it is transferred to the fetch/update unit. This unit combines a set of tokens with a copy of the appropriate instruction to produce an executable instruction. A prerequisite for this method is the extension of data tokens by tags specifying the token's context. To determine matching tokens, their tags are compared and this is called token matching [TBH82].

1.2 Associative acceleration of dataflow control mechanisms

Regardless of the method used to determine executable instructions, dataflow architectures all show a pipelined ring structure. The dataflow control operations *updating* and *fetching* or *matching* and *fetching*, respectively, are performed with each instruction of a given program like incrementing the program counter in a von Neumann architecture. Thus, the implementation of the control operations has a strong effect on the architecture's performance.

1.2.1 Token matching

Since token matching is based on the comparison of a tag to the tags of all tokens in the matching unit, this operation performs best with an associative memory as the matching unit [ABU91]. Associative or content-addressable memories (CAM) are able to select items from a set of data according to a specific search function σ that is typically the Boolean equivalence. Data selection can be performed in parallel. This fact has been considered in the MIT tagged-token architecture, which conceptually provides an associative matching unit [AuN90]. Due to the low capacity of associative memories, this approach has not been pursued. Other dataflow computers, such as the SIGMA-1, use hashing techniques to match tokens [HSN84].

1.2.2 Token storage with associative retrieval of executable instructions

Although the use of associative memories in the implementation of token storage is not essential, advantages in static dataflow architecture performance can be gained when associative memories are used for token storage. A first approach to accelerate the retrieval of executable instructions in a static dataflow architecture has been made in the LAU-System [Pla76]. An associative instruction control memory (ICM) determines the executability of instructions. An ICM word consisting of three bits is assigned to each instruction, and the three bits indicate the availability of two operands and whether the instruction has already been executed or not. The configuration 111 at address m indicates that the corresponding instruction is executable. The search for 111 configurations in the ICM is performed in parallel. Unfortunately, executable instruction addresses are read sequentially and are transferred to the LAU-System's local memory for instruction retrieval.

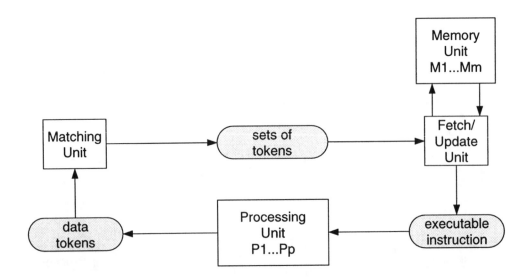

Figure 3. Dataflow architecture with token matching. [TBH82].

Parallel read/write access is not provided by conventional associative memories; thus, input/output operations are usually performed sequentially. Figure 4 shows the organization of a conventional associative memory [Koh87]. During the selection, data items are labeled by tags in the response store. Since the CAM array provides only a single-word output, matching memory words must be read sequentially. A multiple-response resolver provides the encoder with single matches to facilitate the encoding. Encoded addresses are fed into the address selector + decoder to select a memory word for reading.

1.2.3 Token storage with associative updating

The LAU-System uses an associative memory only to select executable instructions, but memory updating could also be performed efficiently by associative memories. Token storage based on conventional RAM causes multiple write accesses for each generated result, depending on the number of addresses in the destination fields of an instruction. This can be avoided with an associative memory. The content-oriented addressing mechanism of associative memories facilitates the simultaneous addressing of multiple memory words. In contrast to the read access described above, write access may be performed in parallel if a single value is stored in multiple memory words. This is the prerequisite for a parallel memory updating.

Associative updating is performed by a content-oriented addressing of the destination instructions for a given data token, as shown in Figure 5. Each operand is specified by a unique identifier. Thus, a data token consists of a result value (val_res) together with its identifier (id_res) replacing the destination address. The computer uses a result's identifier as a search argument to select the destination instructions and compares it to the identifiers of all operands in the instruction words. The other fields are irrelevant and ignored by masking. Following this procedure, all destination instructions are addressed simultaneously and the operand value may be stored into several instructions concurrently. Together with the storage of operand values, the availability flags f of the operands are set. They are used to determine executable instructions. Based on the content-oriented addressing of destination instructions, sequential storage operations are avoided and updating time is minimized.

Since some fields in the instruction word are never used for content-oriented memory access, storing those fields in the CAM array would be a waste of expensive associative hardware. Alternatively, a catalog memory can be used as an instruction store [Koh87]. The identifiers and the availability flags are used as keywords for the associative access in the directory while the operand values and the result identifier are stored in the data memory. The associatively coordinated dataflow concept proposed in [Rol88] provides associative memory updating and determination of executable instructions similar to the method described above.

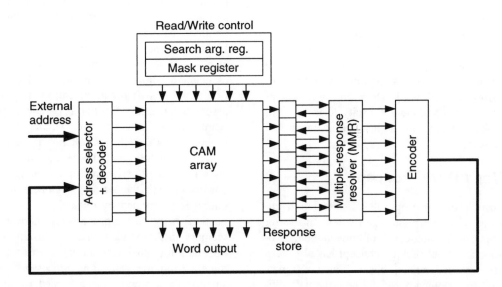

Figure 4. Organization of a conventional associative memory [Koh87].

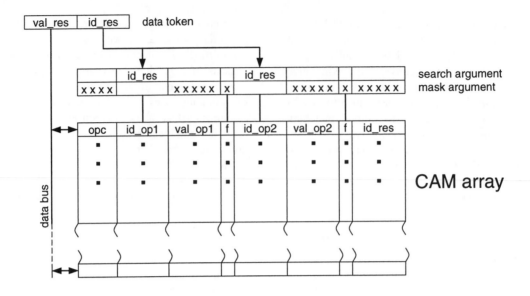

Figure 5. Associative memory updating.

1.2.4 *Further improvements*

Although we've been discussing concurrent updating for single data tokens, in a dataflow multiprocessor numerous tokens may be generated concurrently. This requires concurrent memory updating as well. Even if updating the memory with a single token may be accelerated by the multiwrite capability of associative memories, they do not facilitate parallel memory updating with multiple tokens. This requires the support of multiple search arguments and a very complex data bus structure in the memory. A further problem, not yet solved, is parallel-read access to executable instructions and the data transfer between memory unit and processors.

Besides the improvement of associative memories to accelerate the dataflow control mechanisms, the bandwidth of the communication facility connecting the memory unit to the processing unit also influences system performance [Den80]. Therefore, a communication network with sufficient capacity to transfer all the result tokens and executable instructions in parallel would be desirable.

2 The ADARC concept

As described, previous proposals of associative implementations of the token storage method still suffer from the input/output bottleneck of conventional associative memories. The ADARC concept has also been derived from token storage, but it contains a new memory updating method based on the program's efficient distribution onto the system's processors. Memory updating is performed by an intelligent communication mechanism, computed results are exchanged via

an associative communication network, and the executability of instructions is determined by the processors themselves. This approach is close to the model of dataflow graphs where results are transferred immediately from producing to consuming nodes and the nodes are triggered by an internal firing rule of the node.

2.1 Concept introduction

Figure 6 is an overview of ADARC, which consists of a processing unit and an associative communication network. The network overcomes the problems described earlier by providing the functionality of a common associative updating unit as well as non-blocking communication between the processors. It also serves as input/output unit for the system. The associative communication network has the structure of a crossbar switch and is controlled by a distributed associative memory facilitating parallel inquiries. Each word-cell of the associative memory gains the functionality of a switch controller. The network's structure provides full-parallel access to all generated operands in a single-write, multiple-read mode, which is consistent with the single assignment principle. Updating is performed by dynamically routing the connections between the processors. There is no operand memory in ADARC. Instruction results that serve as operands for other instructions are transferred immediately from the generating processors to their consumers. Data storage is performed by local operand registers of the consuming processors. This may cause redundant storage of several operands, but it enables full-parallel memory access.

input

results

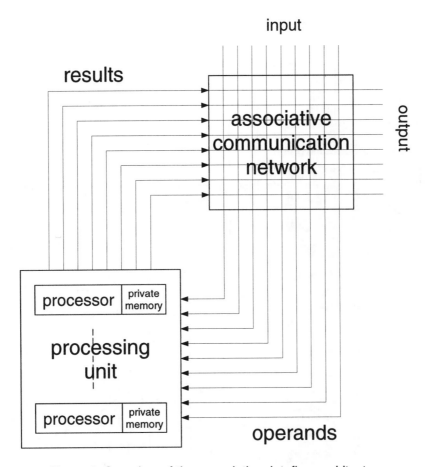

output

operands

Figure 6. Overview of the associative dataflow architecture.

ADARC processors have a private memory unit. These private memories contain parts of the dataflow program that are generated at compile time by a pre-scheduler and assigned during initialization. The program's instruction sequence derives from an analysis of the data dependencies contained in a given dataflow graph. The pre–runtime–scheduling facilitates sequential execution of predefined threads without offending the data-driven nature of computing. The current instruction of a processor is executed as soon as all input operands have been received.

2.2   Architecture description

Figure 7 shows a block diagram of ADARC. The processing unit consists of a number of processors, connected via the associative communication network, computing dyadic operations. The processors may have different arithmetical capabilities. The only re-

quirements are a private memory and three ports as the network interface. Two of these ports receive operands. The result of the latest instruction is transmitted into the network via the output port, each of which has a fixed connection to one of the network's vertical output lines. Each input port is driven by a horizontal input line that is connected to all vertical output lines in the network via associatively controlled switches (denoted by the circles). Thus, data provided at any output port is available for all system processors. Since the switches are controlled individually, single connections, and multicast or broadcast communication, are available. The system input is realized by additional associative switches on each input line. Data output is performed via the output lines. Using the input and output lines as an interface to the environment offers a high communication bandwidth. The fact that all results can be observed at the system outputs affords a high potential for system monitoring and program debugging.

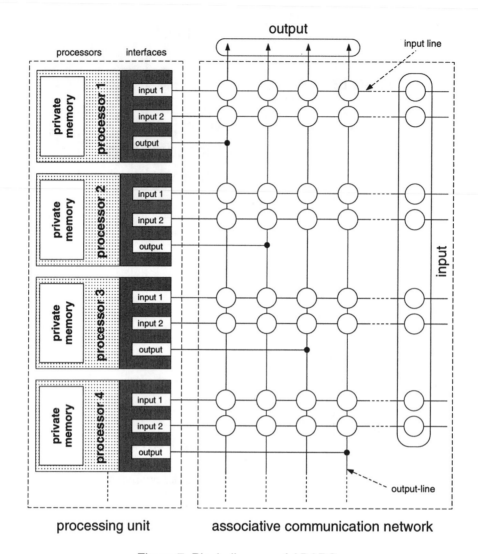

processing unit   associative communication network

Figure 7. Block diagram of ADARC.

Figure 8 shows a more detailed schematic of ADARC for a small configuration consisting of two processors and an appropriate network. The processors consist of an ALU, two input registers, and an output register. All processors are provided with private memory. The control mechanism of the network is based on the associative updating in a token storage system as described in section 1.2. The fields of the instruction format used for ADARC's associative updating mechanism are classified as associative information. In Figure 8 those fields are shaded grey. The opcode that controls the ALU is stored with the associative information in the processors' private memory. The values are not stored in the memory—they are transferred immediately from the producer to the consumer(s) where they are stored in the input registers. According to the distinction of identifiers and values, the communication lines are partitioned into identifier lines and value lines. The associatively controlled

switches that connect input lines and output lines contain a small associative memory consisting of a search argument register and a single CAM word. The CAM word's *match* signal controls the connection between the value lines. A connection is enabled if the search argument matches the contents of the CAM word.

2.3 System operation

To execute the current instruction, two input operands are required. The identifiers of the requested operands are sent into the network via the identifier lines of the input ports. These identifiers must be compared to the identifiers of all available results and are stored redundantly in the CAM word of each associative switch on the input line. After generating a result, the result of the comparison value is provided at the value line of the output port. The result identifier is sent to the search argument register of the associative switches

88

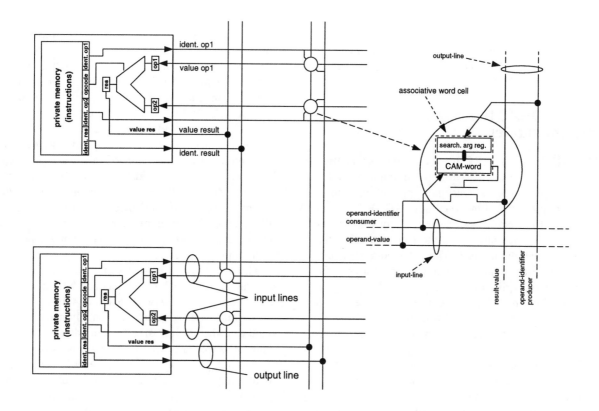

instruction format

| opcode | ident. op1 | value op1 | ident. op2 | value op2 | ident. res. | value res. |

Figure 8. Detailed diagram of ADARC.

located at the assigned output line. Since the associative memory is distributed over the network, multiple inquiries are performed simultaneously. After the comparison, all connections required to provide the processors with their requested operands are activated. As soon as both operands are available, an instruction is executed. Requests for the next operands are sent into the network simultaneously with the execution of the current instruction. To save communication time, each processor may check internally whether it is the consumer of its own current result. In this case, operand values may be transferred immediately between internal registers.

An earlier approach to determine destinations for computed results is the common data bus implemented in the IBM System/360 Model 91 [Tom67]. It supports concurrency between multiple execution units by an intelligent control of operand transfer. In this approach, operand transfer is performed via a bus connecting all units. Tags specifying the generating unit of the next operand to be received are dynamically as-

signed to the input registers of all units. Data transfer is controlled by comparing the tags of operands on the bus with the registers' tags. ADARC's method of controlling operand transfer is more general. An individual identifier is assigned to each operand so that its identification is independent of the generating processor.

ADARC also shows the pipelined ring structure that is typical for dataflow architectures, but it avoids the bottlenecks mentioned previously. All processors may transfer their results in parallel. Since operands are not stored between instructions, there is network latency but no memory latency. This architecture is close to the principle of dataflow graphs, where the edges do not provide storage capacity and operands are transferred immediately from node to node.

With a rising number of processors, the associative network grows in square space complexity, but since it has a regular structure it can be extended easily by using identical building blocks. Current VLSI technologies facilitate the design of such building blocks as integrated circuits. This offers the opportunity to build systems of different size according to the specific requirements by combining an appropriate number of building-blocks.

3 ADARC hardware implementation

After validating ADARC by a functional simulation with Cadence Systems' Verilog, we implemented a hardware prototype to investigate applications and to optimize processor functionalities. ADARC is not restricted to specific processors; it does have requirements concerning the interface between the processors and the network. The processors must provide appropriate connections and support a specific communication protocol. To achieve a high degree of flexibility in ADARC's current implementation phase, we can emulate the instruction sets of different types of processing units with a high-performance microprocessor.

Except for the associative communication network, we based the hardware implementation on standard, off-the-shelf components. We chose Texas Instruments' signal processors (TMS320C30), which has a peak performance of 40 Mflops. It is equipped with 2 serial ports offering a high I/O bandwidth and an appropriate interface to the communication network.

Since ADARC's performance depends on the efficient implementation of the associative communication network, we designed an ASIC. The associative crossbar module (ACM) is a VLSI building block for the modular construction of the associative communication network. ACM chips may be cascaded to realize associative networks of different sizes.

We designed a processor board and a motherboard (see Figure 9) for the ADARC hardware prototype. The processor board holds up to 1 Mbyte of local memory. ROM modules store the operating system and the interpreter for a dedicated instruction set. Additionally, each processor board provides two serial and a parallel interface for system input/output and program monitoring.

The motherboard provides an associative communication network for 8 processors and 8 slots for processor boards. The network consists of 4 16-node ACM chips, which are cascaded horizontally and vertically to increase the network size. To provide an associative communication network for more processor boards, several motherboards may be cascaded. Each motherboard is equipped with connectors for horizontal and vertical cascading. The system is connected to a host via a standard serial interface, also implemented on the motherboard. The serial interface loads the instruction sequences generated by the prescheduler into the private memories of the processors.

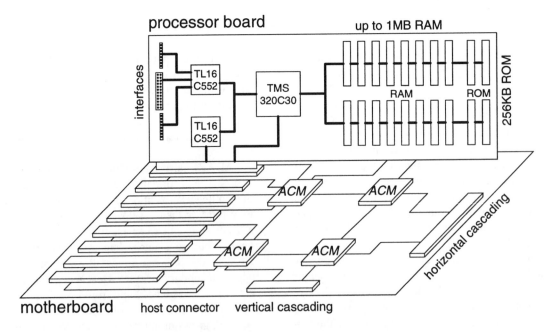

Figure 9. ADARC hardware structure.

3.1 The associative crossbar module

The associative crossbar module is a VLSI building block for the associative communication network. One chip interconnects up to 4 processors. Several ACM chips may be cascaded to increase the network size. Since the network grows in square space complexity, $\frac{p}{4}^2$ ACM chips are required to connect ρ processors. The chip's processor interface has been adapted to the serial ports of the TMS320C30 signal processor. Data transfer between the ACM and the processor is performed in a fixed-burst mode [Tex91] with a word-length varying from 8 to 32 bits in 8-bit steps. The communication between the processors and the associative communication network is completely controlled by the ACM chips.

Design and fabrication of the ACM ASIC has been performed in the framework of EUROCHIP, using a 1.5μm standard cell library. Our first implementation has a complexity of 18,871 transistors requiring a chip area of 42 mm^2 and 72 pins. A result of the first design was that the chip area of this small ACM is determined by the number of pad-cells. The chip core requires 10 mm^2 only. Since the pin number grows linearly, an associative communication network for 8 processors could be realized on a single chip using the same technology. With more sophisticated technologies, larger networks could easily be implemented on a single chip.

The ACM may be used in two modes:

1. *Associative crossbar switch.* In this mode, the connections between input lines and output lines are controlled by the associative switches. Data transfer is performed in three phases.

   - The identifiers of the requested operands are sent into the network simultaneously by all processors.

   - A bit-serial comparison between identifiers of operands and of results is performed. Simultaneously, the result values are transferred to the network and buffered in registers.

   - According to the results of the comparison phase, the value lines of inputs and outputs are connected, and the buffered results are transferred to the appropriate processors.

2. *Programmable crossbar switch.* In this mode, fixed connections between the processors are programmed during an initialization phase.

Programming is performed by setting the match signals in the associative switches according to the desired network topology.

In both modes, a counter checks whether an input line is driven by more than one output line. Because multiple drivers of an input line may cause a short circuit, this situation is avoided and any attempt is indicated by an error signal. Hardware testing of the integrated circuit is supported by a scanpath connecting all match flip-flops to a shift register. This scanpath is also used for programming the fixed connections.

4 ADARC programming environment

The execution of programs on ADARC is based on the dataflow programming paradigm; thus, the base language for ADARC is dataflow graphs. The programming environment of ADARC is mainly based on the transformation of a given dataflow graph into instruction sequences to be executed by the processors. This is performed by a prescheduler. Since dataflow graphs are a very low-level program representation, we added several, more comfortable programming tools. For example, a tool for compiling a high-level programming language into dataflow graphs is included, as are several tools to transform application-specific representations into dataflow graphs. Currently, tools for the transformation of artificial neural nets and genetic algorithms are available. Figure 10 shows the ADARC programming environment.

To achieve acceptance from programmers accustomed to imperative programming languages, ADARC's high-level language resembles C [Bir94]. The following piece of code describes the computation of the factorial.

```
{
    input    int   n;
    output   int   fak;

    int  i;

    fak  =   1;
    i    =   2;
    while   (i <= n)
    {
        fak =   i * fak;
        i   =   i + 1;
    }
}
```

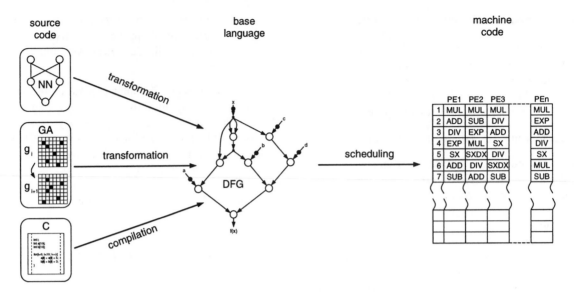

Figure 10. ADARC programming environment.

4.1 Basic considerations

Since new results computed in each instruction cycle are not buffered, they are available for a limited period only. This fact must be considered when instructions are assigned to the processors. The assignment strategy depends on the relation between the number of processors and the number of nodes in the dataflow graph. If the number of processors is equal to or greater than the number of nodes in the dataflow graph, all instructions can be assigned to different processors. In this case, each processor is active only once during a program run. New program runs can be started while previous runs are still in progress. This is useful for applications like signal processing where identical processing of incoming data is repeated permanently so that the architecture operates like a pipeline.

If the number of processing elements is smaller than the number of nodes, a static assignment between instructions and processors is impossible. Each processor has to execute several instructions. The assignment of instructions to processors has to be performed at compile time by a prescheduler, considering the fact that operands are available temporarily only. The pre–runtime-scheduling is based on an analysis of the data dependencies defined by the dataflow graph.

The degree of an algorithm's parallelism can be determined by partitioning the dataflow graph into disjoint horizontal layers. All nodes on the same layer compute in parallel. The layers are linearly ordered with respect to their precedence constraints [LHF91]. The complete parallelism of an algorithm is exploited if all instructions represented by the nodes on one layer are executed concurrently. In this case, the number of processors must be greater than or equal to the degree of parallelism. The dataflow graph is processed layer by layer so that instruction sequences may be assigned to one processor. The availability of consumers for the operands is guaranteed by a sufficient number of processors and by keeping the precedence constraints.

A degree of parallelism higher than the number of processors disables the concurrent execution of all instructions on one layer. Layers must be partitioned according to the number of available processors and processed sequentially. To avoid the loss of data, results must be buffered for several instruction cycles.

4.2 The prescheduler

The prescheduler that generates the instruction sequences from dataflow graphs was implemented at J.W. Goethe-University Technische Informatik in two steps. First, a scheduler for acyclic dataflow graphs was developed and implemented [App94]. In a second step, the tool was extended to process cyclic dataflow graphs as well [Wei95]. The input for both schedulers is a special language to describe dataflow graphs. The description of a dataflow graph corresponding to the program code for the computation of the factorial is presented below. The scheduling process is as follows. Cyclic DFGs are decomposed into acyclic parts called basic blocks. Next, a schedule for the basic blocks is computed. The dataflow subgraphs corresponding to the basic blocks are processed by the scheduler for acyclic graphs. The instruction sequences generated from the basic blocks are assembled according to the schedule of the blocks to form the complete threads for the processors.

// NodeNr	OpCode	op. 1	op. 2	further operands
1:	SETI	#2		
2:	SETI	#3		
3:	SETI	#1		
4:	CMERGE	3,		
		I.2	I.3	I.1,
		I.5	I.7.T.2	I.8
5:	ADDI	I.7.T.1	I.1	
6:	CMPI_LE	I.4..1	I.4..2	
7:	BRANCH	I.6,	3,	
		I.4..1	I.4..2	I.4..3
8:	MULI	I.7.T.1	I.7.T.3	
9:	OUTI	I.7.F.3		

The acyclic subgraphs are processed in two phases. The first phase performs an analysis of the dataflow graph. For each node in the graph, the most expensive path from the node to a leave is computed. This computation considers different execution times for the operations represented by the nodes. The first phase also computes the sequence of nodes to be processed in the second phase. The second phase performs the assignment between instructions represented by the dataflow graph nodes and processors. During the assignment phase, the instructions are mapped on the available processors. In this phase, the prescheduler detects the requirements of result buffering. To guarantee the availability of operands, different types of SAVE- and LOAD-instructions may be inserted. The result of this pre–runtime-scheduling is instruction sequences to be processed concurrently by the system's processors.

5   Performance evaluation

We evaluated system performance and validated the scheduler based on the computation of artificial neural nets. Since nets are data-driven by nature, they can easily be transformed into dataflow graphs. By decomposing the computations performed by the neurons, a high degree of parallelism can be achieved. This effect is demonstrated in Figure 11, which shows the dataflow graph of one learning cycle of an XOR net with 4 neurons.

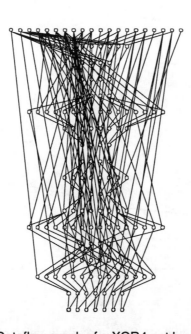

Figure 11. Dataflow graph of a XOR4 net learning cycle.

Performance measurements have been made based on the learning phase of a backpropagation algorithm performed by different neural nets shown in Figure 12 [Bro94].

The results of the performance analysis presented in Figures 13 and 14 show that an efficiency of approximately 0.5 can be reached as long as the ratio between the degree of parallelism and the number of processors is nearly 1. As soon as the number of available processors exceeds the degree of parallelism, the slope of the speedup curves becomes very small and thus the efficiency decreases. The speedup grows linearly with a sufficient degree of parallelism provided by large neural networks.

Net	Topology	Neurons
XOR4	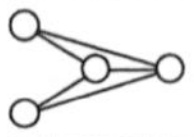	4
XOR5	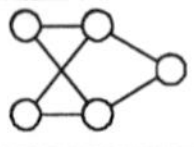	5
NOT	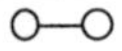	2
PAR4I	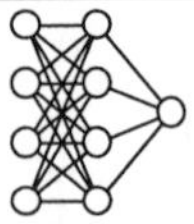	9
ENCIDE	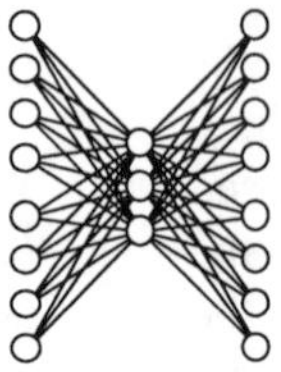	19

Figure 12. Neural nets used for performance evaluation.

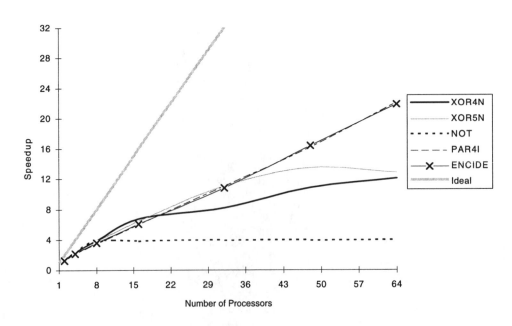

Figure 13. Speedup of a learning cycle.

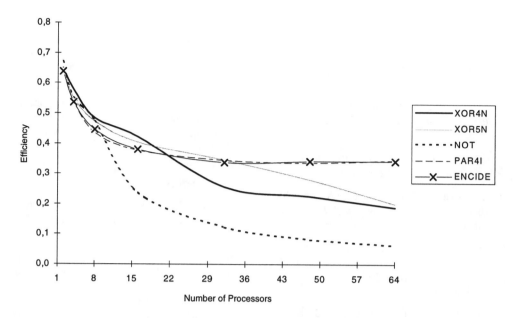

Figure 14. Efficiency of a learning cycle.

6   Conclusion

We presented the new dataflow architecture, ADARC. Our design goal for ADARC was to increase the architecture's speed by an efficient implementation of the dataflow control mechanisms. Associative methods were chosen for the control mechanisms' implementation. An investigation of former approaches led to the new concept of an associative updating unit. This unit consists of a distributed associative memory coupled with a nonblocking communication unit. Updating is performed by an intelligent routing of connections between the system's processors. This method is supported by a pre–runtime-scheduling of the program instructions, according to their data dependencies.

The ADARC concept was validated by simulation and a hardware prototype was implemented. The programming of ADARC is supported by means of a high-level programming language. To facilitate the computation of artificial neural nets, appropriate network descriptions may automatically be transformed into dataflow graphs exploiting the neurons' implicit parallelism.

References

[App94] S. Appelhans, "Entwicklung und Implementierung eines Preschedulers für eine assoziative Datenflußarchitektur" [Development and Implementation of a Prescheduler for an Associative Dataflow Architecture], master thesis, Dept. of Computer Sci., J.W. Goethe-University, Frankfurt, May 1994.

[AuN90] Arvind and R.S Nikhil, "Executing a Program on the MIT Tagged-Token Dataflow Architecture," *IEEE Trans. Computers*, Vol. 39, No. 3, Mar. 1990.

[ABU91] Arvind, L. Bic, and Th. Ungerer, "Evolution of Dataflow Computers," from *Advanced* Topics *in Data-Flow Computing*, Prentice-Hall, Englewood Cliffs, N.J., 1991.

[Bir94] J. Birken, "Entwicklung einer Programmierschnittstelle für repetierenden Betrieb auf einer assoziativen Datenflußarchitektur" [Development of a Programming Interface for Repeated Computations on a Dataflow Architecture], master thesis, Dept. of Computer Sci., J.W. Goethe-University, Frankfurt, Nov. 1994.

[Bro94] B. Brodnik, "Simulation neuronaler Netze auf feinkörnigen parallelen Datenflußrechnern" [Simulation of Neural Networks on Fine Grain Dataflow Computers], master thesis, Dept. of Computer Sci., J.W. Goethe-University Frankfurt, Sept. 1994.

[Den74] J.B. Dennis, "First Version of a Data Flow Procedure Language," *Lecture Notes in Computer Sci.*, Vol. 19, Springer-Verlag, Berlin, 1974.

[DaM75] J.B. Dennis and R.P. Misunas, "A Preliminary Architecture for a Basic Dataflow Processor," *Proc. 2nd Ann. Symp. Computer Architecture*, IEEE CS Press, Los Alamitos, Calif., 1975.

[Den79] J.B. Dennis, "The Varieties of Data Flow Computers," *Proc. 1st Int'l Conf. Distributed Computing Systems*, IEEE CS Press, Los Alamitos, Calif., 1979.

[Den80] J.B. Dennis, "Data Flow Supercomputers," *Computer*, Vol. 13, No. 11, Nov. 1980.

[HSN84] K. Hiraki, T. Shimada, and K. Nishida, "A Hardware Design of the SIGMA-1—A Dataflow Computer for Scientific Computations," *Proc. Int'l Conf. Parallel Processing*, IEEE CS Press, Los Alamitos, Calif., 1984.

[HaB85] K. Hwang and F.A. Briggs, *Computer Architecture and Parallel Processing*, McGraw-Hill, Singapore, 1985.

[Koh87] T. Kohonen, *Content-Addressable Memories*, Springer-Verlag, Berlin, Heidelberg, 1987.

[LHF91] B. Lee, A.R. Hurson, and T.Y. Feng, "A Vertically Layered Scheme for Data Flow Systems," *J. Parallel and Distributed Computing*, Vol. 11, No. 3, Mar. 1991.

[Pla76] A. Plas et al., "Lau System Architecture: A Parallel Data-Driven Processor based on Single Assignment," *Proc. 1976 Int'l Conf. Parallel Processing*, IEEE CS Press, Los Alamitos, Calif., 1976.

[Rol88] G. Roll, "Ein mikroprogrammierter Bit-Slice-Assoziativprozessor zur Unterstützung paralleler Rechnerarchitekturen" [A Mikroprogrammable Bit-Slice-Associative Processor supporting Parallel Computer Architectures, doctoral dissertation, Dept. of Computer Sci., J.W. Goethe-University, Frankfurt, 1988.

[TBH82] P.C. Treleaven, D.R. Brownbridge, and R.P. Hopkins, "Data-Driven and Demand-Driven Computer Architecture, *Computing Surveys*, Vol. 14, No. 1, Mar. 1982.

[Tex91] Texas Instruments Corp., "TMS320C3x User's Guide," 1991.

[Tom67] R.M. Tomasulo, "An Efficient Algorithm for Exploiting Multiple Arithmetic Units," *IBM J. Research and Development*, 1967.

[Wei95] H.-J. Weimer, "Entwicklung und Implementierung eines Preschedulers für zyklische Datenflußgraphen" [Development and Implementation of a Prescheduler for Cyclic Dataflow Graphs], master thesis, Dept. of Computer Sci., J.W. Goethe-University, Frankfurt, Mar. 1995.

A Dynamic Associative Processor for Machine Vision Applications

Massively parallel associative processors may be well suited as coprocessors for accelerating machine vision applications. They achieve very fine granularity, as every word of memory functions as a simple processing element. A dense, dynamic, content-addressable memory cell supports fully parallel operation, and pitch-matched word logic improves arithmetic performance with minimal area cost. An asynchronous reconfigurable mesh network handles interprocessor communication and image input/output, and an area-efficient pass-transistor circuit counts and prioritizes responders.

Frederick P. Herrmann

Charles G. Sodini

Massachusetts Institute of Technology

Recent technological advances have led to two developments with exciting implications for machine vision. First, massively parallel supercomputers have come of age. With many thousands of processing elements and some Gbits of total memory, these systems may be the most promising technology for high-level, image-understanding applications. Second, designers are applying VLSI to low-level, or *early*, vision problems. High density and low power make single-chip solutions feasible, perhaps on the same chip as the imager.

Somewhere between the massively parallel supercomputer and the application-specific analog solution a need exists for a simple, low-cost, very fine-grained machine. There is a class of applications in early and middle vision for which million-dollar supercomputers are overkill, yet analog solutions are insufficiently general. The associative parallel processor can fill this niche.

In the early years of associative processing, the pioneers of the field recognized picture processing as a promising source of applications for their new machines.[1,2] Image processing problems can be rich in inherent parallelism, with many thousands of pixels receiving identical processing steps. The low precision of image data (typically 8-bit integers) and the often modest computational requirements at each pixel match the limitations of bit-serial arithmetic. Associative processors are an attractive solution, because they are by nature fine-grained machines in which every word of memory functions as a tiny processing element (PE). Modern VLSI technology provides the density necessary to produce large arrays at low cost, with each PE assigned to a single pixel.

As shown in Figure 1 on the next page a 2D network connects the PEs and handles image input and output. A host computer broadcasts instructions to all PEs in the array. Two data conversion steps are needed to load the array with a digitized image. First, the imager makes an analog electronic signal representing the image. The acquisition domain is typically optical, but the imager could be an electron microscope, a medical magnetic resonance imager, or a radio telescope.

After any analog-domain processing, an analog-to-digital converter produces a digital signal for the associative processor. The edge of the network provides a high-bandwidth port for image input and output. This system can serve as the front end of a hierarchical architecture for image understanding[3] or as a stand-alone processor for pattern recognition and image processing tasks.

Reprinted from *IEEE Micro*, Vol. 12, No. 3, June 1992, pp. 31–41.

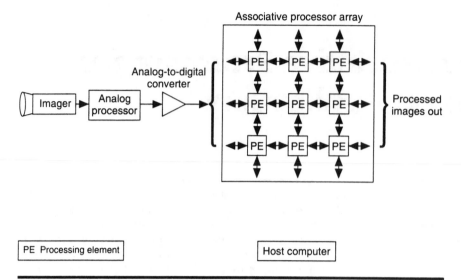

Figure 1. Vision system incorporating an associative processor.

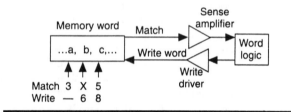

Figure 2. Associative PE.

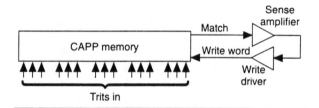

Figure 3. PE with direct match-write feedback.

Figure 2 is a generalized diagram of a single associative PE. The memory word stores patterns, which may have several fields (*a,b,c,...*). A match operation finds PEs that match one or more fields; unused fields are masked with don't cares (X). For example, the operation Match (3, X, 5) would identify all PEs with *a* = 3 and *c* = 5, and would set their sense amplifier outputs to 1. Each PE's match result passes to its word logic, which in turn controls the write driver. Thus, match results condition write operations. If the write driver is not enabled, the PE is masked, and its memory remains unchanged.

Fields within a word can also be masked, so we can modify some fields while preserving others. For example, Write (–, 6, 8) will set *b* = 6 and *c* = 8 while leaving the contents of the *a* field unchanged.

Associative parallel processors may be bit serial/word parallel or fully parallel. In the first case, match and write operations may examine or modify only one bit of each memory word at a time. Multibit operations take several cycles, and combining results of the single-bit matches requires relatively complex word logic. Fully parallel systems perform multibit matches and writes as single operations and therefore may use simpler word logic. The advantage of the bit-serial approach is that designers can use conventional RAM cells, while fully parallel systems require special content-addressable parallel processor memory.

This CAPP memory has historically been relatively expensive compared to standard RAM. However, a new dynamic cell[4] uses only five N-channel transistors and with equivalent technology should achieve a density similar to that of a CMOS SRAM. This new technology should make fully parallel systems competitive, especially in applications requiring many relatively simple PEs.

The dynamic CAPP cell (see box) stores the three ternary digits (trits) 0, 1, and X. The match operation compares the stored trit to a presented datum, with every trit matching itself, and the don't care (X) matching every trit. All the cells of a word perform the match comparison in parallel, and the word match result is the logical And of the individual cell match results.

The write operation modifies the cell contents. If a masked Write (–) is presented, the cell contents will be preserved. Otherwise the cell will take the value of the presented trit. Of course, none of the cells in the word will be modified unless the word logic activates the write enable driver.

The cell also supports a read operation, but the associative processor system does not use it. Instead, the processor array outputs data through the interprocessor communication network.

Word logic

In an area-efficient design the word logic must match the vertical pitch of the memory cells. This constraint is a strong incentive to reduce word logic complexity. Consider, as a design exercise, the simplest logic element imaginable: a wire.

Figure 3 is a fully parallel associative PE with the sense

Dynamic content-addressable parallel processor cell

Figure A is a circuit diagram of the dynamic CAPP cell used in the fully parallel associative processor. The cell uses five N-channel MOS transistors, including two overlapping dual-gate structures available in MIT's CCD/CMOS process.

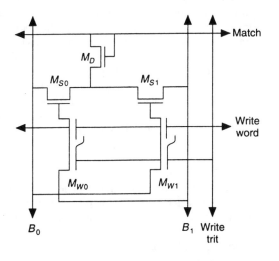

Figure A. Dynamic content-addressable parallel processor cell.

Charge is stored on the gates of M_{S0} and M_{S1}, which are written through the M_W devices. The diode-connected transistor prevents shorting the bit lines ($B_{0,1}$) of adjacent cells through the match line M. Three states (trits) may be stored in the cell: 0 or 1 by charging the gates of M_{S0} or M_{S1}, and X (don't care) by discharging both (see Table A). Because it is difficult to charge both gates simultaneously, no fourth state is used.

The cell performs match, read, and write operations. The match operation begins with the match line precharged to a high potential. The bit lines are then driven with the match trit (Table B), and a mismatch will cause the match line to be discharged. For example, a 1 is presented by dropping B_0 while B_1 remains high. If the cell is storing a 0, then M_{S0} will be on, and current will flow through M_D and M_{S0}. Similarly, a 0 is presented by dropping only B_1. If both bit lines remain high, then an X has been presented, as there can be no discharge path and a match is guaran-

teed. Finally, if both bit lines are driven low, the cell will indicate a mismatch if either storage device is on. This fourth (can't match) datum is denoted with the symbol Ø. Its primary use is to detect stored X's during refresh.

The read operation is similar to the match, except that the match line is used to pull up the bit lines, instead of the bit lines discharging the match line. If a 0 is stored in the cell, B_0 will be pulled up through M_D and M_{S0}. A stored 1 will cause B_1 to rise. If the cell is in the X state, both storage devices will be off, and both bit lines will remain low.

Two write lines are necessary to provide write enables in two dimensions. The word logic controls the write-word line, which runs horizontally. The write-trit line runs vertically and is used for trit-column masking. The cell is written by raising both write lines and driving the bit lines to the appropriate potentials. If the write-trit line is held low, the write is masked, and the state of the cell will remain unchanged. The symbol "–" denotes this masked write.

Table A. Three states stored in the cell.

State	Storage nodes	
	$V_{GS}(M_{S0})$	$V_{GS}(M_{S1})$
0	High	Low
1	Low	High
X	Low	Low

Table B. Control of match and write operations.

Operation	Control lines		
	B_0	B_1	Write trit
Match 0	High	Low	Low
Match 1	Low	High	Low
Match X	High	High	Low
Match Ø	Low	Low	Low
Write 0	Low	High	High
Write 1	High	Low	High
Write X	Low	Low	High
Write –			Low

amplifier output fed directly back to the write enable driver. Match and write patterns are presented to the CAPP memory word on the trit lines, which run vertically through the PE array. Surprisingly, even this simple PE can perform useful operations. We use a sequential state transformation process.[1]

Table 1 is a truth table for the destructive single-bit full add,

$$A + B + C \rightarrow A, C.$$

Table 1. Full-add truth table and transformations.

State	Previous state			New state		Transform
	A	B	C	A	C	
0	0	0	0	0	0	√
1	0	0	1	1	0	
2	0	1	0	1	0	
3	0	1	1	0	1	√
4	1	0	0	1	0	√
5	1	0	1	0	1	
6	1	1	0	0	1	
7	1	1	1	1	1	√

Table 2. Full-add procedure.

Step	Instruction	Pattern		
		A	B	C
1	Match	0	0	1
2	Write	1	–	0
3	Match	1	0	1
4	Write	0	–	1
5	Match	1	1	0
6	Write	0	–	1
7	Match	0	1	0
8	Write	1	–	0

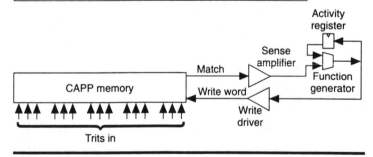

Figure 4. PE with improved word logic.

The least-significant bit of the sum replaces the value of A, and the carry bit C receives the most-significant bit. A quick examination of the table reveals that no work needs to be done in the checked states; the new values of A and C are the same as the old values. The other four states need to be transformed, as indicated by the arrows. Each transformation will require one match and one write operation, as shown in Table 2.

The first match operation selects all PEs in the 001 state. The Write $(1-0)$ modifies the A and C bits appropriately, transforming state 1 into state 4. Steps 3 and 4 transform state 5 into state 1, and subsequent operations handle the remaining transformations. The procedure requires eight operations, but some are redundant: The four write instructions use only two write patterns. Perhaps a different choice of word logic could reduce the total number of operations.

Figure 4 shows the word logic actually used in this associative processor design. It includes a two-input function generator and one bit of state, the activity register (AR). The function generator can compute any of the 16 binary Boolean functions of two inputs. We define two operations:

- *Match*. The function generator is evaluated using the old values of the AR and sense amplifier (SA). The AR takes the function generator output as its new value, and the SA value is replaced by the match result on the CAPP memory word.
- *Write*. After evaluation, the function generator is used to enable the write driver. The AR and SA values remain unchanged.

Table 3 shows an add procedure for the improved word logic. In the first step, the processor performs a match with the pattern XX1. This loads C into the sense amplifier. In step 2, the function generator passes the sense amplifier result to the activity register, while the sense amplifier takes on the value B. The exclusive-Or $(B \oplus C)$ is computed in the third step, while the value of A is loaded into the sense amplifier.

After three matches, the SA and AR contain the information necessary to enable the writes. Step 4 uses the function $SA' \wedge AR$ to enable the instruction Write $(1-0)$, transforming states 1 and 2 of Table 1. The last write transforms states 5 and 6.

The function generator and activity register reduce the number of instructions required for a full add from eight to five. Table 4 presents results for other arithmetic operations and shows that the improved word logic can increase performance by a factor of two or more. (These figures represent per-bit requirements, excluding constant-time initialization or cleanup instructions.)

We must weigh the performance benefits provided by the word logic against its cost in silicon

Table 3. Add procedure for the improved word logic.

Step	Instruction	Function	Pattern A	B	C	Sense amplifier contents	Activity register contents
1	Match		X	X	1	C	
2	Match	(SA)	X	1	X	B	C
3	Match	(SA $\oplus$ AR)	1	X	X	A	$B \oplus C$
4	Write	(SA' $\wedge$ AR)	1	–	0	A	$B \oplus C$
5	Write	(SA $\wedge$ AR)	0	–	1	A	$B \oplus C$

area. Fortunately, this cost is small. The activity register is almost cost free, since it shares many transistors with a shift register, which is required for testing. The function generator occupies about 5,000 square microns in 2-μm design rules or a little more than four memory cells. In the experimental chip discussed later, the function generators accounted for less than 5 percent of array area.

One might consider further increasing word logic complexity to provide greater performance. For example, a three-input functional unit, such as a full adder, might replace the two-input function generator. Doing so would trim the destructive add algorithm modestly, from five operations down to four, but word logic area would more than double. We deemed the two-input function generator a more appropriate trade-off between performance and area, consistent with our stated goal of very fine granularity.

Experimental implementation

We built an associative processing test chip in MIT's 2-μm CCD/CMOS process[5] as a first step toward complete implementation. Along with other key circuits, the chip includes an array of 64 PEs, each with 64 trits of CAPP memory (see Figure 5). We chose the number of trits per PE after considering the memory needs of several low-level vision algorithms. To ease the pitch constraint, however, the memory is actually implemented with two 32-trit words for each PE. In this way, two word pitches are available for laying out the sense amplifier, function generator, and activity register. A match line multiplexer allows these circuits to be shared by the two words, however each PE requires two write drivers and two match drivers.

Our prototype design relies on off-chip control logic, timing, and instruction decoding. Plans for the final implementation include these subsystems on chip, along with interprocessor communication and response resolution circuits. The anticipated density is 256 PEs per chip in 2-μm technology.

Table 4. Cycles required for arithmetic operations.

Operation	Notation	State transformation	Improved word logic
Destructive add	$A + B + C \rightarrow A, C$	8	5
Nondestructive add	$A + B + C \rightarrow \Sigma, C$	12	5
Scalar add	$A + s \rightarrow A$	4	3
Absolute value	$|A| \rightarrow A$	6	3

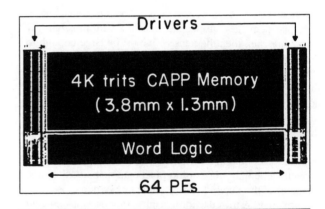

Figure 5. Detail from photomicrograph of experimental chip, showing array of 64 PEs with 4,096 trits total memory.

Interconnection

Interprocessor communication is an important consideration in the design of any parallel processor, and this associative processor is no exception. However, the associative processor's fine grain creates a different set of constraints than that which might limit a coarse-grained design. For example, an often-repeated maxim says that in modern VLSI systems, "Wires are expensive, and transistors are cheap." In a pitch-matched lay-

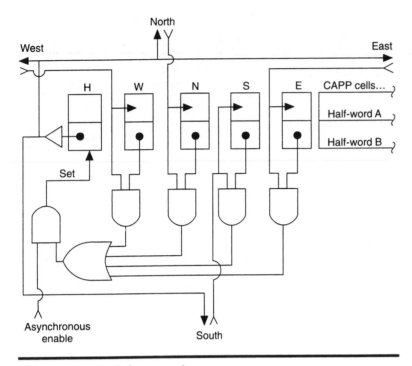

Figure 6. Special cells for network.

out, however, transistors are expensive too. Output circuits in particular demand considerable area. If a wire runs halfway across the chip, then the transistors must be large enough to drive several picofarads.

Efforts to reduce network wiring may result in false economies if they require additional drivers or if they require additional control signals to be routed through the array. Extensive multiplexing is more appropriate for interchip communication than for on-chip networks in very fine-grain systems.

Fortunately, most early vision algorithms have modest communication requirements. A 2D rectangular mesh topology provides a natural processor-to-pixel mapping, and the large diameter of the network is not a limitation when most communication is restricted to local neighborhoods. Unlike higher order networks, the mesh readily extends across chip boundaries at present and anticipated levels of integration.

How can we add network capabilities to the simple PE of Figure 4? The most common model treats the network as an extension of the word logic, adding special-purpose communication registers. Since the present word logic has only one register, this would considerably increase its complexity. Instead, our design preserves the word logic and extends the CAPP memory word with special network cells.

Figure 6 shows the 10 special cells for networking. Since the CAPP memory is already organized into two 32-trit words, we grouped the 10 cells into five cell pairs. The B half of each pair may be written and matched like a standard CAPP

cell, except that it stores only two states. The A halves are simple match-only cells; network functionality does not require them to be writable.

There are four cell pairs–N,E,W, and S (one for each compass direction)–and a fifth Home cell pair. When a PE writes to the B half of its H cell (H_B), that value is transmitted to the PE's four nearest neighbors. It is then matchable in their corresponding NEWS cells. A PE can examine its neighbors' H cells by performing match operations on its own NEWS cells. Only one output driver is required per PE; the NEWS cells function only as receivers.

Move-and-add procedure. Bit-serial arithmetic algorithms can incorporate network operations. Table 5 presents the move-and-add procedure $A + B_N \rightarrow A$, in which the north neighbor's B field is added to the local field A. The first three instructions copy bit B to the special network cell H_B. If the first match is successful, the next write will set H_B to 1. Otherwise, the write in step 3 will set H_B to 0.

The remainder of the algorithm duplicates the destructive add discussed earlier, except that step 5 matches the net cell N_A instead of the local B cell. In this way, the PE obtains the value of its north neighbor's H_B cell, which will contain the copy of B_N written in the first three steps.

Combining arithmetic and communications operations in this way is faster and more memory efficient than the naive approach of copying the entire B field and performing a local addition.

Asynchronous-mode communication. The example in Table 5 used the network's synchronous mode of operation, which requires several instructions to move information from one PE to its neighbor. This works well for local communication, but results in unacceptable delays over longer distances. We can get better performance by providing a separate asynchronous communication path where gate delays–not clock cycles–limit propagation time. Illiac III[6] was an early machine to use this technique. Its network circuitry provided a flash-through mode.

Another desirable feature is connection autonomy, the ability of individual PEs to configure their net connections independently. The polymorphic torus[7] and gated-connection network[8] are representative. The fully parallel associative processor uses an asynchronous reconfigurable mesh (ARM). The ARM network provides functionality similar to the gated-connection network but is implemented quite differently.

Figure 6 shows that each of the four NEWS inputs is Anded with the B half of its corresponding network cell pair. If the

Step	Instruction	Function	Pattern					SA contents	AR contents
			A	B	C	H_B	N_A		
1	Match		X	1	X	X	X	B	
2	Write	(SA)	–	–	–	1	–	B	
3	Write	(SA')	–	–	–	0	–	B	
4	Match		X	X	1	X	X	C	
5	Match	(SA)	X	X	X	X	1	B_N	C
6	Match	(SA $\oplus$ AR)	1	X	X	X	X	A	$B_N \oplus C$
7	Write	(SA' $\wedge$ AR)	1	–	0	–	–	A	$B_N \oplus C$
8	Write	(SA $\wedge$ AR)	0	–	1	–	–	A	$B_N \oplus C$

Table 5. Move-and-add procedure.

B cell contains a 1, asynchronous signals from the neighbor are enabled, and a unidirectional communication link is established. When a 1 is received from a neighbor, the H_B cell is set, and the signal propagates through the PE to all four neighbors.

Each PE can independently reconfigure its ARM links by writing to its B cells. Figure 7 shows some possible connections: a unidirectional wire (with a branch), and two bidirectionally connected regions. Once connected, the ARM network provides for simultaneous broadcasting within connected regions, using the following procedure.

- PEs configure their NEWS cells to define connectivity.
- All PEs write 0 to their H_B cells.
- Asynchronous mode is enabled.
- Senders write 1 to their H_B cells, and the network is allowed to settle.
- Each PE examines its H_B cell. If it finds a 1, it knows it is connected to a sender.

The ARM network logically Ors the outputs of multiple senders in the same region. The ability to broadcast over connected regions of arbitrary shape is particularly useful for labeling connected components and finding their corners.[3]

Note that the And and Or gates of Figure 6 are drawn only to show logical function. The actual implementation makes extensive use of precharged logic to reduce circuit complexity. The NEWS cells use only N-channel transistors and are only slightly larger than the CAPP memory cells.

Response resolution

When a content-addressable memory performs a match operation, we call the memory words that match the presented pattern *responders*. In an associative processor, the responder set may be identified by the logical combination of several match results. In either case, if more than one responder can occur, the system should have a multiple-re-

sponse resolution circuit. The response resolver produces summary information about the state of the array and feeds it back to the host computer and/or the individual PEs.

The ARM network performs simple Some/None response resolution. In the previous example, the H_B cell will match 1 if some senders are in the region and will match 0 if there are none. Responder prioritization and counting are examples of more sophisticated resolution tasks. The first task selects a single responder from a set of many. This procedure could be repeated to count the number of responders, or additional hardware may be provided to perform the count in time independent of the responder set's size.

Once again, the need to fit circuits on the memory pitch bounds the space of available solutions. The fastest response resolvers use tree and shower topologies[9,10] that do not lay out well in memory arrays. Linear chains are easier to lay out, but their delays increase with length. A good compromise solution is to use linear chains within each subarray, combin-

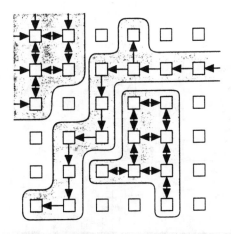

Figure 7. Reconfigurable connections of ARM network.

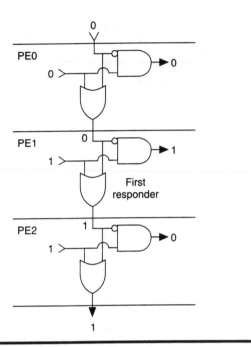

Figure 8. Prioritizing chain with Or gates.

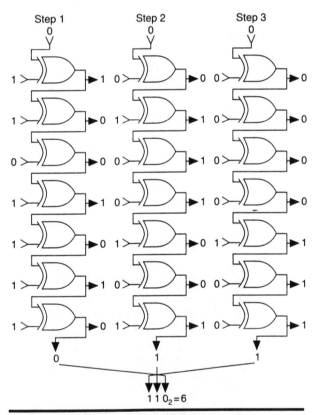

Figure 9. Counting responders with XOR chain.

ing the chain results in a tree structure.

Figure 8 shows a logic diagram for an Or gate prioritizing chain. Each input on the left side of the chain corresponds to one PE and is asserted if that PE is a responder. The output on the right side is asserted only if the PE is a responder and there are no higher priority responders. In the figure, PE1 is the first responder; it passes a 1 down the chain to inhibit PE2 and lower priority responders. The bottom of the Or chain produces a Some/None result for all PEs in the chain.

A chain of exclusive-Or gates can count responders in $\log_2 N$ steps, with N equal to the length of the chain. Figure 9 shows the three steps of the procedure for a chain of seven PEs.

The six 1 inputs on the left indicate six initial responders. The exclusive-Or chain computes the parity, and the last gate outputs a 0. This is the least significant bit of the count. Then every other responder is disabled, so three remain. The bottom of the chain outputs a 1. Finally, the even responders are again disabled, and the most significant bit 1 is obtained. Taking the bits in reverse order gives $110_2 = 6$, the number of initial responders.

Both the Or and XOR chains can be implemented with a single pass-transistor network, as shown in Figure 10. The lines $T_{1,0}$ pass 2-bit tokens from one PE to the next. The match-only cell H_A reflects the state of the chain, with each trit mapped to a 2-bit token,

$$00 \leftrightarrow X$$
$$10 \leftrightarrow 0$$
$$01 \leftrightarrow 1.$$

The 11 token is not used. The B half of the H cell serves as a responder flag. If the PE is not a responder, then $H_B = 0$. Transistors M_1 and M_3 will be on; they pass the token unchanged. However, if $H_B = 1$, then M_2 will pass $T_{1,in}$ to $T_{0,out}$ while M_4 passes $T_{1,in}'$ to $T_{1,out}$. In this way, responding PEs

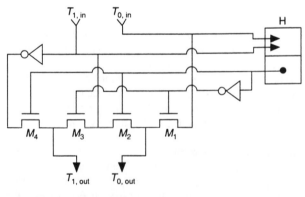

Figure 10. Pass transistor implementation of responder chain.

reverse 01 and 10 tokens, performing the Xor function. If the top of the chain is loaded with a 10 token, the bottom of the chain will produce the exclusive-Or of all the responder flags.

In priority mode, the top of the chain is loaded with two 0 bits. The 00 token propagates down to the first responder, which converts it to a 10. Lower priority responders will exchange the 10 and 01 tokens but cannot restore the 00. The chain is equivalent to a cascade of Or gates under the identification

$$00 \leftrightarrow 0$$
$$01, 10 \leftrightarrow 1.$$

Any PE finding a don't care (00 token) in its H_A cell recognizes there are no higher priority responders.

Note that no additional circuitry is necessary to implement the And function of Figure 8. After a PE examines its H_A cell with a match operation, it can compute the And in its function generator.

Applications

The active research in machine vision algorithms exceeds the scope of this article. Here we briefly discuss some simplified applications intended to demonstrate the utility of the associative processor in basic vision tasks, not to represent exemplary solutions to particular vision problems.

Smoothing and segmentation. Figure 11a shows an unprocessed image of a toy block. Higher level vision algorithms might require a preprocessing step to remove noise and smooth the texture. We could use a simple low-pass filter, but this would destroy useful edge information. Ideally, we want to filter only the connected regions and preserve segment boundaries.

We implemented a smooth-and-segment algorithm on a software simulator of the associative processor. The two-step procedure is a discrete-time analog of the fused resistor approach.[11]

In the smoothing step, the image is convolved with a 2D kernel such as the approximate Gaussian in Figure 12a on the next page. In the segmentation step, each pixel compares its value with its neighbors', and a segmentation flag is set if the difference is greater than a given threshold. The next smooth step will not cross a boundary if this flag is set. For example, if a pixel's east segment flag is set, it will use the modified kernel in Figure 12b in the next smooth step.

In a simulation with 8-bit pixels, the associative processor requires up to 330 match and write operations to execute both the smooth and segment steps, depending on the threshold value and the sharpness of the kernel used. We used 1,000 iterations with varying thresholds and kernels to produce the image in Figure 11b. With a 10-MHz instruction clock, the associative processor could achieve real-time performance, processing more than 30 frames per second.

Binocular stereo. Stereo matching gauges depth information by comparing two images displaced in space. It is similar to optical flow, which estimates motion by comparing

Figure 11. Original image (a) and smoothed and segmented image (b).

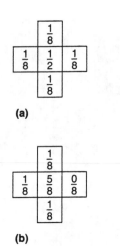

(a)

(b)

Figure 12. A 2D kernel (a) and a modified kernel (b).

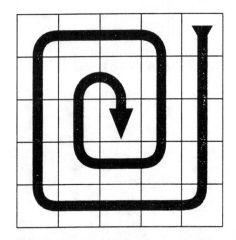

Figure 13. Accumulation path for 5 × 5 support region.

two images displaced in time.

Although they differ in their refinements, most stereo matching algorithms perform the essential task of repeatedly comparing and shifting the two images. In a typical massively parallel implementation, each PE is assigned a corresponding pair of pixels from the left and right images. The PE compares its two pixels, and examines the results of all comparisons in a support region of neighboring PEs. Then the right image is shifted relative to the left, and the process repeats with a new disparity. When the PE has tested all allowed disparities, a decision procedure determines the actual disparity at each pixel, from which the depth can be computed.

If we use a simple decision procedure (such as winner take all), then the most computationally expensive part of the procedure will be the summation of comparison results in the support region. The associative processor computes this sum using the move-and-accumulate procedure,

$$A_N + B \rightarrow A,$$

which is similar to the move-and-add described earlier. The contents of the A field are replaced by the sum of the local B field and the north neighbor's A field. The procedure requires nine match and write operations per bit.

Figure 13 shows an accumulation path for a 5 × 5 support region. Suppose the PE in the northeast corner is initialized with $A = B$. Four northerly move-and-accumulate iterations will collect all the B fields on the east edge into the southeast PE's A field. Four easterly iterations are then performed; the southwest corner will accumulate all the Bs from the east and south edges. After 24 iterations, the center PE will obtain the sum over the entire region. And because all PEs are working in parallel, every PE in the array will obtain the sum for its neighbors in the same period.

Simulation results indicate that associative processors can perform stereo algorithms similar to those appropriate for analog implementation[12] at about the standard video frame rate. This result depends on the support region area and the maximum allowed disparity, which must be chosen for each particular application. However, as in the smooth-and-segment case, image size does not impact performance.

THIS ASSOCIATIVE PARALLEL PROCESSOR architecture emphasizes high density, fine granularity, and massive parallelism. The design style is device intensive, similar to memory design rather than microprocessor design. The memory, word logic, network, and response resolution circuits all fit on pitch, and a minimum of random glue logic is required. In short, every transistor counts.

Fine granularity is achieved as each 64-trit memory word becomes its own PE. A dynamic content addressable memory cell supports fully parallel operation and allows the use of simpler word logic than is practical with a bit-serial approach. In fact, it is possible to perform useful work without any word logic at all. However, the addition of an activity register and two-input function generator significantly improves arithmetic performance with only a modest area penalty. The PEs communicate over an asynchronous reconfigurable mesh that provides a mechanism for simultaneous broadcasting over multiple connected regions. The network and response resolver use special-purpose memory cells to save area and keep the word logic simple. The target applications for the system are low- to intermediate-level machine vision and image processing tasks. Configured as a coprocessor with a desktop workstation host, the associative parallel processor may provide a low-cost, flexible alternative to the massively parallel supercomputer. ▯

Acknowledgments

We gratefully acknowledge the contributions of Craig Keast, Phil Chu, and Shih-Jih Yao in device fabrication and application simulation. We thank Andrew Ellenberger of IBM and Terry Potter of Digital Equipment Corporation for the insights they have shared with us in many fruitful conversations. We also gratefully acknowledge Digital Equipment Corporation, IBM, and the National Science Foundation (Contract MIP-9117724) for supporting this research.

References

1. R.H. Fuller and R.M. Bird, "An Associative Parallel Processor with Applications to Picture Processing," *Proc. of AFIPS Fall Joint Computer Conf.*, Spartan Books, Washington, D.C., Vol. 27, 1965, pp. 105-116.

2. M.A. Wesley, S.K. Chang, and J. H. Mommens, "A Design for an Auxiliary Associative Parallel Processor," *Proc. of AFIPS Fall Joint Computer Conf.*, AFIPS Press, Montvale, N.J., Vol. 41, 1972, pp. 461-472.

3. C.C. Weems, "Architectural Requirements of Image Understanding with Respect to Parallel Processing," *Proc. IEEE*, Institute of Electrical and Electronics Engineers, Piscataway, N.J., Vol. 79, No. 4, Apr. 1991, pp. 537-547.

4. F.P. Herrmann et al., "A Dynamic Three-State Memory Cell for High-Density Associative Processors," *IEEE J. Solid-State Circuits*, Vol. 26, No. 4, Apr. 1991, pp. 537-541.

5. C.L. Keast and C.G. Sodini, "A CCD/CMOS Process for Integrated Image Acquisition and Early Vision Signal Processing," *Proc. SPIE Vol. 1242: Charge-Coupled Devices and Solid State Optical Sensors*, Society of Photo-Optical Instrumentation Engineers, Bellingham, Wash., 1990, pp. 152-161.

6. B.H. McCormick, "The Illinois Pattern Recognition Computer– ILLIAC III," *IEEE Trans. Electronic Computers*, Vol. EC-12, No. 6, Dec. 1963, pp. 791-813.

7. H. Li and M. Maresca, "Polymorphic-Torus Network," *IEEE Trans. Computers*, Vol. 38, No. 9, Sept. 1989, pp. 1345-1351.

8. D.B. Shu et al., "Implementation and Application of a Gated-Connection Network in Image Understanding," *Reconfigurable Massively Parallel Computers*, H. Li and Q.F. Stout, eds., Prentice Hall, Englewood Cliffs, N.J., 1991, pp. 64-87.

9. C.C. Foster and F.D. Stockton, "Counting Responders in an Associative Memory," *IEEE Trans. Computers*, Vol. C-20, No. 12, Dec. 1971, pp. 1580-1583.

10. G.A. Anderson, "Multiple Match Resolvers: A New Design Method," *IEEE Trans. Computers*, Vol. C-23, Dec. 1974, pp. 1317-1320.

11. P.C. Yu et al., "CMOS Resistive Fuses for Image Smoothing and Segmentation," *IEEE J. Solid State Circuits*, Vol. 27, No. 4, Apr. 1992, pp. 545-553.

12. M. Hakkarainen et al., "Interaction of Algorithm and Implementation for Analog VLSI Stereo Vision," *Proc. SPIE Vol. 1473: Visual Information Processing: From Neurons to Chips*, SPIE, Apr. 1991, pp. 173-184.

Direct questions or comments about this article to Frederick P. Herrmann, Department of Electrical Engineering and Computer Science, Massachusetts Institute of Technology, Cambridge, MA. 02139; or via e-mail at fritz@mtl.mit.edu.

An Associative Architecture for Genetic Algorithm-Based Machine Learning

Kirk Twardowski, Loral Federal Systems – Owego

Machine-based learning will eventually be applied to solve real-world problems. Here, an associative architecture teams with hybrid AI algorithms to solve a letter prediction problem with promising results.

Systems architects have continually sought to design machines with ever-greater levels of human-like autonomy and intelligence. It is widely recognized that the potential for such machines is nearly limitless, as evidenced by recent achievements involving autonomous agents, database mining, speech processing and translation, adaptive vision systems, visualization systems and animation. The results promise radical change in how we will eventually interact with our computers. Currently available systems, of course, are far from attaining real-world performance in such areas, largely due to a lack of computational power.

Researchers of massively parallel artificial intelligence seek to capitalize on advances in computer architecture to develop novel AI techniques that fully exploit the parallel capabilities of such powerful machines. The combination of AI and massively parallel computing will couple sophisticated knowledge-processing models with vast computational resources, which has the potential to eliminate the computational bottleneck that now prevents many AI systems from offering practical solutions to real-world problems.

This article describes an investigation and simulation of a massively parallel Learning Classifier System (LCS) that was developed from a specialized associative architecture joined with hybrid AI algorithms. The LCS algorithms were specifically invented to computationally match a massively parallel computer architecture, which was a special-purpose design to support the inferencing and learning components of the LCS. The LCS's computationally intensive functions include rule matching, parent selection, replacement selection, and, to a lesser degree, data structure manipulation.

Learning Classifier Systems

Learning Classifier Systems, introduced by Holland[1], are general-purpose machine learning systems designed to operate in uncertain, noisy environments that provide infrequent and often incomplete feedback. An example of such an environment might be a chemical plant, where an LCS would perform process control. An LCS comprises three layers: a parallel production system, a credit assignment algorithm, and classifier discovery algorithms. The production system models the problem domain as clusters of highly standardized rules called *classifiers*, and it provides

Reprinted from *Computer*, Vol. 27, No. 11, Nov. 1994, pp. 27–38.

a basic match-select-act inferencing cycle with parallel-classifier activation. The credit assignment algorithm evaluates a strength for each classifier based on feedback from the environment. This strength serves as a measure of a classifier's utility to the LCS and is used both in the inferencing process and in the discovery of classifiers. Classifier discovery algorithms are typically a combination of genetic algorithms and several heuristic methods. Together, credit assignment and classifier discovery are the techniques that endow the LCS with its adaptive capability, which is what enables machine learning systems to respond to changing conditions in a problem domain.

Rule-based production system. The LCS production system layer bears many similarities to rule-based expert systems. In particular, the production system's knowledge is encoded in a set of classifiers processed by a cyclic match-select-act inferencing algorithm. The primary difference between the two system types lies in the production system's mechanisms for simultaneous classifier activation, which makes it a parallel-classifier-based system. On the other hand, expert systems are sequential in nature, permitting only one rule to be processed at a

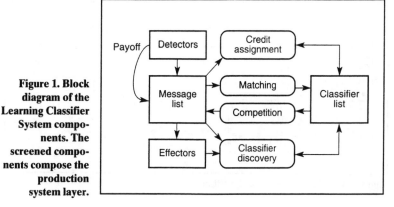

Figure 1. Block diagram of the Learning Classifier System components. The screened components compose the production system layer.

time. Short-term working memory is maintained on a global *message list* that stores internally generated messages as well as input and output environment communication messages. A set of detectors and effectors provides the message-based interface to the environment. An example of a detector is a temperature sensor, whereas an example of an effector is a robotic arm or a valve.

Each classifier has a simple IF *condition(s)*, THEN *action* syntax (for example, IF temperature is greater than 100°, THEN open valve). Conditions and actions are fixed-length strings and are typically identical in length for all classifiers. The

symbol alphabet used to compose both the condition and action strings is {0, 1, #}. The # symbol represents a don't-care character that can match either 0 or 1. Messages are identical in structure to conditions and actions, except they contain no # symbols.

An LCS production system, therefore, consists of a classifier list, a message list, a set of detectors, a set of effectors, and a feedback mechanism (see Figure 1). Also shown are the credit assignment and classifier discovery components (layers). The basic execution loop governing the interactions between these components consists of six steps in a single execution cycle:

Glossary

Bias — Many of the decisions made in the Learning Classifier System are of a stochastic nature. They are controlled by the bias, which is a numeric value stored with each individual classifier in the LCS.

Bid — A fractional amount of strength paid by a classifier for the right to post a message that is used in the bucket brigade algorithm.

Classifier — A basic component of knowledge representation in an LCS that is analogous to a rule in expert or production systems.

Classifier discovery — That part of the system that uses heuristics, most notably the genetic algorithm, to explore new concepts by creating new classifiers.

Competition — A process, which is based on a classifier's strength, that decides which classifiers are granted access to limited system resources (that is, the message list).

Crossover — A basic operator in the genetic algorithm that generates a new classifier from subsections of parent classifiers.

Detectors — Sensors that translate environment conditions into the messages processed by the LCS.

Effectors — Environment manipulators used by the LCS to perform actions.

Fitness — A relative measure of a classifier's utility to the LCS in solving a given problem.

Genetic algorithm — A search-and-optimization algorithm based on the mechanics of biological evolution.

Payment — The strength value transferred between two classifiers within the bucket brigade algorithm. Payment is made to the classifier that generated a message from the classifier that matches the message.

Payoff — The scalar reinforcement value received from the environment as a form of reward or punishment.

Spatial locality — The physical distribution of classifiers within the array of processing elements where parents and replacement classifiers are selected such that they are physically colocated.

Specificity — A measure of the number of different messages that can match a classifier. A classifier can match from one to hundreds of messages that are either internally generated by the LCS or issued from the environment. Classifiers that are very general match many messages and therefore handle default conditions. Classifiers that are very specific match few messages and therefore handle special cases in the environment.

Strength — Numeric estimate of fitness that controls many aspects of a classifier's behavior in the LCS, that is, in the competition to post new messages and its probability of being selected as a parent or a replacement.

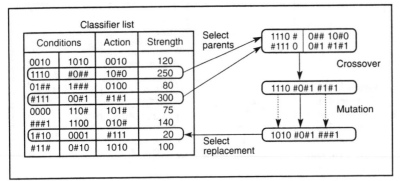

Figure 2. Example of a genetic algorithm cycle.

(1) any messages from the environment detectors are added to the current message list, (2) the contents of the message list are matched against all the conditions of all the classifiers, (3) those classifiers whose conditions were matched compete for the right to post messages to the message list such that those with greater strength are favored to win, (4) the winners of the competition create new messages based upon their actions and the matching messages, (5) the new messages are added to the message list, and (6) the effectors perform any actions specified in the message list.

Credit assignment. Credit assignment has long been recognized as a difficult problem inherent in any learning system composed of many interacting components (for example, classifiers) that contribute, over time, to the overall performance. The purpose of credit assignment in an LCS is to distribute feedback from the environment in the form of a scalar reinforcement value such that beneficial classifiers are rewarded and detrimental classifiers are penalized with respect to the desired outcomes.

Holland's[1] proposed *bucket brigade* algorithm is a mechanism that can potentially solve the credit assignment problem in an LCS. The objective of the bucket brigade algorithm is to distribute payoffs received from the environment to the appropriate classifiers in the form of strength adjustments. When the environment determines that the LCS has acted in a beneficial way (for example, correctly regulates temperature in controlling a process), it rewards (pays off) the system in terms of added strength. Conversely, if the LCS has acted in a harmful way, the environment penalizes it by taking strength away. This is important because these adjustments shape the adaptive (learning) ability of the LCS: Classifiers whose strength has been increased are more likely to be selected when a similar problem next needs to be solved, while those whose strength has been diminished are less likely to be selected.

As the term bucket brigade implies, strength is taken in small quantities from those classifiers that lead directly to payoff (active when payoff is received) and given to those classifiers that lead indirectly to payoff ("stage-setting" classifiers). Conceptually, the bucket brigade algorithm operates on chains of classifiers in which strength is being passed backward from the payoff-receiving classifier to previously active classifiers. The algorithm consists of two steps for each posting classifier: (1) reduce the classifier's strength by an amount equal to a fraction (approximately 1/10) of its strength, and (2) distribute this amount among classifiers that generated, in the previous time-step, the messages that satisfied this classifier. Classifiers posting effector-actuating messages when payoff is received share the payoff amount, and have their strengths updated accordingly.

Classifier discovery algorithms. While the bucket brigade is an effective mechanism for the temporal aspects of credit assignment, it cannot modify the system's knowledge structure. The ability to modify the system's internal knowledge structures is crucial for an LCS to learn new behaviors or adapt to a changing domain. What is needed is the ability to create new classifiers and delete those that have proven to be of little value.

The primary classifier discovery mechanism in an LCS is the *genetic algorithm*,[2] which is why a simplistic string representation is used for classifiers. The genetic algorithm is a heuristic search procedure modeled on natural evolution in an attempt to capture evolution's adaptive and optimizing features in a practical algorithmic form.

In an LCS, the genetic algorithm is periodically invoked to create new classifiers. The algorithm's basic execution cycle is:

(1) from the classifier list, randomly select pairs of parent classifiers such that higher-strength classifiers have a greater chance of selection,
(2) create new classifiers by applying genetic operators to the parents, and
(3) randomly select those classifiers to be replaced by the newly generated classifiers such that lower-strength classifiers have a greater chance of selection.

In the prototypical genetic algorithm, there are two genetic operators: *crossover* and *mutation*, which are applied to the selected parent classifiers to create new classifiers. To form a new classifier, the crossover operator pieces together sections from two parents, while the mutation operator, with a very low probability, alters randomly selected bits within a classifier.

Figure 2 shows a single genetic algorithm cycle that has been applied on classifiers with two 4-bit conditions. For emphasis, selection of parent and replacement classifiers is shown as a maximum or minimum function, respectively. Crossover occurs between the fifth and sixth bits, while bits 2 and 10 are mutated.

The associative architecture

There were two key reasons compelling the choice of a specialized associative architecture: (1) searching occurs frequently during LCS functions (rule matching, parent selection, replacement selection, and data structure manipulation), and (2) the independent nature of the individual classifiers made them well suited to the SIMD (single instruction, multiple data) paradigm of associative computing. For these reasons, we believed a computationally efficient implementation was well worth investigation.

To date, two notable parallel LCSs include Robertson's[3] *CFS on the Connection Machine and Dorigo's[4] Alecsys, which runs on an array of transputers. Of these, *CFS is most similar to the approach described here because it is a SIMD massively parallel system. Neither *CFS nor Alecsys, however, incorporates

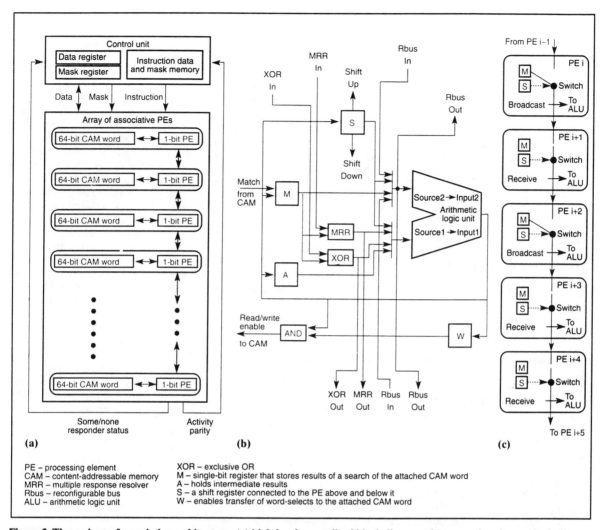

Figure 3. Three views of associative architecture: (a) high-level generalized block diagram; (b) processing element logic diagram showing the four single-bit registers: *M* **stores results of a search of the attached CAM word;** *W* **enables transfer of word-selects to the attached CAM word;** *S* **is a shift register connected to the PE above and below it; and** *A* **holds intermediate results; (c) reconfigurable bus operation.**

a parallel GA model as does our implementation as described later. A parallel genetic algorithm is important for two reasons: (1) it extracts as much parallelism from the algorithms as possible, and (2) it improves system performance with respect to the number of classifiers. Accurate execution times are not available for either system, so a meaningful performance comparison will not be possible until further research is conducted.

The architecture is a linear array of fully associative processing elements that consist of 64 bits of content-addressable memory, coupled with a 1-bit row processor to provide response processing, activity control, multiple response resolution logic, and inter-PE communication. Memory and PE size determina-

tion was based on commercially available CAM chips or on those in development, as described in the literature[5] and by Stormon during the "Associative Processing and Applications Workshop" presented at Syracuse University in 1992.

Figure 3a shows a high-level view of the architecture. The array of PEs operates in a SIMD mode and therefore has a controller that is responsible for generating and broadcasting instructions and data to the array, as well as accumulating and testing global feedback information. The controller contains a data register, which holds the data broadcast to the array, and a mask register that determines which bit columns of the array are active during writes and matches. This architecture is an example of traditional,

fully parallel associative processing, and it provides essential associative computing capabilities, such as

- fully parallel search of all memory,
- constant time responder/no responder status,
- multiple response resolution to select a single processor from many,
- efficient broadcast of data and instructions from controller to array, and
- efficient one-to-one data transfer between processing elements and the control unit.[6]

In addition, the architecture provides an extended communication capability in the form of a reconfigurable bus similar to those found in many of the more re-

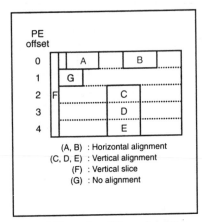

PE offset				
0		A		B
1	G			
2	F		C	
3			D	
4				E

(A, B) : Horizontal alignment
(C, D, E) : Vertical alignment
(F) : Vertical slice
(G) : No alignment

Figure 4. Examples of the various alignment cases possible when variables are mapped onto processing elements.

cent VLSI implementations of associative processors.[7-9]

Processing element. Figure 3b is a detailed diagram of the 1-bit processor within each PE. There are four single-bit registers used for dedicated functions, temporary results storage, or both. The M register stores the results from a search of the attached CAM word. The W register, since it enables the transfer of the word-selects to the attached CAM word, effectively controls local activity (that is, whether the PE executes instructions broadcast to it). The S register is a shift register connected to the PE directly above and below. The A register primarily holds intermediate data. The ALU (arithmetic logic unit) can calculate any function of two inputs and can be loaded into any of the four registers.

The multiple response resolver (MRR) behaves like a priority circuit. Its output is a single bit that corresponds to the topmost active bit in the M register. The MRR resolves the situation that results when multiple PEs, which need to be processed individually, respond to a match pattern.

Output of the M register feeds one input of an XOR (exclusive-OR) gate, with the other input being the output of the XOR in the PE directly above, thus forming a chain of XOR gates that connects all PEs. The XOR chain has two functions: to enumerate the active responders and quickly count responders.

In addition to the shift register, a reconfigurable bus (Rbus) lets the PEs be connected as arbitrary contiguous segments. For operations such as a parallel-prefix add, a more significant perfor-

mance gain can be realized through the Rbus, which is more effective for long-distance communication between PEs than for simple shifts of data. Communication on the Rbus is unidirectional and occurs in either a downward or upward direction. Each segment starts at a broadcasting PE and continues to the next broadcasting PE, where the S register controls the connectivity, as shown in Figure 3c. It is important to note that Figure 3c is a logical, not physical, representation of the design.

Instruction set. The instruction set allows the simultaneous execution of three different operation types — array, shift, and ALU. Within each PE, the read, write, and match instructions control the operation of the CAM word. At the locations activated by the word-select lines, read returns data and write modifies the contents of the CAM array. The data register stores data that is written, and the mask register's contents determine the bit columns to be modified. The match instruction determines those locations in the CAM array that match the value in the data register. The bit columns to be searched are specified by the mask register; therefore, individual bits or subfields within the array can be isolated for a search. The shift and ALU operations control the S register and the ALU outputs, respectively. The shift operation results in an unconditional change of the S register in all PEs.

Programming model. The programming model typically employed in fully parallel associative architectures is often called *data parallel* and is the same as that found on many of the bit-serial massively parallel machines such as the DAP, Thinking Machine's Connection Machine CM-1, and the MasPar MP-1. In the data-parallel model, there is a copy of each parallel variable in every PE within the array; thus, if a machine contains 8,192 PEs, there will be 8,192 copies of each parallel variable. In fully parallel VLSI implementations of CAM, however, the length of the CAM word can be a limiting factor. While a single CAM word appears to be adequate for image processing tasks,[9,10] CAM word length severely limits most other kinds of processing that require more PE memory. In these instances, a logical-to-physical mapping is necessary to allocate a set of PEs to each set of variables being processed in parallel.

In the programming model selected for the LCS design, a contiguous set of physical PEs is allocated as a logical PE that processes a record. *Record* refers to a collection of data-parallel variables to be processed by a single logical processor. This set of PEs, acting as a single processor, then processes the data within that record. This model is in direct contrast with, for example, the C* Connection Machine programming language, where a single physical PE can support as many virtual PEs as will fit within available memory. In many cases with our LCS model, there is a loss of parallelism as only one of N physical PEs within a logical PE performs useful work at any given time. Occasionally, however, it is possible to exploit parallelism within a record so that more than one physical PE per logical PE is active.

The variables within each record consist of a contiguous set of bits within a single PE. Unlike a conventional computer that can use a single address parameter to identify and locate a variable, the associative processor under our programming model requires three parameters:

- the starting bit position of the variable with a PE,
- the variable's length in bits, and
- the offset of the PE containing the variable.

The starting bit position is analogous to the address in a conventional machine. A variable requires a length because there are no predetermined lengths for variables; a variable can be anywhere from 1 bit long to as long as, or longer than, the entire CAM word. The offset identifies the PE containing this variable out of all physical PEs that constitute the logical record.

Mapping data onto CAM. The memory organization of the logical PE is a two-dimensional array of bits with one dimension being the physical PE offset and the other being the starting bit position. It is essential therefore to consider the alignment relationships between a record's variables when they are mapped onto the PEs. These relationships determine the amount of parallelism that can be extracted from the array. The alignment relationships, depicted in Figure 4, can be classified as horizontal alignment, vertical alignment, no alignment, or vertical slice.

Horizontal alignment applies to items

Table 1. Execution time of primitive operations.

Name	Function	Scalar	Vector	Segmented
			Mode	
Increment	$x_1 = x_1 + 1$	$3 + 3m_1$		
Decrement	$x_1 = x_1 - 1$	$3 + 3m_1$		
Add	$x_1 = x_1 + x_2$	$7 + 4m_1$	$7 + d_{12} + m_1(4 + d_{12})$	
Subtract	$x_1 = x_1 - x_2$	$7 + 4m_1$	$7 + d_{12} + m_1(4 + d_{12})$	
Multiply	$x_3 = x_1 * x_2$	$7 + f_1 + (m_{con}/2)$ $(2 + m_1(4 + d_{12}))$	$5 + f_1 + 2d_{12}$ $+m_2(9 + 2d_{13} + f_2 + m_1(4+d_{12}))$	
Divide	$x_3 = x_1/x_2$	$9 + f_1 + 2d_{13} + m_3$ $(10 + f_1 + d_{13} + 6m_1)$	$9 + f_3 + d_{13}$ $+m_3(15 + f_1 + d_{13} + d_{12} + m_1(7 + d_{12}))$	
Reduce Add	$x = \Sigma^i_{j=1} x_j$	$m_i + (2 + \lg(N))$		
Scan Add	$x_i = \Sigma^i_{j=1} x_j$		$3 + \lg(N)(9 + 2d_1 + 5m)$	
Shift			$3 + m_1(3 + d_{12})$	
Compare		$7 + f_1 + 1.5m_1$	$10 + 2f_1 + m_1(4 + d_{12})$	
Minimum		$1 + 2m_1$		$18 + 4f_1 + 7m_1$
Maximum		$1 + 2m_1$		
Move Field			$3 + m_1(3+d_{12})$	
Count		$\lg N$		
Enumerate			$4 + 2\lg(N)$	
Random			$9 + f_1 + 4m_1$	
Send Field			$15 + f_1 + f_2 + 2m_1$	
Spread				$17 + 5f_1 + 5m_1$

Notes:

m_i length, in bits, of operand

f_i distance between operand x_i and start of record

d_{ij} distance between PEs holding operands x_i and x_j

N number of active PEs

that must be stored in the same PE. For example, the destination and source operands of a multiply operation should be within the same word to minimize inter-PE communication overhead. *Vertical alignment* specifies that two items stored in different PEs are to be aligned so that they both start at the same bit position. The conditions of each classifier are an example of this relationship; storing them in a vertically aligned manner means both can be matched simultaneously against messages. Vertical alignment exemplifies parallelism between record variables. *No alignment* is suitable for those items that have no interdependencies and can be placed anywhere within the allocated PEs. A *vertical slice* is a single-bit column that extends the entire length of the PE array and is an exception to the programming model introduced above since it consumes a bit at every PE. Vertical slices typically provide storage for main-

tenance purposes or for temporary storage of a PE's register contents. A vertical slice can also hold data that is processed in a bit-parallel manner by all the ALUs.

Associative primitives. Implementing the LCS algorithms requires a core set of arithmetic, logic, and communication primitives. These algorithms are inherently bit serial, since the PE is only a single bit wide. Consequently, operations can take many more computation cycles to complete than with bit-parallel algorithms. However, since many operations are performed simultaneously, the increase in cycles is amortized over the total number of results generated, giving a superior throughput. This does assume that the parallelism is great enough to sufficiently amortize the cost. Furthermore, since the architecture lets operands be any length, efficiency gains are often achieved at the expense of precision,

which suits our purposes in the model.

Table 1 lists the primitive operations used by the LCS algorithms, and Table 2 describes the higher-level primitives. Each column of Table 1 shows the execution time in machine cycles, for each of three possible execution modes. The *scalar* mode applies when the controller broadcasts a scalar value to the active set of PEs. *Vector* mode occurs when all operands are contained within the PE array. *Segmented* mode supports the execution of segmented scans and reduction primitives[11] as well as long-range communication via the Rbus.

As is evident in Table 1, some of the operations (for example, scan add in segmented mode) were not implemented, primarily because the LCS algorithms did not require them. The architecture, however, has no limitations that would prohibit the rest of the operations from being developed.

Execution time parameters have two

Table 2. Higher-level associative primitives.

Name	Description
Count	Using the XOR logic, assemble a count of the number of active PEs.
Enumerate	Assign consecutive numbers to the active PEs via the XOR logic.
Random	Generate a random number in each active PE, via a one-dimensional cellular automata algorithm.
Send Field	An Rbus communication primitive to transmit fields between specially marked PEs. Restricted to transmitting between nonoverlapping pairs of PEs due to the nature of the single-wire bus connection between PEs.
Spread	A segmented broadcast from one PE to a set of physically adjacent PEs as controlled by a bit vector that establishes how the array is broken into segments.
Segmented Minimum	Find the minimum value in each segment of the array, where the segmentation is controlled by a bit vector contained in one of the PE registers.
Scan Add	Tabulate a running sum over all the currently active PEs. Scan Add uses the Enumerate primitive to control the connectivity on the Rbus.

dimensions: m_i represents the length of operand i, and d_{ij} represents the distance between the PEs containing operands i and j. As an example, consider an add instruction that adds two variables and stores the result in the first variable. If these two variables are located on different PEs, the contents of the second variable must be bit-serially shifted to the first as the add progresses. Thus, if the operands are m bits long, $m \times d$ cycles will then be required in addition to the four cycles needed to read the operand bits, calculate the new data and carry bits, and update the CAM word. The additional $7 + d$ cycles are mainly "cleanup" code for overflow and underflow cases.

Associative implementation of LCS

All three LCS layers were implemented with the primitive operations just described. Next, we examine the mapping of program data structures onto the CAM and how the primitive operations were applied.

CAM data structure. Our LCS contains two primary data structures: the message list and the classifier list. There are three ways to map them onto the associative processor — store messages in the PE array (message-parallel), store classifiers in the PE array (classifier-parallel), or store both in the PE array

(jointly parallel). This specific LCS implementation is based on the classifier-parallel approach for two reasons: (1) it minimizes transferring messages between the array and the controller, and (2) technology already exists to support 1,000 to 10,000 classifiers in a design that could be easily adapted for a desktop PC application, as explained by Stormon at the Syracuse University workshop in 1992.

Record size considerations. In addition to conditions, action, strength, and specificity, each classifier requires a number of

flags and temporary storage; all the variables that compose a classifier are allocated to a single record. To attain the approximately 280 bits of memory required by a classifier record, a minimum of five PEs (320 bits) must be allocated per record. Figure 5 shows the memory map for the classifier record that was used for the simulation experiments. The minimum number of PEs has been allocated to each record to maximize the number of classifiers that can be supported.

Figure 5 identifies the record variables that are statically defined for the dura-

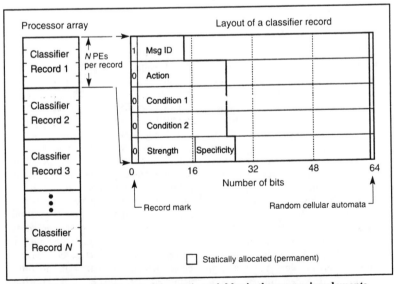

Figure 5. Memory map layout of the static variables in the processing elements.

114

tion of the program. Note that conditions 1 and 2 are vertically aligned to speed up message matching, since both can be compared simultaneously. Remaining space is allocated for temporary storage as needed. The first bit of all five PEs is the record mark that identifies the start of each record. Next to the record mark are the action, conditions, and strength. The first PE has a message identification variable that is reserved for linking classifiers with the messages they posted. The last bit of each PE holds the state of a cellular automaton that generates random numbers.

Condition and action representation. The fully parallel associative architecture, due to its capability to selectively mask search bits, has the ability to store a don't care (#). The don't care will match either a one or a zero in the search pattern. This is particularly useful for representing the conditions and action of a classifier, which use the # symbol in just that manner. Each condition and action symbol uses two CAM bits, where a $0 \equiv 01$, $1 \equiv 10$ and $\# \equiv 11$. The search patterns are #1 for a zero and 1# for a one: Both of these match the 11 used to represent the # in conditions and action, as well as their respective symbol.

The production system layer. The core processing loop within the LCS is the five-step match-select-act process listed in Table 3: (1) match classifiers, (2) create messages, (3) post new messages, (4) extract messages, and (5) process effectors. The continual repetition of these five steps constitutes the largest portion of the computational effort. Note that this processing loop differs in two respects from

the earlier processing loop description: (1) the add detector messages step has been disregarded since this doesn't involve the array, and (2) the order of the create message and post message steps has been reversed to simplify the parallel implementation.

Match classifiers. A special-purpose associative architecture was selected for the LCS largely due to the matching requirements of the match classifier step. The CAM-based design reduces the runtime of this step virtually to a constant, regardless of the number of classifiers. Moreover, the associative organization means that match status can be maintained without pointers or intermediate structures. Unlike associative processing, sequential processing would, in order to reduce runtime, need to establish a linked list of candidate classifiers, each with its own list of matching messages. The associative architecture avoids this situation by using status flags that can be matched in parallel or, since the match cost is very low, by reprocessing the message list. Our LCS features both techniques.

The message list is processed in two passes. In the first, all candidate classifiers are determined. During the second pass, a copy of the matching message is stored at each candidate classifier and marked as "used." Each candidate classifier matching an internal message — one posted by a classifier on the previous cycle — has a match count incremented. The message stored with the candidate classifiers is used for the *create messages* step, and the credit assignment layer later uses this match count to determine strength-payments distribution to classifiers active in the previous time-step.

Create messages. The action component of each classifier is the template for new-message construction. Recall that the symbols in the action are from the set: {0, 1, #}. The 0, 1 is copied directly to the new message, whereas the # is a "pass-thru" token that accepts the corresponding bit from a matching message. This algorithm is similar to a field-move operation, except that it conditionally copies bits from the source field. As implemented, new-message creation moves only 0s and 1s from the action variable to the message variable containing the message stored during the match step. The #'s found in the action are not copied into the message variable, which lets the matching message define the new message at these bits.

Post new messages. The message list is a constrained resource in the system as it has space enough for only a limited number of messages. Furthermore, there is a limit to the number of each message type permitted on the list. Consequently, the primary task of message posting is to count the number of new messages. If there are too many of the given type, then the system runs a competition to determine those that will actually be posted. Another task performed during this step is bid calculation for each prospective message. The bid is used to bias the competition and is stored with each message for reference by the bucket brigade algorithm. Typically, the bid is a function of strength and specificity; in our LCS implementation it is strength times specificity.

The competition operation conducts a parallelized random selection by first performing a scan-add of the bids and, for each message to be selected, generating a random number between zero and the

Table 3. Core processing loop in the production system layer.

Step	Name	Description
1	Match classifiers	Each message is matched against all classifier conditions. Each classifier with all conditions matched becomes active.
2	Create messages	Each active classifier, based on its actions and a matching message, creates a new candidate message for posting to the message list.
3	Post new messages	If required, a competition is run to see which messages are posted to the message list; if not, all messages are posted to the message list.
4	Extract messages	Messages to be posted are read from the array and loaded into the message list in controller memory. A tag is associated with each classifier/message pair for use in the credit assignment layer.
5	Process effectors	The message list is processed by the effectors, and messages are consumed by any effector that they match.

sum of all the bids. Each random probe searches the array to find the classifiers whose bid is greater than that probe. The MRR then selects the topmost classifier as the winner for this step.

Extract messages. Message extraction requires three passes through all new messages. The first pass assigns each message and its generating classifier a tag that links them together for the bucket brigade algorithm in the credit assignment layer. Each message identifies its generating classifier from the tag via a single match instruction. The 8-bit tag variable is incremented whenever a message is generated, with the assumption that fewer than 128 messages are created during each cycle of the production system layer. The remaining passes read the messages and bids, then insert them in the message list.

Process effectors. Effector processing is an inherently sequential operation that loops through the message list to see if any messages satisfy an effector. If so, that effector performs its function, and the respective message is removed from the list.

The credit assignment layer. The bucket brigade algorithm is the sole function performed by this layer, and its operation is driven by the contents of the message list. Each message specifies a transfer of strength to the classifier that posted the message from the classifiers it matched. Also at this time, the bid is deducted from the classifier that generated the message.

First, each classifier calculates a payment value; this is the bid divided by the number of internal messages it matched, because an equal share of the bid is paid to each message-generating classifier. Next, each internally generated message is processed sequentially. The message is first matched against the active classifiers to find those from which a payment is to be collected. Next, a reduce-add primitive calculates the total payment owed to the classifier that generated the message. Finally, the classifiers are searched again, this time with the message tag, to locate the generating classifier and store the payment it has received. After all messages are processed, all classifiers receiving a payment from a message have their strengths simultaneously updated with an add-vector variable primitive.

The associative search function of the

array simplifies the execution of this algorithm by allowing a low overhead mechanism to quickly identify links between messages and classifiers. A sequential machine, on the other hand, would have to maintain a number of lists that link classifiers with messages and messages with their posting classifiers.

Classifier discovery layer. The classifier discovery layer is the most complex of the three LCS layers and uses a genetic algorithm as the discovery heuristic. There are nine steps involved that make heavy use of the communication bus as well as numerous other processor capabilities. It is worth noting here that our LCS implementation replaces the standard genetic algorithm with a parallel

---

Parallel genetic algorithms build a model that more closely resembles natural evolution by introducing the concept of spatial locality.

GA.[12] Parallel GAs employ the characteristics of parallel computers to build a model that more closely resembles natural evolution by introducing the concept of *spatial locality*. The standard GA selects parents and replacements from the entire pool of strings without any bias other than the weighted selection process. This is not, however, a realistic model of how evolution actually occurs. In reality, parents are most likely to reside within close proximity of one another. By limiting the distance between parents and the string their offspring will replace, a parallel computer becomes the logical choice to implement the parallel GA because of greatly reduced communication costs inherent in the architecture. Moreover, algorithm processing improves twofold. First, as expected, parallel processing increases the algorithm's execution speed. Second, a more subtle improvement results from the spatial relationships between the population members, which has the effect of allowing small pockets of the population to evolve

somewhat independently from the rest. Consequently, as each subpopulation searches a different area of the solution space, a larger area of the solution space is searched simultaneously.

Mark eligible parents. This step globally searches various classifier tags and numeric values to mark those classifiers that can be considered as potential parents.

Calculate fitness. A biased version of strength, called fitness, is used during parent selection. The bias increases the chance that those classifiers with higher strength will be selected. Fitness is normally calculated by raising strength to a prespecified power. These LCS simulations, however, simply set fitness equal to strength.

Select parents. The same parallelized random selection algorithm that was used in the competition to post messages is applied to parent selection, with the exception that the algorithm is now based on the fitness value just calculated. The number of parents selected is twice the number of classifiers to be generated, which is a fixed percentage of the total number of classifiers.

Implicit in a sequential genetic algorithm is the grouping of parents together for applying the crossover operator. In a fine-grained parallel genetic algorithm, this is problematic as it introduces the need for the classifiers to establish pairwise groupings. One parent of each group must then send a copy of its conditions, actions, and strength to its "mate." However, the reconfigurable capability of the Rbus suggests a method of grouping parents that maximizes bus utilization and is computationally less demanding. All parents are labeled as either even or odd depending on their location in the array, with the topmost parent being even. Each even parent is grouped with the odd parent immediately below it. Grouping the parents in this fashion is important as it splits the array into spatially disjoint segments that can make use of the Rbus without contention. Thus, all "even" parents can simultaneously broadcast to their "odd" mates via the Rbus, using the send-field primitive.

Send parents. Offspring generation by means of the crossover operator requires the conditions, actions, and strengths of the two classifiers. The send-field primitive supports this communication based

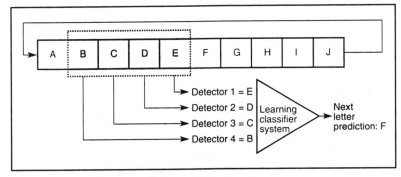

Figure 6. Letter sequence prediction problem domain.

on the parent grouping just described. In order to minimize communication time during offspring generation, vertical alignment is set up between the respective classifier components that will become offspring after the following step (create offspring). All even parents are then disabled; further processing occurs at the odd parent.

Create offspring. Offspring creation proceeds by first applying the crossover operator on selected parents at the odd mate location and then applying the mutation operator on the offspring thus generated. Both steps extensively use random number generation to determine the outcome of many decisions that are part of these steps. Decisions include determining

- which offspring are to be created by crossover as opposed to just copying,
- crossover point locations,
- the type of crossover to perform, and
- the number and location of mutations.

Crossover is similar to message creation since one variable is being conditionally copied into another (that is, the odd parent into the new offspring). The *copy state*, initially set to "no copy," controls the conditional copying of the odd parent. Crossover proceeds bit by bit through the entire classifier. The copy state is updated prior to the generation of each bit of the offspring, such that all PEs whose first crossover point matches the current bit set their copy state to "copy." All PEs whose second crossover point matches the current bit set their copy state to "no copy." Thus, for the range of bits between the two crossover points, the offspring originates from the odd parent.

Mutation changes up to three bits in each offspring, and for each one of these possible mutations it maintains a *mutation position* variable and a *mutation-active* flag. Like crossover, mutation proceeds bit by bit over the entire classifier, but now, when the current bit matches a mutation position in a classifier that has the respective mutation-active flag set,

that classifier undergoes a mutation at this bit position.

The final step of creating the offspring is to calculate the new strength for the offspring. In this implementation, an average of the parent strengths is applied.

Duplication check. There is nothing to prevent the offspring generation step from producing many identical classifiers. In particular, high-strength classifiers have a tendency to reproduce rapidly, quickly dominating the entire set of classifiers and degrading system performance. A duplication check limits the number of duplicates by reading each offspring from the array and comparing it with the current classifier list. If the number of responders is greater than permitted, the offspring is eliminated.

Select replacements. Replacement selection relies on the segmented minimum primitive to build a local neighborhood around each offspring. From this neighborhood, a classifier is selected that will be replaced by the offspring. The size of the neighborhood, N, is typically a small integer. In our LCS simulations it was three.

Use of the segmented primitives requires that the segment boundaries be set up beforehand. Segment boundaries are created with a two-step process in which first the high, and then the low, segment boundaries are propagated outward from each offspring. Taken together, the upper and lower segment bounds demarcate the neighborhood of the offspring from which the replacement will be selected. If two offspring are within N of each other, their neighborhoods are

Table 4. Average number of active processing elements per call by primitive operation.

Primitive	Avg. cycles	Percent total	Number of classifiers					
			200	400	600	800	1,000	1,200
Subtract	118	19.94	24.1	59.6	101.8	165.7	198.1	268.1
Multiply-vector	957	17.49	28.6	44.0	69.2	27.4	46.1	38.6
Scan Add	992	14.15	47.1	87.1	120.4	229.7	203.3	210.3
Compare	87	13.48	46.2	113.2	177.6	391.0	416.4	559.9
Move Field	67	7.51	19.9	54.8	69.6	84.5	111.0	117.8
Add-vector	78	1.46	5.5	3.5	4.3	3.5	4.3	4.47
Reduce Add	119	1.24	200.0	400.0	540.0	688.0	998.6	1198.9
Random	68	0.95	...	...	...	...	...	...
Maximum	54	0.79	47.1	87.2	120.4	229.7	203.3	210.3
Decrement	59	0.55	200.0	400.0	600.0	800.0	1,000.0	1,200.0

merged and one of the two will be discarded, depending on the location of the replacement. If the two offspring are within 2*N*, but further than *N*, then the lower bound of the topmost bound is shortened so it doesn't overlap that of the second. The segmented minimum primitive then selects the lowest strength classifier within each segment, which is then marked for replacement.

Send offspring. Following the replacements selection, the spread primitive broadcasts the offspring to the replacement.

Calculate specificity. The specificity for the offspring is calculated at its new location to minimize communication costs. Since specificity is just a count of the number of 0s and 1s in the conditions and actions of the offspring, the desired result is obtained by performing bit-by-bit compares and incrementing the specificity variable for each.

Performance evaluation

An associative architecture simulator was developed on a MasPar MP-1 system that consisted of 8,192 4-bit processors. The simulator served as a highly instrumented testbed on which the performance of various algorithms was investigated. Additionally, the use of the MP-1 parallel computer with an architecture closely matched to that of the simulated machine proved highly effective in reducing the runtime of the simulations.

The LCS algorithms were exercised on this simulator and tested on a letter prediction problem. In this problem, the LCS detectors were a sliding window over a continually repeated sequence of letters, and the desired output of the LCS was a prediction of the next letter to become visible in the window, as shown in Figure 6. This was a difficult problem as the system had no knowledge of the problem domain to begin with, and had no meanings associated with its detector inputs or effector outputs. From a qualitative reinforcement signal that merely indicated "right" or "wrong," the LCS had to create a set of prediction rules.

Many simulations, which varied the number of classifiers from 200 to 1,200, were performed to test the effect on execution time. The number of processing el-

Figure 7. Total number of execution cycles for a varying number of classifiers, showing the number of cycles contributed by each of the three layers: production system, credit assignment, and classifier discovery.

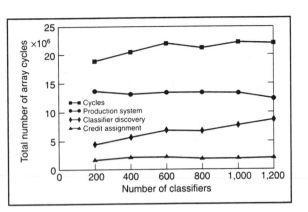

ements involved was five times the number of classifiers, or from 1,000 to 6,000. Figure 7 shows the total number of machine cycles required to complete a simulation run of 4,000 cycles. In general, execution time increased slightly with respect to the number of classifiers. The total number of cycles that were attributed to each layer is also shown in Figure 7. As expected, the production system layer accounted for most of the cycles. It is interesting to note that the

Arithmetic operations accounted for most of the execution cycles. Communication operations accounted for very few.

classifier discovery layer, while not invoked at every cycle, was still responsible for the next largest block of cycles and that it grew with the number of classifiers. Consequently, the increase in total execution time was due to the classifier discovery layer.

In all simulations, primitive operations accounted for approximately 78 percent of the total number of cycles. In particular, it is important to know the degree of parallelism exercised within each of the primitives. Table 4 shows the ten primitives that consumed the most cycles, sorted in descending order by the percent of the total number of execution cycles they contributed. Next to each prim-

itive is shown the average number of cycles executed per call; the percent of the total number of cycles; and, for a range of different numbers of classifiers, the average number of active PEs per call. From this table, it can be concluded that the arithmetic operations were directly responsible for the largest portion of the total number of execution cycles. Furthermore, it is also clear that the communication operations comprised an insignificant portion of the total number of cycles. The data for the random primitive is left out as that primitive was coded to generate a random number in all classifier records.

An important concern was whether there were enough active PEs to justify the use of bit-serial algorithms, or whether the work should have been performed sequentially in the controller with bit-parallel hardware. Those primitives where the average number of active PEs was less than the average number of cycles are *multiply-vector*, *scan add*, and *add-vector*. By moving these operations to the controller, approximately 12 percent of all cycles were eliminated. However, since the number of active PEs often varied greatly between individual calls, it was important to preface each routine with a test of the number of active PEs to determine where to perform the calculation.

A lthough this article focused on a single type of encoding for the classifiers, the architecture, while highly specialized, is quite capable of easily supporting any number of genetic algorithm encodings. This is due to the very flexible way in which the CAM data can be processed. Furthermore, the architecture will enable the development of many different algorithms for both the credit assignment and classifier discovery layers, in conjunction with new research results on LCSs.

The work reported here shows that associative architectures with the correct communication support, such as a reconfigurable long-distance communication bus, are effective for building Learning Classifier Systems. In particular, the experimental data showed that the runtime of the system increased only slightly even as the number of classifiers was increased sixfold.

Research to date has investigated the development of a specialized associative architecture to support inductive rule-based machine learning with genetic algorithms. Future development of intelligent systems with broad-based machine learning and adaptive capabilities may benefit directly from such specialized architectures. These architectures offer valuable potential for achieving a high degree of reactivity to inputs from the environment. In particular, as is possible with this architecture, it is important that ever-larger knowledge bases be supported in a manner that does not significantly affect runtime. ■

References

1. J.H. Holland, "Escaping Brittleness: The Possibilities of General-Purpose Learning Algorithms Applied to Parallel Rule-Based Systems," in R.S. Michalski, J.G. Carbonell, and T.M. Mitchell, eds., *Machine Learning: An Artificial Intelligence Approach*, Morgan Kaufmann, Los Altos, Calif., 2nd edition, 1986, pp. 593-623.

2. L.B. Booker, D.E. Goldberg, and J.H. Holland, "Classifier Systems and Genetic Algorithms," *Artificial Intelligence*, Vol. 40, Sept. 1989, pp. 235-282.

3. G. Robertson, "Parallel Implementation of Genetic Algorithms in a Classifier System," L. Davis, ed., *Genetic Algorithms and Simulated Annealing*, Pitman, London, 1987, pp. 129-140.

4. M. Dorigo, E. Sirtori, "Alecsys: A Parallel Laboratory for Learning Classifier Systems," *Proc. 4th Int'l Conf. on Genetic Algorithms*, Morgan Kaufmann, Los Altos, Calif., 1991, pp. 296-302.

5. C.D. Stormon et al., "A General-Purpose CMOS Associative Processor IC and System," *IEEE Micro*, Vol. 12, No. 6, Dec. 1992, pp. 68-78.

6. *Associative Computing: A Programming Paradigm for Massively Parallel Computers*, J.L. Potter, ed., Plenum Press, New York, 1992.

7. C.C. Weems et al., "The Image Understanding Architecture," *Int'l. J. Computer Vision*, Vol. 2, No. 3, Jan. 1989, pp. 251-282.

8. R.M. Lea, "WASP: A WSI Associative String Processor," *J. VLSI Signal Processing*, Vol. 2, No. 4, May 1991, pp. 271-285.

9. F.P. Herrmann and C.G. Sodini, "A Dynamic Associative Processor for Machine Vision Applications," *IEEE Micro*, Vol. 12, No. 3, June 1992, pp. 31-41.

10. R.H. Storer et al., "An Associative Processing Module for a Heterogeneous Vision Architecture," *IEEE Micro*, Vol. 12, No. 3, June 1992, pp. 42-55.

11. G.E. Blelloch, *Vector Models for Data-Parallel Computing*, MIT Press, Cambridge, Mass., 1990.

12. H. Muhlenbein, M. Gorges-Schleuter, and O. Krämer, "New Solutions to the Mapping Problem of Parallel Systems — the Evolution Approach," *Parallel Computing*, Vol. 4, No. 3, June 1987, pp. 269-279.

Flag-Oriented Parallel Associative Architectures and Applications

Djamshid Tavangarian, University of Hagen

Flag transformation, a new design concept for parallel associative memory and processor architectures, maps word-oriented data into flag-oriented data. A flag vector represents each word in a set. The flag position corresponds to the value of the transformed word, and all flags in a vector are processed simultaneously to obtain parallel operations. The results of complex search operations performed by modular, cascadable hardware components are also represented by flags and retransformed into word-oriented data.

This transformation method allows parallel processing of associative or content-addressable data in uniprocessor architectures, expedites IC design rule checks, and accelerates complex memory tests. It can also be used to develop associative processor architectures and to emulate very fast, modular, cascadable artificial neural networks.

Content-addressable memory

A content-addressable memory (CAM), also known as an associative memory (AM), uses contents — not locations — to access data. Parallel processing in AMs, which is related to multiprocessing, allows simultaneous execution of command sequences over many data sets. Thus, AMs effectively handle many information processing problems. Various forms of AMs are used in different associative processor architectures, but we will focus on a classical word-oriented AM to explain an AM's function. (See the sidebar "Associative processor architectures.")

A word-oriented AM with n-bit word length generally has n-bit search and mask arguments. The minimum outputs of an AM with a multiple-match-resolving circuit are a 1-bit match or hit signal and an n-bit output word. The output word can contain $n + k$ bit positions if a word in the memory is composed of an n-bit, content-addressable part and a k-bit data part. Figure 1 shows the structure of a typical CAM. Search and mask registers store search and mask arguments, respectively. Content-addressable data is stored in the first memory field, and data that is not content-addressable is stored in the second field.

> A flag-oriented
> architecture contains
> one processing unit
> capable of executing
> complex functions
> in parallel.

As a simple example, consider the 5+7 bit-per-word memory in Figure 1. Suppose the problem is to find all words that contain the data, X1X01, where X is 0 or 1, a "don't care" or masked-search bit position.

The conventional approach is to individually restore each word from memory and determine whether it matches the criteria. Obviously, this can be time-consuming if the memory contains many words. However, a CAM with parallel-search capability permits asking all words in memory to simultaneously perform a comparison (match) with the search argument register, but only when the bit position in the mask register is 0. Each word has a bit output that indicates if the pieces of data in that word match the information for which the memory is being searched. The match output shows a 1 if at least one hit is in the memory. The next operation would be to ask if any of the words match, count the words that match,

---

Associative processor architectures

The two most significant features of associative processors are (1) their content-dependent extraction and selection of data and (2) their method of processing selected information (preferably in parallel). Figure A lists several types of control units and associative memory units, the two main modules of an associative processor.

In Flynn's classification scheme, most associative processors can be classified as single-instruction-stream, multiple-data-stream (SIMD) architectures. Unlike multiple-instruction-stream, multiple-data-stream (MIMD) architectures, SIMD architectures do not need any special mechanism to control actions in parallel, since only one instruction is executed by many processors at the same time, on different data. These architectures require only one control unit to organize the instruction stream, control the processing or arithmetic and logic units, and distribute the data. Furthermore, their central control units allow them to process array- or field-structured data like vectors or matrices.

Programmable logic arrays and other arrays can be used to convert the control unit to a sequential network. A more flexible control unit is a RISC, CISC, or bit-slice microprocessor. Sometimes the host computer is set to control the associative memory unit.

Content-dependent access and data processing can be organized by fully parallel or bit-serial, word-parallel associative memories and serial-working associative-memory emulators with conventional RAMs or by an ensemble of network-coupled processor elements with a single control unit.

Another kind of associative memory system, an artificial neural network, is a parallel, distributed information structure consisting of processing cells (neurons) connected via unidirectional signal channels. Each cell accesses a local memory and carries out localized information-processing operations. Each cell also has a single output, which is connected to the other cell inputs as required. Factors such as processing time, number of inputs, complexity, and application domain can influence the design of an artificial neural network. Variations include an ensemble of connected analog cells, digital circuits, and an emulation of networks with single or multiprocessors.

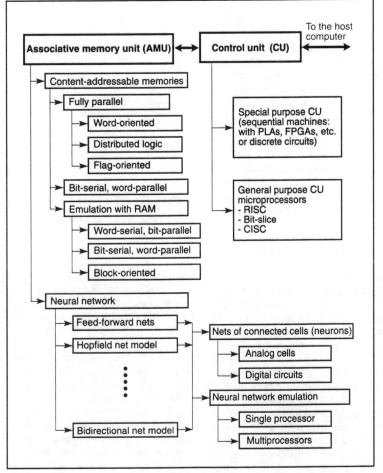

Figure A. Associative-processor architectures.

121

or sequentially read the matching words to learn what data those words are holding in the masked bit positions.

The ability to search for stored data based on contents can be a powerful asset in many applications. However, the CAM also forms the basis for the more sophisticated case of general associative data processing. ADP deals with the interrelations among data and sets of data. The simple match process (which a CAM can perform) can be iterated for the more complex operations of set definition and set positioning (such as greater than, less than or equal to, next greater, next lower, between limits, and searches for maximum or minimum). Consequently, it is possible to rapidly extract the data from an ADP content-addressable memory in a subset that matches certain characteristics based on complex searches.

Consider, for example, an associative algorithm that extracts the word with the maximum value from a CAM where bit positions have been assigned a binary-weighted order. The first operation might be to search the most significant bit in each word for a 1 and define all other bits as "don't care" (masked search): $1XXX \ldots X$. If only one word indicates a match, then the maximum-word search is completed. If several words indicate a match, then the CAM is accessed again, this time for $11XX \ldots X$. However, if no word indicates a match in the first search, then the second search is conducted for $01XX \ldots X$. Hence, an n-bit-per-word memory requires no more than n cycles to determine the maximum-valued word regardless of the total number of words, and the complexity of these operations is $O(n)$.

A CAM that can be accessed in parallel for simple — and some extended — searches requires a complex logic part at each bit position in the memory. Furthermore, existing CAM concepts realize ICs with only limited memory capacity compared to RAMs. A fully parallel CAM as a modular, cascadable IC that executes only a compare operation between a masked search argument and each word in memory is sophisticated. If it becomes necessary to increase the word length of the CAM by adding some CAM modules, each module must give a hit signal for each memory word to the next CAM module. Fully parallel searches can be executed in the entire CAM array only when this condition is fulfilled. Therefore, a CAM chip's number of pins determines its memory capacity. This is known as the "pin limitation problem,"

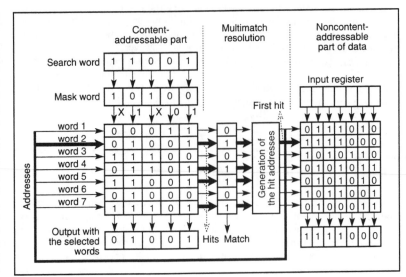

Figure 1. Basic structure of a conventional content-addressable memory.

and it restricts the number of memory words per CAM module. Concepts that use serial compare operations are not influenced by this problem, but have a relatively long execution time.

The flag transformation method allows parallel processing of associative or content-addressable data in a uniprocessor architecture. This method converts word-oriented data into flag-oriented data to make it suitable for further processing in parallel.

Flag-oriented hardware system

Flag transformation represents a new concept for developing VLSI circuit modules for storage and fully parallel processing of content-addressable data (such as identification, searches, or search operations combined with arithmetic and logic operations). Examples of flag-oriented hardware systems include associative RAMs (ARAMs),[1] associative coprocessors, and the associative reduced-instruction-set computing (RISC) processor architecture called Astra.[2]

A flag-oriented associative hardware system generally includes three main parts: the transformation, the processing unit, and the inverse transformation.

The flag transformation transforms n-bit words into flag-oriented data. This data is represented by a bit vector of 2^n ordered cells (0 through $2^n - 1$) in which

each word is represented by a flag. The position — or address — of the flag is defined by the value of the corresponding data. The transformed data is processed when the flags are switched. The original domain of the word-oriented data is called the word domain. As usual, this data consists of n bit positions. Descriptions of transformed data and corresponding flags are contained in a new domain, called the flag domain.

The second part of this hardware system, the processing unit, uses the flags as operands. Since the operands are represented as 1-bit information in the flag domain, they can be processed simultaneously. Boolean functions are constructed via patterns derived from special axioms and laws, which are based on set theory and Boolean algebra. These axioms and laws consider the special attributes of the flag vector and shape an isomorph to set theory, called flag-algebra (See the sidebar "Mathematical basis for flag-oriented operations.") Flag algebra describes parallel, flag-oriented search, arithmetic, and logic operations in the flag domain and the theoretical basis for realizing suitable circuits to execute them. The hardware complexity of large systems based on this concept should be acceptable, in spite of their fully parallel mechanisms.

The results of operations with flag-oriented operands are represented by flags, and parallel operations with many operands can produce several. A sequential mechanism is required to isolate single results. The third part of a flag-oriented

Mathematical basis for flag-oriented operations

Flag transformation. A set of n-bit data is given as:

$$S' = \{S'_1, S'_2, \ldots, S'_q\}$$

The indicator-function FLAG of each set, S', in the word domain is now introduced to compute the Boolean vector $F \in \{0,1\}^{2^n}$ (with 0 = false, 1 = true) in the flag domain:

$$Flag : (P(S) \rightarrow \{0,1\}^{2^n})$$

$$Flag\ (S') = F = (f_0, f_1, f_2, f_3, \ldots, f_j, \ldots, f_{2^n-1})$$

with $f_j = 1 \leftrightarrow S_j \in S'$ and $\wedge\ j \in \{0 \ldots (2^n - 1)\}$

The flag transformation converts any set of n-bit data from the word domain to the flag domain as a bit vector F with a length of $L(F) = 2^n$.

A position f_j in the vector F represents the word S_j and is called the flag of S_j. The vector F holding the flags is called the flag vector. To process data, the operations are executed with the flag vectors. The flag-oriented data in the flag vectors are always sorted, and this supports these operations.

Flag algebra. Flag algebra is an isomorph of Boolean algebra; the same axioms and theories are valid. Most of the laws and definitions of flag algebra are given in Tavangarian.[1] Flag algebra is needed for arithmetic computations on the flag vectors and implementations of associative functions on the data represented by flag vectors. The following aspects briefly describe the basic computations on flag vectors with 2^n-bit length each:

Complement of flag vectors:

$$\overline{F} = \{\overline{f_j}; j = 0..(2^n - 1)\}$$

Union of flag vectors:

$$F_U = F_1 \cup F_2 = \left[f_{U_j} = f_{1_j} \vee f_{2_j}, j = \{0 \ldots (2^n - 1)\} \right]$$

Intersection of flag vectors:

$$F_I = F_1 \cap F_2 = \left[f_{I_j} = f_{1_j} \wedge f_{2_j}, j = \{0 \ldots (2^n - 1)\} \right]$$

Two flag vectors are disjoint if the result of the intersection is an empty flag vector.

Equivalence:

$$F_{EQ} = F_1 \equiv F_2 = \left[f_{EQ_j} = f_{1_j} \equiv f_{2_j}, j = \{0 \ldots (2^n - 1)\} \right]$$

Exclusive (XOR):

$$F_{EX} = F_1 \oplus F_2 = \left[f_{EX_j} = f_{1_j} \oplus f_{2_j}, j = \{0 \ldots (2^n - 1)\} \right]$$

The union, intersection, equivalence and exclusive OR operations are provided by more than one operand. Since the operands are Boolean values, the computation laws of Boolean functions (such as commutative and associative laws and cal-culations with constants) must be considered.

Unsymmetrical difference:

$$F_{UNSYM} = (F_1 - F_2) = \left[f_{UNSYM_j} = (f_{1_j} - f_{2_j}) = f_{1_j} \cap \overline{f_{2_j}}, j = \{0 \ldots 2^n - 1\} \right]$$

The results of the investigated computations on flag vectors are always flag vectors. There are many more operations that yield non-flag-vector-type results. For example, operations on two or more flag vectors can result in multidimensional vector systems. Such a result is yielded by the product of two flag vectors, F_1 and F_2, that have the same length, meaning $L(F_1) = L(F_2)$.

Examples. For the execution of operations with flag vectors, the vectors are stored in registers or memory words of conventional microprocessors. The basic functions of a standard ALU can be used for the execution of operations.

For example, we can find all identical data words in two sets, S_1 and S_2, that both contain p elements. This problem can be solved with the original data in word domain via the bucket-sort algorithm with a complexity of $O(p)$.

The same operation can be conducted for $O(1)$. The equivalence function can be applied to use the flag-oriented data to represent the sets as flag vectors, F_1 and $F_2 : F_{RESULT} = F_1 \cap F_2$.

Compared to standard methods, performance is increased significantly.

The complements of the flag vectors yield some basic operations. For example, complements of the operands can be used to construct the following functions:

$F_{RESULT} = F_1 \cap \overline{F_2}$ returns all data contained in F_1, but not in F_2 (unsymmetrical difference).

$F_{RESULT} = \overline{F_1} \cap \overline{F_2}$ returns all data contained in neither F_1 nor F_2.

Other examples can be derived from search operations using the complements of the operands.

Inverse flag transformation. The flag-oriented data being processed in the flag domain needs a conversion to equivalent data in the word domain. This conversion for a flag vector,

$$F = (f_0, f_1, \ldots, f_j, \ldots, f_{2n-1}),$$

is done by the inverse flag transformation, $FLAG^{-1}$:

$$FLAG^{-1}(F) : (\{0,1\}^{2n} \rightarrow P\{S\})$$

$$FLAG^{-1}(F) = S' = \{S'_1, S'_2, \ldots, S'_j, \ldots, S'_q\}$$

with $S'_j \in S' \leftrightarrow f_j = 1$ and $\forall j \in \{0 \ldots (2^n - 1)\}$

If the inverse flag transformation is done in ascending (descending) order beginning with $f_0 (f_{2^n-1})$ the sorted set, S', is obtained.

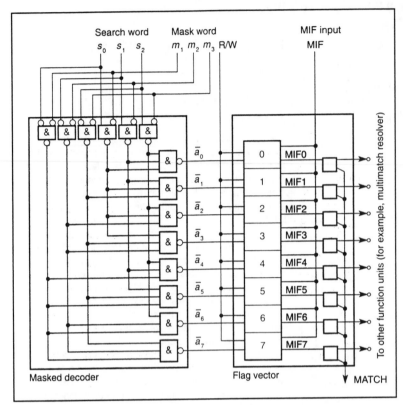

Figure 2. Circuit of a masking decoder of a flag-oriented associative memory with match-indicating flag cells.

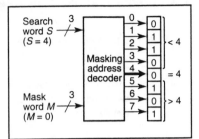

Figure 3. Relevant parts of the flag vector for search operations greater-than, equal-to, and less-than 4.

system accomplishes this and converts results in the flag domain into word-oriented data in the word domain. This mechanism is called the inverse flag transformation.

Associative RAM

The most important part of an associative RAM (ARAM) is the masking address decoder (MAD). This unit transforms the n-bit search word, $S(n)$, and n-bit mask word, $M(n)$, into one or more addresses for a conventional one-bit RAM cell vector, the flag vector. The cells store the flags.

Figure 2 shows the circuitry in an $n = 3$-bit ARAM. The circuit includes inputs for write/read, match-indicating flag (MIF), and output match operations. The $2^3 = 8$ cell addresses are a_0 through a_1. During the write period (WR = 0), the addressed cells will be set to MIF = 1 if the data is to be stored, or reset to MIF = 0 if the data is to be erased from memory. In a search operation, part of the cells are addressed simultaneously, depending on the masked

search argument. During the search period (WR = 1), a match signal (MATCH) will be generated if at least one addressed MIF-cell is set. This is accomplished by a wired-OR connection of all MIF-cell outputs that avoids any comparisons between stored and searched data. Finally, searched data is read (WR = 1) by encoding the position of the matched MIF cell in the MIF memory vector. Multiple matches are read sequentially by means of a multimatch resolver. Both the transformation of associative data into MIF addresses and the encoding of searched data from the match addresses are operations that could easily be cascaded for search and mask words with expanded word length, because they are realized by cascadable hardware decoder components.

An ARAM can be characterized by the following features:

- A set's associative data is not stored, itself, but represented by flags.
- Associative data is stored in flag vectors, in ascending order.
- A parallel associative operation is executed by simultaneous addressing

and reading/writing of flag cells.

- An ARAM, like a conventiona RAM, is cascadable for increasing word length and memory capacity. The realization of an ARAM as an IC is not restricted by the pin limitation problem.

Complex search operations. A flag-oriented memory allows a search for stored values, which is essentially a search for equality. Because the data in a flag vector is stored in ascending order, an ARAM also allows complex searches (such as greater-than or less-than). A greater-than-or-equal-to or less-than-or-equal-to search operation can address the relevant parts of the flag vector simultaneously. If an addressed flag cell contains the value 1, then the result of the search will contain at least one match. Figure 3 is a very simple example of how the addresses of relevant parts of the flag vector are specified and characterized for a search operation.

Figure 3 shows the address decoder and flag cells of a 3-bit ARAM. Appropriate flags decide which of the eight (2^3) numbers, 0 through 7, are stored into memory. The values 1, 2, 5 and 7 are stored, but the values 0, 3, 4, and 6 are not, because they do not contain a 1 in the appropriate flag cell.

To determine the values greater than or equal to the search arguments ($S = 4$), cells 4 through 7 are addressed simultaneously as relevant parts. The output lines of the flag cells are connected by a wired OR. If one of the addressed cells contains a 1, a match signal exists. The match signal shows that at least one value greater than the search argument (S) is stored in the addressed part. Cells 0 through 4 must be addressed to determine which values are less than or equal to S.

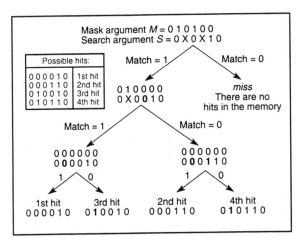

Mask argument $M = 0\ 1\ 0\ 1\ 0\ 0$
Search argument $S = 0\ X\ 0\ X\ 1\ 0$

Possible hits:

0 0 0 0 1 0	1st hit
0 0 0 1 1 0	2nd hit
0 1 0 0 1 0	3rd hit
0 1 0 1 1 0	4th hit

Match = 1   Match = 0

0 1 0 0 0 0
0 X 0 0 1 0   *miss*
                   There are no
                   hits in the memory

Match = 1   Match = 0

0 0 0 0 0 0   0 0 0 0 0 0
0 0 0 0 1 0   0 0 0 1 1 0

1   0   1   0

1st hit   3rd hit   2nd hit   4th hit
0 0 0 0 1 0 0 1 0 0 1 0 0 0 0 1 1 0 0 1 0 1 1 0

Figure 4. Algorithm for the separation of hits with a mask word.

It is easy to develop circuits that enable simultaneous addressing of relevant parts. These simple combinatorial circuits are extensions of the masking decoder. There are three possible circuit forms: fully parallel, serial, or parallel-serial. Circuits that work in parallel can shorten execution and response times. The search operation executes in only one cycle. However, this is a relatively expensive approach. The serial circuit method is cheaper, but slower. The parallel-serial method is a favorable compromise, especially for cascading ARAM chips. In this case, the calculation is carried out in parallel inside a chip. Search operations between chips can be organized serially with special carry signals. The corresponding circuits are specified in Tavangarian.[1]

Another possibility is to generate a new flag vector that specifies the relevant part for a search. For example, the vector for greater-than-or-equal-to 4 would be ($F = 00001111$), where a 1 in each flag cell represents a value greater than or equal to 4 and each remaining cell contains a 0. A Boolean AND between the stored data in the flag vector (F) and F separates all the possible solutions:

$$
\begin{aligned}
F_{solution} &= F\ \&\ F_{GE} \\
&= 0\ 1\ 1\ 0\ 0\ 1\ 0\ 1\ \& \\
&\quad \underline{0\ 0\ 0\ 0\ 1\ 1\ 1\ 1} \\
&\quad 0\ 0\ 0\ 0\ 0\ 1\ 0\ 1 = F_{solution}
\end{aligned}
$$

In the same way, various other complex search operations (such as equal, less than, less than or equal to, between limits or outside limits) are possible. These operations can be conducted by simultaneous addressing of all appropriate flag cells.

Nevertheless, some search and arithmetic-logic operations (such as searches for minimum or maximum and searches for next less or next higher) use the contents of flag cells in addition to their addresses.[1] For example, a minimum search would require the flag cell containing a 1 in the first cell of the flag vector to be addressed. A maximum search would require the flag cell containing a 1 in the last cell of the flag vector to be addressed. In other words, determining the greatest or smallest value in memory requires only contents of the flag cells needed to choose the appropriate addresses. In a minimum search operation, flag cell i is addressed if it contains a 1 and the preceeding cells (0 through $i - 1$) do not:

$$
a_{1_{min}} = f_i \wedge \bigwedge_{j=0}^{i-1} \bar{f}_j \text{ with } i = 0, 1, \ldots 2^n - 1
$$

In a maximum search operation, flag cell i is addressed if it contains a 1 and the cells following it ($i + 1, \ldots, 2^n - 1$) each do not contain a 1:

$$
a_{1_{max}} = f_i \wedge \bigwedge_{j=i+1}^{2^n-1} \bar{f}_j \text{ with } i = 0, 1, \ldots 2^n - 1
$$

These relations are used directly for combinatorial circuit realizations of minimum and maximum search operations. Realizations of other search operations, such as searches for next greater or next lower and searches for similar words, are determined the same way. Once again, parallel, serial, or parallel-serial methods can be chosen. However, the hardware expenditure for the serial circuit form would be at least three gates per word. Parallel search operations in an ARAM

array can also be executed by an appropriate carry-look-ahead mechanism.[1]

Multimatch resolving. In the first step of a search operation, the relevant part of the flag vector is addressed with the help of search and mask arguments. If the search results in a match, then at least one hit exists in the memory. When there are multiple matches, hits in the output must be separated. This problem can be solved with hardware or software.

The hardware solution uses a priority network, which always separates the first hit in memory. After output, the separated hit is deleted so that the next hit becomes the first one, can be separated, and so on. Hence, the priority circuit can be used as a maximum or minimum search.

The software solution uses mask and search word inputs in a binary tree search algorithm. Figure 4 shows the principal flow for a given example, which includes a search argument with two bit positions masked by M. The existence of two masked bits means four hits (2^2) are possible, because the masked bit positions of S can each be 0 or 1.

The algorithm starts with the $M = 010100$ and $S = 0X0X10$. All four flag cells are addressed simultaneously with the mask word. If there is no match (match = 0) in the first step, there will be no hits in the memory because none of the addressed cells contain a flag. If the match output shows a 1, at least one of the four cells contains a flag.

In the second step, one bit position is unmasked and the unmasked position of S becomes 0. To check for a match, the second masked bit is removed and the new unmasked bit position is set to 0. If there is a match, the first hit has been separated. If not, the new bit position of the search word must be changed to 1. This word must be a hit, since the match in the first step indicates at least one match in this path. Thus, the third hit is separated. The search in the second step is continued so that the second and fourth hits can be separated.

The number of steps required to separate the first hit depends on the number of masked bit positions. For n-bit words, the maximum number of masked bit positions and the maximum number of steps to find the first hit are both n. So the complexity of the algorithm is $O(n)$.

If the separated hit is removed from memory (the selected flag cell is set to 0), the next hit can be separated by a repeat of the algorithm. The number of steps in the repeating processes depends on the number of hits existing in the memory. Saving the data base in the flag vector requires a copy of the flag vector used to execute the separating algorithm.

This algorithm is very fast yet does not require any additional hardware.

Accelerating tasks with flag-oriented structures

Flag-oriented structures can be used efficiently to accelerate various data processing tasks. Flag-oriented conceptions can equip ICs or stand-alone processors normally used as workstation coprocessors to handle special problems.

Flag-oriented systems can consist of one or more dimensions. The basic form of a flag vector is a linear, one-dimensional order of flag cells. A two-dimensional flag system is built from a set of flag vectors like a matrix of cells. A three-dimensional flag system is a cube of flag cells.

Applications of flag-oriented structures include

- the acceleration of design rule checkers (DRCs) that check geometrical violations in IC layouts. The problem is solved with an associative coprocessor consisting of a one-dimensional flag-oriented memory system.
- the usability of a two-dimensional flag-oriented system inside a VLSI chip. The flag-oriented circuits, which are used as extensions of conventional RAM circuits, allow functional tests to be accelerated by one or two orders of complexity.
- a neural network formed with the help of a flag-oriented memory system.

DRC acceleration. VLSI circuits cannot be designed in an acceptable amount of time without efficient design tools. Therefore, in the last decade, industry and research laboratories have developed design systems that provide tools for the design and validation of ICs in homogeneous user environments.[3] Apparently, data structures for layout description and algorithms for layout manipulation are more adapted to associative data processing (see the first sidebar) than to conventional von Neumann computers.[4]

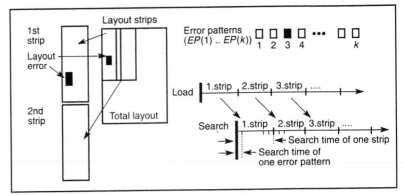

Figure 5. Simultaneous comparison of a single error pattern with all windows of the layout strip.

Associative DRC algorithms. DRC concepts can generally be divided into three classes: pixel-oriented, which are based on the raster scan method; polygon-oriented or algebraic, which normally include distance calculations and intersections of different layers by Boolean operations; and edge or corner-based, which concentrate on corners or edges of layout structures to find geometrical layout violations.

The edge method is normally more efficient than the pixel-oriented method if complex search operations, such as threshold and double-limit searches, are available. A detailed presentation of these conceptions and their realizations is given in Strugala.[4]

The pixel-oriented method is the easiest to explain. The layout is cast onto a square grid, where spacings are determined by the grid width that is equivalent to the minimum structure size of the actual process. Each square is characterized by its x and y coordinates on the associated layout layers. Design rules are transformed into reference patterns and compared to the actual layout window, which is sized to overlap the largest reference pattern by one grid width. The comparison is repeated when the layout window is moved line by line across the grid. Any discrepancies between the tested and reference patterns indicate a design rule violation. In this method, the basic operations are comparisons, which are well suited for a hardware implementation, especially with associative coprocessors.

Layout in content-addressable memory. The content-addressable memory (CAM) approach uses the pixel-oriented

method through a comparison of layout structures with fixed reference patterns that describe design rule violations.

Figure 5 introduces a model to explain this concept. The raster bit map of the layout indicated in the model is completely stored in a CAM. Layout errors are defined by reference patterns consisting of $n \times n$ bit cells.[3] Each of these error patterns is used as a search argument for the associative array, so that the search for layout errors can be done simultaneously in the entire layout. If a complete set of error patterns is applied to the array, all design rule violations are flagged as matches. A special multimatch resolution sequentially informs the layout positions of design rule violations. The total execution time for DRC depends directly on the number of error patterns checked.

The adaptation of this model to layouts with arbitrary geometrical dimensions makes it necessary to split the raster bit map into strips, which are sequentially processed with the associative array (Figure 5). The layout strips are checked using the same procedures described for the model. However, overlapping strips must be introduced to detect errors at the transition line between adjacent layout strips. This operation renders successive loading of bitmap strips into the CAM. System performance can be improved if the associative memory is divided into two parts of the same memory capacity. Load and search operations are executed alternately in both parts of the array. During the search operation in one part, the other memory section is loaded by direct memory access (DMA) from the host computer. Thus, search and load operations are run in parallel, which reduces the execution time of

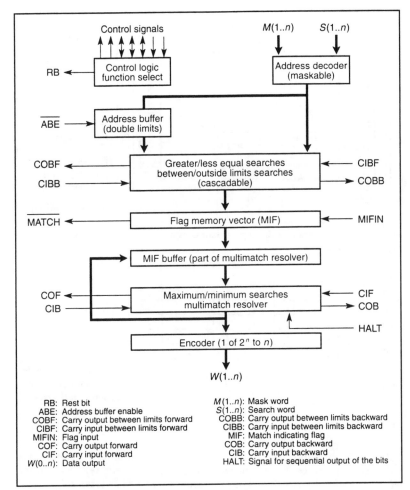

Figure 6. Block diagram of an associative RAM chip.

RB: Rest bit
ABE: Address buffer enable
COBF: Carry output between limits forward
CIBF: Carry input between limits forward
MIFIN: Flag input
COF: Carry output forward
CIF: Carry input forward
W(0..n): Data output

M(1..n): Mask word
S(1..n): Search word
COBB: Carry output between limits backward
CIBB: Carry input between limits backward
MIF: Match indicating flag
COB: Carry output backward
CIB: Carry input backward
HALT: Signal for sequential output of the bits

all possible error patterns, EP(1)...EP(k), can be stored in the associative-memory array as reference patterns. In this case, the layout is split into windows and used as search arguments for the associative memory, so that all error patterns can be compared in parallel.[4]

Associative memory of a coprocessor for DRC. The main functional unit of an associative coprocessor for the implementation of a DRC accelerator is a fully parallel associative-memory array based on the ARAM concept. The fully parallel search functions within flag-oriented memory modules at the IC level with relatively low expenditures include searches for equality, matches greater/less than a limit, and matches between/outside two limits.

Each of these functions can be executed with masked or unmasked search arguments and can be completed by a search for a maximum/minimum value in the stored data set. So, 47 different functions are available.[5] Matched data is restored from memory in ascending or descending order, because all data kept in ARAM is automatically sorted during write operations. Since the associative data can be accessed in parallel, the execution of each operation takes only one memory cycle. Figure 6 shows the hardware components within the memory module performing their various functions.

Different versions of the ARAM have been realized as ICs.[1,4-6] An associative-memory array designed with these ICs is cascadable and can be expanded by adding further memory modules. The memory capacity of this array working in parallel is no longer restricted and can be varied depending on the desired application. Signals from a chip-select generator select the actual memory module in the array, and a remaining-bit generator identifies it as the module reads matched data. A status exchange between the modules involved in the operation lets search operations be executed fully in parallel. This exchange is established by so-called carry signals, which are processed by carry-look-ahead (CLA) circuitry. This circuitry is connected to a peripheral memory unit, which acts as a gate array.[5]

The ARAM arrays can be connected hierarchically with CLA circuits of rising levels, as shown in Figure 7. Each CLA circuit of level 0 can be applied to a maximum of eight ARAM modules; a CLA

the DRC. A balanced distribution of search and load time is attained when the suitable load time — and, therefore, the size of a raster-bit-map strip — is determined by the search time required to verify all error patterns. Because of this, the dimension of the strip depends on the number of error patterns checked in the layout.

The raster bit map representing the layout is kept in a RAM. In a second example, called the *error-patterns-in-CAM approach,*

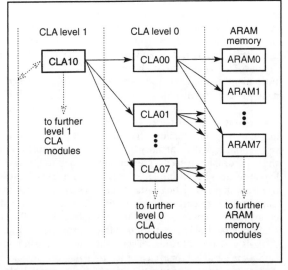

Figure 7. Schematic illustration of a hierarchical associative RAM array with carry-look-ahead modules.

circuit of level l controls up to eight CLA circuits of level 0; and so on. For example, the construction of a memory array with a flag vector of 2^{20} cells (1-Mword capacity of 20 bit lengths per word) would require 16 ARAM modules with 2^{16} flag cells (64-Kwords with 16-bit word lengths each) and three CLA circuits positioned in two levels.

Besides flexible cascading of IC modules, the ARAM concept offers two other important advantages. First, search operations are executed fully in parallel without external control. Second, after the search arguments and functions have been specified, an asynchronous, demand-driven output of matched data is provided by the host computer. Both features support the installation of the memory array as an associative coprocessor for workstations. Hence, dedicated problems, such as sort and search operations, which are normally solved by service routines can be managed within the ARAM array.

PC implementation. An associative coprocessor with ARAM modules has been implemented for a PC with a Xenix operating system.[6] The main objectives have been to

- realize the coprocessor in an environment with a sufficient number of software tools and hardware resources;
- implement a "system call" interface for C language, since the DRC is also programmed in C; and
- separate the associative-memory array and controller interface to guarantee flexibility in the hierarchy of the ARAM-array components.

Therefore, the hardware consists of two parts placed in a PC: a controller board and a memory board. The controller board contains register banks and top-level cascading circuitry. The PC interface and DMA controller in this circuitry allow it to control eight memory submodules. (See Figure 8.) The controller communicates with the host via the system bus, but provides control signals, search arguments, and matched data via a special associative-array interconnection bus.

A software interface for the programming of associative functions is as important as a hardware interface. This interface should not require the user to have detailed information about the coprocessor: only a list of possible functions

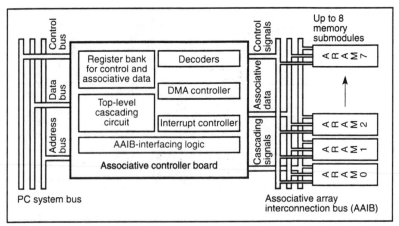

Figure 8. Block diagram of the coprocessor comprising controller-board and memory submodules.

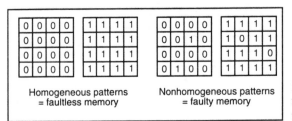

Homogeneous patterns = faultless memory

Nonhomogeneous patterns = faulty memory

Figure 9. Homogeneous and nonhomogeneous patterns.

and a mechanism to specify them and the processed data. The Xenix operating system provides a hierarchical file system, which handles devices (such as terminals, disks, and printers) as files. To provide the user with system consistency, the same interfacing technique accesses the associative coprocessor. System calls such as open(), close(), read(), and write() have standard meanings, but the system call, ioctl(), controls access rights for the device and starts write, test, and read operations. These functions can be used as supplements to the standard C language in the Xenix environment.

Accelerating RAM tests. The minimization of circuit structures has led to exponential growth in memory capacity, which, in turn, has placed a greater burden on testing. For example, according to recent estimates, testing costs as a percent of total chip costs have risen from just over 20 percent for 16-Mbit DRAMs to approximately 40 percent for 64-Mbit DRAMs and are still rising.[7] Two main reasons are the linear (or even more complex) dependence of sequential test algorithms on the number of cells per chip and the growing complexity of the faults viewed.[8]

Development of test algorithms has produced systematic tests with linear complexity based on logic fault models, but fault localization is possible only in some cases. With architectural modifications, several memory cells in a RAM can be tested in parallel, reducing the test length by the constant factor of the cells tested in parallel. However, this method succeeds only if testing is restricted to fault detection, and this entails a somewhat considerable circuit expenditure.

Proposed method. In an effort to curb increasing test costs, the contents of all memory cells are interpreted as a pattern or picture.[9,10] If all memory cells viewed in parallel store the same information, for example, a value of 0 (1), they are defined to represent a homogeneous pattern. But if there is at least one faulty cell storing a dual value of 1 (0) in this pattern, it is defined as nonhomogeneous (see Figure 9). This transforms the test problem into a pattern-recognition problem that can be treated in parallel with flag-oriented structures and their associative search algorithms.

A homogeneous pattern is associated with a fault-free memory if all cells viewed in parallel are written with the

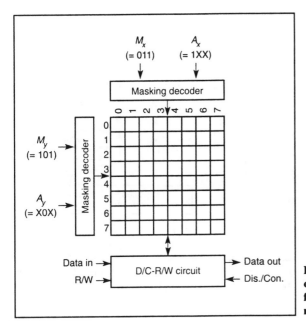

Figure 10. Example of an extended functional-memory model.

Faults	Fault detection		Fault localization	
	Known	New	Known	New
AF+TF+SAF	$21 \cdot 10^6$	115	–	$638 \ldots 1.4 \cdot 10^9$
CF+AF+TF+SAF	$42 \cdot 10^6$	358	$3.5 \cdot 10^{12}$	$2464 \ldots 9.6 \cdot 10^9$
ANPSF+SAF+TF	$187 \cdot 10^6$	1037	$680 \cdot 10^6$	$2312 \ldots 544 \cdot 10^6$

Figure 11. Number of test patterns needed for fault detection and fault localization.

same value, whereas an inhomogeneous pattern is associated with a faulty memory. The memory is defined as a flag-oriented AM and the faulty cells as flags in the memory. When all the fault-free cells in a homogeneous pattern are 0, a flag in the memory is shown as 1, and vice versa. The associative searches are conducted by superposing the patterns of the actual value (read from the memory) on the set value (derived from the test pattern generator). Differences between the two patterns can now be detected easily. A disjunction of all memory cells read in parallel detects a faulty memory storing at least one value of 1 instead of a set value of 0. A conjunction allows at least one faulty value of 0 to be detected in a set value of 1 for all memory cells read in parallel.[10]

Parallel access is achieved by a two-dimensional, fully associative (masked) decoding of memory cell addresses in x- and y-directions.[6] For example, if a 3-bit x-mask word (M_x = 011) and a corresponding x-address word (A_x = 1XX) are used, the cells with the x-addresses 100, 101, 110 and 111 are accessed. With M_y = 101 and A_y = X0X, the y-addresses generated by a y-decoder are 000, 001, 100, and 101. Figure 10 shows the 16 accessed cells of an extended 64-bit memory for these address inputs.

Disjunctions and conjunctions of all data read in parallel require only a few gates to change the read/write circuit into a disjunction/conjunction-read/write circuit (D/C-R/W circuit). The memory cells, themselves, do not need to be modified.

The successive-approximation method (binary search, Figure 4) localizes a faulty memory cell by successively halving the number of cells read in parallel until only one faulty cell is read. The address of the

faulty cell is made available by the test pattern generator. Multiple faulty cells are localized using a method based on backtracking.

Based on these circuit modifications, test algorithms for the new test method have been developed for both fault detection and fault localization. They take into account faults in the memory cell array, the modified address decoder, and the modified read/write circuit. Fault detection is based on parallel access and manipulation of selected parts of a RAM. Cells in these parts are addressed in parallel. Faults in the read/write circuit can be mapped onto faults in the memory cells. Thus, no extra tests for faults in the read/write circuit are necessary, but the sources of these faults are not distinguishable in some cases. Faults before and in the address decoder can be mapped onto faults behind the address decoder and partly onto the memory cell array. Thus, they can be detected with tests of the memory cell array if they fulfill some read/write requirements.[8] Tests of the masking feature of the address decoder are conducted at the same time as tests for common-address-decoder faults.

Applying this concept accelerates all the usual test methods, such as tests for stuck-at faults (SAFs), transition faults (TFs), neighborhood-pattern-sensitive faults (NPSFs), coupling faults (CFs), and address-decoder faults (AFs).

Test acceleration. The new fault-detection algorithms reduce complexity by one or two orders of complexity. For stuck-at faults, transition faults and neighborhood-pattern-sensitive faults, the known test algorithms have linear complexities of $O(N)$, (where N = number of memory cells). These complexities are reduced to a constant complexity of $O(1)$ for the newly developed test algorithms with flag-oriented structures. The complexity of test algorithms for coupling faults and address-decoder faults is reduced from $O(N)$ to $O(\log N)$.

The test complexity for fault localization can be reduced for SAFs, TFs, and NPSFs from $O(N)$ to $O(k \log N)$, (where k = number of faulty cells in a memory); and for CFs and AFs from $O(N^2)$ to $O(k (\log N)^2)$. Whereas test complexity depends on the number of memory cells, the test length depends on the number of faulty cells. Since the number of faulty cells is lower than the total number of cells, the test length for fault localization can be further reduced.

Figure 11 illustrates achievable test acceleration by showing the number of test patterns needed for three test algorithms. In each case, a memory capacity of 4 M-bits is assumed. In the entries for fault localization, a range of test pattern numbers are specified. In the last column, the first number represents the number of test patterns needed when only a single faulty cell is present in the memory cell array. The second number represents the maximum number of test patterns needed if a large number of cells (more than 50 percent) are faulty.[10]

Neural network with a flag-oriented system. The flag-oriented concepts can be applied to various types of very fast artificial neural networks (ANNs), such as feed-forward ANNs and optimization ANNs. An artificial neural network is a computing system consisting of a set of equal, highly interconnected processing elements (PEs) used for associations.[11,12] (See the first sidebar.) A feed-forward ANN based on flag-oriented architecture is called a flag-oriented artificial neural network (FANN).

Two operational phases of an ANN are the learning phase and the association (search) phase. In the learning phase, the weights connecting the PEs are adjusted when iterative input patterns are applied to the ANN and modifications are made to the weights to produce a dedicated output. In the association phase, which uses the adjusted weights as fixed values, output patterns are derived from input patterns and from information stored during the learning phase. Because one learning phase is often followed by a number of associations, accelerating the ANN association process greatly impacts performance.

A FANN can accelerate the association phase by combining output/input association with parallel processing. Its modular structure makes it highly suitable for cascading into large FANNs. In general, the weight values of an ANN that has passed the learning phase are preprocessed into association information for the FANN. The flag transformation allows parallel use of this association information.

Each neuron in the association phase calculates a product sum of input values and their corresponding weights and applies a threshold function (such as a sigmoid function) to this product sum.(See Figure 12.) In a feed-forward FANN, the sum is calculated for all possible inputs and stored in the neu-

ron during a preprocessing step. In the association phase, an input value selects a product sum for further processing. After a flag transformation, a threshold function can be applied very quickly. In particular, a hard limiter function ($y = 1$ for $x > x_0$, $y = 0$ otherwise) is very suitable here. For a cascadable FANN, only the sums of a subset of all inputs (for example, eight) are calculated and stored in partial sums, and this minimizes hardware expenditures. Thus, a module to process partial sums can be cascaded for the required number of inputs. (See Figure 12.)

Theoretically obtained FANN performances have been verified by the development and simulation of two different FANNs. Net A has been developed with four input neurons, three hidden neurons, and two output neurons. Net B contains 512 input neurons, 512 hidden neurons, and 50 output neurons. In both cases, logic gates with 5 ns delay, a maximum fan-in of 4, and a maximum fan-out of 10 have been used. The time required for one association in net A (net B) is 440 ns (13 µs), which leads to a performance of about 2 giga-connections per second (30 GC/s). The sum of the required capacities of the partial-sum memories is 27 Kbytes (13.5 Mbytes). The difference in association times is due to the technical requirements (differences in sequential stages of each circuit).

Calculations show that FANN outputs differ from the conventional ANN outputs for about 7 percent of all possible inputs. This is due to some flag-oriented operations and the use of a hard limiter threshold function instead of a sigmoid function. However, if needed, this loss in capacity can be offset by appropriate adaptation of learning parameters, number of neurons, and learning patterns.

V arious functions and capabilities of the proposed flag-oriented architectures have been demonstrated by three examples: an ac-

celerator as a coprocessor for design rule checks of IC layouts, circuit structures for the acceleration of tests in integrated RAMs, and a model of a fast, modular artificial neural network. All of these applications share one characteristic: the number of data-word bits is not too long. Because of the complexity of flag vectors for long data words, these words are separated into smaller subwords before the flag transformation that gets the flag vector is executed. In this case, the fully parallel concept is reduced to a parallel-sequential concept. The level of parallelism depends principally on the number of separated subflag vectors, since the flags of the operands can be processed simultaneously, regardless of their settings. However, the achievable accelerations still compare to those obtained through conventional solutions.

Our current research includes transferring the flag-oriented test method for RAMs to other computer components. The basic approach at the IC level involves flag-oriented cross-checks in electronic components (like PLAs and gate or cell arrays). Another research project considers new flag-oriented conceptions for ANN designs with various applications.

Other institutions are also considering flag-oriented applications. Several applications may use flag-oriented concepts to construct alternative architectures capable of achieving very good performance characteristics. ∎

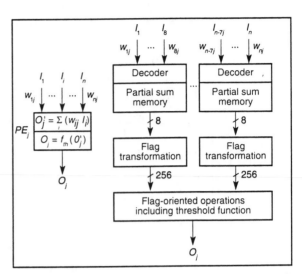

Figure 12. Hidden neuron and realization in a feed-forward flag-oriented artificial neural network.

Acknowledgments

Several parts of this research work were sponsored by the German Ministry of R&D within the EIS project and the German National Science Foundation. Partial support of this work came from the Commission of European Communities in the Eurochip project. I gratefully acknowledge all the colleagues, students and members of my group at the University of Hagen for their invaluable discussions and support for this research. I especially appreciate everyone who has assisted in technical questions and during the development of this article, including Olav Borgmeier, Cordula and Christian Elm, Gunther Hipper, Michael Klein, Michael Koch, and Inge Schlemper.

References

1. D. Tavangarian, *Flag-Oriented Associative Memory and Processors*, (in German), Springer, Berlin, 1990, pp. 40-45.

2. D. Tavangarian and M. Beck, "Astra: An Associative RISC-Architecture," *Euromicro Congress '90*, North-Holland, Amsterdam, 1990, pp. 41-48.

3. C. Mead and L. Conway, *Introduction to VLSI Systems*, Addison-Wesley, Reading, Mass., 1980.

4. M. Strugala et al., "An Associative Processor as a Design Rule Check Accelerator," *Proc. CompEuro '87*, IEEE CS Press, Los Alamitos, Calif., Order No. FJ773, 1987, pp. 426-431.

5. B. Soucek and M. Soucek, *Neural and Massively Parallel Computers*, John Wiley & Sons, N.Y., 1988, pp. 357-368.

6. M. Schulz et al., "An Associative Coprocessor Architecture with Unix Operating System for the Acceleration of CAD Tools," *MIMI Congress*, North-Holland, Amsterdam, 1988, pp. 102-106.

7. T. Yamada et al., "COM (Cost Oriented Memory) Testing, *Proc. Test Conf., 1992 Int'l (ITC '92)*, Baltimore, 1992, p. 259.

8. A. van de Goor, *Testing Semiconductor Memories, Theory and Praxis*, Wiley & Sons, Chichester, West Sussex, England, 1991, pp. 24-64.

9. D. Tavangarian, "Design of Easily Testable RAMs Using Flag-Oriented Circuit Structures," *Proc. IEEE Hawaii Int'l Conf. on System Science*, IEEE CS Press, Los Alamitos, Calif., Order No. HICSS91, 1991.

10. C. Elm and D. Tavangarian, "Associative Search Based Test Algorithms Acceleration in FAST-RAMs," *IEEE Workshop on Memory Testing*, IEEE CS Press, Los Alamitos, Calif., 1993, pp. 38-43.

11. T. Kohonen, *Self-Organization and Associative Memory*, Springer, Berlin, 1984.

12. J.J. Hopfield and D.W. Tank, "'Neural' Computation of Decisions in Optimization Problems," *Biological Cybernetics*, No. 52, Springer, Berlin, 1985, pp. 141-152.

Readers can contact the author at the University of Hagen, Dept. of Computer Science, PO Box 940, D-58084, Hagen, Germany, e-mail d.tavangarian@fernuni-hagen.de.

ASTRA
A Multilayer Parallel Processing System

I.P. Jalowiecki and C. Anyanwu
Brunel University
Uxbridge, UK
{Ian.Jalowiecki, Chijioke.Anyanwu}@brunel.ac.uk

Abstract

The application of parallel processing systems to the solution of computationally intensive problems is a well-established strategy in many application areas. However, in a number of these fields, such as natural language processing and computer vision, the operations and data structures vary widely in size and complexity so that no single processor will be ideally suited to the entire range of problems. Heterogeneous computing environments, composed of diverse high-performance computers connected by high-speed networks, have been proposed for these applications. An alternative approach would be to incorporate the principle of heterogeneity in a machine whose topology is compatible with the range of problems. ASTRA, a multilayer parallel processing system developed for image analysis applications, is an example of such a system and its architecture and performance are discussed here.

1   Introduction

Any computer application exhibits a number of defining characteristics for architectural features desirable in a computer that is to be applied to solve the problem. For many tasks, these architectural requirements are satisfied by appropriately configured general-purpose computers, but for others performance can be significantly improved by employing architecturally compatible systems. Thus, for instance, vector processors have long been used for operations on large vectors and procedures requiring identical operations on arrays of data benefit from arrays of processors able to perform these operations in parallel on all data elements. However, a number of applications comprise operations with varying and conflicting architectural requirements that cannot all be met by a homogeneous computing environment composed of one or more processors of the same type.

This is typically the case in computer vision where operations may be classified into low-, intermediate-,

and high-level categories with data size decreasing, and data and operation complexity increasing, from low to high levels. Computer vision applications, particularly real-time vision, lend themselves to a layered structure in that the image is pipelined from the lower levels to the higher levels, each level performing, concurrently where necessary, some amount of processing until a solution is extracted at the highest level.

Pyramid structures [uhr86] provide such a hierarchical arrangement but traditional pyramids [abu88,can87,tan87,mer86] have tended to be homogeneous machines capable only of SIMD (single instruction, multiple data) or limited multi-SIMD operation and, therefore, somewhat inadequate for general computer vision. Various other multilayer heterogeneous machines such as the image understanding architecture [wee89], Warwick pyramid machine [nud92], and the Simon Fraser University hybrid pyramid [ens92] have followed. These all have an array of simple processors at the lowest level and two or more layers of successively fewer, but more powerful, processors at higher levels. The heterogeneous vision architecture [dul89] possesses similar characteristics but incorporates a digital signal processor module that may be configured to lie at the bottom of the hierarchy.

The ASTRA is a multilayer heterogeneous system based on a linear array of associative processors. This fundamental processor that makes up the array, the ASP, is introduced next, then subsequent sections describe the ASTRA system, its architecture, operation, and performance.

2   The associative string processor

An associative string processor (ASP) substring is made up of a number of associative processing elements (APEs), each connected to an inter-APE communication network (IAPECN), three buses (activity, data, and control) and a match reply line as shown in Figure 1.

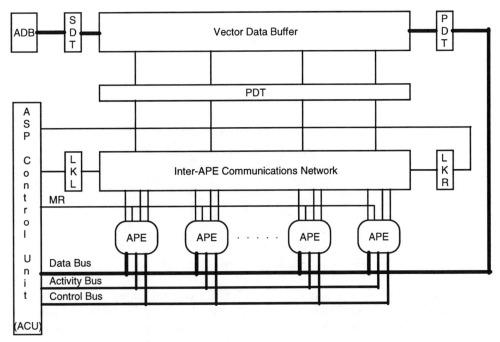

Figure 1. The associative string processor (ASP).

Each APE is a fully bit-parallel, word-parallel associative processor with 70 bits of memory, a parallel comparator, a number of single-bit registers, and a bit-serial full adder [lea88].

Data is transferred between APEs: either bit-parallel over the 32-bit data bus, providing single source to single or multiple destination transfers, or bit-serial through the IAPECN, allowing for multiple APE communication.

Data transfer between substring and external devices is either

1. through an ASP data buffer (ADB), a vector data buffer (VDB) and associated primary data transfer (PDT) and secondary data transfer (SDT) channels, or

2. through the ASP control unit (ACU).

In the former method, data entering or leaving the ASP passes through the ADB memory, then undergoes a secondary data transfer into the VDB, a bit-parallel operation that can be overlapped with APE processing.

The data loaded into the VDB may be transferred to or from the APEs through a bit-serial primary data transfer that performs a very high bandwidth (APE-parallel) transfer via the IAPECN or through a bit-parallel PDT that performs a lower speed (essentially APE-sequential) transfer over the data bus.

The ACU controls APE instruction execution using the activity and control buses and is capable of

sourcing or sinking data arguments via the data bus. The results of conditional associative operations can be monitored via the match reply line. The ACU is also able to inject signals into, and sense signals from, the IAPECN through the link-left (LKL) and link-right (LKR) ports.

ASP implementation has followed advances in device technology, and the current production device, the VASP/E1, is a full-custom VLSI ASP chip implemented in 2-micron CMOS and containing 64 APEs. A more recent VLSI processor version, known as VASP/E3, in 0.7-micron CMOS and containing 256 APEs, is due for production in the near future, following successful completion of a 128-APE prototype (VASP/E2). Samples of multichip module (MCM) versions have been fabricated for investigations into the feasibility of these implementations.

3   ASTRA structure

ASTRA (ASP system testbed for research and applications) was developed primarily as a physics image processing workstation for off-line processing of 6-Mbyte (2K × 3K × 8 bits) images produced by the CERN (European Organisation for Nuclear Research) NA-35 streamer chamber experiment [a02] and represents the first full implementation of an ASP-based system.

ASTRA's design, as illustrated in Figure 2, incorporates, in addition to a 16K-PE ASP substring, a three-level control and processing hierarchy.

133

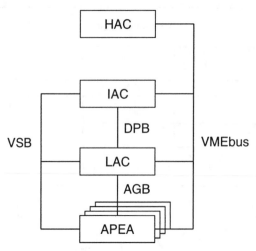

Figure 2. Basic structure of ASTRA.

The lowest (ASP) level is made up of a number of APE array (APEA) cards, each of which contains an ASP substring and associated ADB. The ASP control unit (see Figure 1), which is directly responsible for issuing instructions to the APEA forms the next higher level and is known in the system as the low-level ASP controller (LAC). Following this is the intermediate-level ASP controller (IAC) that, among other tasks, performs scalar processing and is responsible for data transfer to and from the APEA, while at the highest level is the high-level ASP controller (HAC) that is responsible for overall system control and provides the user interface to the machine.

The four subsystems are linked through a system of four buses. A VMEbus connects together all the modules while a VME subsystem bus (VSB) provides a further link between IAC, LAC, and APEA. The LAC is further connected to the IAC through an 8-bit DMA (direct memory access) peripheral bus (DPB) that is used for data exchange between the two units, and to the APEA card by the ASP global bus (AGB), a high-speed synchronous bus that provides the path for direct exchange of control information and data between the two components.

The basic design of the system allows for the upgrading of the various subsystems without requiring a complete system redesign. This is particularly true of the APEA where increasing the number of APEs involves little more than replacing the original boards with more powerful boards and making minimal modifications to affected software.

3.1 APE array card

The APEA card (Figure 3) comprises two main functional blocks, one containing the ADB and the other the APE array.

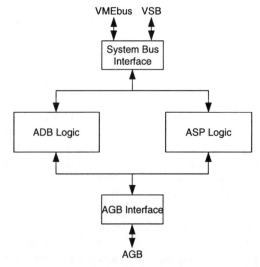

Figure 3. Block diagram of the APE array card.

The system, as currently implemented, contains no VDB, therefore a primary data transfer operation involves word-sequential, bit-parallel transfers of data from the ADB into the APEs over the data bus. The ASPA (ASP array) is organized as four channels of eight VASP/E1 chips providing a total of 2,048 APEs per card.

The ADB contains two planes (implemented by two 4,096 × 32-bit dual-port memories) providing output and input channels for the ASPA. These planes are further partitioned into two pages, A and B, which are managed by the ADB logic to ensure that host (SDT) and ASP (PDT) accesses are made to alternate pages. This arrangement not only allows for simultaneous host and ASP access to the ADB but provides a two-page buffer for data transfers, as well as limited local storage for temporary results that cannot be accommodated in the ASPA during processing.

3.2   Low-level ASP controller

The low-level ASP controller (LAC), whose essential features are illustrated in Figure 4, is a purpose-designed module for controlling one or more APEA boards. It contains all the logic necessary to generate APEA instructions and provide data for ASP routines. It comprises the following major blocks:

3.2.1   Microprogram unit (MPU)

The MPU is directly responsible for control of the LAC and thus the APEA. It consists of an AMD 29331 sequencer, a 64K × 152-bit microinstruction buffer (MIB) that holds the card's operating system and LAC/ASP application code (the microprograms that represent low-level executable procedures), and support logic. The sequencer causes sequences of microinstructions, for LAC and APEA components, to be output from the MIB starting at a location specified by a procedure call queue (LPCQ). The sequencer supports conventional sequential, loop, and conditional microinstructions sequences (conditional on the state of the board and the APEA). The low-level programming model defines that ASP instructions are grouped into low-level ASP procedures (LAPs).

3.2.2   Low-level ASP procedure call queue (LPCQ)

The LPCQ provides the means by which the IAC can call procedures to run on the LAC. It contains a 256 × 99-bit FIFO, assembly registers, a LPCQ process identifier (lpcqPid) counter, and control and status registers. The size of the LPCQ assembly register fields allows for a limited number of parameters to be passed to the LAC in addition to the entry point of the low-level ASP procedure (LAP) in the MIB. The MPU increments the host-visible lpcqPid counter by one on completion of each LAP, presenting the IAC with a means of monitoring call execution on the LAC, which is executing as a concurrent thread. The lpcqPid therefore provides a means of low- to intermediate-level synchronization.

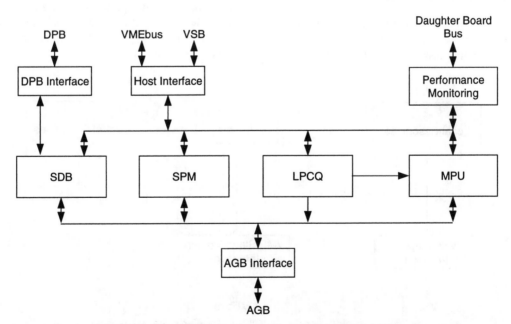

Figure 4. Block diagram of the low-level ASP controller.

135

3.2.3 Scratch pad memory (SPM)

The SPM, which is completely host accessible and may be accessed by LAC resources through a data register, serves primarily as a temporary data store for LAC procedures although it is possible to use it, with increased overheads, for passing program-scalar data.

3.2.4 Scalar data buffer (SDB)

The SDB provides a path for scalar data exchange between both the LAC and APEA, and the IAC. It comprises two $1K \times 32$-bit FIFOs:

- the rdfifo, used to pass data from the ASP via the LAC, and

- the swfifo, used to pass data to the ASP via the LAC

The SDB provides flags that signal the state of the FIFOs to the MPU and the DPB Interface, so that these devices do not attempt to read from an empty FIFO or write to a full one.

3.2.5 Performance monitoring

The performance monitoring block provides a number of counters, incremented by the MIB during program execution, that allow the host to monitor various LAC functions and also connects, via the daughterboard bus, to a histogram card capable of counting the number of occurrences of specified MIB instructions.

3.3 Intermediate-level ASP controller

The IAC consists of two commercially available cards: a CPU card and a VME interconnect card (VIC), the latter being necessary because the IAC is connected to

the HAC, located in a different crate, by a VMVbus (a bus that provides a means for connecting two or more VMEbus or VSB crates together).

The IAC CPU card is a 68020-based VME board whose components may be grouped into a set of local resources, accessible only from on-board devices, and a set of global resources, accessible from both on- and off-board devices, as shown in Figure 5.

Included in the local resources are a floating-point unit and a four-channel DMA controller that is able to support transfers between memory and input/output (I/O) devices, the latter by means of an 8-bit peripheral bus (a subset of which forms the DPB in ASTRA). The device is configured in ASTRA to provide dedicated channels for data transfers to the SDB swfifo and ADB write plane and from the SDB rdfifo and ADB read plane.

The global resources include 512 Kbytes of RAM that forms part of the ASTRA shared memory and is used for data (program and control) exchange between the HAC and IAC, as well as the next layer of local memory for the LAC/APEA cards associated with the IAC. Finally, four communications FIFOs provide hardware support for message passing between the HAC and IAC.

The four FIFOs are divided into two channels, control and service, each of which provides one FIFO for HAC to IAC message passing and another for message passing in the opposite direction. The control channel is the physical link of the cross-level message (XLM) passing system, used to pass control information between the HAC and IAC parts of a program while the service channel is used during downloading and debugging IAC programs as well as for application program I/O. The FIFOs do not themselves act as I/O channels; rather, they allow the passing of pointers to the data item(s) in shared memory.

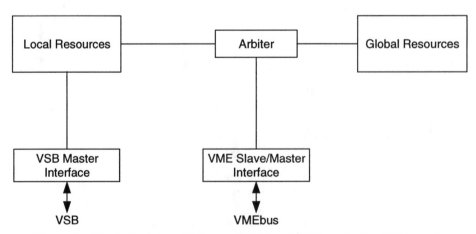

Figure 5. Block diagram of intermediate-level ASP controller CPU card.

Access to global resources is through an arbiter that defaults to providing a connection to the local master. The structure allows the CPU to proceed with local processing, or even access a VSB resource, while an external master is engaged in a transaction with a global resource.

3.4 High-level ASP controller

The HAC initially consisted of a Sun 3 workstation with a VIC card for VMVbus interfacing. The Sun 3 provided additional shared memory in the form of its framestore but provided no other special-purpose hardware to specifically support ASTRA.

Three VMEbus-accessible 1-bit mailbox registers on the HAC VIC were used by the IAC to inform the HAC whenever it had written a message for it in one of the communications FIFOs (see Figure 6). These remain the synchronizing events in the cross-level message passing scheme.

4 System operation

The operation of ASTRA is managed by a three-part distributed operating system, ASTRA OS, and its programs are written in modules individually targeted at the HAC, IAC, or LAC.

This section will look at how ASTRA programs are structured, describe the ASTRA OS, and then examine how the operating system supports program execution.

4.1 Application programming

ASTRA application programs are written in modules, each targeted at a specific controller level. High-level application modules (HAMs) and intermediate-level application modules (IAMs) are written in Modula-2 while LAMs are written in the LAM (low-level ASP module) programming language (LPL), which is based on (and is a subset of) Modula-2.

HAMs are responsible for the user interface, disk I/O, while the IAMs are typically targeting at scalar processing and data flow management (that is, support for data movement, such as secondary data transfers). Code at the intermediate level may not undertake file I/O or make host OS system calls. The LAMs, naturally, provide the low-level instruction to the ASP processor.

As in normal Modula-2 programming, all levels may have implementation and definition modules. The implementation modules each contain a number of procedures (high-, intermediate-, and low-level procedures: HAPs, IAPs, and LAPs) but only a HAM implementation module may contain a main module. An ASTRA program is thus written to run on the high-level controller and calls can then be made to IAPs as necessary using a mechanism known as a cross-level procedure call (XPC). The operation of this process is such that the HAC may proceed with normal program execution while the called procedure executes on the IAC. IAPs may in a similar manner make calls to LAPs so that it is possible for all three levels to work concurrently on different aspects of a task, a feature that is beneficial in a hierarchical parallel computer. Procedures can be cross-level exported from LAMs to IAMs and from IAMs to HAMs, as may types and constants.

The example HAM module shown in Text Box 1 illustrates the cross-level import of an intermediate-level procedure. Such cross-level import/export is applicable to all procedures, constants, types, and so forth.

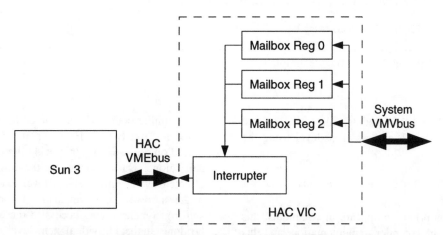

Figure 6. Basic structure of the high-level ASP controller.

```
(*$$ HighLevel ASP *) MODULE  HighLevelExample;

FROM IntermediateLevelExample IMPORT
IntermediateApplicationProcedure;

BEGIN (* main program *)
IntermediateApplicationProcedure
END HighLevelExample.
```

1 High-level ASP module (HAM) code template

```
(*$$ IntermediateLevel ASP *) MODULE IntermediateLevelExample;

(*$$ EXPORT CROSS LEVEL IntermediateApplicationProcedure; *)

FROM LowLevelExample IMPORT LowLevelApplicationProcedure;

PROCEDURE IntermediateApplicationProcedure;
BEGIN
   LowLevelApplicationProcedure
END IntermediateApplicationProcedure;

END IntermediateLevelExample.
```

2 Intermediate-level ASP module (IAM) code template

```
(*$$ LowLevel ASP *) MODULE LowLevelExample;

(*$$ EXPORT CROSS LEVEL LowLevelApplicationProcedure *)

PROCEDURE LowLevelApplicationProcedure
BEGIN
   (* low level code here *)
END LowLevelApplicationProcedure;

END LowLevelExample.
```

3 Low-level ASP module (LAM) code template

An intermediate-level module, illustrated by the example in Text Box 2, exports cross-level using the primitive:

```
(*$$ EXPORT CROSS LEVEL ExportedItem *)
```

Although this primitive appears in comments, this is an artifact of the compiler implementation, and this must be read as an essential code statement.

A similar code style is adopted for the LAM, illustrated in Text Box 3. However, more restrictions are placed on cross-export, this being limited to procedure calls alone. Data transfers to the low level must be effected by the intermediate level loading the appropriate hardware data channels (for example, ADB, swfifo). Synchronizing access to these resources may be done at the individual item level (swfifo), or per data block (ADB) using hardware semaphores.

Standard Modula-2 instructions and types may be used in HAMs and IAMs and application libraries that define new types and provide a number of ASTRA-specific procedures are provided at both levels. A LAM library is also provided to minimize coding effort.

4.2 Compilation

Compilation is performed by the ASP compiler (aspc), which actually presents a front end to three compilers, OEM compilers for HAMs and IAMs, and a custom compiler for LAMs. The aspc determines the level of each module and calls the appropriate compiler to compile the code.

4.3 ASTRA OS

The operation of ASTRA is managed by three operating systems—the HAC-OS, the IAC-OS, and the LAC-OS—that collectively make up the ASTRA operating system.

The HAC-OS is integrated within the Sun's operating system and is thus similar to any other Unix-like OS. The HAC-OS, however, provides a number of additional commands as well as HAM system calls and libraries that enable it to initialize ASTRA and interface with the IAC.

The IAC-OS is a simple single-thread operating system made up of a standard supplied part and a suite of library procedures that is automatically downloaded by the HAC whenever an application program containing calls to IAPs is executed at that level. When the application program executable code has been loaded into the IAC, control passes to the IAC-OS kernel, a library procedure that runs in a continuous loop polling the communications FIFO (control channel) for messages from the HAC and reacting appropriately when one is found.

The LAC-OS is a simple operating system that controls the MPU's operation and provides various libraries for the LAMs. The operating system is downloaded, along with application code, into the MIB by the HAC when a program containing calls to LAPs is run on the system and, when enabled, enters a continuous loop, polling the LPCQ for IAC calls.

4.3.1 Cross-level message passing

The ASTRA OS supports a cross-level message-passing (XLM) scheme for communication between the HAC and IAC parts of an application program. An XLM is a 32-bit word (4 bits message identifier and 28 bits message data) passed between the HAC and IAC over the control channel (see also Figure 6).

A HAC-to-IAC XLM will typically be sent when a HAM calls an IAP and will cause the IAC-OS kernel

to start up the required procedure. On completion of the IAP, the IAC-OS notifies the HAC by sending it an XLM (and also writing to a HAC mailbox, thus generating an interrupt on the HAC). Other XLMs may be used to deallocate shared memory.

On both levels, an attempt to write to a full control channel results in the calling process being blocked until the message can be sent.

4.3.2 Cross-level procedure calls

As mentioned earlier, cross-level procedure calls (XPCs) provide the means by which programs running on one level call on procedures to run on a lower level in a process that is transparent to the applications programmer.

During compilation of a program containing cross-exported procedures, the aspc performs a number of operations specifically in support of these procedures and generates, among others, a number of client stubs and one or two cross-level entry point (XLEP) tables. A client stub, essentially a representation of a cross-exported procedure at the importing level, is a piece of code that transmits the parameters and entry point for a procedure during an XPC and returns a process identifier (pid) for that call. The XLEP table (the HAC and IAC each have one) is built up during initialization of the ASP application program and contains the entry point (in the MIB for the IAC XLEP or IAC local memory for the HAC XLEP) for each cross-exported procedure.

When a cross-exported procedure is encountered during program execution, the corresponding client stub is called, which then consults the XLEP table before passing parameters and entry point to the target level using a mechanism that depends on the type of XPC.

HAC to IAC XPC. To perform an XPC, the HAC-OS first builds a pid for the call and allocates a block of shared memory, the size of which it computes based on the number of parameters being passed. It then writes into this block the remote IAP's entry point, the pid, the parameter size area, and finally the portion of the client stub's stack frame that holds the parameters. It then sends an "xpcCall" XLM, containing a pointer to this block, down the control channel, which is then detected by the IAC-OS kernel. Finally, the HAC-OS returns the pid to the caller. This pid may be used by the caller to effect synchronization on a given intermediate-level procedure that is running as a concurrent thread.

The IAC-OS kernel subsequently extracts the pointer, transfers the parameters to the IAC stack, then passes control to the IAP located at the specified entry point. Upon completion, control returns to the kernel that then writes an "xpcReturn" XLM, containing the same memory pointer, to the control channel. The "xpcReturn" may be analyzed by the HAC to detect completion of an intermediate procedure.

IAC to LAC XPC. Before proceeding to set up an XPC, the IAC-OS checks to ensure that the LPCQ is not full; if it is, the procedure will block until space becomes available. The client stub's parameters and LAP entry point are then written into the relevant LPCQ assembly registers and the LAC instructed to push them onto the LPCQ FIFO from where the LAC MPU can fetch the call when it is ready. Finally, a pid is built for the call and returned to the caller.

As is apparent from the preceding discussion, both forms of XPCs are nonblocking (ASTRA OS, however, provides—on the HAC and IAC—the system call Wait should a blocking action be required on these levels) so that program execution on the calling level may continue while the called procedure executes. It is, therefore, possible for all ASTRA levels to work concurrently on different aspects of a task, a feature desirable in a hierarchical parallel computer.

4.3.3 Data passing

Data passing between the HAC and IAC is carried out using shared memory that may be located in the HAC, IAC, or some VMEbus-accessible external memory.

Between the IAC and LAC, data passing is generally carried out by means of the SDB (usually for scalar data) or ADB (normally vector data). However, since various host-accessible resources exist that may

be referenced in LAPs, other possibilities for data passing between these levels exist.

5   ASTRA implementation

The full ASTRA system is currently implemented in two formats:

1. Comprising two VME crates, one containing the HAC and the other the IAC, LAC, and APEA cards, connected by a VMV bus. The second crate also contains a CCD camera interface and a 16-Mbyte VMEbus memory card. A standard Sun 3 monitor and keyboard are connected to the HAC crate and provide the user interface.

2. Comprising a single VME crate incorporating the HAC in the standard chassis by utilizing an OEM SPARC board. The VMV interconnect is rendered unnecessary. All other system components remain the same.

The LAC and APEA are implemented using hyperextended triple Eurocard form factor (9U) multilayer printed circuit boards, to VXIbus specifications. Thus, in addition to the P1 and P2 connectors provided to VMEbus specifications, to connect the VMEbus and VSB, a P3 backplane is available that is used in the system for the AGB.

Figure 7 shows a photograph of the APEA card (designation 1102). The array of 32 VASP/E1 chips is clearly visible.

Figure 7. APE array card.

Figure 8 shows a photograph of the LAC card. It shares the hyperextended triple Eurocard form factor of the APEA card. In contrast, the IAC CPU card, the VIC, and the SPARC HAC card (if present) are standard 6U VME extended Eurocard format. These occupy complete slots in the card cage, utilizing the P1 and P2 connectors on the backplane.

6 Image processing on an ASP

Early concept validation of the ASP was primarily carried out using image and vision-related processing tasks. While not limited to such applications, they have proved a fertile environment for the development of ideas and the validation of concepts.

On the ASP, images or image-derived or related objects are distributed across the APE array, utilizing either a single APE or a cluster of APEs per item.

Pixel-based image processing generally utilizes a single APE per pixel, with processing carried out on an image patch, sized to match the delivered APE array. For more complex image analysis tasks, image-derived objects are typically represented as a collection of features (for example, line segments and their intersections at corners), which will normally be assigned to a cluster of APEs. Hence, an image object, comprising multiple features, is similarly distributed over a number of APEs or clusters of APEs, connected via the inter-APE communications network (IAPECN), enabling each feature to be processed in parallel.

In a typical implementation of a computer vision scenario using the ASP, an unknown scene is first digitized and loaded into the ASP as an array of pixels, one per APE, with image lines concatenated to suit the string format of the basic processor.

The APE array may be thought of as a patch processor in this mode, repeatedly processing rectangular patches of the image, transferred into the APE array from the appropriate designated memory area by the IAC, via the ADB using the secondary data transfer protocol and hence into the array during the primary data transfer. Results may be held in-situ, or swapped out to local memory, or transferred out to IAC memory for subsequent IAC processing, data redistribution, or reloading into the ASP array.

In the image processing scenario, pixel processing identifies candidate features (for example, edge points may identified in parallel; marked and straight line segments are fitted to edge points using a least-squares estimate). Features may be grouped (such as intersecting lines grouped into corner features), which may then be matched in parallel with corresponding corner features in a model database using templatelike verification steps based on the ASP's associative processing nature.

Figure 8. Low-level ASP controller card.

141

6.1 ASP performance

As an aid to system and program development, an ASP simulator was implemented before ASTRA came on line. In vision-related benchmark tests, the ASP concept had consistently been one of the best performers [kri91]. In the Abingdon Cross benchmark [pre89], for example, on the basis of two figures of merit, the ASP placed first and second, respectively, among machines that were tested. Furthermore, the ASP was also a top performer on the DARPA II benchmark, an integrated vision problem that is more representative of real-world computer vision tasks [wee91a].

7 ASTRA performance

The ASTRA development has been the first opportunity to integrate an ASP processor into a realistic hierarchical systems environment and thereby to develop an understanding of the systems issues when trying to achieve the full performance potential of the ASP.

Since the ASTRA machine has become available, effort has continued to be focused on applications in the area of image-related processing. The approach has been to demonstrate a variety of applications. In addition to a wide range of general-purpose arithmetic, logical and relational application libraries, specification demonstration applications include:

- Abingdon Cross
- Fingerprint classification
- Discrete cosine transform
- Motion vector estimation
- DARPA II benchmarks

The Abingdon Cross benchmark was one of the first such tasks to be coded for ASTRA and provided a means for demonstrating correct system operation once the entire machine had been assembled. We shall use it here as an example of the problems and pitfalls relating to the first-generation ASTRA architecture.

The code is a series of image-to-image transforms, comprising image smoothing through the application of several iterations of a local window operator, followed by the iterative application of a series of binary masks to compute the image skeleton.

This algorithm has a high I/O content compared to the processing cycle. It became an ideal vehicle to assess the ASTRA I/O performance. An illustration of the activity of the ASTRA system's three layers, when executing a single patch process cycle for the Abingdon Cross application, is shown in the thread diagram below (Figure 9).

The speedup, relative to a minimally configured machine (with a single APEA board), for systems with up to 8 APEA boards (that is, 2K to 16K APEs) is shown in Figure 10 (thick, solid line), and is seen to be clearly sublinear. Referring to Figure 9, this can be attributed to the increasing secondary data transfer (SDT) time as the array size increases, while the primary data transfer (PDT) and processing time remains relatively invariant.

Although minor system tuning allows the SDT time to be more effectively overlapped with the processing and PDT operations, the undesirable SDT time (*overhead I/O* and *essential I/O*; see below) will become unbalanced for operations that do not have significant parallel processing content. Tuning the system to meet the application requirements and achieve a better balance between processing and overlapped

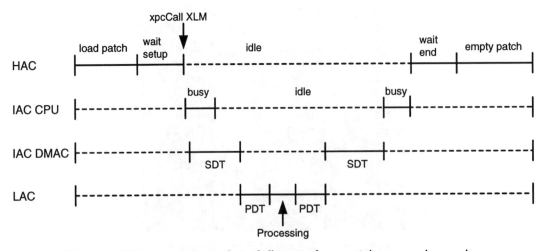

Figure 9. Timing sequence thread diagram for a patch processing cycle.

secondary I/O can be done by adjusting the number and effectiveness of the primary data transfer channels, and the size of the array. However, the corresponding optimization of secondary I/O (especially the minimization of overhead I/O) remains an essential priority for next-generation systems. Since the main identified source of overhead I/O is the swapping of image patches into intermediate level storage for data redistribution, then this presents opportunities for enhancement by minimizing such transfers by augmenting the low-level memory and memory module sharing.

In general, the results shown in Figure 10 were not totally unexpected considering that the percentage of total benchmark execution time spent on processing by the LAC/APEA (L_{exec} is an indication of the proportion of parallel code) is approximately 14 percent for the single APEA system—a figure that reduces dramatically as the performance (size) of the array is increased. This further degrades the potential to achieve balance between secondary I/O and processing, and hence to achieve the optimum overlap of these tasks. Figures 11 and 12 indicate the breakdown of activity for the three-layer hierarchical system, for:

- a single LAC/APEA system, and
- a single LAC with 8 APEA cards.

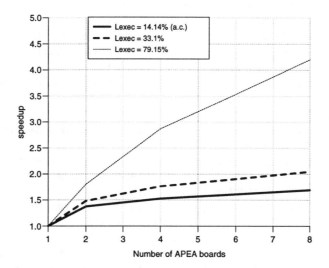

Figure 10. ASTRA system performance with varying parallel processing loads.

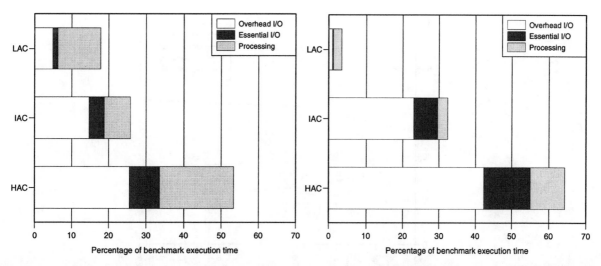

Figures 11 and 12. Processing and I/O characteristics of minimum (2K) and fully configured (16K) ASTRA configurations.

143

Clearly, the key parallel processing component of the system is heavily underutilized in this processing example. A key factor to note is the high percentage of so-called overhead I/O, which constitutes image swapping back to shared memory for the purpose of redistributing data in the array. This is in contrast to essential I/O, which constitutes original and final image transfers to and from the framestore.

Also of note is the significant HAC load. This is also illustrated by the utilization of key system components, shown in Figure 13, and indicates that the HAC is the most-used resource in this application, although none of the resources are being used to their fullest.

Although minor system tuning may allow much of the HAC activity to take place in parallel with intermediate and low-level tasks, the load on the HAC must be brought into balance with the other layers, primarily by off-loading data movement tasks onto the IAC or dedicated data movement Controllers.

As expected, the absolute LAC processing time per patch process cycle remains constant regardless of the number of APEA boards, although the number of patch I/O cycles decreases. This means that the LAC utilization (this is the proportion of time spent by the LAC/APEA levels on processing IAC calls) falls, while bus (this refers to VMEbus; the VSB was not used in this application) and HAC utilization rises, with increasing number of array boards.

7.1 Performance scalability

Considering the effect of applications with increased low-level content, from tenfold to one hundredfold

greater than that of the Abingdon Cross (factors consistent with the level of complexity inherent in other representative vision-related tasks), L_{exec} values of 33.1 percent and 79.15 percent, respectively, were obtained experimentally for multiple APEA board systems. The resulting performance is shown, with the Abingdon Cross results, in Figure 10, while Figures 14 and 15 show the resulting resource utilization for the two cases.

As is evident from the performance characteristics, the scalability of the ASTRA system approaches linearity as L_{exec} increases, as is to be expected from a well-designed parallel processing system. LAC utilization rises accordingly, and bus and HAC utilization falls.

However, such scalable characteristics can be achieved only for the case where the overhead I/O and essential I/O remains relatively low. In practice, this is unlikely to be the case for overhead I/O, and therefore enhancements to the low-level local memory and memory sharing will be necessary.

8   Conclusions

The ASTRA system is a first-generation ASP-based machine and has provided a vehicle for investigating the integration of the ASP processor into a hierarchical computing environment. A complete system has been implemented and its performance on vision-related tasks studied.

The hierarchical structure of the ASTRA processor has proved to be an attractive environment for our experiments, allowing real and conceptual modular systems to be rapidly assembled or modeled for these vision-related tasks.

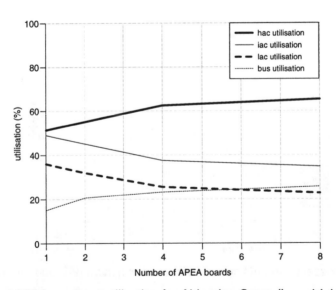

Figure 13. ASTRA resource utilization for Abingdon Cross (L_{exec}=14.14 percent).

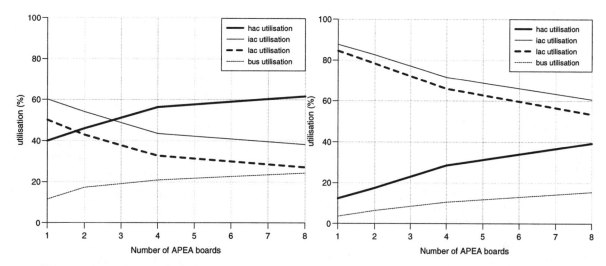

Figures 14 and 15. ASTRA resource utilization for L_{exec}=33.1 percent and L_{exec}=79.15 percent.

For the Abingdon Cross benchmark, results indicate that, at substantially below 20 percent utilization, the low-level parallel processing array is underutilized, an undesirable situation particularly as it is potentially the most expensive component in the system.

This is partly because the application, as implemented, is disproportionately I/O-limited and does not require significant low-level processing, thereby minimizing the opportunity to load-balance with the associated I/O and other related high and intermediate activity.

Nevertheless, significant observations may be made, pointing the way toward more appropriately optimized system solutions. Chief among these are:

1. Tuning the system to meet the application requirements and achieve a better balance between overlapped secondary I/O, which can be done at a coarse level by adjusting the number and effectiveness of the primary data transfer channels, and the size of the array. This presupposes a suitable modular structure, which must exploit VLSI or multichip module (MCM) technology more effectively than the first-generation ASTRA system.

2. Minor tuning will allow the intermediate-level operations (especially SDT handling) to be carried out more effectively in parallel with low-level tasks.

3. The further minimization of secondary I/O (especially the minimization of overhead I/O) remains an essential priority for next-generation systems. Since the main identified source of overhead I/O is the swapping of image patches into shared memory for data redistribution, then enhancements to the low-level shared memory and memory module sharing will be significant.

4. Although minor system tuning may allow much of the high-level ASP controller activity to take place in parallel with intermediate and low-level tasks, the load on the HAC must be brought into balance with the other layers, primarily by off-loading data movement tasks onto the IAC or, preferably, dedicated data movement controllers.

Investigations into the impact of these changes indicate that performance improvements for this class of application of up to sixteenfold may be expected over the initial ASTRA configurations at relatively modest additional cost.

A growing number of application programs, some now available in libraries, continue to be written for ASTRA. The machine may be said to have validated the ASP concept, although it does not necessarily deliver the full potential of the processor. With various improvements, arising both from exploitation of technological advances, and from software and architectural enhancements based on broader evaluation studies (including those presented here), the next generation of ASP-based machines are expected to provide further improvement in performance and increased capability.

Acknowledgments

The authors acknowledge the staff contributions of Aspex Microsystems, in particular J. Lancaster and Anargyros Krikelis.

145

References

[uhr86] L. Uhr, "Parallel Hierarchical Software/Hardware Pyramid Architectures," in *Pyramid Systems for Computer Vision*, V. Cantoni and S. Levialdi, eds., Springer-Verlag, Berlin, 1986, pp. 1–20.

[abu88] Z. Abumedhi, "The GAM II Pyramid," *Proc. 2nd Symp. The Frontiers of Massively Parallel Computation*, IEEE CS Press, Los Alamitos, Calif., 1988, pp. 443–448.

[can87] V. Cantoni and S. Levialdi, "PAPIA: A Case History," in *Parallel Computer Vision*, L. Uhr, ed., Academic Press, New York, N.Y., 1987, pp. 3–13.

[tan87] S.L. Tanimoto, T.J. Ligocki, and R. Ling, "A Prototype Pyramid Machine for Hierarchical Cellular Logic," in *Parallel Computer Vision*, L. Uhr, ed., Academic Press, New York, N.Y., 1987, pp. 43–83.

[mer86] A. Merigot et al., "A Pyramidal System for Image Processing," in *Pyramid Systems for Computer Vision*, V. Cantoni and S. Levialdi, eds., Springer-Verlag, Berlin, 1986, pp. 109–124.

[wee89] C.C. Weems et al., "The Image Understanding Architecture," *Int'l Conf. Computer Vision* Vol. 2, No. 3, 1989, pp. 251–282.

[nud92] G. Nudd et al., "Hierarchical Multiple-SIMD Architecture for Image Analysis," *Machine Vision and Applications*, Vol. 5, No. 2, Spring 1992, pp. 85–103.

[ens92] J Ens et al., "A Hybrid Pyramidal Vision Machine for Real Time Object Recognition," in *Transputer Research and Applications*, A. Veronis and Y. Paker, eds., Vol. 5, IOS Press, Amsterdam, 1992, pp. 90–103.

[dul89] A.W.G. Duller et al., "An Associative Processor Array for Image Processing," *Image and Vision Computing*, Vol. 7, No. 2, 1989, pp. 151–158.

[lea88] R.M. Lea, "The ASP: A Cost-Effective Parallel Microcomputer," *IEEE Micro*, Vol. 8, No. 5, Oct. 1988, pp. 10–29.

[a02] "System Specification for the Trax-1 Physics Image Workstation," Aspex Microsystems Ltd., Brunel University, Uxbridge, UK, Issue 1, Mar. 1989.

[kri91] A. Krikelis, "Computer Vision Applications with the Associative String Processor," *J. Parallel and Distributed Computing*, Vol. 13, No. 2, 1991, pp. 170–184.

[pre89] K. Preston Jr., "The Abingdon Cross—Benchmark Survey," *Computer*, Vol. 22, No. 7, July 1989, pp. 9–18.

[wee91a] C. Weems, E. Riseman, and A Hanson, "The DARPA Image Understanding Benchmark for Parallel Computers," *J. Parallel and Distributed Computing*, Vol. 11, No. 1, Jan. 1991, pp. 1–24.

An Optical Associative Parallel Processor for High-Speed Database Processing

Theoretical Concepts and Experimental Results

Ahmed Louri and James A. Hatch Jr., University of Arizona

This architecture exploits optics to perform word-parallel and bit-parallel relative magnitude searches. As the present system evolves, it will substantially exceed current database processing speeds.

With its many communications advantages, optics continues to receive increasing attention as a way to provide the storage, speed, and massive interconnections needed in future computing systems. We have devised a novel architecture that exploits the advantages of optics for performing word-parallel and bit-parallel equivalence and relative magnitude searches of database tables in constant time. Moreover, our experimental optoelectronic implementation of the associative processing portion of this architecture has achieved encouraging preliminary results.

Associative processing is advantageous for performing symbolic computing tasks for several reasons, as explained in the Guest Editor's Introduction to this issue. However, there have been many obstacles to commercially successful associative processors. Some of these obstacles include the higher cost and poorer storage density of associative memory compared with conventional memory, the lack of efficient broadcasting and funneling, and the lack of parallel access to data.

A potential solution to many of these shortcomings is to integrate such alternate technologies as optics with conventional electronics. First, the use of free-space and fiber-based optical interconnects can alleviate the wiring complexity of associative processing systems[1] by migrating the implementation of wiring into the third dimension, that is, free space. This decreases the chip area used for routing signals between chips and boards and increases the area available for gates. Moreover, the large bandwidth of optics will provide higher interconnection densities with lower power dissipation.[1] The ease with which optical signals can be expanded (which allows for signal broadcasting) and combined (which allows for signal funneling) can also be exploited to solve the interconnect design problem and alleviate network latency problems. Furthermore, since photons do not readily interact with each other, optical signals are less prone to crosstalk, thus potentially allowing higher interconnect densities than with electronic signals.

Reprinted from *Computer*, Vol. 27, No. 11, Nov. 1994, pp. 65–72.

147

The OCAPPRP architecture

Our experimental architecture, called the optical content-addressable parallel processor for relational database processing (OCAPPRP), supports parallel relational database processing by fully exploiting the parallelism of optics. First we address the searching capacity of the architecture and the problem of execution-time differences for equivalence and relative magnitude ($<, >, \leq, \geq$) searches.

The OCAPPRP compares a search string (comparand) with each entry of a database table in parallel. The search of a single comparand through an entire table is referred to as a one-dimensional search in this article. A two-dimensional search increases the system throughput by a factor of n by searching multiple comparands through the *same* database table in parallel, where n is the number of comparands. Regardless of the search dimensionality, relational database processing can be decomposed into two types of searches, equivalence and relative magnitude. Equivalence searches merge tables (relations) on the basis of the presence of identical entries in either of two relations. Relative magnitude searches retrieve data from a single relation, as in, say, the search for all articles published after 1990.

In a high-speed database system, it is important to perform both of these operations in a bit-parallel manner. By bit-parallel we mean that an operation's execution time is independent of the number of bits per word (the word size). To do this, all bits must factor directly into the output. As the word size increases, the wiring complexity of the operation can restrict its electronic implementation.

Optical equivalence searches are easily implemented as bit-parallel operations. Since a mismatch in *any* bit position of two words indicates their inequality, a simple funneling (beam-merging) operation determines the result. However, optical relative magnitude searches are not as simple. For two words that are not equal, the relative magnitude is not immediately

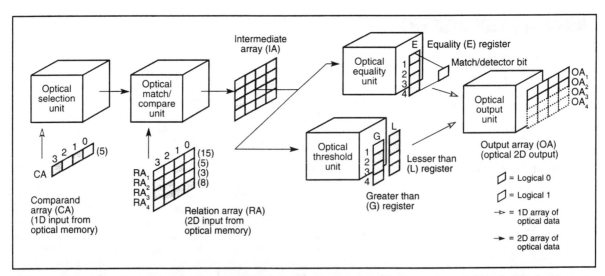

Figure 1. Structural organization of the OCAPPRP. The number 5 in the comparand array (lower left) is simultaneously compared with each of the four rows of the RA. The *E*, *G*, and *L* registers store the search results. As an example, we use the search for all RA entries that are greater in value than the number 5. As reported in the *G* register, rows RA₁ and RA₄ satisfy the search and are transferred to the output array by the output unit.

148

known because only the first bit position to result in a mismatch, beginning with the most significant bit, is relevant.

The problem of isolating this bit position has limited relative magnitude searches to bit-serial implementations, requiring up to m iterations, where m is the word size. We exploit the interconnection capabilities of optics in developing a new word-parallel and bit-parallel technique for isolating this bit position, which allows constant-time operation, that is, $O(1)$ operations; hence, our approach is a single-step algorithm.

OCAPPRP description. Figure 1 shows a preliminary organizational structure for the OCAPPRP. The architecture consists of a selection unit, a match/compare unit (MCU), an equality unit, a threshold unit, an output unit (OU), and a control unit (not shown). The selection unit is intended to enable word and bit slices of a search string (comparand) called the comparand array. The CA and other optical inputs can be supplied by either optical disks or page-oriented holographic memory (POHM). In a POHM, many pages of data (approximately $1,000 \times 1,000$ bits/page for an area of 1 square millimeter)^2 are stored as multiple subholograms on a single substrate. They offer storage densities of more than a terabyte, with transfer rates exceeding 100 Gbytes/s.

The MCU searches the comparands through a data array known as the relation array, which stores the database table (relation) being searched. The RA consists of k tuples of word size m. The search of a comparand through the RA begins with the bit-by-bit search for mismatches within input word-pairs (see Figure 2).

At this point, the search is not complete. The intermediate results, represented by the right-hand side of Equation 1 in Figure 2 and called the intermediate array, merely indicate the match/mismatch of the corresponding words on a bit-by-bit level. A zero in the IA indicates the equality of the corresponding CA and RA bits, while a one indicates their inequality. To determine the equality/inequality and relative magnitude on the word level, we need to further process the IA in the equality and threshold units, respectively.

The equality unit determines matches among input word-pairs by scanning the IA for mismatches. This is accomplished by ORing the bits along the IA rows, since bit-by-bit mismatches are represented by ones. Thus, a single mismatch

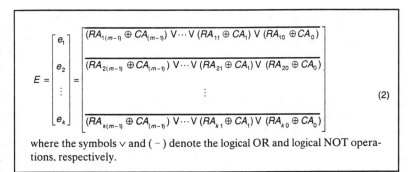

The search of a comparand through the RA is accomplished by bitwise XORing the CA with each RA entry, where a comparand $CA = ca_{(m-1)} \ldots ca_1 ca_0$ and

$$[ca_{(m-1)} \ldots ca_1 ca_0] \oplus \begin{bmatrix} ra_{1(m-1)} & \cdots & ra_{11} & ra_{10} \\ ra_{2(m-1)} & \cdots & ra_{21} & ra_{20} \\ \vdots & & \vdots & \vdots \\ ra_{k(m-1)} & \cdots & ra_{k1} & ra_{k0} \end{bmatrix} = \begin{bmatrix} ra_{1(m-1)} \oplus ca_{(m-1)} & \cdots & ra_{11} \oplus ca_1 & ra_{10} \oplus ca_0 \\ ra_{2(m-1)} \oplus ca_{(m-1)} & \cdots & ra_{21} \oplus ca_1 & ra_{20} \oplus ca_0 \\ \vdots & & \vdots & \vdots \\ ra_{k(m-1)} \oplus ca_{(m-1)} & \cdots & ra_{k1} \oplus ca_1 & ra_{k0} \oplus ca_0 \end{bmatrix}$$

(1)

where the symbol $\oplus$ represents the XOR operation.

Figure 2. Searching a comparand through the relation array.

$$E = \begin{bmatrix} e_1 \\ e_2 \\ \vdots \\ e_k \end{bmatrix} = \begin{bmatrix} \overline{(RA_{1(m-1)} \oplus CA_{(m-1)}) \vee \cdots \vee (RA_{11} \oplus CA_1) \vee (RA_{10} \oplus CA_0)} \\ \overline{(RA_{2(m-1)} \oplus CA_{(m-1)}) \vee \cdots \vee (RA_{21} \oplus CA_1) \vee (RA_{20} \oplus CA_0)} \\ \vdots \\ \overline{(RA_{k(m-1)} \oplus CA_{(m-1)}) \vee \cdots \vee (RA_{k1} \oplus CA_1) \vee (RA_{k0} \oplus CA_0)} \end{bmatrix}$$

(2)

where the symbols $\vee$ and $(\,^-\,)$ denote the logical OR and logical NOT operations, respectively.

Figure 3. The formation of the equality register E.

Figure 4. The equality unit determines the match/mismatch of input word-pairs from the comparand array and the relation array by detect-

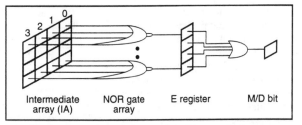

Intermediate array (IA) NOR gate array E register M/D bit

ing at least one mismatched bit position in a given row of the intermediate array.

in any bit position indicates the mismatch of the two words. The result is then inverted, a step needed only if the "positive logic" representation is desired. These operations are demonstrated by the expression shown in Figure 3. This expression forms a $k \times 1$ column vector known as the equality register. The E register is represented as $E = \{e_1 e_2 \ldots e_k\}^T$, where a 1 in element e_i represents the equality of the CA with the ith RA entry, RA_i. The equality unit is demonstrated schematically in Figure 4. We see that element $e_2 = 1$ indicates that row RA_2

matches the CA. This register is then vertically ORed to form the match/detector (M/D) bit. The condition $M/D = 1$ indicates that at least one entry of the RA matches the CA. The value of this bit gives a quick indication of whether there are any matches.

The threshold unit (where the term threshold is synonymous with relative magnitude) processes a second copy of the IA for the word-parallel and bit-parallel relative magnitude search of the CA and the RA in a single step. Recall that the rows of the IA indicate the bit-by-bit

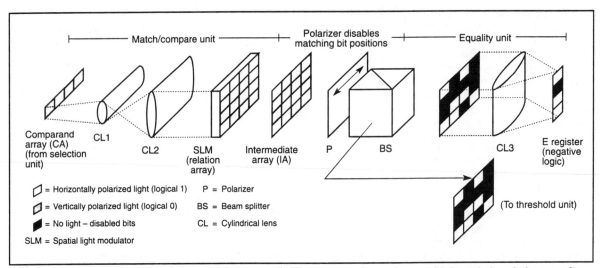

Figure 5. Optical implementation of the match/compare unit. The comparand array is searched through the relation array by expanding (broadcasting) and imaging it onto the relation array, which is stored in the spatial light modulator. The two are bitwise XORed, and the result is used for bit-parallel equivalence and relative magnitude searches.

equality/inequality of the CA and the RA. To compute the relative magnitude of a row on the word level, we must isolate the first bit position of the IA, beginning with the most significant bit, to result in an inequality. The relative magnitude of this bit position determines the relative magnitude of the entire word. Since our algorithm isolates this bit position in a single step, it eliminates the need for iterating through bit slices. We provide a complete, detailed description of this operation and its optical implementation elsewhere.[3,4]

The threshold unit creates two sets of registers called the greater-than (G) register, where $G = \{g_1\ g_2\ ...\ g_k\}^r$, and the lesser-than ($L$) register, where $L = \{l_1\ l_2\ ...\ l_k\}^r$. The condition $g_i = 1$ indicates that RA_i is greater than the CA, and $l_i = 1$ indicates that RA_i is less than the CA. In Figure 1, elements g_1 and g_4 are set, which indicates that rows RA_1 and RA_4 are greater than the CA. Likewise, the value of l_3 indicates that row RA_3 is less than the CA. The OU then transfers selected tuples of the RA to the optical output array (OA). It dynamically maps nonconsecutive input tuples onto consecutive rows of the OA. In Figure 1, rows RA_1 and RA_4 are mapped onto rows OA_1 and OA_2, respectively.

OCAPPRP implementation. Below, we describe in detail the optical implementation of the match/compare and equality units of the OCAPPRP. Because the

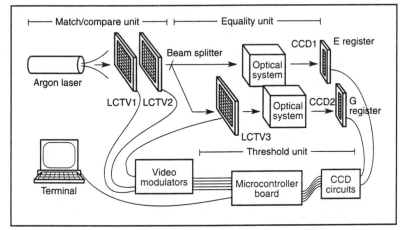

Figure 6. Organization of the experimental system. The video modulators create video signals that write data patterns on the liquid crystal televisions. The output of a search is collected by linear CCD arrays, which are then read by circuits that sample, threshold, and digitize the CCD output. New inputs are created on the basis of the results, and another pass through the system begins.

threshold unit is so complex, we refer readers interested in its optical implementation to our previously published work.[3]

Figure 5 illustrates the detailed optical implementation of the MCU. To search the CA through each entry of the RA in parallel, the CA from the selection unit is first scaled in the vertical dimension by cylindrical lenses CL1 and CL2. It is then imaged onto the spatial light modulator (SLM), which holds the RA. An SLM is a real-time reconfigurable device capable

of modifying the amplitude (or intensity), phase, or polarization of an optical wavefront as a function of position across the wavefront.[5] The SLM for the bitwise XOR operation is a liquid crystal device that rotates the polarization of the incident light by 90 degrees in the bit positions that contain logical 1's. Thus, the polarization of the incident light is rotated by 0 or 180 degrees for the 00 and 11 cases, respectively, yielding vertically polarized light, and 90 degrees for the 01 and 10

Figure 7. Laboratory arrangement of the initial experimental version of the OCAPPRP. To the right of the optical table is the microcontroller-based control unit for the system. The lens system performs the optical matching. An IBM PC displays the search results.

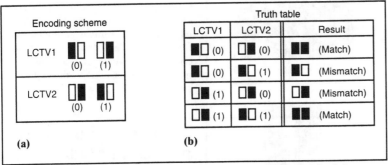

Figure 8. (a) The spatial encoding scheme for representing binary-valued data as optical signals. (b) The truth table for using the encoding scheme to perform matching in our experimental system.

cases, yielding horizontally polarized light in the IA. Lohmann provides more information on polarization-encoded logic.[6] The polarizer "disables" the equalities in the IA by blocking the vertically polarized light. Without light, these bit positions can no longer factor into computations. The resulting data plane is then duplicated by the beam splitter, with one copy going to the equality unit and the other going to the threshold unit. In the equality unit, cylindrical lens CL3 sums all the bits along each RA row to search for mismatches. A negative logic representation of the E register is formed at the focal point of CL3. An optional SLM

may be inserted to generate the positive logic form shown in Figure 4.

An experimental OCAPPRP. First we describe the laboratory setup, including the devices and components used, then we present some of the results we obtained experimentally.

System setup. We are building, at the University of Arizona, Department of Electrical and Computer Engineering, an experimental OCAPPRP. Our initial version uses a bit-serial relative magnitude algorithm instead of the single-step relative magnitude algorithm discussed pre-

viously. Future versions will include this advanced single-step feature. Figure 6 illustrates the system's organization, which allows for everything to be controlled by a microcontroller board. Active-matrix liquid crystal television screens (LCTVs) are used as spatial light modulators, since they are cost-effective devices for demonstration purposes. Video generation ICs interfaced to the microcontroller generate the write patterns for the LCTVs. After a set of patterns is written to the LCTVs and the search is performed, linear CCD (charge-coupled device) arrays detect the output. Auxiliary circuits sample and threshold the CCD output to form a digital data stream, which is then read by the microcontroller. New data patterns are generated and the search continues.

The optical portion of the demonstration system in Figure 6 operates as follows: The digital patterns are impressed on a beam from an argon laser by LCTV1 and LCTV2. The two LCTVs store the CA and RA, respectively. The CA is copied electronically into each row of LCTV1, and the beam expansion optics (cylindrical lenses CL1 and CL2 in Figure 5) are eliminated to reduce complexity and cost. The search array is simultaneously written into LCTV2. The superposition of the two data planes performs the optical matching, whose result is split into two paths. One path is focused to a vertical line, forming the E register, which is then imaged onto a linear CCD array. Here, electronic circuits sample, threshold, and digitize the data for the microcontroller. This path represents the equality unit. To implement the bit-serial relative magnitude algorithm, the other path uses LCTV3 to disable bit slices during iterations. This forms the G register and the L register (not shown). Figure 7 shows the laboratory setup.

Experimental results. We performed a sample search with our experimental laboratory system. For this initial version, we are using a different encoding scheme because commercial LCTVs have a limited contrast ratio (the amount of light transmitted in the "on" state compared with that transmitted in the "off" state). Other liquid crystal devices, such as ferroelectric liquid crystals (FLC),[5] exhibit the necessary contrast but are more expensive. In this scheme, both a binary value and its complement are used to encode a single bit, as in the expression $x\bar{y} + \bar{x}y$. The encoding scheme and truth table are illustrated in Figures 8a and 8b.

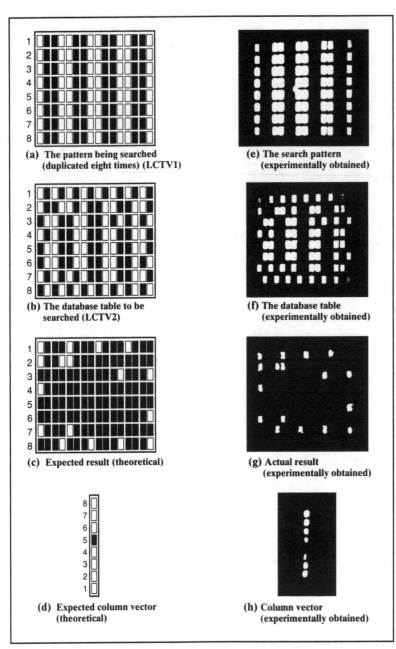

(a) The pattern being searched
(duplicated eight times) (LCTV1)

(b) The database table to be
searched (LCTV2)

(c) Expected result (theoretical)

(d) Expected column vector
(theoretical)

(e) The search pattern
(experimentally obtained)

(f) The database table
(experimentally obtained)

(g) Actual result
(experimentally obtained)

(h) Column vector
(experimentally obtained)

Figure 9. The theoretical and experimentally obtained system results.

A black square represents an opaque LCTV pixel, whereas a white square represents a transparent one. The patterns on the two LCTVs are superimposed to perform the logical operation. In the result, if both pixels corresponding to a single bit are dark, then the two inputs are logically equivalent. The presence of light in either pixel of a bit indicates a mismatch between the two inputs.

To map these patterns onto the devices, the LCTV display areas are partitioned into eight rows with 16 squares per row. Thus, we are demonstrating an 8×8 data array. Note that this is a proof-of-principle system. Our word size, m, is limited solely by the contrast ratio of the devices and not by the architecture. As mentioned above, other currently available devices have the necessary contrast ratio to support a minimum word size of 128 and even 256 bits.

Figure 9 illustrates the various data planes for the search. Figure 9a is a

graphical representation of the pattern written to LCTV1, while Figure 9b is the pattern written to LCTV2. The data plane in Figure 9c illustrates the theoretical results of the optical matching operation. We see that row 5 is completely dark because of the perfect match between the search string and the fifth array entry. A single pixel is illuminated in rows 4 and 6, indicating a single mismatch between these array entries and the search string. Moreover, the column vector in Figure 9d illustrates the theoretical output of the horizontal summing of Figure 9c, which is vertically inverted by the optical system. Again, row 5 is dark relative to the others.

To demonstrate the system's operation, we include photographs of the input patterns written to LCTV1 and LCTV2 (Figures 9e and 9f, respectively). In Figure 9g, we report the experimentally obtained results of the optical matching, which fulfill our expectations from Figure 9c. Furthermore, the photograph in Figure 9h illustrates the experimental generation of the output column vector. Overall, the results satisfy our expectations and successfully demonstrate the system's ability to perform optical parallel-string searches. The final step is to detect this optical result with a CCD array and report the results electronically to the microcontroller.

Theoretical performance analysis

The system's execution time (T_{ex}) can be expressed by

$$T_{ex} = T_{set} + T_{proc} + T_{trf} \qquad (3)$$

where T_{set} is the setup time, T_{proc} is the processing time of the optical system, and T_{trf} is the time needed to transfer the result to the host computer. Since T_{set} and T_{trf} can be overlapped with the processing time (assuming heavy pipelining), they need not be considered in this preliminary analysis. The term T_{proc} can be expanded as

$$T_{proc} \approx T_{page} + T_{prop} + 2T_{SLM} + T_{detect} \quad (4)$$

T_{proc} represents the equivalence search path, T_{page} is the time needed to read a page of data from holographic memory,

T_{prop} is the light propagation time between components, T_{SLM} is the SLM switching time, and T_{detect} represents the speed of the detector. The value of T_{prop} is negligible (on the order of picoseconds) and $T_{page} \approx 20$ nanoseconds, while $T_{detect} \approx 30$ ns and T_{SLM} is on the order of microseconds. Therefore, the dominant factor in Equation 4 becomes $2T_{SLM}$. Johnson et al.[7] note that currently available optically addressable ferroelectric liquid crystal arrays have been demonstrated in sizes of 128×128. Electrically addressable versions of FLC arrays have been demonstrated in sizes of $1,280 \times 1,120$ pixels. Although the switching time of the liquid crystal itself is approximately 2 microseconds, the time needed to charge the photoconductive layer currently limits the optical addressing time to about 3 milliseconds. However, with improved integration techniques, we believe this value can eventually be reduced to tens of microseconds, judging by the incredible (gigahertz) operating speeds of current discrete phototransistors.

The number of tuples that the system can match per second is found by dividing the SLM size by the execution time. We estimate that for $T_{ex} = 6$ ms ($2T_{SLM}$), an OCAPPRP built with this technology would be capable of matching 2×10^4 tuples/second in a 1D system and 3×10^6 tuples/s in a 2D system. Using a power analysis that relates the necessary optical power to the bit rate, we estimate that the optical power requirements for the 1D system operating at a BER (bit error rate) = 10^{-17} is approximately 50 milliwatts for equivalence searches. Expectations are that $1,028 \times 1,120$ optically addressed arrays will be operating at $T_{SLM} = 30$ μs.[7] For future 1D systems with $T_{ex} = 60$ μs, we can expect to match 1×10^7 tuples/s with an optical power requirement of approximately 1W. Using another technology, such as self-electro-optic-effect devices,[5] which have write times in the nanosecond range, we should be able to match approximately 1×10^{10} tuples/s. Since data transfer rates greater than 100 Gbytes/s are currently possible with page-oriented holographic memory,[2] an OCAPPRP will have no problem supporting these predicted processing rates. Such performance is possible because data is retrieved from memory in parallel as pages and is then processed as pages.

Note that the above execution-time analysis excludes the speedup realized

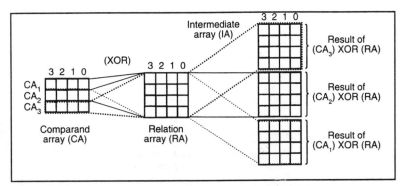

Figure 10. The 2D match/compare unit implements Equation 1 (Figure 2) for each entry of the comparand array. The results of these parallel operations appear in the intermediate array, which will later be processed by the equality and threshold units.

when selection is based on relative magnitude searches. The use of our new single-step algorithm, even for current word sizes of 64 bits, will provide even greater performance increases. Others are performing similar research in this area,[2] and our predicted performance is very close to their most recent estimates of 1×10^9 tuples/s.

Future work

Work on the OCAPPRP is ongoing. One of the most substantial improvements is the extension of the MCU to 2D. Although we have already completed this extension, we omitted it from this article so that the architecture described would match that of the experimental system. Nevertheless, we can briefly explain the main concepts.

We generalize the search of Equation 1 to 2D by representing the comparand array as CA_h, where $h = 1, 2, ..., n$ and $CA_h = ca_{h(m-1)} ... ca_{h1} ca_{h0}$. Fundamentally, 2D searches can be viewed as n 1D searches in parallel. To perform 2D searches, the MCU must be scaled from a 1D to a 2D implementation. The operation of a 2D MCU is described schematically in Figure 10, where the n intermediate results form the IA. Corresponding to each of the intermediate results, we will also have n E, G, and L registers (not shown), one for each comparand. Similar to the 2D notation for the CA, these column vectors are denoted as $E_h = \{e_{1h} e_{2h} ... e_{kh}\}^T$, $G_h = \{g_{1h} g_{2h} ... g_{kh}\}^T$, and $L_h = \{l_{1h} l_{2h} ... l_{kh}\}^T$. More details regarding the operation and optical implementation of a 2D MCU are available in the literature.[4]

We have targeted some additional

work for the experimental system. The first task is to replace the electronically connected paths with optics to obtain purely optical feedback. Other tasks will include the experimental demonstration of the 2D MCU and the single-step relative magnitude search algorithm. In short, future generations of the system should more closely meet our goal of producing a hybrid optoelectronic machine that exploits the domains of both electronics and optics.

As we have shown, the proposed architecture has the potential to process approximately 1×10^{10} tuples/s. Nevertheless, with available optical switching devices (SLMs) the proposed system clearly cannot compete with its electronic counterparts because the switching time of current optical device technology is slow. However, many improvements are being made in optical and optoelectronic device technologies. With advances in SLM technology, we can expect the proposed optical system to become a viable and cost-effective alternative for parallel and high-speed database processing. ∎

Acknowledgment

This research was supported by National Science Foundation Grant No. MIP 9113688.

References

1. F.B. McCormick, *Photonics in Switching*, Vol. 2, Ch. 4, Academic Press, Boston, 1993.

2. P.B. Berra et al., "Optical Database/Knowledge Base Machines," *Applied Optics*, Vol. 29, No. 2, Jan. 1990, pp. 195-205.

3. A. Louri and J.A. Hatch Jr., "Optical Implementation of a Single-Iteration Thresholding Algorithm with Applications to Parallel Database/Knowledge Base Processing," *Optics Letters*, Vol. 18, 1993, pp. 992-994.

4. A. Louri and J.A. Hatch Jr., "An Optical Content-Addressable Parallel Processor for High-Speed Database Processing," to be published in *Applied Optics*, 1994.

5. J.A. Neff, R.A. Athale, and S.H. Lee, "Two-Dimensional Spatial Light Modulators: A Tutorial," *Proc. IEEE*, Vol. 78, May 1990, pp. 826-854.

6. A.W. Lohmann, "Polarization and Optical Logic," *Applied Optics*, Vol. 25, Mar. 1986, pp. 1,594-1,597.

7. K.M. Johnson, D.J. McKnight, and I. Underwood, "Smart Spatial Light Modulator Using Liquid Crystals on Silicon," *IEEE J. Quantum Electronics*, Vol. 29, No. 2, 1993, pp. 699-714.

Readers can contact Louri at the University of Arizona, Dept. of Electrical and Computer Engineering, Tucson, AZ 85721. His e-mail address is louri@ece.arizona.edu.

Optical Associative Processing

Leo J. Irakliotis, George A. Betzos, and Pericles A. Mitkas

Optoelectronic Computing Systems Center and
the Department of Electrical Engineering
Colorado State University
Fort Collins, Colorado 80523
{mitkas, irakliot, betzos} @LANCE.ColoState.EDU
http://www.lance.colostate.edu/optical

Abstract

Optical and optoelectronic schemes for associative processing are presented and reviewed. We discuss both analog and digital associative processing techniques with an emphasis on nonnumerical processing applications such as image processing and relational database operations. A brief review of optical storage systems and other necessary optical components precedes the discussion of system implementation.

1   Introduction

It has been known since antiquity that the human brain stores and recalls information associatively. Associative information retrieval is a natural model for fast and parallel access to large data sets and can have a tremendous impact in terms of speed and efficiency in applications such as image processing, low-level machine vision, relational database operations, and text processing. In image processing we very often need to extract certain features from a scene. To do so, we need to determine whether these features are present in the image, which is clearly an associative process. A fundamental operation in relational database processing is selection. A fraction of records contained in a database are retrieved according to a specific selection criterion. Such a content-based search can be optimally executed in an associative manner. Since any relational operation can be decomposed into a series of selections and projections [ULL88], the importance of associative processing in relational databases is evident [SU88]. Finally, text processing often requires scanning many documents to locate occurrences of specific words or phrases and retrieve the corresponding documents. An associative processor for text processing can retrieve a document based on its content in a single step without actually scanning the text sequentially.

In addition to these well-documented applications, associative processing can be used with a number of emerging applications, such as interactive television, and offer better control over broadband entertainment and information services [NEG95]. As an example, consider the ability of a VCR set to record programs based on their content without the need for the user to program the VCR unit with the broadcast date, time, channel, and duration. Also, consider an interactive television set potentially capable of accessing programs based on their content and broadcasted by many stations, then joining them together and replaying them as a single program. These are examples of applications that can be greatly enhanced and made more user-friendly by employing associative processing.

Electronic associative memories and processors, due to their parallel search capabilities and fine granularity, are very well suited for information retrieval and low-level machine vision applications. However, because of the prohibitively expensive extra matching and processing logic, which results in hardware implementations with a limited number of cells, associative processors and memories have been restricted mainly to research prototypes. The best known commercially available associative processor, STARAN [BAT74], was 200 times more expensive per memory bit than contemporary random access memories [FOS76]. Recent advances in VLSI technology have enabled commercial production of CAM chips with up to 64 Kbits of memory capacity [MUS92]. However, with the exception of network routing, these CAM chips have not found their way into other applications.

Apart from the problem of low density, electronic associative processors and memories feature limited communication capabilities between cells. For example, architectures targeted for machine vision applications [WEE89, KRI91, HER92] have primarily a nearest-neighbor communication pattern between processing elements and have to resort to additional levels of hardware to achieve long-distance communication.

Optics has emerged recently as the technology of the future, because VLSI technology will soon reach its limits in terms of density and signal propagation speed, and because its two-dimensional nature limits the number of possible interconnections that can be reasonably implemented in hardware. Optics offers an alternative, attractive solution to the implementation of global interconnects [MID93] for various reasons. Optical interconnects are far less susceptible to cross-talk noise since light beams do not interact with each other, even when they cross each other. Free-space optical interconnects offer the flexibility of processing data electronically or otherwise on a 2D topology and use the third dimension for signal propagation. Because associative processors require a large number of interconnections with sometimes complex patterns, it seems that optical implementation may be an alternative solution to electronic approaches. We believe that it is a particularly viable alternative for image processing applications and relational database operations. In fact, the fundamental operation of an all-parallel content-addressable memory, that of broadcasting the search argument to the memory words, while it may become time-consuming and expensive in VLSI terms, as the memory becomes larger, it is a rather straightforward operation with optics.

In addition, optical secondary storage media, especially these of a 3D nature, have the potential of achieving high bit densities. Such media have the advantage that data can be retrieved in parallel, one whole page at a time, resulting in a significant increase in memory/processor bandwidth. The memory output can be transported through free space to an optical/optoelectronic associative processing system operating at the page level, rather than the word level, as is the case with electronic associative memories. Obviously, such a parallel interface can also alleviate the problem, common with electronic CAMs, of updating the contents of the associative memory array.

In summary, optical systems, although still at an early stage, can have a significant impact on associative processing because they combine: (1) the massive data capacities of 3D parallel optical memories, (2) increased memory bandwidth due to parallel memory access, (3) global interconnectivity through free space, (4) fine processing granularity, and (5) the ability to receive and process optical data with a high degree of parallelism. Furthermore, in the case of holographic memories, as we shall see later, the readout mechanism is inherently associative and can be used directly in various ways for associative processor implementation.

This article deals with two classes of optical associative processing: (1) image correlators and neural networks, and (2) relational database operations. Traditionally, image correlators have been realized using analog optical setups [VAN64, VAN92]. Recent advances in optoelectronic devices, however, allow the implementation of optical correlators using digital approaches as well. Optical implementation of neural networks has been also demonstrated using discrete digital components [PSA85]. On the other hand, optical implementation of relational database operations was proposed not long ago [BER89, BER90, MIT93] and systems have been designed and demonstrated only recently [MIT94, LOU94, SNY95]. Optical systems for relational database operations are digital.

We follow the analog/digital classification to describe optical associative processing in this article, but we believe that a new classification, which reflects a more fundamental difference between the two classes reviewed here, is in order. The main difference between images and relational data is that the former are unformatted data sets while the latter are strictly formatted. Therefore, associative processing could be classified as:

- Formatted data associative processing: for example, relational operations, and

- Unformatted data associative processing: for example, image processing, text retrieval.

From a systems perspective, relational operations are strictly boolean-based manipulations of data typically on a bitwise arrangement. At the same time image correlators and neural networks do not in general employ Boolean algebra. Also, relational operations, when performed optically, require straight pass optical interconnects. Image processing and neural networks employ more complex interconnect schemes.[1] The reader can see here that a number of alternative classification schemes exist and that more can be proposed.

We begin our discussion with a brief introduction of machinery, components, and devices used to implement optical associative processing systems. We then present a number of optical implementations for image correlators and neural networks, followed by a review of optical systems for relational operations. We conclude our review with a summary of our findings and some discussion on the future of optical associative memories.

---

[1] Although in the case of image correlators we cannot specifically define an interconnection pattern in terms of discrete light paths, in general each point at the output plane is affected by each point at the input plane. Therefore, a virtual global interconnection pattern does exist.

2   Supporting technologies

Optical implementation of associative processors requires a number of components and devices that may be unfamiliar to some readers. Such components and devices include optical storage systems, light modulation devices, bulk lenses and microlens arrays, and holograms, among others. Here we briefly review these enabling technologies.

2.1   Lenses, microlens arrays, and diffractive optics

Most readers are familiar with bulk lenses used in magnifying glasses, prescription glasses, and cameras. The purpose of a lens is to route light to a specific point or plane. Advances in the field of optoelectronic devices such as microlasers and 2D photodetector arrays with logic incorporated into them (see next section) dictated the need for the development of microlens arrays. These are integrated arrays of small lenses, each a few tens of micrometers in diameter. Their intended use is in optical interconnect systems where they ensure that light emitted from a specific microlaser device in a source array will reach a specific photodetector element in a receiver array without crosstalking to other photodetectors. In general, microlenses allow better control of light beams than bulk lenses, especially when we are dealing with arrays of discrete light sources.

Most of us deal with refractive optical elements in everyday life. Prescription glasses, camera lenses, copy machine lenses—all are refractive optical elements. As light propagates through a material with an index of refraction different from that of air, it bends and therefore is directed to the desired point. Another not-so-well-known class of optical elements is diffractive optics. An everyday example of diffractive optical elements is car headlights: On closer inspection you will see that the cover glass (or plastic) exhibits a specific surface pattern with numerous edges. Diffraction of light at these edges directs most of the light onto the road surface.

Diffractive optical elements (also known as binary optics when the surface relief is a binary pattern) exhibit a number of advantages over their refractive counterparts and in particular over refractive microlens arrays. Specifically, diffractive elements do not exhibit spherical aberrations. Also, diffractive microlens arrays are easier to fabricate and in most cases are less expensive than refractive microlenses. A diffractive optical element is typically a surface relief that can be fabricated with photolithography/etching techniques [SWA89].

2.2   Optoelectronic devices

In optical implementations of associative processors, and in optical systems in general, a number of optoelectronic devices such as laser sources, light modulators, and photodetectors are used to produce, control, and detect light. Light sources include arrays of microlasers or light-emitting diodes. Microlaser arrays of choice appear to be 2D arrays of vertical-cavity surface-emitting lasers (VCSELs) [JEW91]. Photodetector arrays include a large variety of devices such as p-i-n detectors, charged coupled device arrays (CCDs), phototransistors, and avalanche photodiodes [BHA94].

Light modulators typically change one or more properties of light across a surface or a spectral distribution. Among the most important modulators are the spatial light modulators (SLMs) that can be loaded electrically or optically with an image or a data page and that change the amplitude, phase, or polarization of transmitted or reflected light with respect to the spatial distribution of their contents, as shown in Figure 1 [NEF90]. Spatial light modulators are found in digital watches and clocks, which use liquid crystal displays, and on portable computers, which use similar display technology. SLMs can be used to compose images and data pages and provide the input to an optical processor.

Optoelectronic logic can be implemented in a variety of ways [GIB86, MCA91, MID93]. In our systems we make use of heterojunction phototransistor (HPT) arrays that can be integrated with VCSELs in order to form *smart pixels*. A smart pixel is an optoelectronic device that accepts optical inputs and produces an optical output, which is a function of the received inputs. Optoelectronic implementations of AND and XOR functions using HPT/VCSEL-based logic are shown in Figure 2. Depending on the value (high or low intensity) of the optical inputs A and B received by each phototransistor in the gates shown in Figure 2, the devices will be either enabled or remain inactive, thus causing current to flow (or not) through the VCSEL, which provides the optical ouput of the gate.

2.3   Optical storage systems

Optical storage technology is one of the most important and further advanced aspects of optical computing. In principle, the data density in an optical storage system is much higher than in an electronic or magnetic storage system. In addition, optical storage allows the use of all three geometric dimensions and a number of generalized coordinates to be used in order to create a multidimensional storage space.

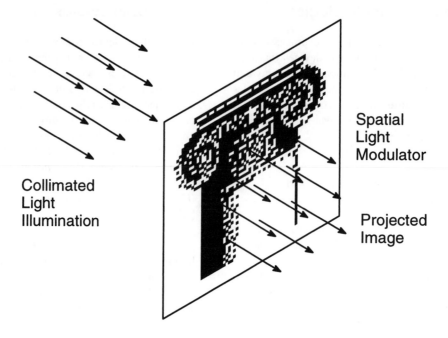

Figure 1. A transmissive 2D spatial light modulator with a binary image loaded.

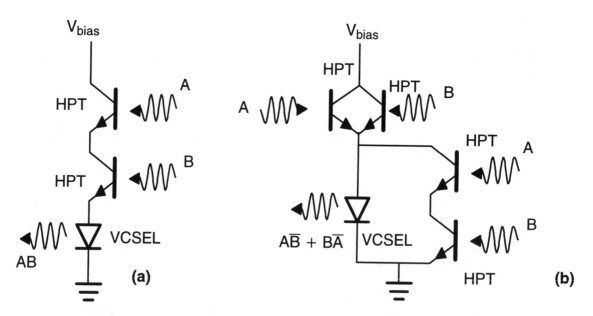

Figure 2. Optoelectronic implementation of (a) AND gate and (b) XOR gate using HPT/VCSEL-based smart pixels.

In the early 1960s the laser was invented. Its introduction gave scientists a powerful tool to probe matter at higher electromagnetic field intensities and narrower spectral lines. This led to the discovery of a number of nonlinear phenomena that today constitute the field of nonlinear optics. Lasers have a number of

advantages over conventional light sources. Further research into light-matter interaction using laser sources revealed several mechanisms that can be used to record information optically. These recording processes are reversible, and the development of rewritable/erasable media is possible. In addition to these all-optical storage mechanisms, in the 1980s optical disks were introduced. These are planar media that can be either erasable or nonerasable. In the case of nonerasable media, data are recorded permanently on the disk's surface. The recording mechanism does not have to be necessarily optical. Compact disks (CDs), for example, are molded with the data being engraved during this process. Write-once/read-many (WORM) disks, on the other hand, are recorded optically; a laser beam creates a permanent mark (optical damage) on the surface of the disk thus recording a bit value.

To better appreciate the potential of optical storage machinery for associative processing applications, we review a few promising systems for optical storage. These are the optical disks in general, the photorefractive volume holographic storage, and the two-photon 3D storage.

2.3.1 Optical disks

Optical disks were the next step in planar storage, following magnetic disks. Data retrieval from optical disks occurs by reflecting a laser beam off the surface of the recording medium, which is typically enveloped in hard plastic to prevent scratches and other damages. The incident beam is modulated by the surface properties at the specific spot, and the reflected beam carries that signal to a photodetector, which determines the bit value at that spot as illustrated in Figure 3.

Modulating properties at the surface of the disk include polarization rotation and light reflectance, among others [MAR90]. Polarization rotation is used on magneto-optical disks where different magnetization on the surface will cause different rotation of polarization through the Kerr effect. Reflectance modulation is the mechanism of choice for CDs and WORM

disks. Maximum storage density on a disk is approximately $\lambda^{-2}/2$ bits/cm^2, where λ is the wavelength used to record the data.

A monochromatic light beam can be focused on a spot of diameter λ, that is, the spot cannot be made smaller than the wavelength of beam without having diffraction-limited distortion come into effect. The area of such a spot is $\pi\lambda^{-2}/4$, and it can be approximated by λ^{-2}. If we leave a blank space between successive bits, interleaving this pattern as shown in Figure 4, then the data density is in the order of λ^{-2} as we mentioned already.

For red light emitted at approximately 600 nm the data density reaches approximately 1.2 Gbits/cm^2 or 33 Mbytes/cm^2. For magnetic disks, the areal data density varies between 40 Kbytes/cm^2 to 19 Mbytes/cm^2.

2.3.2 Photorefractive volume holographic storage

Photorefractive volume holographic storage (PVHS) uses electro-optic crystals such as lithium niobate (LiNbO3), which exhibit the photorefractive effect. This is the spatial modulation of the index of refraction in proportion to the intensity of incident light. If the incident light corresponds to the interference pattern between a reference and an object beam, a hologram is formed and it is stored in the crystal volume. If the object beam is the scattered light from a data page (such as a picture or tabulated data), then a holographic record is created. Multiple holograms can be stored this way using different reference beams. By illuminating the holographic volume with a reference beam, we can reconstruct the corresponding hologram. In reverse, if we illuminate the holographic volume with the image of a recorded object (or part of it) we can reconstruct the corresponding reference beam.

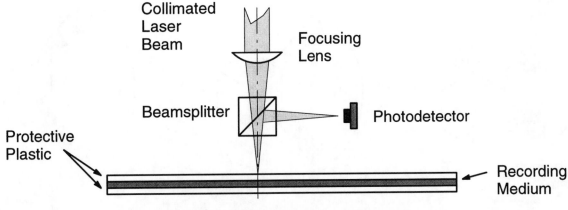

Figure 3. Optical readout of an optical disk.

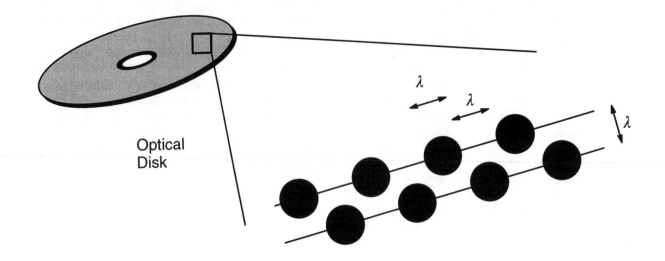

Figure 4. Bit arrangement along the tracks of an optical disk.

As we similarly demonstrated the areal data density for optical disks, we can show that the volume data density for PVHS is in the order of λ^{-3} [YEH93]. In fact, this is the volume storage density for all kinds of optical storage machinery that employ 3D geometric space.

We indicated that multiple holograms can be written in the same volume. Although the physics of multiplexing techniques is quite intriguing, it is beyond the scope of this article, and relevant information can be found in [YEH93] and [HES93]. A generic system description, however, is in order. Figure 5 shows a basic multiplexing technique known as angular multiplexing. By changing the angle between the reference beam and the crystal, we can record multiple holograms in the crystal. Each hologram is identified by a

unique angle, and therefore random access is possible by selecting the appropriate incidence angle for a reference beam.

Holograms have some interesting properties that are very useful when building an associative memory system. A hologram can still reconstruct an image stored in it even if the medium is damaged or broken in several pieces. Assuming that we are dealing with Fourier holograms, that is, with interference patterns between a reference beam and the Fourier transform of the object beam, we spread information about the object all over the hologram. Even when a subset of the original hologram is available, there are probably enough spatial frequency components in the remaining hologram to reconstruct the original image at somewhat lower quality. This fault tolerance of Fourier

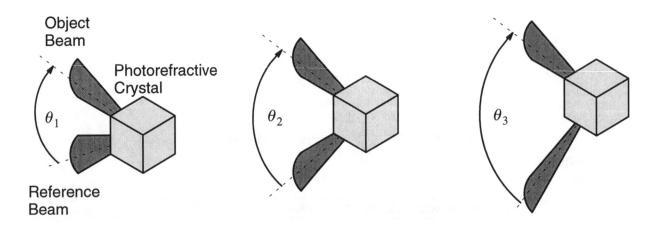

Figure 5. Angular multiplexing in photorefractive volume holographic storage.

holograms is bi-directional in the sense that if a partially damaged on uncompleted version of an object beam is imaged on the hologram, the corresponding reference beam will be reconstructed at a lower SNR. Since the reference beam is essentially the address of that hologram, one can see the associative nature of holography.

Angular multiplexing has a dynamic range of approximately 500 holograms per cm³. Additional capacity is obtained by employing other addressing mechanisms such as spatioangular [BUR94] and peristrophic multiplexing [PU95]. The use of spatioangular multiplexing up to 10,000 holograms has been recorded [BUR94]. This number is expected to reach 160,000 in the near future [BUR95].

Recording in photorefractive crystals is quite persistent and reversible. Persistence time varies from a few minutes to several weeks depending on the host and the impurities. Thermal fixing of the crystal can also increase the storage time. Data can be erased in bulk if the crystal is illuminated by intense white light, which restores the electric field equilibrium in it.

2.3.3 Two-photon three-dimensional memory

Two-photon 3D memory (TPTDM) was introduced in the late 1980s as a potential system for high density optical storage [HUN90]. The underlying mechanism is a two-photon process that causes the molecules of a photochromic material to undergo a structural phase transition. This structural transition is reversible and detectable and therefore can be used for information recording.

Data are stored in planes within the crystal, as shown in Figure 6. Each plane contains a 2D array of volume elements, each corresponding to a bit. A volume element is addressed by two intersecting beams. During the write cycle, the beams are called data beam and address beam. Data beams offer the first photon in the two-photon process, and they originate from a binary page composer such as a spatial light modulator (SLM) and are focused through an autofocus mechanism (not shown in Figure 6) at the selected data plane. At the same time, the data plane is illuminated by a multitude of address beams that provide the second photon required for the two-photon process. The two beams intersect in a volume element and cause the photochromic molecules to undergo a molecular structure transition. If there is no data beam present, that is, the intended bit value corresponds to a zero, then the photochromic material in the volume element does not undergo the molecular transition because the address beam's photons cannot initiate a two-photon process by themselves.

When reading a plane, each volume element is intersected by an address beam and a readout beam. Now all elements in the plane receive beams from the SLM, that is, all the pixels on the SLM are being turned on. If a volume element has undergone a molecular structure transition during the read cycle, photons from the address and read beams will excite it and make it fluoresce. If it has not undergone a transition, then the energy offered by the two intersecting beams is not enough to excite it, and no fluorescence will be detected from that plane.

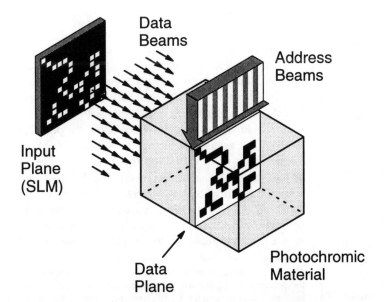 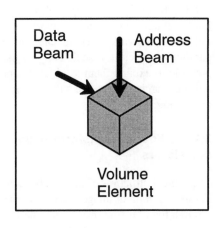

Figure 6. Two-photon 3D memory system. The inset at right shows the addressing of independent bits.

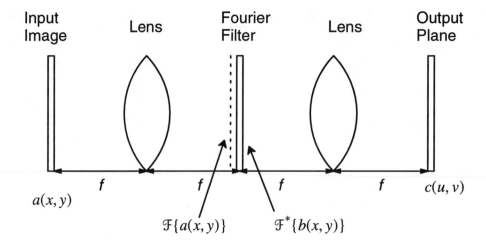

Figure 7. Typical structure of an image correlator. *f* is the focal length of the lenses.

Data stored in photochromic materials via the two-photon process can be maintained for several weeks. Erasure is possible by raising the temperature of the crystal, thus providing enough energy to restore the original molecular structures. Selective erasure is also possible by rewriting a selected bit location.

3   Analog processing

Analog associative processing refers to optical implementation of neural networks with associative capabilities (such as the Hopfield network) and to optical image correlators. We begin our discussion with optical image correlators, which can be classified as either block-oriented associative processors or full and parallel associative processors. Our review here deals with two distinct implementations: (1) correlators based on optical disks and (2) correlators based on volume holographic storage. Next we review optical implementations of neural networks, specifically Hopfield-type networks. These are, in principle, bit-parallel/word-serial associative processors, but it is possible to expand them to block-oriented processors. All these architectures are suitable for autoassociative processing.

3.1   Fourier transform-based image correlators

The typical structure of image correlators is shown in Figure 7. An input image $a(x,y)$ is Fourier transformed through the first spherical lens.[2] The Fourier transform $\Im\{a(x,y)\}$ is then multiplied by the complex conjugate

Fourier transform of a reference image $b(x,y)$. A light modulator (film, SLM, and mask, for instance) located at the back focal plane of the first spherical lens has an amplitude transmissivity proportional to $\Im*\{b(x,y)\}$. Therefore, a priori knowledge of $\Im*\{b(x,y)\}$ is required.

The two Fourier transforms are then multiplied together and the inverse Fourier transform of the product $\Im\{a(x,y)\}$ $\Im*\{b(x,y)\}$ is obtained via the second spherical lens of the setup. The inverse Fourier transform of the product is the correlation[3] function of the two images:

$$c(u,v) = \Im^{-1}\{\Im\{a(x,y)\}\Im*\{b(x,y)\}\}$$
$$= \iint a(x,y)b(x-u,y-v)dxdy \qquad (1)$$

When $a(x,y) = b(x-u,y-v)$ the correlation $c(u,v)$ reaches a maximum. Therefore, it is possible to determine whether images a and b are similar or not.

The presence of the complex conjugate term $\Im*\{b(x,y)\}$ in Equation (1) suggests that the Fourier filter should also carry information about the phase of the Fourier transform of the reference image $b(x,y)$. A. Vander Lugt noticed in 1964 that phase information about $\Im*\{b(x,y)\}$ can be recorded in combination with a second beam with known amplitude and phase distributions [VAN64]. What Vander Lugt essentially described was the use of Fourier transform holograms in image correlators. In 1969 D. Gabor, unaware of

---

[2] It is a well-known property of spherical lenses that they produce the Fourier transform of the input image at the back focal plane [RHO53].

[3] We use the terms *correlation* and *convolution* interchangeably in the present context, because from an optical system perspective, both operations are similar. Strictly speaking, however, the convolution has a folding operation that is not present in the correlation operation [PRO92].

Vander Lugt's work, proposed the use of holograms in associative memories and suggested that the fault tolerance exhibited by the brain in associative recalls is similar to holographic fault tolerance at an abstract mathematical level [GAB69]. In the 1980s, Demetri Psaltis proposed and implemented several associative memories based on Fourier transform holograms [PSA85], [PAE87].

From a system perspective, an image correlator requires a large library of reference images. If an input image resembles one of the stored reference images, a match will be indicated by a strong correlation. In other words the system will recall one of the stored reference images based on partial or distorted input. Therefore, image correlators can be considered as associative memories. There are two points we must address: First, where and how do we store the reference image library? And second, how do we engineer the interaction of the input image with the reference library?

Let us begin with the reference library. This is an optical memory that needs to be fast and of large capacity. Early engineering restrictions also dictated the need for a planar medium. Ideally, the reference library can be stored on an optical disk. Considerable research on this field has been performed by Demetri Psaltis who explored several different configurations of optical disk/Vander Lugt-based correlators [PSA90].

A first approach is shown in Figure 8. The holograms of the reference library images are stored on the optical disk. An input image is projected on the disk surface through the beamsplitter and the spherical lens, which focuses its Fourier transform on the surface of the disk. The amplitude intensity of the input image's Fourier transform illuminates an area of the disk where the Fourier transform hologram of a reference image is prerecorded. The result is a reflection of this area, in other words it's the product of the two Fourier transforms. This product passes again through the spherical lens, and its inverse Fourier transform is imaged onto the correlation plane. The output on the correlation plane is meaningful only when a Fourier transform hologram on the disk spatially coincides with the Fourier transform of an input image on the disk's surface. Therefore, we need look at the correlation plane only at those moments.

In this system, the filter plane—the plane on which the two Fourier transforms are multiplied—is located on the disk's surface. The system requires a 2D array of photodetectors such as a CCD array at the correlation plane. However, it is sensitive to the quality of the disk, alignment requirements, and the time required to produce the Fourier transform holograms for the reference library and produce the optical disk. Because a Fourier transform hologram contains information about the spatial frequencies distribution and the phase of an image, any phase distortion due to poor quality of disk coating, for example, will affect the performance. Because this system multiplies Fourier transforms, alignment is a critical parameter. Disk wobble can introduce a source of misalignment, affecting the system's performance.

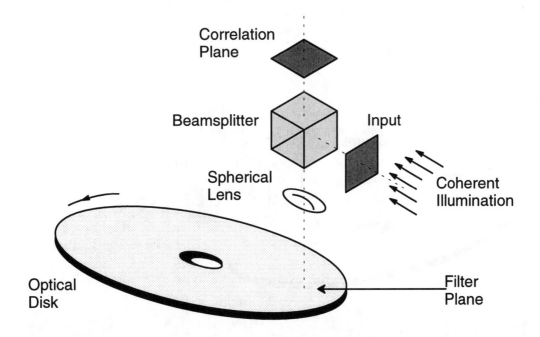

Figure 8. An optical image correlator system based on optical disks.

An alternative configuration, which allows us to overcome the computational overhead of producing computer-generated holograms for the reference library, is to store the reference images on the disk and create their Fourier transform holograms dynamically. In this setup, shown in Figure 9, the filter plane is moved off the disk's surface and the correlation involves two steps. First an input image enters the system through the beamsplitter, and it is Fourier transformed on the photorefractive crystal by the first spherical lens. The photorefractive crystal is also illuminated by a coherent reference beam and acts as a recording medium. Therefore, the Fourier transform hologram of the input image is recorded in the crystal. Next, the Fourier transform of a reference image is used to read out the hologram. If the two images correlate, a strong peak will be detected at the correlation plane [NEI93].

The previous two methods compute the correlation of two images by multiplying their Fourier transforms. Fourier transform-based systems were demonstrated with up to 400,000 correlations/sec [PSA90]. The correlation can be found also by evaluating the double integral in Equation (1). This is illustrated with the help of Figure 10. Let's assume that our inputs are discrete and that both a and b are 2×2 matrices. In this case the integrals are replaced by summation operators. The correlation matrix will be a 3×3 matrix whose elements are shown in Figure 10. The scanning operation is performed in both directions. In terms of a disk topology and assuming proper mapping of the data on the disk's surface, we need to scan both tangentially and radially [PSA90].

As shown in Figure 11, tangential scanning is performed due to the disk's rotation. Radial scan is accomplished with a rotating polygon mirror. The inner product of the two images is collected by the third spherical lens onto the correlation plane. Alignment requirements are relaxed with this setup. The cost, however, is the speed. Each radial scan must be completed before the disk rotates by one pixel along the tangential direction. Therefore, the performance of the system is limited by the scanning rate of the polygon mirror. To improve the situation, it is possible to use an acousto-optic modulator to perform faster radial scanning. Still, for this type of correlation the price is a lower correlation rate, between 400 and 1,400 correlations per second [PSA90].

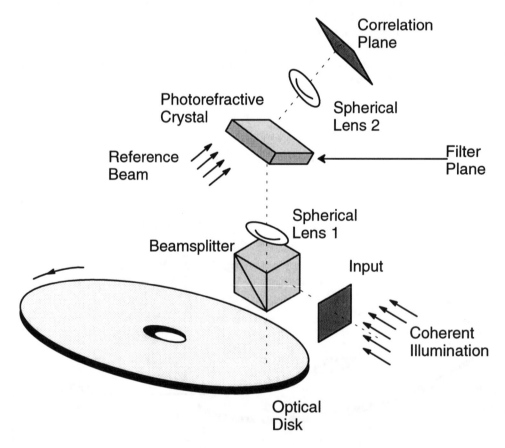

Figure 9. An optical image correlator system based on optical disks using dynamic holograms.

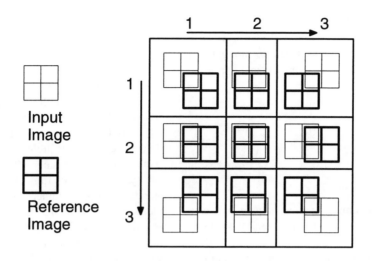

Figure 10. Example of a correlation matrix for two 2×2 discrete inputs.

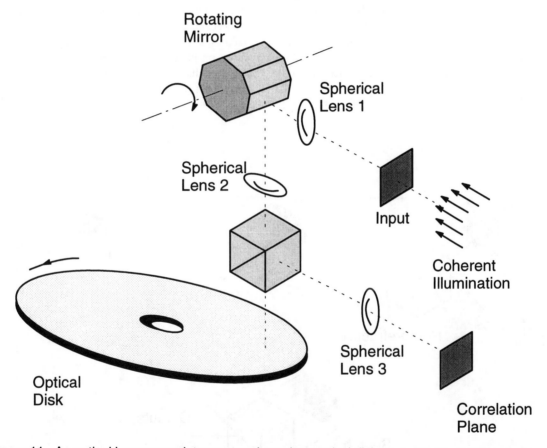

Figure 11. An optical image correlator system based on optical disks operating in the linear space.

3.2 Volume holographic storage and processing

Volume holographic storage offers the potential for full and parallel associative processing. As shown in Figure 12a, multiple data pages can be written in the same volume at different angular addresses. Each data page is recorded with a reference beam coming from a different angle. In this angular multiplexing scheme several conditions must be met in order to ensure that there will be no cross talk between adjacent data pages. If the reference beam can be deflected over an angle θ_h along the horizontal axis and θ_v along the vertical one, then the number of available angular addresses for multiplexing is:

$$\left(\frac{\theta_h}{\Delta\theta_B}\right) \times \left(\frac{\theta_v}{\Delta\theta_B}\right) \qquad (2)$$

where $\Delta\theta_B$ is a the minimum angular step, which is determined by physics laws and more specifically by Bragg selectivity.

In section 2.3.2 we described the associative nature of holography. We can use the inherent associativity of holographic storage to implement image correlators. Here, instead of storing the reference library on a disk, we store it in the holographic volume. Next, if we interrogate the holographic volume using the Fourier transform of a distorted version of one of the stored images, we will obtain the addresses of the corresponding images as shown in Figure 12b. Therefore, it is possible to scan the entire memory in one step.

The time required to complete this step is:

$$t_{\text{scan}} = t_{\text{setup}} + t_{\text{readout}} + t_{\text{detector}} \qquad (3)$$

where t_{setup} is the time required to compose the search argument image on the SLM, t_{readout} is the time required to diffract light from the storage medium, and t_{detector} is the time required by a 2D photodetector to detect the diffracted light. The entire process is completed in approximately 30-500 msec, depending on the system configuration. Although by modern VLSI standards this is rather slow, considering that the memory volume being searched here is in the order of several Gbytes, the performance is satisfactory. Once the 2D photodetector records the diffracted light, which corresponds to the angular addresses of the qualifying images, we can recall them one at a time. This is accomplished by loading the obtained angular addresses on the address mechanism, one at a time, and reading out the corresponding hologram.

Recent experiments on associative searches for databases stored in volume holographic memories based on photorefractive crystals have showed promising results when using small partial inputs as search arguments [GOE96a, GOE96b, RIC96].

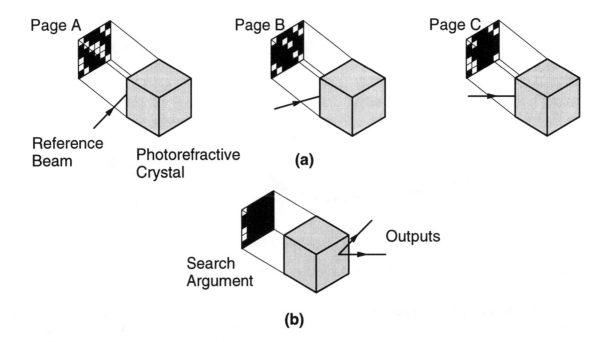

Figure 12. (a) Holographic recording using angular multiplexing; (b) associative recall.

166

3.3 Optical implementation of Hopfield networks

Neural network architectures can be more easily realized as optical systems than as electronics. The 2D topology of electronic implementations limits the number of layers and the globalism of interconnects. Because of electronic limitations, neural networks are treated more like algorithms than computational architectures. As we mentioned earlier, interconnection density and complexity limitations are relaxed in optical systems, and hardware implementation of neural networks is possible.

One of the first neural networks implemented optically was the Hopfield network [PSA85], [OWE87]. A Hopfield network [HOP82] can store a number of N-dimensional binary vectors $V^m = \left(v_1^m, v_2^m, ..., v_N^m\right)$ in a matrix $\mathbf{T}$ whose elements T_{ij} are defined as:

$$T_{ij}=\begin{cases} \sum_{m=1}^{M}\left[(2v_i^m-1)(2v_j^m-1)\right] & \text{if } i \neq j \\ 0 & \text{if } i = j \end{cases} \quad (4)$$

where M is the number of vectors to be stored. If $\mathbf{U}^k$ is a distorted version of vector $\mathbf{V}^k$ then the multiplication $\mathbf{U}^k\mathbf{T}$ will yield $\mathbf{Q}^k$ which is an estimate of the stored vector $\mathbf{V}^k$–$\mathbf{I}$ where $\mathbf{I}$ is the unitary vector $\mathbf{I} =$

(1,1, ... ,1). It has been shown [PSA85] that the signal-to-noise ratio of this memory is:

$$\text{SNR} = \sqrt{\frac{N}{2(M-1)}} \quad (5)$$

For large vectors, $N > M$ the SNR is large enough to allow successful identification of the stored vector based on partial input. The challenge is to be able to successfully recall a pattern even when the SNR is low—that is, when the number of correct bits in $\mathbf{Q}^k$ is less than N. In this case it is possible to use the estimate $\mathbf{Q}^k$ as a new input to the memory, that is, multiply $\mathbf{T}$ by $\mathbf{Q}^k$ in order to obtain a better estimate. This procedure can be repeated until we have successfully recalled the stored vector $\mathbf{V}^k$–$\mathbf{I}$.

The optical realization of a Hopfield network with feedback is shown in Figure 13. An input vector is composed of an array of light sources such as a linear light-emitting diode, or surface emitting laser array, or a one-dimensional spatial light modulator illuminated by a collimated laser beam. A cylindrical lens, which is not shown in the schematics, expands this vector along the horizontal direction, thus effectively multiplying each element of the input vector with all the elements of the corresponding row of the association matrix $\mathbf{T}$. A second cylindrical lens after the association matrix plane collects the products from each col-

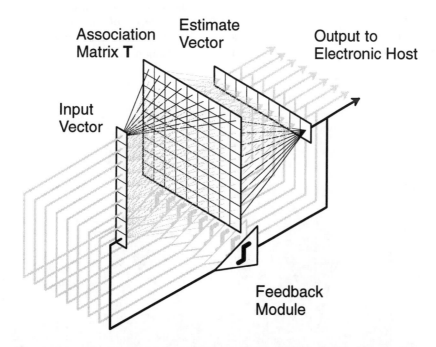

Figure 13. Optical implementation of a Hopfield network with feedback.

umn and focuses them along a linear photodetector array. The association matrix itself is composed on a 2D spatial light modulator.

The estimate vector detected at the output is fed back as the new input vector in order to achieve a better approximation. The feedback module provides some thresholding as well, to ensure that the new input vector is binary, too. The implementation of the feedback module can be either optical, electronic, or hybrid. All three approaches have been demonstrated [PSA85]. After a few iterations, the system will converge to the stored vector with the minimum Hamming distance from the input vector. In a continuous space the convergence can be illustrated with the help of Figure 14. If the estimate vector's location is represented by a rolling ball, it will eventually end up in one of the wells, most probably in the closest one. If the wells represent the stored vectors, then the analogy is clear. Notice that if the space between wells is flat, then the ball will remain there, that is, there will be no convergence to a stored vector. However, if the number of wells is large enough (that is, a large M) and/or the wells are wide (that is, a large N) there will be no flat area on this space, and the rolling ball will eventually end up in a well.

Processing of 2D inputs has also been demonstrated [PSA85]. In this case the association matrix $\mathbf{T}$ becomes a 4D tensor:

$$T_{ijkl} = \sum_{m=1}^{M} V^m(i, j) V^m(k, l) \qquad (6)$$

where $\mathbf{V}^m$ is a 2D input. The challenge here is to find a suitable medium to store the tensor $\mathbf{T}$. The detailed description of the system demonstrated in [PSA85] is beyond the scope of this review. Furthermore, simpler approaches are possible using volume holographic storage techniques as mentioned previously.

4   Digital associative processing

Digital associative processing refers to direct implementation of Boolean functions on data sets in order to evaluate their similarity with a given argument. A suitable application for Boolean associative processing is relational database operations. Optoelectronic implementation of relational database operations has been proposed and discussed in literature over the past five years [BER89, BER90, BRO93, IRA94, IRA95, LOU94, MIT93, MIT94, MIT94a]. These proposals can be classified according to their associative processing capabilities. Volume holographic storage for large databases [BRO93] offers full and parallel associative processing. The optoelectronic data filter [MIT94] and the optical content-addressable parallel processor [LOU94] offer block-oriented associative processing. And finally, the tomographic protocol [IRA94] offers bit-slice associative processing, specifically word-parallel/bit-serial processing.

In the next four sections we will be reviewing these optoelectronic architectures for relational databases, emphasizing their associative processing characteristics. Associative processing is very important in relational database operations because it accelerates selection operations [SU88]. We already mentioned that any relational database operation can be decomposed into a series of selections and projections [ULL88]. Full and parallel associative processing lets us perform a selection in a single step. Block- or page-oriented

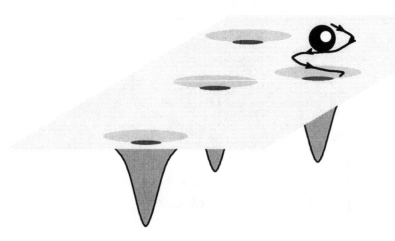

Figure 14. Hopfield convergence in a continuous space.

associative processing architectures perform a selection in k steps where $k = \lceil R/p \rceil$. Here R is the cardinality[4] of the relation and p is the number of tuples per block or page. Bit-serial/word-parallel associative processing takes q steps to complete a selection operation. Here q is the length of the selection attribute.

The methods and architectures we describe here are, in principle, autoassociative memories as were those in the previous section. However, one may argue that relational database associative processing is heteroassociative because based on the partial input of a tuple we can recall the rest of it, and with projection it is possible to eliminate the input attribute, that is, the partial tuple we used to recall the entire one. From this point of view, relational database associative processing is heteroassociative. But in principle, the heteroassociation is artificially embedded at the projection operation following the selection. The selection operation itself is an autoassociation.

4.1 Volume holographic storage for large databases

In section 3.2 we discussed volume holographic storage and processing as a non-Boolean implementation of associative processing. The same approach can be used to implement relational database operations. Specifically, if the reference images stored in the volume holographic memory are tuples from a relation and the query input is a partial tuple, the memory will recall the corresponding tuple's address. Although this is clearly a non-Boolean, analog process it is necessary to briefly mention it here since we are discussing possible ways of implementing relational database operations.

4.2 Optoelectronic data filter for selection and projection

The optoelectronic data filter (ODF) is a block-oriented associative processing architecture designed to operate as an interface between parallel optical memories and electronic computers [MIT94]. Its functionality is aimed at reducing the data transfer rates from a parallel optical memory to an electronic host, by performing on-the-fly selection and projection operations on 2D pages of relational data.

Projection requires masking out the undesired data fields of a page by bringing it, along with a projection argument, on an AND optoelectronic gate array. Selection is performed by comparing the data page to a 2D matrix formed by replicating the selection argu-

ment onto each row of the matrix. The comparison is completed optically in parallel as a bitwise XOR operation between the data bits and the argument bits. The results of all the XOR operations in each row are ORed together to determine matching rows. The selection operation is described by the following equation:

$$
\begin{bmatrix} h_1 \\ h_2 \\ \vdots \\ h_n \end{bmatrix} = \begin{bmatrix} d_{11} \oplus s_{11} + d_{12} \oplus s_{12} + \cdots + d_{1m} \oplus s_{1m} \\ d_{21} \oplus s_{21} + d_{22} \oplus s_{22} + \cdots + d_{2} \oplus s_{2m} \\ \vdots \\ d_{n1} \oplus s_{n1} + d_{n2} \oplus s_{n2} + \cdots + d_{nm} \oplus s_{nm} \end{bmatrix} \quad (7)
$$

where h_j are the elements of a vector identifying matches (if $h_i=0$, there is a match) and $d_{ij} = b_{ij} \cdot f_{ij}$. Here, f_{ij} are the bits of the selection mask pattern, b_{ij} are the data bits received from the optical memory, and s_{ij} are the bits of the selection argument replicated to the 2D array, (therefore $s_{1j} = s_{2j} = \ldots = s_{nj}$, $j = 1,2, \ldots, m$). The presence of a selection mask lets us perform selection only on a specified attribute. The functionality of the selection mask is to alleviate the need for "don't care" values that are not available in the strictly binary encoding scheme employed by this architecture.

Figure 15 shows a system view of the ODF, and Figure 16 is a picture of the early prototype [SNY95]. In the system view of Figure 15, several optical components such as lenses and microlens arrays have been omitted for clarity. Data enter the system from the lower right beamsplitter and are split in two directions. One copy of the data page propagates toward the selection module, and the other is directed to the projection module. Data in the projection module are ANDed with the projection mask, and the output is imaged on the optoelectronic RAM array. The optoelectronic RAM is an ordinary RAM array with an array of photodetectors integrated on top of the memory cells. This lets us write the entire RAM array in a single step by imaging a binary pattern on the photodetector array.

Data entering the selection module will be ANDed with the selection mask, which marks the "don't care" bits as 0-value bits. Then this masked page will be XORed with the 2D replica of the selection argument. The rows of the XOR array output are focused by a cylindrical lens along a linear photodetector array. The cylindrical lens functions as an optical OR gate. As shown in Figure 17, light beams from all the elements in a row are focused by the cylindrical lens onto a point. The light intensity at that point corresponds to the sum of the light intensities of the row elements. Assuming a binary encoding, the focal point represents the OR of the row elements.

---

[4] The cardinality of a relation is defined as the number of tuples (records) contained in it.

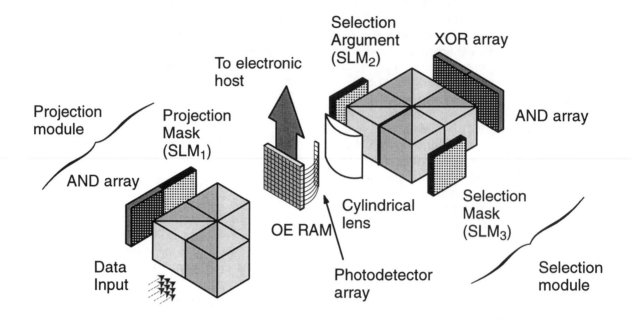

Figure 15. A system view of the optoelectronic data filter prototype.

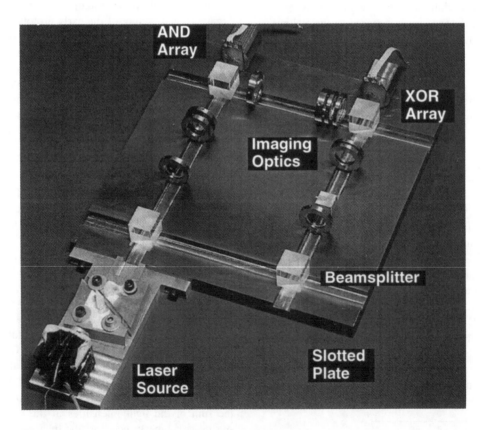

Figure 16. A picture of the optoelectronic data filter prototype at an early stage.

170

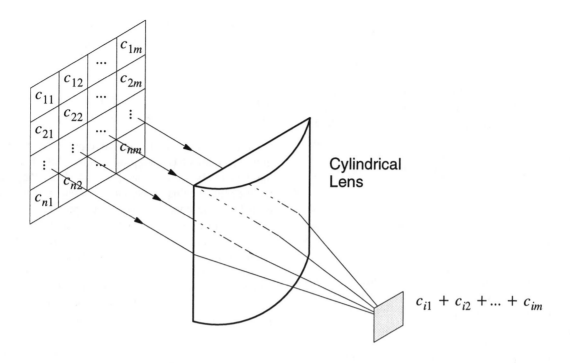

Figure 17. Cylindrical lens acting as an OR gate.

The photodetector array determines which rows of the optoelectronic RAM will be read out and subsequently transferred to the electronic host computer. The combination of the photodetector array and the optoelectronic RAM lets us transfer only those portions of the projection output that match with the selection argument, thus reducing the effective transfer rate between the parallel optical memory and the electronic host. Figure 18 shows the transformations of a data page through its route in the selection module.

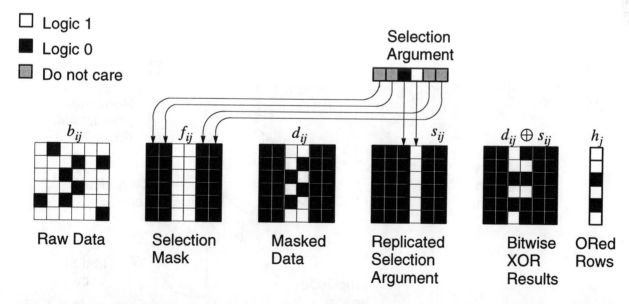

Figure 18. Block-oriented associative processing for the optoelectronic data filter. "Do not care" bits are converted to logic-0 bits because the selection mask masks them out.

Logic operations are carried out on 2D arrays of optoelectronic logic gates, also known as smart pixels. As we mentioned earlier in section 2.2, smart pixels can be implemented as combinations of detectors, emitters, and electronic logic (see Figure 2). We have fabricated our smart pixels using heterostructure phototransistors as detectors and vertical cavity surface-emitting lasers as emitters [IRA95].

The time performance of the optoelectronic data filter for the selection is given by the following equation:

$$t_{select} = t_{setup} + k\left[t_{pagein} + t_{AND} + \max\{(t_{XOR} + t_{PDA}), t_{OERAM}\}\right] \tag{8}$$

where t_{setup} is the time required to load the selection arguments and mask on the SLMs, k is the number of incoming data pages, t_{pagein} is the time required to load a page from the optical memory, t_{AND} is the response time of the AND gate array, t_{XOR} is the response time of the XOR gate array, t_{PDA} is the response time of the photodetector array detecting the h vector given in Equation (7), and t_{OERAM} is the response time of the optoelectronic RAM array receiving data in parallel.

Even though t_{setup} is currently in the order of milliseconds (due to the slow loading times for SLMs), the overall performance of the system is not significantly affected since the SLMs remain unchanged during the selection. The remaining time terms in Equation (8) are in the order of nanoseconds. For a large number of data pages, the response time of the selection operation is bound by O(k).

Based on a similar architecture described here, we can develop optoelectronic look-up tables [MIT93a, IRA95] that are used as heteroassociative memories.

4.3 Optical content-addressable parallel processor for database processing

Another block-oriented associative processor for relational databases has been proposed by Ahmed Louri at the University of Arizona [LOU94, LOU94b]. The functionality of this processor is similar to that of the optoelectronic data filter described previously. However, the optical content-addressable parallel processor (OCAPP) employs a rather complex polarization encoding scheme to perform inequality comparisons. In contrast to the ODF, which can perform only equality comparisons, OCAPP will be capable of performing selections based on other Θ-operators such as < and ≥, in addition to equality comparisons when it is completed.

The design for the selection unit of the OCAPP is shown in Figure 19. The selection argument is vertically replicated on a 2D polarization-based SLM. Orthogonal polarization encoded data from the optical memory are imaged on the SLM. If the polarization state of an SLM pixel is vertical, then light will pass through it without altering its polarization. If, however, the SLM pixel is horizontally polarized, then incident light will experience a 90° rotation of its polarization state. The result of this superposition is an intermediate page whose polarization states are shown in Table 1.

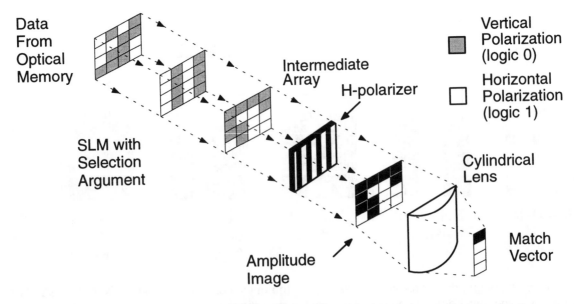

Figure 19. Selection unit of the optical content-addressable parallel processor for databases.

Table 1. Polarization states of intermediate array.

Data Page Pixel	Selection Argument Pixel	Intermediate Array
Vertical	Vertical	Vertical
Vertical	Horizontal	Horizontal
Horizontal	Vertical	Horizontal
Horizontal	Horizontal	Vertical

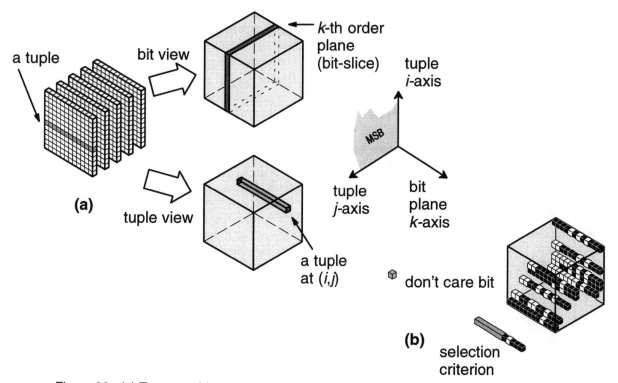

Figure 20. (a) Tomographic mapping; (b) selection operation in the tomographic scheme.

The intermediate array is then filtered through a horizontal polarizer to produce an amplitude image. The horizontal polarizer allows only horizontally polarized light to go through and blocks any incident light with vertical polarization. The filtered image corresponds to the bitwise XOR result between the data page and the selection argument. Next, a cylindrical lens focuses the rows of the intermediate array to form a match vector. This vector identifies those rows from the data page that match the selection argument.

Masking for "don't care" values in the search argument is possible here as well. An additional SLM can be inserted between the data page from the optical memory and the SLM with the selection argument. This SLM will cause the "don't care" values to force logic-0s on the corresponding positions of the data page. Therefore, by loading logic-0s at the corresponding positions on the selection argument SLM, exact matches can be performed.

The time performance of the OCAPP is limited by the response time of the SLM, which is the slowest component in this architecture as well as in the optoelectronic data filter. Again, here, for a large number of data pages, the performance of the OCAPP is bound by $O(k)$, where k is the number of data pages.

4.4   3D tomographic storage scheme

The 3D tomographic storage scheme (TSS) has been proposed as an alternative data format suitable for optoelectronic implementation of database operations [IRA94]. The TSS exploits the ability of volume optical memories to store and retrieve 2D pages of data, each page at a single logical and physical address. Its name has been derived by the Greek words *tomé* and *graphé*, which mean "view of a slice." In the TSS, the data pages correspond to bit slices of all the tuples in the relation as shown in Figure 20a.

In the case of selection, we need to identify the tuples that match the selection criterion. An example of a selection is shown in Figure 20b. The tuples are identified by their Cartesian coordinates on the tuple plane. If the selection criterion s is:

$$[s_{a+1}\ s_{a+2}\ ...\ s_{a+q}];\ 1 \leq a + 1 \leq a + q \leq L \qquad (9)$$

where s_i are bit values, L is the length of the tuple and q is the length of the selection criterion, then the qualified tuples are marked by the table:

$$M(i,j) = \prod_{m=1}^{q} \left[\overline{S_{a+m}(i,j) \oplus B_{a+m}(i,j)} \right]$$
$$= \prod_{m=1}^{q} \left[\overline{S_{a+m}(i,j)} \oplus B_{a+m}(i,j) \right] \qquad (10)$$

where S is a matrix with all its elements set to the current value of the selection argument bit, that is

$$S_l(i,j) = s_l$$
$$1 \leq ij \leq N;$$
$$a + 1 \leq l \leq a + q \qquad (11)$$

and $B_k(i,j)$ is the 2D data bit slice of k-th order.

TSS can be used to perform selections in a bit-serial/word-parallel associative processing scheme. The sequence of steps in the tomographic selection is illustrated in Figure 21. The bits of the selection argument are replicated in 2D arrays of equal size to the bit slices of the relation, one at a time. Then, the 2D selection bit replica is bitwise XORed with the corresponding bit slice from the optical memory. Next, the result of the XOR operation is ANDed with the result of the same operation from the previous slice. To denote the sequential time of these AND operations, Equation (10) is written as:

$$M_m(i,j) = M_{m-1}(i,j) \cdot$$
$$\overline{[S_{a+m}(i,j) \oplus B_{a+m}(i,j)]}\ ;\ 0 < m \leq q \qquad (12)$$

with the initial condition $M_0(i,j) = 1$, $\forall i,j$. From Equations (10) and (12) we can see that the time complexity of the tomographic operation is $O(q)$. After $q+1$ steps, the matrix $M_q(i,j)$ identifies the Cartesian coordinates (i,j) of those tuples matching the selection argument. For the example of Figure 21, these tuples are located at points $(1,1)$ and $(4,3)$.

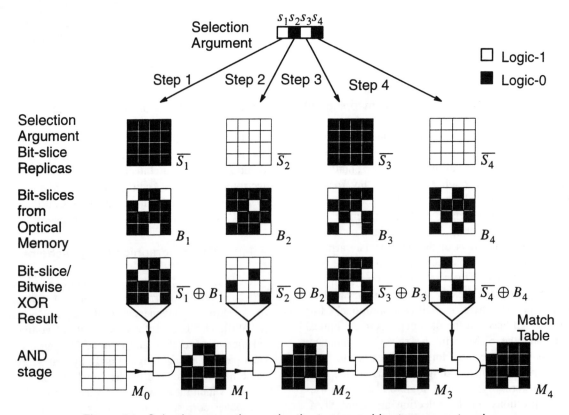

Figure 21. Selection operation under the tomographic storage protocol.

174

From Equation (12) it becomes apparent that we need to hold the results of an XOR operation until a similar operation at the next bit-slice level is completed. Using electronics for the processing, this can be done is a straightforward way by employing flip-flops in a buffer array.

Exact matches can be accomplished with the tomographic protocol. When a "don't care" value is encountered during tomographic selection, it is possible to ignore the corresponding bit slice and skip the XOR operation at that time step.

The TSS appears to be highly suitable for implementation in combination with a two-photon 3D memory, because we can address its contents both in a word-parallel/bit-serial or word-serial/bit-parallel fashion relatively easily.

5   Discussion and conclusions

Associative processing offers fast access to data based on their content even when we do not know their entire content or when our search pattern is distorted. The fault-tolerant nature of associative processing combined with its high degree of parallelism result in a unique solution for alleviating the von Neumann bottleneck in many input/output-intensive applications such as image processing, text retrieval, lexical analysis, and relational database operations.

In this review we have presented several different ways that associative processing can be supported by optical and optoelectronic architectures to perform image processing and relational database operations. At the high end, holography offers full and parallel associative processing, while at the other end, Hopfield networks and the tomographic storage scheme can benefit by bit-slice associative processing. In the middle we have block-oriented associative architectures based on optical disks and smart-pixel arrays. All methods presented here require parallel input/output of 2D pages of data that can be provided by parallel optical memories. The various optical associative processing techniques are summarized in Table 2.

Holography offers an attractive solution because it involves a minimum number of electronic components of low complexity. The actual processing involves optical multiplication of Fourier transforms. Volume holographic storage and processing is highly suitable for image recognition and relevant applications [PU95] and for database processing [BRO93], [MIT94a] where access speed is very important. Holographic associative memories based on optical disks offer a reliable processing architecture for image processing. This is a block-oriented approach that can be very fast if the disk rotates fast enough.

The optoelectronic data filter, which was designed as an interface between parallel optical memories and electronic computers to eliminate bottlenecks between fast secondary storage and slower electronic memories, offers block-oriented associative processing. Therefore, it requires optical memories with page-formatted output. Such memories include optical disks read in parallel, two-photon 3D memories, volume holographic memories, and spectral hole-burning memories. These memories constitute the majority of optical storage technology. The optoelectronic data filter can in principle "see" virtually any wavelength ranging from blue light all the way up to infrared emissions. It can be also made very sensitive to detect the weak emissions of optical memories and to maintain economical power requirements. An early prototype has been demonstrated by the authors and their colleagues at Colorado State University [SNY95].

Table 2. Classification of optical associative processing.

Algorithmic Nature	Data Structure	
	Formatted	Unformatted
Non-Boolean	Neural networks Relational operations	Image correlators Neural networks Text retrieval Lexical analysis
Boolean	Relational operations	Text retrieval

The optoelectronic data filter is limited by two factors. First, spatial light modulators (SLM) based on ferroelectric liquid crystals are not as fast as we would like them to be. Currently available devices operate in the range of a few thousand frames per second, and their size does not typically exceed 128×128 pixels. Alternative devices such as 2D arrays of active matrix displays can perform better. However, these devices exhibit large diffraction effects because of the periodic structure of the thin-film transistor array. Second, large arrays of vertical-cavity surface-emitting laser diodes (VCSELs) have not been fabricated yet. Typically, 8×8 arrays with yields ranging in 50-100 percent per array are available, but for realistic applications arrays with more than 128×128 VCSELs and 100 percent yield will be required. Similar limitations are present for heterojunction phototransistor (HPT) arrays. Finally, one more challenge to address is the monolithic integration of HPTs and VCSELs. At present we use hybrid approaches to wire-interconnect HPT-based arrays of logic gates with arrays of VCSELs.

The optical content-addressable parallel processor is an interesting and sophisticated approach to block-oriented associative processing. However, its severe limitation is that it requires the input data to be encoded in an orthogonal polarized scheme. Since optical memories do not offer polarization encoding, this system requires a preprocessing stage where data are polarization encoded.

Optically implemented Hopfield networks offer an interesting platform to test the performance of neural network applications. At present, optical implementations of Hopfield type networks are word-parallel approaches to associative processing, and they serve only as demonstrators of the potential of optics for realizing neural architectures.

Finally, the tomographic storage scheme that is suitable for bit-slice–oriented associative processing is limited by the lack of large arrays of HPT-based logic gate arrays. Again, here it is desirable to have arrays of 128×128 gates with 100 percent yield. An XOR gate has 4 HPTs, which translate to an array of 256×256 HPTs. Since there is no reason we should limit our choice to the III-V material system, the photodetectors and the logic gates for the tomographic architecture can be fabricated in the II-VI system. This material system uses elements from the second and sixth columns of the periodic table, it is known for its high yields, and it is ideal for VLSI architectures.

Optical associative processors cannot compete very well with electronic systems at present. Optical systems are limited by slow response times of peripheral devices such as SLMs and by the performance characteristics of smart-pixel arrays [IRA95]. How-

ever, the optical systems we reviewed here have the potential to outperform their electronic counterparts. Advances in SLM technology, device fabrication, and smart-pixel integration will eventually lead to optical associative processors that will be competitive alternatives to electronic systems.

In addition to the applications of associative processing we described here, there are a number of emerging applications where optical associative memories and optoelectronic associative processors can have an impact. These applications are mainly focused on broadband information and entertainment services, and further research is required to determine the full potential of optical associative processing in that field.

Acknowledgments

The authors would like to acknowledge the partial support of National Science Foundation through contract EEC-9015128 and of Colorado Advanced Technology Institute through contract GEA-95-0002.

References

[BAT74] H.E. Batcher, "STARAN Parallel Processor Hardware," in *AFIPS Conf. Proc.*, Vol. 43, 1974, pp. 405–410.

[BER89] P.B. Berra et al., "The Impact of Optics on Data and Knowledge Base Systems," invited paper, *IEEE Trans. Knowledge and Data Engineering*, Vol. 1, No. 1, 1989, pp. 111–132.

[BER90] P.B. Berra et al., "Optical Database/Knowledge Base Machines," *Applied Optics*, Vol. 29, No. 2, 1990, pp. 195–205.

[BHA94] P. Bhattacharya, *Semiconductor Optoelectronic Devices*, Prentice Hall, Englewood Cliffs, N.J., 1994.

[BRO93] J. Brown, L.J. Irakliotis, and P.A. Mitkas, "Volume Holographic Storage and Processing for Large Databases," *Proc. OSA Topical Meeting on Optical Computing*, 1993, OSA Technical Digest Vol. 7, 1993, pp. 54–57.

[BUR94] G.W. Burr, F.H. Mok, and D. Psaltis, "Large Scale Volume Holographic Storage in the Long Interaction Length Architecture," in "Photonics for Processors, Neural Networks, and Memories II," J.L. Horner, B. Javidi, and S.T. Kowel, eds., *Proc. SPIE*, Vol. 2,297, 1994, pp. 402–414.

[BUR95] G.W. Burr, private communication, 1995.

[FOS76] C.C. Foster, *Content-Addressable Parallel Processors*, Van Nostrand Reinhold, New York, N.Y., 1976.

[GAB69] D. Gabor, "Holographic Associative Memories," *IBM J. Research and Development*, Vol. 13, Mar. 1969, pp. 156–159.

[GIB86] H. Gibbs, *Optical Bistability: Controlling Light with Light*, Academic Press, London, 1986.

[GOE96a] B.J. Goertzen, K.G. Richling, and P.A. Mitkas, "Implementation of a Volume Holographic Database System," *Proc. Optical Computing*, 1996.

[GOE96b] B.J. Goertzen and P.A. Mitkas, "Volume Holographic Storage for Large Relational Databases," to be published in *Optical Engineering*, 1996.

[HER92] F.P. Herrmann and C.G. Sodini, "A Dynamic Associative Processor for Machine Vision Applications," *IEEE Micro*, Vol. 12, No. 3, June 1992, pp. 31–41.

[HES93] L. Hesselink and M.C. Bashaw, "Optical Memories Implemented with Photorefractive Media," *Optical and Quantum Electronics*, Vol. 25, 1993, pp. S611–S661.

[HOP82] J.J. Hopfield, "Neural Networks and Physical Systems with Emergent Collective Computational Abilities," *Proc. National Academy of Sciences*, Vol. 79, Apr. 1982, pp. 2,554–2,558.

[HUN90] S. Hunter et al., "Potentials of Two-Photon-Based Three-Dimensional Optical Memories for High Performance Computing," *Applied Optics*, Vol. 29, No. 14, 1993, pp. 2,058–2,066.

[IRA94] L.J. Irakliotis and P.A. Mitkas, "Tomographic Storage Scheme for Three Dimensional Implementation of Database Operations," in "Photonics for Processors, Neural Networks, and Memories II," J.L. Horner, B. Javidi, and S.T. Kowel, eds., *Proc. SPIE*, Vol. 2,297, 1994, pp. 359–367.

[IRA95] L.J. Irakliotis et al., "Optoelectronic Parallel Processing with Surface-Emitting Lasers and Free-Space Interconnects," accepted for publication, *J. Lightwave Technology*, 1995.

[JEW91] J.L. Jewell, J.P. Harbison, and A. Scherer, "Microlasers," *Scientific American*, Nov. 1991, pp. 86–94.

[KRI91] A. Krikelis, "Computer Vision Applications with the Associative String Processor," *J. Parallel and Distributed Computing*, Vol. 13, No. 2, Oct. 1991, pp. 170-184.

[LOU94] A. Louri and A. Hatch Jr., "An Optical Associative Parallel Processor for High-Speed Database Processing," *Computer*, Vol. 27, No. 11, Nov. 1994, pp. 65–72.

[LOU94b] A. Louri and A. Hatch Jr., "Optical Content-Addressable Parallel Processor for High-Speed Database Processing," *Applied Optics*, Vol. 33, No. 35, Dec. 10, 1994, pp. 8,153–8,163.

[MAR90] A.B. Marchant, *Optical Recording: A Technical Overview*, Addison-Wesley, Reading, Mass., 1990.

[MCA91] A.D. McAulay, *Optical Computer Architectures*, John Wiley & Sons, New York, N.Y., 1991.

[MID93] J. Midwinter (ed.), *Photonics in Switching*, Vols. I and II, Academic Press, Boston, Mass., 1993.

[MIT93] P.A. Mitkas and P.B. Berra, "PHOEBUS: An Optoelectronic Database Machine Based on Parallel Optical Disks," *J. Parallel and Distributed Computing*, Vol. 17, 1993, pp. 230–244.

[MIT93a] P.A. Mitkas et al., "Optoelectronic Look-Up Table Using VCSEL-Based Logic," *Proc. LEOS 6th Ann. Meeting*, 1993, pp. 71–72.

[MIT94] P.A. Mitkas et al., "Optoelectronic Data Filter for Selection and Projection," *Applied Optics*, Vol. 33, No. 8, 1994, pp. 1,345–1,353.

[MIT94a] P.A. Mitkas and L.J. Irakliotis, "Three-Dimensional Optical Storage for Database Processing," invited paper, *J. Optical Memory and Neural Networks*, Vol. 3, No. 2, 1994, pp. 217-229.

[MUS92] *The MU9C1480 LANCAM Handbook*, MUSIC Semiconductors, Colorado Springs, Co., 1992.

[NEF90] J.A. Neff, R.A. Athale, and S.H. Lee, "Two-Dimensional Spatial Light Modulators: A Tutorial," *Proc. IEEE*, Vol. 78, 1990, pp. 826–855.

[NEG95] N. Negroponte, *Being Digital*, Alfred Knopf, New York, N.Y., 1995.

[NEI93] M.A. Neifeld and D. Psaltis, "Programmable Image Associative Memory Using an Optical Disk and a Photorefractive Crystal," *Applied Optics*, Vol. 32, No. 23, Aug. 10, 1993, pp. 4,398–4,409.

[OWE87] Y. Owechko et al., "Holographic Associative Memory with Nonlinearities in the Correlation Domain," *Applied Optics*, Vol. 26, No. 19, May 15, 1987, pp. 1,900–1,910.

[PRO92] J.G. Proakis and D.G. Manolakis, *Digital Signal Processing Principles, Algorithms and Applications*, Macmillan, New York, N.Y., 1992.

[PSA85] D. Psaltis and N. Farhat, "Optical Information Processing Based on an Associative-Memory Model of Neural Nets with Thresholding and Feedback," *Optics Letters*, Vol. 10, No. 2, 1985, pp. 98–100.

[PSA90] D. Psaltis et al., "Optical Memory Disks in Optical Information Processing," *Applied Optics*, Vol. 29, No. 14, 1990, pp. 2,038–2,057.

[PAE87] FOR EXAMPLE Paek and D. Psaltis, "Optical Associative Processing Using Fourier Transform Holograms," *Optical Engineering*, Vol. 26, No. 5, May 1987, pp. 428–433.

[PU95] A. Pu, R. Denkewalter, and D. Psaltis, "Robot Navigation Using a Peristrophic Holographic Memory," in *Optical Computing 1995*, OSA Technical Digest Series, Vol. 10, 1995 pp. 137–139.

[RHO53] J.E. Rhodes Jr., "Analysis and Synthesis of Optical Images," *American J. Physics*, Vol. 21, 1953, pp. 337–343.

[RIC96] K.G. Richling and P.A. Mitkas, "Characterization of Volume Holographic Associative Searching," *Proc. OSA Topical Meeting in Holography*, 1996.

[SNY95] R.D. Snyder et al., "Desing and Demonstration of Projection and Selection Modules for a VCSEL/HPT-Based Database Filter," *Optical Computing 1995*, OSA Technical Digest Series, Vol. 10, 1995, pp. 204–206.

[SU88] S.Y.W. Su, *Database Computers: Principles, Architectures and Techniques*, McGraw-Hill, New York, N.Y., 1988.

[SWA89] G.J. Swanson, "Binary Optics Technology: The Theory and Design of Multi-Level Diffractive Optical Elements," Technical Report No. 854, MIT Lincoln Laboratory, Lincoln, Mass., 1989.

[VAN64] A. Vander Lugt, "Signal Detection by Complex Spatial Filtering," *IEEE Trans. Information Theory*, Vol. IT-10, 1964, pp. 139–145.

[VAN92] A. Vander Lugt, *Optical Signal Processing*, John Wiley & Sons, Inc., New York, N.Y., 1992.

[ULL88] J.D. Ullman, *Principles of Database and Knowledge-Based Systems*, Vol. 1, Computer Science Press, 1988.

[WEE89] C.C. Weems et al., "The Image Understanding Architecture," *Int'l J. Computer Vision*, Vol. 2, No. 3, 1989, pp. 251–282.

[YEH93] P. Yeh, *Introduction to Photorefractive Nonlinear Optics*, John Wiley & Sons, New York, N.Y., 1993.

Section III
Associative Processing Software

Associative Computing Environment

Jerry L. Potter
Kent State University
Kent, Ohio 44242
potter@mcs.kent.edu

Abstract

This paper points out the need for improved software productivity. It shows how associative computing with a tabular data structure and natural language syntax can be combined to provide an associative computing environment (ACE) suitable for introducing data parallelism to elementary algebra students and bypassing the Basic-Pascal-C intermediate stages. This ACE approach also provides considerable promise for improved productivity.

1 Introduction

Ever since my introduction to programming over 30 years ago, two concepts have fascinated me. One is the concept of writing a program that generates a program; the second is the concept of accessing data by content instead of address. Over these 30 years the hardware has changed drastically. Computing power selling for a few thousand dollars today would have cost millions not long ago. Software productivity, however, has scarcely changed at all. A crude but useful measure of software productivity is the number of lines of code needed to program a problem. Using this metric, the Fortran of 1964 is not a lot different from the C of today.

It can be argued that a QWERTY[1] syndrome has prevented the advancement of software productivity. That is, the programming style and techniques developed for primitive, slow, expensive machines still dominate today. Modern languages and algorithms are based on the classic von Neumann architecture and on the inherent implication that computing power (CPUs) are expensive while memory is cheap. The relative relationship may still be true, but the advances of inte-

---

[1] QWERTY is the term used to express the concept that established practices are difficult to change even though they are widely recognized to be inefficient. Examples include using imperial measures instead of metric, or using the "standard"—that is, QWERTY—typewriter keyboard that was designed specifically to slow down a typist when many better keyboard designs have been developed.

grated circuitry makes it irrelevant. That is, a factor of two or three to one when talking about a few dollars is irrelevant compared to the cost of programming. Thus an important research issue is whether some of the increase in hardware productivity can be used to increase software productivity.

Content-addressable memories in the form of associative computing has the potential to substantially increase productivity. Associative computing is a paradigm that is easily mapped onto massively parallel hardware configurations. Data parallelism is an inherent component of associative computing. Associative computing does not use pointers, and it eliminates the need for sorting; this makes it simple to use. Comparisons have shown that it has the potential to increase productivity by a factor of three [Potter, 1992, p.108].

The first advance in software productivity was achieved by replacing assembly language programming with Fortran and Pascal. This was achieved predominately by reorganizing the course sequence to teach Pascal or Fortran first and then assembly language programming as a second auxiliary language. Accordingly, this paper describes an associative computing environment (ACE) suitable for introducing data parallel and associative computation at the high-school algebra level. The intent is to bypass the Basic-Pascal-C-parallel sequence taught in high schools today.

2 Associative computing

The concept of content-addressable memory seems of limited use in that it is the ability to access a word of memory which is already at least partially known. However, if the definition of "word of memory" is expanded to several thousand bytes to allow entire records (not just fields) of data to be stored, then the concept is one of retrieving entire records based on a portion of their contents. When content-addressable records are accessed, entire thoughts—sentences or paragraphs of information—can be obtained by a description of part of them.

The everyday utility of this capability is demonstrated by the question, "What is the price of the red

Lamborghini?" The data record consists of "car type, color, price, and fuel economy." Two of the known values, color and car type, are used to reference a third, price. Note that the above "program" is easy to understand, there are no data declarations, indices, or loop specifications, for example. The associative computing paradigm is based on a "universal" two-dimensional data structure and a natural language interface to access and process it.

2.1 Data structures

Most data is inherently organized in a tabular form or can easily be mapped onto one. For example, "car type, color, price, and fuel economy" records are organized into a file as shown in Table 1. The file is a 2D tabular data organization that can be accessed by content.

Other data structures—such as stacks and queues,

lists, trees, arrays, and graphs—are easily mapped onto tables using structure codes as explained in detail in [Potter, 1992]. Tables 2 and 3 illustrate queues and trees. Many mathematical problems, such as matrices and imagery, have a natural 2D form.

2.2 Accessing data

Mathematical data organizations are accessed using data-parallel extensions of conventional algebraic expressions. The scalar/parallel dichotomy of associative data parallelism matches naturally with the singular/plural dichotomy of natural language. A $ is used as the plural/parallel marker to avoid the irregularities of English plurals. Thus, if there is a table of hours and rates, the wages may be calculated using data parallelism by

$$\text{wage\$ = hour\$ X rate\$.} \quad (2.2.1)$$

Table 1. A tabular organization.

Car Type	Color	Price	Fuel Economy
Lamborghini	Red	$90,000	8 mpg
Ford	Blue	$10,000	25 mpg
Chevy	Green	$12,000	32 mpg

Table 2. An associative stack and queue.

Time Tag	Task ID		Time Tag	Task ID		Time Tag	Task ID
0	10		0	10		0	10
not	used		5	17		not	used
2	15		2	15		2	15
4	20		4	20		not	used
3	35		3	35		3	35
1	100		1	100		1	100
before			after push 17			after pop ⇒ 20	

Associative stack

Time Tag	Task ID		Time Tag	Task ID		Time Tag	Task ID
0	10		0	10		not	used
not	used		5	17		not	used
2	15		2	15		2	15
4	20		4	20		4	20
3	35		3	35		3	35
1	100		1	100		1	100
before			after queue 17			after next ⇒ 10	

Associative queue

181

Table 3. A tree organization.

Object Name	Structure Code	Value
List	100	This
List	210	is
List	221	a
List	222	list

List = (This (is (a list)))

The expression

```
wage = hour X rate.
```

refers to a single record (row) of scalar variables and is ambiguous in isolation, because no individual record has been identified. Records may be identified by associative search using a natural language syntax. Thus, "What is the price of the red Lamborghini?" is an associative search that identifies one or more entries in the car data structure, and "Whose rate is $5.00?" is a search in the wage data structure.

2.3   Natural language

As a rule of thumb, actions (verbs) are named and objects are described (using noun and prepositional phrases) in natural language. Thus, more formally, the syntax for a command is

```
verb noun_phrase
{prepositional_phrase}*.
```

Accordingly, an alternative command for the price query is

```
Find the price of the red
Lamborghini.
```

The form of a data-parallel computation is

```
Multiply the hour$ times the
rate$. Store the result$ into the
wage$.
```

This latter form is identical to the above algebraic form (2.2.1). It can be used when it is desirable to "document" as well as specify the actions of a program.

2.4   Pronouns

Once individual records have been identified, they may be referenced by using pronouns. Thus

```
Find the price of the red
Lamborghini. Find its fuel
economy.
```

is a shorthand alternative for

```
Find the price of the red
Lamborghini. Find the fuel
economy of the red Lamborghini.
```

When a singular form is used, it implies that at least one matching record exists in the table. However, in general, more than one may match. If so, one is picked at random. Plural statements encompass the singular mode so that even if only one record matches a plural statement, it is processed. The plural form of the above query is

```
Find the price$ of the red
Lamborghini$. Find their fuel
economy$.
```

2.5   Multiword identifiers

Note that in the above, "fuel economy" is a multiword identifier. That is, the column in the table that contains the fuel economy data is so labeled, as shown in Table 1. Underscored or run-together forms such as fuel_economy and fuelEconomy are not needed or used. The multiword identifier form allows table entries to be identified naturally. It may be used for column and row identification. Columns must be labeled, but row labels are optional. For example, in Table 4, the phrase "Aunt Jane's new car" is the associative natural language way to reference "Lamborghini."

2.6   Common knowledge

The careful reader has noticed that "Find the price of the red Lamborghini" identifies the column of the table (that is, price) from which the information is to be obtained. However, the columns to be searched for "red" and "Lamborghini" are not named. This is in

Table 4. Labeled rows and columns.

	New Car	Old Car
Aunt Jane	Lamborghini	Dodge
Uncle Bob	Ford	Chevy

keeping with the concept of common knowledge. Everyone knows that "red" is a color so that you obviously look for "red" in the color column. Common knowledge is achieved in ACE by parsing the data when it is input. At that time, an "inverted list," mapping values to column names, is generated. The inverted list is used to compile the command.

3   Examples

The intent of the associative computing environment is to introduce associative parallel computing to high schools and colleges at the elementary algebra level. The approach is to use the charting technique of story problems as an introduction to 2D data structures and the natural-language concepts described above for programming. Two examples of problem presentations, with explanatory notes, follow. The first presentation introduces data parallelism and discusses the format of the column labels. The second presentation introduces scalar/parallel mixed-mode and restricted-scope computation. Finally, a few computer science applications are discussed.

Problem 1: Compound rates and times

The XYZ company received a large order for widgets. As a result, Mary had to work 6.5 hours of overtime. Mark worked 5 hours of overtime, and Martin worked 8. They all worked a normal 40-hour week in addition. Mary earns $5.50 an hour; Mark, $4.75, and Martin, $6.00. Because the order was very profitable, they all earned extra overtime pay of $2.10 an hour. Thus Mary got $7.60, Mark got $6.85, and Martin got $8.10 an hour for overtime. What is the XYZ payroll for the week?

Analysis:

This problem requires a straightforward extension of the wage formula. Wages are asked for, but two different hours and rates are required. Thus the extended wage equation is:

$$rate_1 \times time_1 + rate_2 \times time_2 = wage$$

Chart: (*organize the facts into chart form*)

	(rate × time) + (over rate × over time) = wage				
Mary	5.50	40	7.60	6.5	w
Mark	4.75	40	6.85	5.0	w
Martin	6.00	40	8.10	8.0	w

Solution:

Step 1:   Write an equation from the chart. $5.50 \times 40 + 7.60 \times 6.5 = w$

Step 2:   Solve the equation symbolically (*Perform each step in the solution of the equation, but do not carry out the arithmetic computations*). $2 = 5.50 \times 40 + 7.60 \times 6.5$

Step 3:   Replace the numbers by their names from the chart. Since the same formula is used for all computations, the statement can be written in data-parallel form.   wage\$ = rate\$ × time\$ + over rate\$ × over time\$

Program:

Step 1: Type ACE.

Step 2: Enter the program (*the program name, the chart, the solution, and END*).

Calculate XYZ Payroll

	(rate × time) + (over rate × over time) = wage				
Mary	5.50	40	7.60	6.5	w
Mark	4.75	40	6.85	5.0	w
Martin	6.00	40	8.10	8.0	w

wage$ = rate$ × time$ + over rate$ × over time$

END.

Step 3: Type the problem name (*Run the program and compute the answer*).
Calculate XYZ Payroll.

Programming Note—Multiple names

As the chart and table in Problem 2.6 illustrates, when column names have multiple parts, the column widths can become overly wide. A common alternative for charts is to double up as below:

```
|      | (rate × time) + (over  × over ) = wage  |
|      |                   rate    time          |
```

ACE supports this alternative form but requires that all "punctuation" be repeated in every row. A single column label may be in any row. For example,

```
|      | (rate × time) + (over × over ) = wage  |
|      | (      ×     ) + (rate × time ) =      |
```

```
|      | (      × time) + (over × over ) = wage |
|      | (rate ×      ) + (rate × time ) =      |
```

and

```
|      | (rate ×      ) + (over × over ) = wage |
|      | (      × time) + (rate × time ) =      |
```

are equivalent. By moving rate, time, and wage from the top row to the bottom, eight different combinations are possible. All are acceptable, but the first one above is preferred.

Problem 2: Extended ratio factor relational equations

A chemical substance has an extended ratio of 2:5:7 with a total mass of 168 grams. Determine the mass of each part.

Analysis:

This problem uses the factor-only relational formula. The chart has three rows, one for each part of the substance. Addition is used in the row equation.

Chart: (*organize the facts into chart form*)

	unknown × ratio = mass		
part1 +	p	2	2p
part2 +	p	5	5p
part3 =	p	7	7p
total			168

Solution:

Step 1:   Write the row equation from the chart. $2p + 5p + 7p = 168$

Step 2:   Solve the equation symbolically (*Perform each step in the solution of the equation, but do not carry out the arithmetic computations*).

$2p + 5p + 7p = 168$
$p(2 + 5 + 7) = 168$
$p = 168 / (2 + 5 + 7)$

Step 3:   Replace the numbers by their names from the chart.

unknown = total mass / (part1 ratio + part2 ratio + part3 ratio)

Program:

Step 1: Type ACE.
Step 2: Enter the program (*the problem name, the chart, the solution, and END*).

Calculate masses:

	unknown	ratio	mass
part1	p	2	2p
part2	p	5	5p
part3	p	7	7p
total			168

unknown = total mass / (part1 ratio + part2 ratio + part3 ratio);
for part1, part2, and part3:
        mass$ = unknown x ratio$.
END.

Step 3: Type the problem name (*Run the program and compute the answer*).
Calculate masses.

In order to demonstrate the range of ACE, some computer science applications will be illustrated next.

"First in, first out" and "last in, first out" queues can be implemented using a table of tasks and associative time stamps as shown in Table 2. The phrase

    Find the task id with the largest
    time tag

implements a "last in, first out" queue.

    Find the task id with the
    smallest time tag

implements a "first in, first out" queue. Note that the same tabular structure can be used for all kinds of queues and that the code for accessing it describes exactly the queue's operation.

A mathematical example is convolution, which is an algebraic formula but is presented here in natural-language form. This problem is presented in three

185

routines. The first, in Table 5 below, defines the "operator" that sums three column elements into one. The second, in Table 6, defines the "operator" that multiplies neighboring values by the appropriate scaling factors, and the third, in Table 7, inputs the image, applies the operators, and outputs the resulting image.

Table 5. Convolution problem—routine 1.

Define column sum:

Input Column	Element
First	
Second	
Third	

Output Column	Element
First	
Second	
Third	

Sum   the input column's first element,
           the input column's second element and
           the input column's third element.
Put the result in the output column's second element.
END.

Table 6. Convolution problem—routine 2.

Define weight matrix multiply:

Weight Column One	Weight Column Two	Weight Column Three

Mask Column One	Mask Column Two	Mask Column Three

Sum   the column sum$ of weight column one$ times mask column one$,
                weight column two$ times mask column two$,
and
                weight column three$ times mask column three$.
Put the result$ in mask column two$.
END.

Table 7. Convolution problem—routine 3.

Problem convolve:

Input Image	Column ...
row :	

Kernel			
	0	-1	0
	-1	4	-1
	0	-1	0

Output Image	Column ...
row :	

Read input image$$.
/* Set the scope for the boundary conditions */
for input image column$2 . . column$511:
For input image row2$ . . row511$:
    weight multiply input image$$ by kernel$$.
Put the result$$ in output image$$.
Write output image$$.
END.

4 Conclusion

I have described a methodology for introducing productive but easy to learn programming techniques that utilize the vast increase in computing power to simplify the programming tasks. Associative programming concepts improve programming productivity by reducing the complexity of the data structures and the attendant number of lines of code. Yet the techniques are simple enough to be taught at the high school level. Moreover, the techniques are appropriate for the massively parallel and associative computers of the future.

4.1 Future directions

Object-oriented programming is the latest in the evolution of conventional sequential languages. Some of the advantages of object-oriented programming are operator overloading (polymorphism), class inheritance, "program-code" bundling (objects), and class libraries. These advantages are significant, and by the "lines of code" metric, a definite improvement in that the libraries allow fewer lines of code to accomplish a specific task. Object-oriented programming with its constructors and destructors and dynamic classes are close to writing a program that generates a program which is then executed. Is it possible to add the advantages of OOP to associative computing?

The basic approach of associative computing resembles OOP. In associative computing, the code and the data are global but very distinct: not intermingled and encapsulated. The protection that encapsulation provides in OOP is accomplished in associative computing by associative search. In essence, data is tagged with a unique code (its description) that the program must "match" before the data is processed. Thus by definition, data *cannot* erroneously be processed even if the control of flow is in error. Instead of wild transfers and core dumps when pointers get confused, erroneous associative commands are simply ignored by the data.

Associative search can also be used with structure codes to implement inheritance. Thus data could be organized hierarchically with hierarchical structure codes. Many of the OOP's advantages can be added to associative computing to complement associative computing's advantages, such as inherent parallelism, simple data structures, and natural-language-like syntax. This is an area for future research.

5 References

J.L. Potter, *Associative Computing*, Plenum Press, New York, N.Y., 1992.

ASC: An Associative-Computing Paradigm

Jerry Potter, Johnnie Baker, Stephen Scott, Arvind Bansal,
Chokchai Leangsuksun, and Chandra Asthagiri

Kent State University

Associative computing evolved in an era when associative memories were both relatively new and, because they required a comparator at each bit of memory, relatively expensive. In the early 1970s, Goodyear Aerospace improved upon early associative processing techniques with its Staran SIMD (single instruction, multiple data) computer.[1] Goodyear realized that the massively parallel search capability of bit-serial SIMDs could simulate associative searching, with the cost advantage of sharing the comparison logic (that is, the processing elements) over all the bits in an entire row of memory. This approach provided two additional benefits: The word widths could be very large (from 256 bits to 64 kilobits), and the data could be processed in situ using the same PEs.

However, today's lower hardware costs and increased computing speeds allow parallel techniques to be effectively emulated on conventional sequential machines. Accessing data by associative searching rather than addresses and processing data in memory require a new programming style. One goal of our research is to develop a parallel programming paradigm that is suitable for many diverse applications, is efficient to write and execute, and can be used on a wide range of computing engines, from PCs and workstations to massively parallel supercomputers.

Our associative-computing (ASC) paradigm is an extension of the general associative processing techniques developed by Goodyear. We use two-dimensional tables as the basic data structure. Our paradigm has an efficient associative-based, dynamic memory-allocation mechanism that does not use pointers. It incorporates data parallelism at the base level, so that programmers do not have to specify low-level sequential tasks such as sorting, looping, and parallelization.

Our paradigm supports all of the standard data-parallel and massively parallel computing algorithms. It combines numerical computation (such as convolution, matrix multiplication, and graphics) with nonnumerical computing (such as compilation, graph algorithms, rule-based systems, and language interpreters).[2] This article focuses on the nonnumerical aspects of ASC.

The ASC model

The ASC model is the basis of a high-level associative-programming paradigm and language. As described in the sidebar, "Properties of the ASC model," the extended model provides a basis for algorithm development and analysis similar to the

> **Today's increased computing speeds allow conventional sequential machines to effectively emulate associative computing techniques. Here is a parallel programming paradigm designed for a wide range of computing engines.**

PRAM (parallel random-access memory) models, with the additional provisions that hardware can be built to support this model and that its primitive operations are sufficiently rich to allow efficient use of massive parallelism.[3] These features let us develop parallel algorithms for large problems that can be abstractly analyzed and executed. Furthermore, algorithms based on a common model will have greater applicability and retain their importance longer than ones based on a specific computer that may be out of production within a few years. Briefly, the model calls for data-parallel execution of instructions, constant-time associative searching, constant-time maximum and minimum operations, and synchronization of instruction streams using control parallelism. The simplest ASC model assumes only one instruction stream (IS). This model can be supported on existing SIMD computers and is assumed throughout unless we state otherwise.

The sidebar lists the specific properties that the hardware must have to support the model. Reflecting these specifications, the ASC language is characterized by built-in associative reduction notation, associative responder iteration, responder-based flow of control, responder reference and selection mechanisms, and a multiple instruction stream capability that provides dynamic control parallelism on top of data parallelism. ASC supports recursion and special command constructs with automatic backtracking for complex context-sensitive searching. Fundamental to the nonnumerical focus of ASC are the unique structure code features and dynamic memory allocation. The most important features of ASC are discussed below. (ASC language syntax is described in detail in Potter.[2])

Associative programming techniques

Generally, a few basic techniques determine the "feel" of a programming paradigm, such as pointers in C and tail recursion or list processing in Lisp and Prolog. In ASC, the associative search is the fundamental operation, and its influence is felt in constant-time operations, tabular representation of abstract data structures, responder processing, and control parallelism.

Constant time operation. Data parallelism is a basic model used in many languages. ASC uses data parallelism as the basis for associative searching, which takes time proportional to the number of bits in a field, not the number of data items being searched. Thus, assuming

---

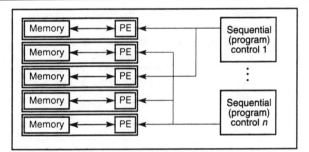
---

that all the data fits in the computer, it executes in constant time,[2] just as comparison, addition, and other data-parallel arithmetic operations do. In addition to basic pattern searching, ASC makes extensive use of constant time functions[4] (maximum, minimum, greatest lower bound, and least upper bound). The constant time functions have corresponding constant-time associative index functions (maxdex, mindex, prvdex, and nxtdex), which are used for associative reduction. For example, the query "What is the salary of the oldest employee?" requires a maximum search on the age field, but the associated salary, not the age, is the desired item. The maxdex function in "salary[maxdex(age$)]" expresses the association between the maximum age and the associated salary. Computers with the properties specified in the sidebar can execute these functions in constant time. In addition, today's sequential computers are powerful enough to emulate these operations for many problems.

Tabular data structures and structure codes. Tabular data structures (that is, tables, charts, and arrays) have two advantages for ASC. First, they are ubiquitous; tables and arrays are a common and natural organization for databases and many scientific applications, and users need only a minimal introduction to manipulate them effectively. Second, the concept of processing an entire column of a table simultaneously is easy to comprehend.

There are a number of common abstract data structures, including stacks, queues, trees, and graphs, that are normally implemented using address manipulation via pointers and indexes. In an associative computer, in contrast, physical address relationships between data are not present. Instead, structure codes, which are numeric representations of the abstract structural information, are associated with the data. The codes are generated automatically, and appropriately named functions — for example, parent(), sibling(), and child() — are used to manipulate them. The programmer need be aware only of the data structure type being used (tree, graph, and so forth) and not the internal structure codes themselves.

One of the major advantages of structure codes is that they allow the data to be expressed in tabular form so that they can be processed in a data-parallel manner. This means that lists, trees, and graphs can be searched associatively in constant time instead of having to be sequentially searched element by element. Tabular organizations are stored one row per cell in an associative computer. Thus, any one field (a column of the table) can be searched in parallel by broadcasting the desired value to all cell PEs, which then compare it with their local values.

---

sponders. It can also restore the previous set of active cells. Each of these actions requires one unit of time.
- Each IS has the ability to select an arbitrary responder from the set of active cells in unit time.
- Each IS can instruct the selected cell to broadcast data on the bus. All other cells listening to this IS receive the value placed on the bus in unit time.

Constant time global operations

- An IS can compute the OR or AND of a binary value in all active PEs in unit time.
- An IS can identify the cells with the maximum or minimum value in each of its active PEs in constant time.

Control parallelism

- Cells without further work to do are called idle cells and are assigned to a specified IS, which (among other tasks) manages the idle cells. An idle cell can be dynamically allocated to an IS in unit time. Any subset of cells can be deallocated and reassigned as idle cells in constant time.
- If an IS is executing a task that requires two or more subtasks involving data in disjoint subsets of the active cells, control (MIMD) parallelism can be invoked by assigning a subtask to an idle IS. When all subtasks generated by the original IS are completed, the cells are returned to the originating IS.

A new programming paradigm called Heterogeneous Associative Computing[7] (HASC) is presently under development at Kent State University. From the ASC model, this paradigm takes the concept of cells and instruction broadcasting. It uses tabular data and massively parallel searches to match commands and data to machines. The result is that, in an extension of polymorphism, commands are executed on the machines best suited for them.

References

1. J.L. Potter, *Associative Computing — A Programming Paradigm for Massively Parallel Computers*, Plenum Publishing, N.Y., 1992.

2. J.W. Baker and A. Miller, "A Parallel Production System Extending OPS5," *Proc. Frontiers of Massively Parallel Computation*, CS Press, Los Alamitos, Calif., Order No. 2772-02, 1990, pp. 110-118.

3. T. Krochta, *Parallel Ray Tracing*, master's thesis, Kent State Univ., Kent, Ohio, 1986.

4. K. Mamoozadeh, *Relational Databases on Associative Processors*, master's thesis, Dept. of Mathematics and Computer Science, Kent State Univ., Kent, Ohio, 1986.

5. C. Asthagiri, *Context-Sensitive Parsing Using an Associative Processor*, master's thesis, Dept. of Mathematics and Computer Science, Kent State Univ., Kent, Ohio, 1986.

6. R. Miles, *Optimizing Associative Intermediate Code*, master's thesis, Dept. of Mathematics and Computer Science, Kent State Univ., Kent, Ohio, 1993.

7. S.L. Scott and J.L. Potter, "Heterogeneous Associative Computing — HASC," *2nd Associative Processing and Applications Workshop*, Syracuse Univ., Syracuse, N.Y., July 1993; Tech. Report CS-9305-05, Dept. of Mathematics and Computer Science, Kent State University, Kent, Ohio, May 1993.

8. C. Leangsuksun, S.L. Scott, and J.L. Potter, "Implicit Task Mapping in a Heterogeneous Environment," Tech Report CS-9409-08, Dept. of Mathematics and Computer Science, Kent State University, Kent, Ohio. May 1993.

9. *Electronic Eng. Times*, Feb. 7, 1994, p. 41.

10. J.W. Baker and J.L. Potter, "A Model of Computation for Associative Computing," Tech. Report CS-9409-07, Dept. of Mathematics and Computer Science, Kent State Univ., Kent, Ohio, Sept. 1994.

Additional information is available via WWW at http://nimitz.mcs. kent.edu/ {~potter, ~chokchai, ~sscott, ~arvind, ~jbaker}.

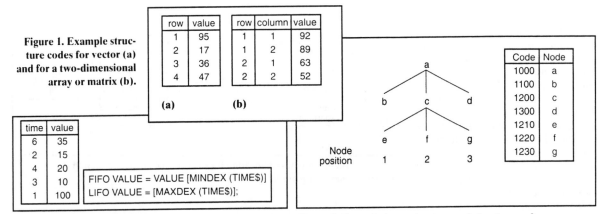

Figure 1. Example structure codes for vector (a) and for a two-dimensional array or matrix (b).

(a)

row	value
1	95
2	17
3	36
4	47

(b)

row	column	value
1	1	92
1	2	89
2	1	63
2	2	52

time	value
6	35
2	15
4	20
3	10
1	100

FIFO VALUE = VALUE [MINDEX (TIME$)]
LIFO VALUE = [MAXDEX (TIME$)];

Figure 2. Associative LIFO and FIFO queues using maximum and minimum function to retrieve associated values.

Code	Node
1000	a
1100	b
1200	c
1300	d
1210	e
1220	f
1230	g

Node position   1   2   3

Figure 3. Canonical tree structure and structure codes as represented in associative memory.

The simplest structure codes are those for arrays. For nonnumerical applications, a vector can be represented by a row field and a value field as shown in Figure 1a. Likewise, we can represent a two-dimensional array or matrix by a row field, a column field, and a value field. In Figure 1b, the matrix value at position (1, 2) can be found in constant time by searching for row 1 and column 2 and retrieving the associated value — 89.

Frequently, we can represent directly useful information in the structure code. For example, the time of arrival is used to implement FIFO and LIFO queues. For example, in Figure 2 the FIFO value in the queue is retrieved using the mindex function to select the first (smallest or oldest) time entry and its associated value.

Trees and graphs require more sophisticated structure codes. If trees are put into a canonical form, and the position of the nodes on every level are numbered from left to right, we can generate a code for every node in the tree by starting at the root of the tree and listing the node numbers along the path to the node in question. If the code is left justified with zero fill, it will support parallel searching, concatenation, insertion, and deletion. Figure 3 gives an example of a tree and its structure codes as represented in an associative memory. The left and right siblings of node *f* can be found in constant time by using the sibdex function — sibdex(code[node$==`f']).

This expression can be read from the inside out. First, the node field is searched for the value *f*; the response is used to select the associated structure-code value (1220), which is passed to the sibdex function. Sibdex combines the greatest-lower-bound and least-upper-bound search functions to identify codes 1210 and 1230 as being adjacent to 1220, and their associated nodes — *e* and *g* — as siblings of *f*. All operations are constant time. This kind of operation is very useful for expression parsing.[5]

Quadsected square codes are structure codes for graphs that can be applied to the generation of node domination, node influencing, and similar information useful in control flow graph analysis. A quadsected square is a square divided into four subsquares. The quadrants of a quadsected square can be recursively subdivided to any level. The quadsected square code calculation and manipulation functions are performed in data-parallel mode for all nodes of a graph. For example, given the code for a node, the dominance relationship between the node and all other nodes in the graph can be computed in constant time independent of the size of the graph.

Figures 4a and 4b illustrate the dual relationship between binary graphs and quadsected squares. The graph's binary

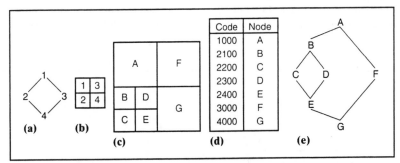

Figure 4. Quadsected square encoding for (a) binary graph, (b) quadsected square, (c) recursively quadsected square, (d) structure codes, and (e) binary graph.

Code	Node
1000	A
2100	B
2200	C
2300	D
2400	E
3000	F
4000	G

fan-out (node 1 branches to 2 and 3) and binary fan-in (node 2 and 3 converge on 4) shown in Figure 4a are mapped onto the location code map shown in Figure 4b. A more complex example is given in Figures 4c, 4d, and 4e, where the control flow starts in quadrant A and flows into the upper left-most subdivision of the two adjacent quadrants (B of BCDE and F). Each subdivision continues this recursive process until the final two quadrants within a subdivision are joined at their right-most subdivision (C and D are joined at E, and E and F are joined at G).

We obtain the structure code for a recursively quadsected square (Figure 4d) by specifying the position of the top-level subdivision first (as the left-most digit), then the position of the next recursive subdivision, and so on, with zero fill used on the right.

Responder processing. The responders of an associative search are those cells that successfully matched the associative search query. Data-parallel operations

191

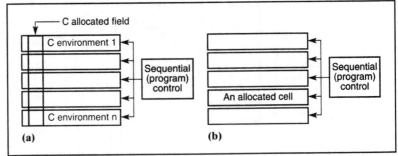

Figure 5. Dynamic memory allocation for (a) C-based environment and (b) the associative computing model.

applied to the responders essentially act as substitutes for the index-based loops used in Fortran and C. However, it is sometimes desirable to process each responder individually. In responder iteration, a responder is arbitrarily selected and processed using both sequential and parallel operations. When processing is complete, the responder is idled and another responder is selected for processing. Responder iteration is an effective way of using parallel searching to avoid sorting unordered data.

We use responder selection to achieve constant-time memory allocation. Idle cells are assigned to a single instruction stream. When an IS needs one or more new cells, they are arbitrarily selected from the idle pool and allocated to the requesting IS. When that IS no longer needs those cells, they are identified by

associative search, released in parallel, and returned to the idle IS. Figure 5 illustrates the difference between associative-memory allocation and C-based data-parallel memory allocation, where additional fields, not cells, are allocated

to the active processors. (The "loop while" statement in Figure 6 is an example of responder iteration.)

Control parallelism. To this point our discussion has centered on data paral-

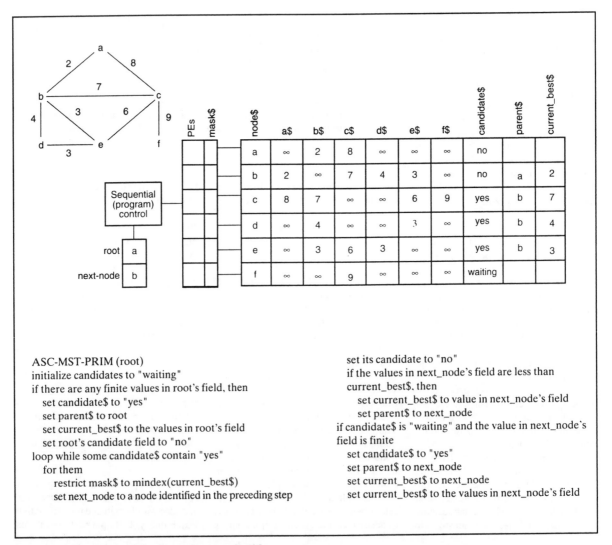

```
ASC-MST-PRIM (root)
initialize candidates to "waiting"
if there are any finite values in root's field, then
    set candidate$ to "yes"
    set parent$ to root
    set current_best$ to the values in root's field
    set root's candidate field to "no"
loop while some candidate$ contain "yes"
    for them
        restrict mask$ to mindex(current_best$)
        set next_node to a node identified in the preceding step
```

```
    set its candidate to "no"
    if the values in next_node's field are less than
    current_best$, then
        set current_best$ to value in next_node's field
        set parent$ to next_node
if candidate$ is "waiting" and the value in next_node's
field is finite
    set candidate$ to "yes"
    set parent$ to next_node
    set current_best$ to next_node
    set current_best$ to the values in next_node's field
```

Figure 6. An associative minimal spanning tree algorithm.

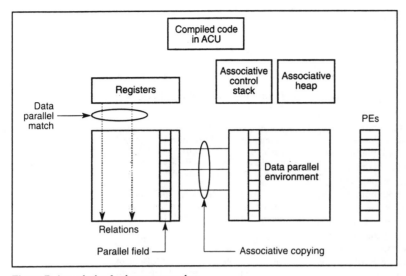

Figure 7. Associative logic programming.

lelism. However, the ASC model accommodates both data and control parallelism so that the computer can efficiently use all its cells. The control-parallel component depends on the dynamic manipulation of instruction streams in response to associative searches. The mechanism relies on partitioning the responders into mutually exclusive subsets. For example, the evaluation of an IF's conditional expression divides the active cells into two mutually exclusive partitions: one containing the cells that respond TRUE and one containing the cells that respond FALSE. These partitions can be processed using control parallelism by forking the process: One IS is assigned to execute the THEN portion of the IF statement with the TRUE responders, and another IS is assigned to execute the ELSE portion with the FALSE responders. The IS's execute in parallel, each in a data-parallel mode. The programmer needs no control-parallel statements, such as FORK or JOIN, since the control parallelism is inherent in the statements. Case statements are another example of control parallelism, except that there are n partitions — one for each of the n cases — instead of two partitions as in the IF-THEN-ELSE.

A significant speedup of up to k in the runtime of certain algorithms is possible using an associative computer with a constant number k of instruction streams. Moreover, if the number of instruction streams is not restricted to being constant, then new algorithms with lower complexity times may be possible.

Example applications

An ASC version of Prim's minimal spanning tree (MST) algorithm[3] using associative-computing techniques with only one IS is given in Figure 6. The values given there indicate the state of the algorithm after the first iteration through the "loop while." All the statements in the algorithm execute in constant time. The data for each node is stored in a record, and the records are stored with at most one record per cell. The cell variables are identified with a "$" symbol following the variable name. The cost of an edge from node x to node y is stored in the $x\$$ field of node y and the $y\$$ field of node x. Each record also has the additional variables, candidate\$, parent\$, and current_best\$. Root and next-node are scalar variables. If root = n, then the terminology "root's field" refers to the field $n\$$. Since one tree edge is selected by each pass through the loop and a spanning tree has $n - 1$ tree edges, the runtime of this algorithm is $O(n)$. This is a cost-optimal parallel implementation of Prim's original MST algorithm, which has a sequential running time of $O(n^2)$. Moreover, no additional overhead is incurred as the size of the graph increases, because the algorithm only requires additional cells and is thus easily scalable to larger data sets. Finally, since no networks are used and no task-forking or join operations are needed, we have minimized the communications and synchronization overhead costs.

ASC has been combined with logic programming to achieve high-performance intelligent reasoning, data-parallel scientific computing, and efficient information retrieval from large knowledge bases.[6] The strategy in the design of the associative-logic programming system is to maximize the use of bit-vector and data-parallel operations and to minimize the movement of scalar data. Facts, relations, and the left-hand sides of rules are represented as records (associations) of parallel fields with one record per cell. The right-hand sides of the rules are compiled into an abstract instruction set. A simplified schematic of the model is given in Figure 7.

Some advantages of combining associative and logic computing are

(1) the speed of knowledge retrieval is independent of the number of ground facts,
(2) knowledge retrieval is possible even if the information is incomplete, making knowledge discovery possible,
(3) relations with a large number of arguments are handled efficiently with little overhead,
(4) associative lookup is fast, allowing the tight integration of high-performance knowledge retrieval and data-parallel computation without any overhead due to data movement or data transformation, and
(5) the model is efficient for both scalar and data-parallel computations on various abstract data types such as sequences, matrices, bags, and sets.

These advantages suggest that this paradigm can be successfully applied to data-intensive problems such as geographical information systems, image-understanding systems, statistical knowledge bases, and genome sequencing. For example, in geographical information systems, spatial data structures such as quadtrees and octtrees are represented associatively with structure codes. As a result, different regions having the same values can be identified using associative searches in constant time.

The integration of data-parallel scientific computing, knowledge base retrieval, and rule-based reasoning provides necessary tools for image-understanding systems. Statistical queries can directly benefit from associative searches, associative representation of structures, data-parallel arithmetic computations, and data-parallel aggregate functions. Genome sequencing requires integration of knowledge retrieval, efficient insertion and deletion of data elements, and efficient manipulation of matrices for the heuristic matching of sequences.

The associative techniques of the 1970s augmented with new techniques — such as structure codes, dynamic memory allocation, responder iteration, multiple instruction streams, associative selection, and reduction notation and pronouns — form the basis of a programming paradigm that makes use of today's inexpensive computing power to facilitate parallel programming. The ASC paradigm uses a tabular-data organization, massive parallel searching, and simple syntax, so that the paradigm is easily comprehensible to computer specialists and nonspecialists alike. Furthermore, the ASC paradigm is suitable for all levels of computing, from PCs and workstations to multiple instruction stream SIMDs and heterogeneous networks. ∎

Acknowledgments

The authors thank Selim Akl for his helpful comments. Stephen L. Scott's work on heterogeneous associative computing is supported by a NASA GSRP-HPCC fellowship and by NRaD.

References

1. K. Batcher, "Staran Parallel Processor System Hardware," *Proc. National Computer Conf.*, AFIPS, 1974, pp. 405-410.

2. J.L. Potter, *Associative Computing — A Programming Paradigm for Massively Parallel Computers*, Plenum Publishing, N.Y., 1992.

3. J.W. Baker and J.L. Potter, "A Model of Computation for Associative Computing," Tech. Report CS-9409-07, Dept. of Mathematics and Computer Science, Kent State Univ., Kent, Ohio, Sept. 1994.

4. A. Falkoff, "Algorithms for Parallel Search Memories," *J. Associative Computing*, Mar. 1962, pp. 488-511.

5. C. Asthagiri and J.L. Potter, "Associative Parallel Common Subexpression Elimination," Tech. Report CS-9405-06, Dept. of Mathematics and Computer Science, Kent State Univ., Kent, Ohio, May 1994.

6. A. Bansal, J.L. Potter, and L. Prasad, "Data-Parallel Compilation and Extending Query Power of Large Knowledge Bases," *Proc. Int'l Conf. Tools With Artificial Intelligence*, CS Press, Los Alamitos, Calif., Order No. 2905-02, 1992, pp. 276-283.

Associative Data Structures

Jerry L. Potter
Kent State University
Kent, Ohio 44242
potter@mcs.kent.edu

Abstract

Structure codes allow the functionality of conventional data structures to be implemented in associative memories and computers. Structure codes have been developed for stacks, queues, and trees. However, graphs are commonly stored in associative memories by specifying their edges. Although this allows the edges to be searched and processed in parallel, the overall structure of the graph that is important for such application as flow analysis must be analyzed sequentially. The quadsected-squares graph-encoding technique described in this paper allows flow graph information to be calculated and manipulated associatively.

1   Introduction

Associative computing is based on accessing data to be processed by specifying a portion of its contents. For example, the triples (car, color, red) and (chair, color, red) can be associatively accessed by specifying (?, color, red). It is obvious that associative access is not limited to triples but can be extended to records of any size. SIMD processors such as Loral Defense Systems' ASPRO, Active Memory Technology's DAP, and MasPar Corporation's MasPar can be programmed for associative computing by storing one record per PE-memory cell. This organization achieves parallel associative searching and data-parallel processing of associatively matched records.

In this paper, I describe the use of structure codes in associative computing, first with a brief background and then some introductory examples of structure codes. Then I describe the quadsected-squares structure codes and show how they may be used to perform data flow analysis on binary graphs.

2   Background

Many conventional data organizations such as stacks, queues, vectors, arrays, trees, and graphs, are based on address manipulation. However, physical address re-lationships between data are not necessarily preserved in an associative computer. Therefore, an alternative mechanism such as structure codes must be used for achieving the equivalent functionality of these data structures. Structure codes are numeric representations of structural information that can be associated with the data.

To be useful, structure codes must possess certain properties and admit basic operations. In particular, they must produce a unique code for every position in the structure. They must be easy to calculate. They must support parallel computation (associative searching), and they must be extensible. That is, they must be applicable to any size of data structure. Structure codes must be designed such that the data structures they encode can be combined, modified, and deleted efficiently. The specific code operations desired depend on the application, but in general, the basic operations—first code, last code, next larger code and next smaller code—are desired.

On a bit-serial SIMD, these operations can be performed in constant time by using the classic Maximum and Minimum functions [Falkoff 1962] and their derivatives. If the Minimum function is applied to the structure code field, the smallest or first code is found. Similarly, Maximum will find the last code. The Sibdex function [Potter 1992] is an enhancement of the Maximum and Minimum algorithms that can find the largest code less than a specified value and the smallest code larger than a specified value in constant time. Given a code, Sibdex provides the next larger code and next smaller code operations.

3   Structure codes

The simplest structure codes are those for dimensioned arrays.

The code is simply the row, column, or row and column position of the element as illustrated in Figure 1. Given that a scalar variable such as Index contains a specific code, the next larger code is obtained by the increment operator, that is, Index++, the next smaller by Index--. The first and last Indexes can be obtained

row	value
1	95
2	17
3	36
4	47

row	col	value
1	1	92
1	2	89
2	1	63
2	2	52

Figure 1. Row and Row-Col structure codes.

by applying the Minimum and Maximum functions to the parallel field containing the indices.

Frequently, directly useful information can be used as the structure code. For example, in Figure 2 the time of arrival is used instead of a row number to implement FIFO and LIFO queues using the Maximum and Minimum functions. (The larger time_tag values indicate later arrivals).

More sophisticated structure codes are required for trees and graphs. If trees are put into a canonical form as shown in Figure 3, and the nodes on every level are numbered from left to right, a code for every node in the tree can be generated by starting at the root of the tree and listing the node numbers along the path to the node in question. If the code is left justified with zero fill, it will support tree concatenation, insertion, and deletion [Potter 1992, pp. 134ff]. Figure 4 gives an example of a tree, its structure codes, and its representation in an associative memory.

Tree structure codes can be used for graphs. One of the nodes of the graph is designated as the root, and the other nodes are organized into levels. The nodes on level one are all one edge from the root. The nodes on level two are two edges away. The path from the root to a node is obtained in the same manner as for a tree. The problem with using tree codes for graphs is that there may be multiple paths from the root to a given node and thus multiple codes. In general, this is unacceptable as each additional code increases the computational effort required to process the graph. The next section describes the quadsected-square encoding technique, which produces a unique code for each node in a binary graph.

TIME _TAG	VALUE
0	10
2	15
4	20
3	35
1	100

FIFO = MINIMUM (TIME_TAG);
LIFO = MAXIMUM (TIME_TAG);

Figure 2. Associative queues.

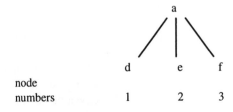

node numbers   1   2   3

Figure 3. Tree node numbering.

196

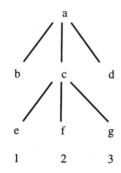

code	node
1000	a
1100	b
1200	c
1300	d
1210	e
1220	f
1230	g

node numbers   1   2   3

Figure 4. Tree structure codes.

4 Quadsected-squares structure codes

Binary graphs are important because (1) all graphs can be converted into binary graphs, and (2) the flow graphs of structured programs can be easily represented as binary graphs.

Figure 5 illustrates the dual relationship between a quadsected square and a binary graph. Quadsected squares are often used in image processing and are modeled and referred to as quadtrees. However, as noted above, tree codes are not suitable for graphs, thus the quadsected-square encoding scheme was developed. By rotating the dual of the quadsected square 45°, it is easily seen that the quadsected square has binary fan-out (A branches to B and C) and binary fan-in (B and C converge on D). Quadsected squares can be recursively divided to represent any binary graph. Figure 6 shows a more detailed example. Quadsected squares can be used as an abstract form of a flow graph. Each node of the graph is a basic block. For simplicity, back edges in the graph are ignored. However, it should be noted that the rules of structured code dictate that back edges always go from a fan-in node (such as V) to a fan-out node (such as A). When control flows into a quadrant, it enters the leftmost lowest subdivision. When it leaves, it leaves the rightmost lowest subdivision. For example, in Figure 6, control flows from node A into B and I, and from node O and H into node P.

4.1 Code mapping

The location code for each node of a quadsected square is shown in Figure 7a. The code for a recursively quadsected square is obtained by specifying the position of the top-level division first (as the leftmost digit), then the position of the first recursive subdivision, and so on. Zero fill is used on the right. Figure 7b gives a simple example.

Figure 8 shows how statements are mapped onto quadsected squares. Figure 9a shows how the nested IFs of Figure 9b map onto a recursively quadsected square. The keywords of the statements are associated with the entry and exit point of the quadsection as shown.

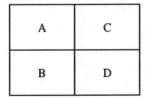
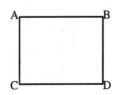

Figure 5. A bisected square and its graph dual.

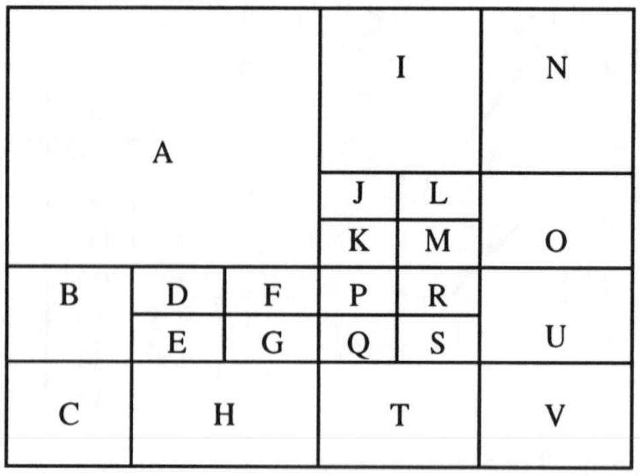

Figure 6: recursively bisected square diagram with labels A, I, N, J, L, K, M, O, B, D, F, P, R, E, G, Q, S, U, C, H, T, V.

CODE	NODE
400	A
340	I
330	N
324	J
323	L
322	K
321	M
310	O
240	B
234	D
233	F
232	E
231	G
220	C
210	H
144	P
143	R
142	Q
141	S
130	U
120	T
110	V

Figure 6. A recursively bisected square.

Figure 7 (a): quadsected square with cells 4, 3, 2, 1. (b): labeled nodes A, B, C, D, E, F, G.

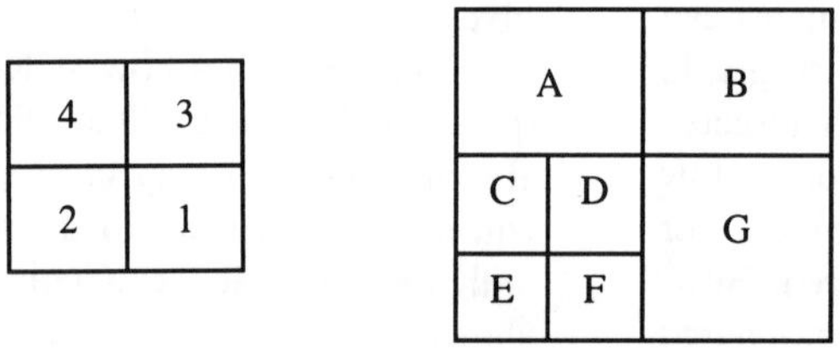

A	40
B	30
C	24
D	23
E	22
F	21
G	10

Figure 7. Quadsected square encoding: (a) code map; (b) labeled nodes and associated codes.

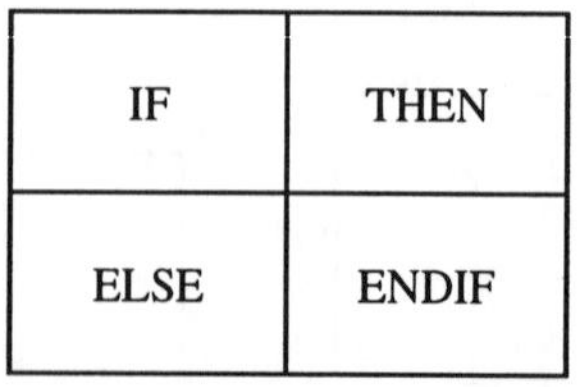

Figure 8: square divided into four cells labeled IF, THEN, ELSE, ENDIF.

Figure 8. IF statement mapping.

	THEN1 codeb cond2 IF2	THEN2 codec
codea cond1 IF1		
	ELSE2 coded	ENDIF2 codee
ELSE1 codef	ENDIF1 codeg	

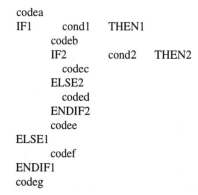

Figure 9. Recursive IF mapping.

4.2 Code operators

The first code, or root code, for the data structure is obtained using the Maximum function on the code field. The Minimum function finds the code of the exit (last) node.

4.3 Code manipulation

The binary graphs of structured code can be used for data flow analysis. Three important concepts in data flow analysis are (1) the set of nodes that can be influenced by a given node, (2) the set of nodes that can influence a given node, and (3) node domination. An important property of quadsected codes is that they can support the generation of this information.

Given a node with code xxYxx, it can influence all other nodes with codes in the ranges generated by the following procedure:

Process the digits in the code from right to left, producing pairs of ranges.

- If Y is a 1, no range is generated.
- If Y is a 2 or a 3, generate the range of codes xx199–xx000.
- If Y is a 4, generate the range xx399–xx000.

For example, processing node **a** with code 3223 generates the ranges 3221–3220, 3219–3200, 3199–3000, and 1999–0000. The first three ranges are contiguous and can be combined into the single range, 3221–3000. Every node in the quadsected graph with codes that fall strictly between[1] the ranges >3000–<3221 and >0000–<1999 can be influenced by node **a**.

Similarly, given a node, **b**, with code xxYxx, all nodes with codes strictly in the ranges produced by the following algorithm can influence it:

---
[1] Codes equal to the boundary codes are not included.

Process the digits in the code from right to left, producing pairs of ranges.

- If Y is a 1, generate the range xx199–xx999.
- If Y is a 2 or a 3, generate the range xx301–xx999.
- If Y is a 4, do not generate any range.

For example, node Q from Figure 6 has code 142 and produces the search ranges >143–<149 and >200–<999. Again from Figure 6, we can see that nodes A–P are within these ranges and therefore can influence Q.

A node, **a**, in a binary graph is said to *dominate* another node, **b**, if every path from the root to **b** passes through **a**. Given two nodes, **a** and **b**, **a** dominates **b** if the code for **a** is processed digit by digit, and the corresponding digit for **b** has the following relationship.

- If **a**'s digit is 0, **b**'s corresponding digit may be anything.
- If **a**'s digit if 1, **b**'s corresponding digit is a 1 or a 0.
- If **a**'s digit is 2, **b**'s corresponding digit is a 2 or a 0.
- If **a**'s digit is 3, **b**'s corresponding digit is a 3 or a 0.
- If **a**'s digit is 4, **b**'s corresponding digit may be anything.

For example, from Figure 6, we see that node P dominates node T because the code for T, 120, meets the requirements specified for the code for P, 144. Conversely, K does not dominate L because the rightmost digit (2) of K's code (322) requires that the rightmost digit of the code for L, 323, be a 2 or a 0.

It is important to recognize that all three of the above algorithms execute in time that is independent of the number of nodes in the graph for any one node.

The complexity analysis depends on the number of digits in the code. Each algorithm can be performed in data parallel for all nodes of the graph. So, for example, given the code for node **a**, the dominance relationship between node **a** and *all* other nodes in the graph is computed in time independent of the size of the graph.

5   Applications

"Reaching definition" and "available expression information" are used for conventional compiler optimization routines such as common subexpression elimination. A definition, **d**, in block B reaches block P, if B dominates P and there are no redefinitions of **d** in the intersection of the nodes that B influences and the nodes that influence P.

An expression, E_1: g+h, is available at B if a copy of E_1 is on every path from the root to B and none of the elements of E_1 (that is, g or h) are redefined after the closest evaluation to B on each path.

Once influencing information is calculated as described in the previous section, the available expression and reaching-definition information can be generated using a small and fixed number of logical operations per expression as shown in Figure 10.

In associative computing, more direct compilation techniques are often used [Asthagiri and Potter 1993]. Common subexpression elimination is performed on source code during initial parsing. In this environment, it can be assumed that all higher order operators have been reduced and that the current operator being checked for common subexpressions is about to be reduced. This means that it is the leftmost, highest priority operator.

The common subexpression steps are

1. Flag all nodes that are (a) dominated by the current node **a** and (b) contain a copy of the current operation.

2. Find all common subexpressions,

   i) If none—done.

   ii) If one or more, select the leftmost one, **b**. (that is, the one with the "largest" structure code).

   a) Flag all nodes between **a** and **b**. (Determined by the intersection of nodes influenced by **a** and the nodes influencing **b**).

   b) For every back edge entering the graph between **a** and **b**, determine the source node. Find the source node with the "smallest" code, **s**. Extend the range of the flagged area to the nodes between **a** and **s**.

   c) Are either of the operands of **a** redefined in the flagged region? If yes, exit. If no, make the common subexpression substitution.

```
START:
  I = 0;
  Idle Code$[I] = 4;
ONIF:
  Idle Code$[I] = 3;
  I++;
  Idle Code$[I] = 4;
  Flag$ = False;
  IFON[I] = True;
ONELSE:
  IF code$[I] ==4 and Flag$ == True Then code$[I] = 0;
  Idle Code$[I-1] = 2;
  Idle Code$[I] = 4;
  Flag$ = False;
  IFON[I] = False;
ONEND;
  IF IFON[I] == True Then Do ONELSE;
  IF Code$[I] = 4 and Flag$ == True Then Code$[I] = 0;
  Idle Code$[I] = 0;
  I--;
  Idle Code$[I] = 1;
  Flag$ = False;
OTHER:
  Flag$ = True;
STOP:
  IF I != 0 Then Error;
```

Figure 10. Quadsected code generation.

5.1 Code generation

The quadsected codes for the source statements of a program can be generated during input using the algorithms shown in Figure 11. A '$' suffix signifies a parallel variable. The I index keeps track of the current code digit. The leftmost digit is digit number 0.

6 Conclusion

In this paper I discussed the concept of using structure codes to represent complex data structures in associative processors and content-addressable memories. The regular codes for vector and arrays were reviewed as were the tree structure codes described in [Potter 1992]. A new structure code for binary graphs that is both extensible and unique was described.

I also described an encoding technique for binary graphs. Since structured statements can be easily mapped onto binary graphs, this code can be used to encode the flow graph structure of programs. These codes allow relationships such as "available expression" and "reaching definitions" to be determined. However, they may be most useful for new associative algorithms for direct common subexpression elimination and code motion.

7 References

[Potter 1992] J.L. Potter, *Associative Computing*, Plenum Press, New York, N.Y., 1992.

[Asthagiri and Potter 1993] C. Asthagiri and J.L. Potter, "Parallel Common Sub-Expression Elimination," *2nd APAW*, 1993.

[Falkoff 1962] A. Falkoff, "Algorithms for Parallel-Search Memories," *J. ACM*, Mar. 9, 1962, pp. 488–511.

```
INB - NODES WHICH INFLUENCE B
IF INB THEN
                   E = EXPRESSION INSTANCE
                   FOR XX IN E
                      EIN = NODES INFLUENCED BY NODE WHICH CONTAINS INSTANCE
                         XX OF E.
                      EDOM = NODES WHICH NODE OF E DOMINATE
                      IF EIN THEN
                         ANY ELEMENT OF E REDEFINED
                            STOP-FAIL-EXIT
                         ELSEANY
                            RELEASE EIN FROM INB
                            RELEASE EDOM FROM INB
                         ENDNANY
                      ENDIF
                   ENDFOR XX
ENDIF
ANY INB
                   EXPRESSION NOT AVAILABLE
ELSENANY
                   EXPRESSION AVAILABLE
ENDANY
```

(a)

```
BDOM = SET OF NODES DOMINATED BY B
BIN = SET OF NODES INFLUENCES BY B
INP = SET OF NODES WHICH INFLUENCE P.
IF BIN INTERSECT INP THEN
  ANY REDEFINITION OF D
    STOP - FAIL
  ELSENANY
    P IS REACHED
  ENDANY
ENDIF
```

(b)

Figure 11. Pseudocode: (a) available expression; (b) reaching definitions.

Associative Parallel Common Subexpression Elimination

Chandra R. Asthagiri and Jerry L. Potter
Kent State University
Department of Mathematics and Computer Science
Kent, OH 44242
asthagir@cs.wright.edu
potter@mcs.kent.edu

Abstract

Compilation is a mature, well-studied discipline. However, with the emphasis on more powerful languages and the need for optimization to achieve maximum efficiency, compilation takes a larger portion of computer resources. Thus, techniques improving compilation speed have a rapid payoff. This paper describes an algorithm to remove common subexpression (CSE)s to improve both compilation speed of the source expressions and the execution speed of the resulting code. This algorithm, using massively parallel associative techniques, removes CSEs directly from the source expression at the time of intermediate code generation itself without needing a separate optimization pass. Unlike any other CSE elimination algorithms, it removes noncontiguous CSEs also. A CSE 'x + y' is noncontiguous when it is found in '..x ± Z + y..', '..y ± Z + x..', or other complex expressions, where Z is a substring with no operator whose precedence is less than that of the generic operator '+'. Further, this algorithm removes certain CSEs, which cannot be detected even by the conventional directed acyclic graph method. Furthermore, it uses simpler data structures and programming techniques than conventional algorithms.

1   Introduction

Common subexpression elimination is most useful in minimizing array index computation and expression evaluation in a loop. Optimizing index computation in a loop that executes many times can save considerable execution time. This applies to any language where array index notation and looping (in imperative language) or recursion (in some functional language) is used. This paper describes an algorithm for performing common subexpression (CSE) elimination using massively parallel associative techniques [8] to improve compilation efficiency of the source code as well as the execution efficiency of the resulting code. This algorithm, implemented on an associative SIMD computer, henceforth is referred to as the associative common subexpression elimination (ACSEE) algorithm.

An associative approach proposed earlier [5] could remove only contiguous CSEs, but the ACSEE approach removes noncontiguous CSEs as well. A contiguous CSE is a CSE when the CSE '$x + y$' is found in '$.. x + y ..$' or '$.. y + x ..$'. A noncontiguous CSE is a CSE when '$x + y$' is found in '$..x \pm Z + y..$', '$..y \pm Z + x..$', or other complex expressions, where Z is a substring with no operator whose precedence is less than that of '+' and '+' is a generic operator.

In conventional approaches, it is not practical to remove CSEs from the source expression itself. Usually CSEs are eliminated by constructing directed acyclic graphs (DAGs) from the intermediate code, which requires a separate optimization pass. But ACSEE removes CSEs directly from the source expression at the time of intermediate code generation itself with no need for a separate optimization pass. Furthermore, it removes certain CSEs, which cannot be detected even by the conventional DAG method, and it uses simpler data structures and programming techniques.

The next section provides a brief overview of the associative computing model [8] called single instruction tabular data associative computing (SITDAC) used by ACSEE. Section 3 gives an extended definition for CSE and defines various terms that are essential for further discussion. Sections 4 and 5 develop techniques to eliminate contiguous and noncontiguous CSEs. Section 6 illustrates the application of the associative techniques in implementing these CSE elimination techniques to remove CSEs from the source code itself without needing a separate optimization pass. Also, it gives certain instances of common subexpressions that are removed easily by ACSEE, but which are not detected even by conventional methods. Section 7 shows the compilation and execution efficiency of ACSEE.

2 Background

2.1 SITDAC

With a massively parallel associative SIMD computer and simple tabular data structures as its basic components, the SITDAC model [8] supports the concept of processing an entire file of data in parallel. In effect, the records are mapped onto the rows of the tabular data structure, and each row has a dedicated processor element (PE). ASC is a high-level language that we designed for SITDAC and developed at Kent State University to program massively parallel associative SIMD computers [8]. The ASC compiler can produce code for Thinking Machines Inc. Connection Machine [7], Goodyear Aerospace Staran-E [4], Loral Defense System ASPRO [1], and WaveTracer's DTC [9]. ASC also has an emulation mode that allows program design and testing under Unix or a similar C environment.

Associative SIMD computers emulate associative memory [6] aspects via associative search, but they are more powerful than associative memories in that the responding items are processed in situ either sequentially or simultaneously. Associative or content-addressable memory means a hardware memory with the property that an entire stored item can be retrieved by specifying only a part of it.

An associative SIMD computer, as shown in Figure 1, consists of an array of *processing cells* that are all operated in parallel by a single instruction broadcast from a front-end processor. Each cell has its own memory and a PE. Each PE has a mask bit that can be set selectively to filter the broadcast instructions. A *field* consists of columns of consecutive bits used to store the same data type in the cell memories. A field is inherently parallel, unordered, and allocated cells need not be contiguous. *Field width* refers to the number of horizontal bits used to store a data item. An *association* is a tuple of fields such that given an index, all of the data items in the different fields associated with the index can be accessed. The index is a one-bit field that flags the appropriate association cells. Throughout the following, '$' as in A[$], denotes the column of the field A in all cells currently allocated to A's association, and A[xx] denotes the reduction of the parallel field A to the scalar xx as illustrated in Figure 2. This type of two-dimensional, tabular data organization is referred to as *associative data organization*.

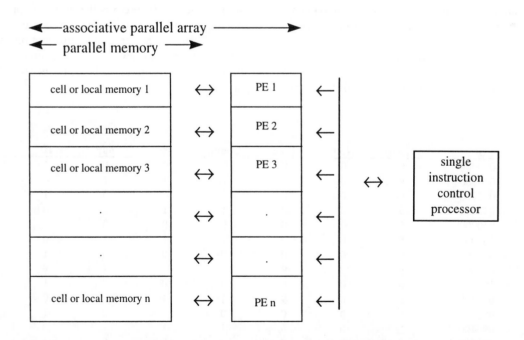

Figure 1. An associative computer configuration.

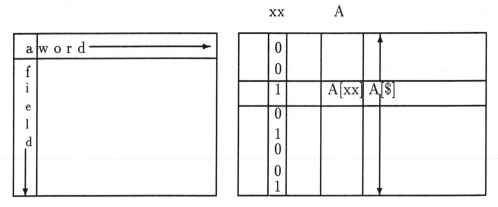

Figure 2. Parallel memory with field A.

SITDAC uses data parallelism [7] as the basis for associative searching, which takes time proportional to the number of bits in a field, not the number of data items being searched. Thus, it executes in constant time [8]. With the constant time-associative search as its fundamental operation, SITDAC has a rich set of constant time operations (which take log n time on a conventional MIMD) such as responder/no-responder (a responder is an active PE that responded positively for an associative search) test, data parallel comparison, numeric computation, and movement, selection of an individual responder, retrieval of a single data item from a field (reduction), certain built-in functions such as *maxdex/mindex* to find the maximum/minimum of a field in the table of records, and the *sibdex* function to find the minimum value larger than the maximum value smaller than a given input value, among others.

2.2   Associative organization

To fully use associative parallelism, the tokens of the source code expression with attributes such as the structure code (SC), associativity, commutativity, priority, and precedence (which are all computed in parallel) are stored as fields within the records in an associative array (See Figure 3).

All the occurrences of an operator get the same value in parallel for the attributes priority, associativity, and commutativity by consulting a table of integer encodings for these attributes. Precedence (Prec) for all operators in an entire expression/program is computed in parallel using the equation 'Prec[$] = priority[$] + Nest[$] * k', where k is a constant (13 in Figure 3) denoting the priority for parenthesis and Nest denotes the number of parentheses enclosing the tokens. See [3] for details on precedence computation. The Prec field in Figure 3 is the result of applying the above equation. The structure code is a unique integer representing the structural information (such as position and nesting level) of each source token and allows all the program tokens to be searched in parallel.

Token	SC	Priority	Nest	Prec	Comm	Assoc	opr	ID	Proc
a	010000	0	0	0	0	0	0	1	0
−	020000	9	0	9	1	1	1	0	0
b	030000	0	0	0	0	0	0	1	0
+	040000	9	0	9	1	1	1	0	0
a	050000	0	0	0	0	0	0	1	0
−	060000	9	0	9	1	1	1	0	0
b	070000	0	0	0	0	0	0	1	0
*	080000	9	0	9	1	1	1	0	0
a	090100	0	0	0	0	0	0	1	0
−	090200	22	0	9	1	1	1	0	0
b	090300	0	0	0	0	0	0	1	0
+	090400	22	0	9	1	1		0	0
c	090500	0	0	0	0	0	0	1	0

Figure 3. Associative organization of '$a - b + a - b * (a - b + c)$'.

2.3 Arithmetic properties

Operators are classified as commutative or noncommutative and left- or right-associative. Commutative means that calculations such as '$a + b$' and '$b + a$' are equivalent. The subtraction operator is noncommutative because '$a - b$' is not equivalent to '$b - a$'. Left-associative means that if an expression consists of a string of operations such as '$a + b + c + d$', the operations should be performed from left to right (that is, an operand goes with the operator on its left) as in '$(((a + b) + c) + d)$'. Some operators such as addition are both left-associative and commutative. Operators like subtraction and shift are left-associative but noncommutative. Right-associative operators are all noncommutative. Noncommutative operators such as subtraction and division are said to be weakly noncommutative ([2, 3]) since their predefined left-to-right evaluation sequence can be relaxed without changing the value of the original expression. Left-associative, noncommutative operators like shift and all of the right associative operators must have their predefined order of evaluation, and these operators are classified as strongly noncommutative.

3 Definitions and notations

This section extends the definition for CSE. It also gives certain instances of CSE elimination and defines certain terms (listed in Figure 4) that are used in this paper.

3.1 Associative common subexpression

Conventionally, an expression E is called a common subexpression (CSE) if E was previously computed and the value of the variables in E have not been changed. This traditional definition applies only to operators and their contiguous operands.

The ASC model allows the practical extension of the above definition to include noncontiguous operands since they can be found associatively in constant time. That is, if a contiguous subexpression E consists of an operator OP and operands a and b, such as 'a OP b', and if operator OP can be found with an adjacent operand (say b) and the other operand (a) can be found in the same expression but not necessarily contiguous with OP, and the latter operator OP with the a and b operands can be replaced with the value of E without changing the value of the original expression, then 'a OP b' is an associative common subexpression.

Consider the expression '$a * b + c + b * z * a$'. After the leftmost instance $a * b$ is reduced into T_1, where T_1 is a temporary to hold the value of $a * b$, '$b *$' with the remote operand 'a' constitutes a CSE ($a * b$) resulting in the replacement of this CSE by the same result temporary (T_1) and the reduction of the original expression into '$T_1 + c + z * T_1$'. Thus, '$a * b$' is an associative common subexpression.

LA = Left Associative, RA = right Associative

LA-COM = Left associative, commutative

LA-NCOM = Left associative, non-commutative

L = left operand of OP, R = right operand of OP

CSE = common sub-expression, PCSE = potentialCSE

PPCSE = partial PCSE, CPCSE = complete PCSE

PCSEopr = operator in the PCSE that matches OP

L_PCSEopnd = Left operand of PCSEopr

R_PCSEopnd = Right operand of PCSEopr

LA-wkNCOM = Left associative, weakly non-commutative

LA-strNCOM = Left associative, strongly non-commutative

B = an expression, E = sub-expression in B, OP = the operator in E

Ti = temporary to hold E's value, i in Ti is an integer

CCSE = contiguous CSE, NCCSE = non-contiguos CSE

L_PCSEopr = nearest left neighbor operator of PCSEopr

R_PCSEopr = nearest right neighbor operator of PCSEopr

L_miss_opr = nearest left neighbor operator to a missing operand

R_miss_opr = nearest right neighbor operator to a missing operand

Figure 4. Abbreviations.

Consider the expression '$a * b + b * a$', which can be viewed as '$a * b + a * b$' with two occurrences of a subexpression '$a * b$'. After the leftmost instance of '$a * b$' is reduced into T_1, all other instances of it can be replaced by the same result temporary (T_1). The result is the generation of a quadruple 'M U L a b T_1' and the reduction of the original expression into '$T_1 + T_1$'.

3.2   Potential CSEs

Let B be an expression, E be a subexpression in B chosen for a normal reduction, OP be the operator in E, T_1 be the temporary variable storing the result of the reduction of E, where $0 \leq i < k$ and k is a constant, and L and R be the left and right operands of OP. Once E is reduced, all of the potential CSEs in B can be checked for their candidacy to be reduced. An expression E1 is a *potential CSE* (PCSE) when it has an unprocessed operator OP with at least one operand matching either L or R. The OP in PCSE, henceforth, is referred to as a potential CSE operator (PCSEopr). If a potential CSE has both the matching operands, then it is a *complete potential CSE* (CPCSE), otherwise it is a *partial potential CSE* (PPCSE). If a CPCSE can be reduced, CPCSE becomes a *contiguous CSE*. If a PPCSE with a remotely placed missing operand becomes legal to reduce, the PPCSE together with the missing operand forms a *noncontiguous CSE*.

The contiguous or noncontiguous CSE can be replaced with the same temporary that was used to store the value of the original reduction of E. For example, in '$a/b + a/b + c/a/b$', the first 'a/b' is the E. The second and the third are potential CSEs. Since the neighboring operators, '+'s, yield to '/', the second one is a contiguous CSE. But the left neighbor '/' for the third 'a/b' does not permit 'a/b' to be reduced. Hence, the third one is just a potential CSE only. In '$a + b + c + b + z + a–b + y + a$', the '$a + b$' is the E. The second '$b+$' with the remote '$a$' in '$z + a$' is a noncontiguous CSE. The third '$b+$' with the remote 'a' in '$y + a$' is just a potential CSE only.

The left and right nearest-neighbor operators of the PCSEopr are called L_PCSEopr and R_PCSEopr, respectively. Similarly, the left and right operands of the PCSEopr are termed L_PCSEopnd and R_PCSEopnd, respectively. The left and right nearest-neighbor operators of the missing operand for a partial PCSE are called L_miss_opr and R_miss_opr, respectively.

4   Elimination of contiguous CSEs

For a contiguous common subexpression, the PCSEopr should have contiguous operands and it can be left- or right-associative and commutative or non-

commutative. When commutative, the operands may appear in any order. Thus '$a + b + c + a + b$' and '$a + b + c + b + a$' have '$a + b$' as common subexpression. When noncommutative, the operands must be in the same relationship in both occurrences. Thus, '$a – b + a – b$' has '$a – b$' as a common subexpression, but '$a – b + b – a$' has no common subexpression.

Because of the contiguous operands, only the nearest-neighbor operators of the PCSE need to be checked as to whether they yield to the PCSEopr. The precedence of a left-associative PCSEopr must be greater than or equal to that of its right neighbor (R_PCSEopr) so that R_PCSEopr yields to the PCSEopr allowing the PCSE to reduce. When PCSEopr is left-associative, there are three cases (PCSEopr may be commutative, weakly noncommutative, or strongly noncommutative) to consider while checking for the nearest left neighbor (L_PCSEopr) of the PCSEopr. For the first two cases, the precedence of the PCSEopr must be greater than or equal to that of L_PCSEopr, and, when equal, the L_PCSEopr must be commutative so that L_PCSEopr yields to the PCSEopr. Thus, the expression '$a \pm b + a \pm b * c – a \pm b + (a \pm b + c) + a \pm b + c * a \pm b$' would be reduced to '$T_1 + a \pm b * c – a \pm b + (T_1 + c) + T_1 + c * a \pm b$'. For the third case, the L_PCSEopr should be strictly less than the PCSEopr in precedence. Thus, the expression '$a << b < d << a << b – c + a << b * c + (a << b < c)$' would be reduced to '$T_1 < d << a << b – c + a << b * c + (T_1 < c)$'.

A right-associative PCSEopr, being always strongly noncommutative, must be greater than its R_PCSEopr and greater than or equal to its L_PCSEopr in precedence. Thus, the second '$a \wedge b$' in the '$a \wedge b \wedge a \wedge b$' is the E, and the first one is just a potential, not an actual, CSE. But the first '$a \wedge b$' in the '$a \wedge b + c \wedge a \wedge b$' is truly a CSE.

5   Elimination of noncontiguous CSEs (NCCSEs)

Since a strongly noncommutative operator needs its operands intact, it can never be a NCCSE operator. Hence, only left associative commutative or noncommutative operators are eligible to be NCCSE operators. Since a missing operand must be brought from outside the partial potential CSE, not only the neighboring operators to the PCSEopr but also the neighboring operators to a remotely placed missing operand, as well as operators in between the PCSEopr and the remote operand, must be considered.

When OP is left-associative and commutative, the right operand of potential CSE (PCSE) can match any operand of OP. But when OP is left-associative and weakly commutative, either the right operand of PCSE should match with the right operand of OP or the left operand of PCSE should match with the left operand of OP because the noncommutativity of OP does not permit interchanging of operands.

The interval of the expression, in which the missing operand for a partial potential CSE can be searched, should not contain any operator X whose precedence is less than that of PCSEopr. This is because of the requirement that both the subexpressions appearing left and right of X should be evaluated independently, and no part of any of these subexpressions should be taken from one side to the other. This fact, henceforth, is referred to as *interval rule*.

A PPCSE (partial PCSE) is said to be a *RightPPCSE* (or *LeftPPCSE*) when its right operand (or left operand) matches one of the operands of E. A search for the missing operand on the left side of the PCSE is referred to as *left search* and a similar search on the right is called *right search*.

5.1 Handling RightPPCSE

Since a RightPPCSE has its matching right operand, the missing operand is searched first on the left side of it. If the missing operand is not found via the left search, a right search is made. In either search, a missing operand, when correctly found, together with the partial potential CSE, forms an actual CSE to be eliminated. This includes marking the PCSE operator and its right operand as processed and replacing the remote operand with the T_i of E. To correctly find a missing operand, if there is one in B (an expression containing E), this section formulates certain rules for the left search and the right search to follow.

5.1.1 The left search rules

A missing operand, if there is one on the left side of the potential CSE (PCSE), can be correctly found when the search is guided by the following requirements:

1. L_PCSEopr ≥ PCSEopr ≥ R_PCSEopr,
2. Observe the interval rule,
3. *L_miss_opr* < *PCSEopr* or (*commutative L_miss_opr* = *PCSEopr*), and
4. *R_miss_opr* = *PCSEopr* in precedence.

By the interval rule, an L_PCSEopr, which appears between the PCSEopr and a missing operand, cannot have precedence less than that of the PCSEopr; when it is greater than or equal to PCSEopr, L_PCSEopr does not lose its strength since its right operand (L_PCSEopnd) belongs to itself rather than to the PCSEopr. R_PCSEopr cannot be greater than

PCSRopr to allow the PCSEopr to reduce. When R_PCSEopr is less than PCSEopr, it yields to the PCSEopr. When it is equal to PCSEopr, it yields to PCSRopr by the property of left-associative operators. R_PCSEopnd therefore belongs to PCSEopr, and PCSE can be reduced.

When *L_miss_opr* > *PCSEopr*, the missing operand belongs to the L_miss_opr and cannot be a part of the potential CSE. Conversely, when *L_miss_opr* < *PCSEopr*, the missing operand does not belong to L_miss_opr. Suppose L_miss_opr is equal to PCSEopr in precedence but is not commutative. Then, the replacement would be a violation since the noncommutative operator using the modified operand (T_i) as its right operand results in an incorrect value. Condition 3 is thus essential for the correct evaluation.

Condition 4 ensures that the CSE elimination is valid with respect to R_miss_opr. By the interval rule, the R_miss_opr, being in between the missing operand and the PPCSE (partial PCSE), cannot be less than PCSEopr in precedence to allow for the left search. The R_miss_opr cannot be greater than PCSEopr, either. Suppose R_miss_opr is greater than PCSEopr. Then, R_miss_opr cannot part with its operand before being used by it. In other words, the missing operand belongs to R_miss_opr, and it should not be modified.

When '*L_miss_opr* < *PCSEopr* = *R_miss_opr*', the missing operand belonging to R_miss_opr can be modified because it is a left operand to a left-associative operator (R_miss_opr). When '*L_miss_opr* = *PCSEopr* = *R_miss_opr*', the missing operand belonging to L_miss_opr can be modified because of the commutative property of the L_miss_opr.

Consider the following expression:

'$a > c - d * k \wedge m \pm n + p \wedge q > p \wedge q + c$'.

The rightmost '$p \wedge q$' is reduced normally, and the other one is reduced via a contiguous CSE elimination, resulting in the following expression:

'$a > c - d * k \wedge m \pm n + T_1 > T_1 + c$'.

which is the first expression given in Figure 5. In that figure, the T_1 in all other expressions also represents the same T_1 as in the first expression.

The first expression reduction in Figure 5 can be interpreted as follows:

Notice that '+' in the '$T_1 + c$' is the nearest neighbor of the recent normal reduction and is higher than its neighbors ('>' and 'ε', where ε denotes a null operator) in precedence. So, '$T_1 + c$' is chosen as E. Now, '+' in '$+T_1$', '±', '>', '>', and '−' are the PCSEopr, L_PCSEopr, R_PCSEopr, '*L_miss_opr*', and '*R_miss_opr*' respectively.

No	Expression	E	PPCSE	Quadruple	CSEE?	
1	$a > \quad c \quad -d*k\wedge m\pm n \quad +T_1 \quad >T_1+c$ $a > \quad T_2 \quad -d*k\wedge m\pm n \qquad >T_2$	$T_1 + c$	$+T_1$	ADD T_1 c T_2	Yes	RightPPCSE Leftsearch
1a	$a > \quad c \quad -d>e*k\wedge m\pm n \quad +T_1 \quad >T_1+c$ $a > \quad c \quad -d>e*k\wedge m\pm n \quad +T_1 \quad >T_2$	$T_1 + c$	$+T_1$	ADD T_1 c T_2	No	
2	$a > \quad +c \quad \pm d*k\wedge m\pm n \quad +T_1 \quad >T_1+c$ $a > \qquad \pm d*k\wedge m\pm n \quad +T_2 \quad >T_2$	$T_1 + c$	$+c$	ADD T_1 c T_2	Yes	RightPPCSE Rightsearch
3	$a>z\pm d*k\wedge m\pm n \quad +T_1 \quad \pm a*b+\ c \quad >c+T_1$ $a>z\pm d*k\wedge m\pm n \quad \pm a*b+\ T_2 \quad >T_2$	$c + T_1$	$+T_1$	ADD c T_1 T_2	Yes	RightPPCSE Rightsearch
4	$a>z\pm d*k\wedge m\pm n+\ T_1 \quad >x\ +c \quad >T_1+c$ $a>z\pm d*k\wedge m\pm n+\ T_1 \quad >x\ +c \quad >T_2$	$T_1 + c$	$+c$	ADD T_1 c T_2	No	
5	$a>T_1 +d*k\wedge m\pm n \ -c \quad >T_1-c$ $a>T_2 +d*k\wedge m\pm n \qquad >T_2$	$T_1 - c$	$-c$	SUB T_1 c T_2	Yes	RightPPCSE Leftsearch
5a	$a>T_1 +d>e*k\wedge m\pm n \ -c \quad >T_1-c$ $a>T_1 +d>e*k\wedge m\pm n \ -c \quad >T_1-c$	$T_1 - c$	$-c$	SUB T_1 c T_2	No	
6	$a+d-c \pm d*k\wedge m\pm n+\ T_1 \quad <T_1-c$ $a+d \quad \pm d*k\wedge m\pm n+\ T_2 \quad <T_2$	$T_1 - c$	$-c$	SUB T_1 c T_2	Yes	RightPPCSE Rightsearch
7	$a>z\pm d*k\wedge m\pm n \ -c \quad \pm a*b+\ T_1 \quad >T_1-c$ $a>z\pm d*k\wedge m\pm n \qquad \pm a*b+\ T_2 \quad >T_2$	$T_1 - c$	$-c$	SUB T_1 c T_2	Yes	RightPPCSE Rightsearch
8	$a>z\pm d*k\wedge m\pm n+\ T_1 \ >x\ -c \ >T_1-c$ $a>z\pm d*k\wedge m\pm n+\ T_1 \ >x\ -c \ >T_2$	$T_1 - c$	$-c$	SUB T_1 c T_2	No	
9	$a< T_1 +d*k\wedge m\pm n \quad + \quad c \quad <T_1+c$ $a< T_2 +d*k\wedge m\pm n \qquad <T_2$	$T_1 +$	$T_1 +$	ADD T_1 c T_2	Yes	LeftPPCSE Rightsearch
9a	$a< T_1 +d<b*k\wedge m\pm n \quad + \quad c \quad <T_1+c$ $a< T_1 +d<b*k\wedge m\pm n \quad + \quad c \quad <T_2$	$T_1 +$	$T_1 +$	ADD T_1 c T_2	No	
10	$a< T_1 -d*k\wedge m\pm n \quad - \quad c \quad <T_1-c$ $a< T_2 -d*k\wedge m\pm n \qquad <T_2$	$T_1 -c$	$T_1 -$	SUB T_1 c T_2	Yes	LeftPPCSE Rightsearch
10a	$a< T_1 -d<b*k\wedge m\pm n \quad - \quad c \quad <T_1-c$ $a< T_1 -d<b*k\wedge m\pm n \quad - \quad c \quad <T_2$	$T_1 -c$	$T_1 -$	SUB T_1 c T_2	No	

Figure 5. NCCSE elimination in the ACSEE method.

These operators follow the conditions 1, 3, and 4. Also, there is no operator between the PCSEopr and the remote operand 'c' with its precedence lower than that of the PCSEopr. So, the left search is successful, and the expression,

'$a > c - d * k \wedge m \pm n + T_1 > T_1 + c$',

becomes

'$a > T_2 - d * k \wedge m \pm n > T_2$'.

Refer to Figure 6 for a pictorial representation of the above interpretation. Similar interpretation applies to the rest of Figure 5's expressions and will not be repeated. While the first expression in Figure 5 represents a successful left search when PCSEopr is left-associative and commutative, the fifth expression represents a successful left search when PCSEopr is left-associative and weakly noncommutative.

The expressions 1a and 5a in Figure 5 are the expressions 1 and 5 with '> e' inserted between 'd' and '*' to demonstrate that the left search works correctly by not bringing a missing operand illegally. Thus, the left search correctly identifies the missing operand.

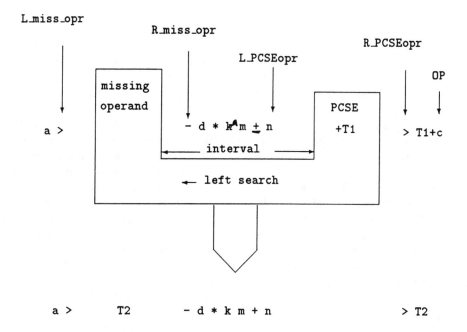

Left Search Rules for RightPPCSE

1. L_PCSEopr >= PCSEopr >= R_PCSEopr

2. No operator in interval < PCSEopr

3. L_miss_opr < PCSEopr or
    (L_miss_opr = PCSEopr and   L_miss_opr is commutative)

4. R_miss_opr = PCSEopr in precedence

Figure 6. Interpretation of expression 1 of Figure 5.

5.1.2 The right search rules to handle a RightPPCSE

This section formalizes the rules to be observed in the right search, which is to be made when the left search fails. A missing operand can be found correctly on the right side of the PCSE only when the right search is guided by the following requirements:

1. PCSEopr = R_PCSEopr,
2. Observe the interval rule,
3. *L_miss_opr = PCSEopr* and L_miss_opr is commutative, and
4. *R_miss_opr ≤ PCSEopr.*

The L_PCSEopnd, which is the right operand of the L_PCSEopr, is not part of the PCSE, so the removal of PCSE by marking it as processed does not affect the left operator. Hence, there is no constraint

on the nature of the left-neighbor operator of the PCSEopr. However, R_PCSEopr has certain constraints. It cannot be less than PCSEopr by the interval rule nor can it be greater than the PCSEopr, since the R_PCSEopnd should not belong to the R_PCSEopr. The right neighbor operator of the PCSEopr must be equal to PCSEopr so that it yields to the PCSEopr. Due to yielding of R_PCSEopr to PCSEopr, the left operand of the R_PCSEopr belongs to the PCSEopr, and the PCSEopr can be reduced legally with that operand. In other words, an operand, which is sandwiched between the PCSEopr on the left and R_PCSEopr on the right, belongs to the left neighbor (PCSEopr) rather than to the right by left-associative property. Thus, condition 2 justifies the removal of the partial PCSE with respect to its neighboring operators.

Since the missing remote operand is replaced with the value of the reduction, the left-neighbor operator of the missing operand must be equal to the PCSEopr and must be commutative, and the right-neighbor operator of the missing operand must be less than or equal to PCSEopr. Because of the property of the right neighbor, the missing operand belongs to its left-neighbor operator; but the commutative property of the left neighbor allows the missing operand to be modified. Thus, the third and fourth conditions justify the replacement of the missing operand by T_i.

For example, consider the expressions 2 and 3 in Figure 5 for a left-associative commutative PCSEopr and the expressions 5 and 6 for a left-associative, weakly noncommutative PCSEopr. The left search for these expressions fails, but the right search succeeds. The expressions 4 and 8 show the failure of the right search due to the occurrence of a '>' operator ('>' < '±') in between PCSEopr and the nearest missing operand. Thus, the left or right search correctly identifies a valid missing operand if there is one in the expression.

5.2   Handling LeftPPCSE

Since a LeftPPCSE has a matching left operand, the missing operand must be searched on its right side. Consider the ninth expression in Figure 5, where '$T_1 +$' is the LeftPPCSE under consideration. In that expression, the missing operand 'c' cannot be chosen from the left side of the LeftPPCSE. Consider all six possible combinations ($c +, + c, c -, - c, Xc, cX$, where X has higher precedence than PCSEopr (here +)). If '$c+$' were on the left side, then it would be the LeftPPCSE that must be considered prior to '$T_1 +$'. If '$+ c$' were on the left side, then it would be a RightPPCSE (PPCSE with matching right operand) that must be treated prior to '$T_1 +$'. If '$c -$' were on the left side, then '$+ T_1$' must be found first, which is again a RightPPCSE. '$- c$' on the left cannot be correct because of the noncommutative '$-$' on the left of 'c'. In the tenth expression in Figure 5, if '$- c$' were found on left of '$T_1 \_$', then that would also become a RightPPCSE. Thus, the missing operand must be found only on the right side of the potential CSE.

5.2.1   The right search rules to handle a LeftPPCSE

The right search for the missing operand for a LeftPPCSE should meet the following requirements:

1. ($L\_PCSEopr < PCSEopr$) or ($L\_PCSEopr = PCSEopr$ and L_PCSEopr is commutative),
2. Observe the interval rule,
3. $L\_miss\_opr = PCSEopr$ exactly, and
4. $R\_miss\_opr \leq PCSEopr$.

When a missing operand satisfying the above four requirements is found, the missing operand and its left operator are treated as the actual potential CSE and they are removed; the left operand of the original potential CSE is replaced by the Ti of E.

Consider the expression 10 in Figure 5. When '$T_1 \_$' is the potential CSE, the missing operand must be found in the form '$- c$'. The value for '$T_1 - c$' cannot be replaced in the second c position because of the left noncommutative operator in '$- c$'. When PCSEopr is left-associative and commutative, the value for the '$T_1 + c$' can be replaced in the second 'c' position. However, to be consistent for both left associative commutative and left-associative, weakly noncommutative CSE operator, look for the missing operand preceded by the same operator as PCSEopr. Then, the missing operand with its left operator can be viewed as a potential CSE, which is the new RightPPCSE for which the missing operand is the matching operand of the original potential CSE. Furthermore, it will be shown shortly that this technique is a right search followed by an implicit application of the left-search technique without checking for the left-search conditions.

If $L\_PCSEopr < PCSEopr$, L_PCSEopr yields to PCSEopr. Therefore, L_PCSEopnd does not belong to L_PCSEopr. When $L\_PCSEopr > PCSEopr$, it does not yield to PCSEopr and the L_PCSEopnd belongs to L_PCSEopr, and thus it cannot be modified before being used by the L_PCSEopr. When L_PCSEopr is equal in precedence to PCSEopr, there are two cases to consider.

L_PCSEopr is commutative and equal in precedence to PCSEopr, and

L_PCSEopr is weakly noncommutative and equal in precedence to PCSEopr.

When PCSEopr is left-associative and commutative, the first case would rather be considered as a RightPPCSE instead of a LeftPPCSE. In the second case, the left operator does not yield to its right equal operator. However, when PCSEopr is left-associative and noncommutative, the commutative operator on the left in the first case allows the PCSEopr to be reduced. But, in the second case, the noncommutative operator on the left does not yield to the PCSEopr. Hence, condition 1 is required.

For example, in the ninth expression, '$a + T_1 +$' or '$a - T_1 +$' would be there in the place of '$a < T_1 +$'. The '$+ T_1$', being a RightPPCSE, is ruled out. The '$- T_1$' in '$- T_1 +$' would violate the '$T_1 +$' to be a PCSE. For a left-associative commutative PCSEopr, the L_PCSEopr must be less than the PCSEopr. In expression 10, '$+T_1-$' or '$-T_1-$' would be there instead of 'T_1-'. The '$-T_1-$' has to be rejected as before. However, '$+T_1-$' form allows 'T_1' in PPCSE to be modi-

210

fied. Thus, L_PCSEopr can be less than or equal to PCSEopr when PCSEopr is LA-wkNCOM. Notice that conditions 3 and 4 are essential to treat the missing operand with the L_miss_opr as a new RightPPCSE. It is shown below that this new RightPPCSE satisfies all the conditions of the left search of a RightPPCSE.

1. Conditions 3 and 4 → 'L_miss_opr = PCSEopr ≥ R_miss_opr'. By considering the L_miss_opr as the new PCSEopr, 'L_miss_opr = PCSEopr ≥ R_miss_opr' ≡ 'new PCSEopr ≥ new R_PCSEopr'.

2. As the interval rule is true for the current right search, there is no operator between the PCSEopr and the remote operand 'c' with its precedence lower than that of the PCSEopr. Therefore, the new L_PCSEopr must be greater than or equal to the new PCSEopr. Thus, 'new L_PCSEopr ≥ new PCSEopr ≥ new R_PCSEopr' is true, and this condition is the first condition of the left search.

3. By step 2, condition 2 of the left search must be true.

4. By considering the L_PCSEopnd as the new missing operand, condition 1 of the right search of the LeftPPCSE case becomes the condition 3 of the left search of the RightPPCSE case.

5. By considering L_PCSEopnd as the new missing operand, the PCSEopr becomes the new R_miss_opr which is exactly PCSEopr, and so condition 4 of the left search 'new R_miss_opr = PCSEopr in precedence' holds.

It is perfectly legal to obtain the missing operand by following the requirements of the right search, and then, treat the missing operand with its left operator as a RightPPCSE and the original L_PCSEopnd as the new missing operand and to consider the new RightPPCSE with the new missing operand as a successful CSE to remove.

For example, in the ninth expression of Figure 5, 'T_1 –' is the original PPCSE and the missing operand is 'c' in '– c'. The '–c' becomes the new PPCSE and the T_1 in 'T_1 –' becomes the new missing operand. This is similar to the first expression, which has been already proved to replace the remote operand with T_i of E and remove the PCSE. Similarly, the tenth expression is similar to the fifth expression if '– c' is treated as the new PCSE and the 'T_1' in the actual PCSE 'T_1 –' as the missing operand. Thus, here the new PCSE is removed; the left operand of the original PCSE becomes the remote operand and gets replaced by the T_i of E.

Expressions 9a and 10a do not have any noncontiguous CSEs due to the presence of '<' operator between the PCSE and the missing operand whose precedence is less than that of PCSEopr.

6   Associative common subexpression elimination

The common subexpression (CSE) elimination techniques described in Sections 4 and 5 of this paper are search intensive. With the associative organization of source tokens in an associative computer, the searches required in testing CSE conditions of these techniques are easily and economically performed by using constant time-associative search and other constant time operations and functions. For example, an operator of the highest precedence is chosen using the maxdex function on the Precedence field in combination with the Operator field. The test 'Opr[$] and maxdex[Prec[$]]' flags all the operators of the same highest precedence. One of these operators can be chosen for the reduction.

After the normal reduction of a chosen operator from an expression, the ACSEE algorithm associatively looks for all of the potential CSEs, both the contiguous and noncontiguous, in that expression. But it removes one at a time if the removal is legal. Thus, at any given time, it removes only one basic subexpression with only one operator. The repeated application of this algorithm combines much larger expressions to remove. For example, by two applications of CSE removal, '$p \wedge q + c$' is removed as a CSE from the first expression of Figure 5.

First, ACSEE flags in parallel all unprocessed operators identical to recently reduced operator (OP) as potential CSE (PCSE) operators. Then it checks the operands of the chosen PCSE operator in parallel to decide whether to handle it as a contiguous PCSE, a noncontiguous PCSE, or neither. If the chosen PCSE operator has operands matching those of the OP, then it replaces the PCSE with the same result variable used for the OP. If the chosen PCSE operator has only one operand matching the OP, and the OP is not strongly noncommutative, then it sets up an interval in parallel to search (also in parallel) for the missing operand. ACSEE continues to process the PCSE only when there is an unprocessed missing operand in the interval. It uses the constant time Sibdex function to locate both operands of a chosen PCSE operator, or to get the two nearest neighboring operators of a chosen PCSE operator or of a chosen missing operand. The properties of the neighboring operators are checked with the simple associative comparison.

As an example for the associative removal of the noncontiguous CSEs, consider the expression '$a + b + c + b + z + a$'. The leftmost instance of $a + b$ is reduced first by generating code (ADD $a\ b\ T_1$) and replacing it by T_1, where T_1 is a temporary to hold the value of $a + b$. Then $+ b$ with the remote operand a constituting a CSE ($a + b$) is replaced with the same result variable (T_1) resulting in the reduced expression '$T_1 + c + z + T_1$' as shown in Figure 7a and Figure 8a. Notice that neither conventional DAG methods nor an associative method proposed earlier [5] can detect this noncontiguous $a + b$ as a CSE.

As an example for the associative removal of the contiguous CSEs, consider the expression '$a + b + b + a + a + b + b + a$', which can be viewed as '$a + b + a + b + a + b + a + b$' with four occurrences of a subexpression '$a + b$'. The leftmost instance of $a + b$ is reduced first by generating intermediate code (ADD $a\ b\ T_1$) for it and replacing it by T_1, where T_1 is a temporary variable to hold the value of $a + b$. All other instances of it are found associatively and replaced in situ by the same result temporary variable (T_1) as shown in Figure 8a. The result is the expression '$T_1 + T_1 + T_1 + T_1$' (see column 1 under the Token field in the right half of Figure 7b). In the reduced expression, '$T_1 + T_1$' is another common subexpression.

| Token | SC | Before Reduction | | | | | | After Reduction | | | | | | | |
		Priority	Nest	Prec	opr	ID	Proc	Token				Proc			
a	010000	0	0	0	0	1	0	T_1	T_2	T_2	T_2	0	0	0	0
+	020000	9	0	9	1	0	0					1	1	1	1
b	030000	0	0	0	0	1	0					1	1	1	1
+	040000	9	0	9	1	0	0	+				0	1	1	1
c	050000	0	0	0	0	1	0	c				0	1	1	1
+	060000	9	0	9	1	0	0					1	1	1	1
b	070000	0	0	0	0	1	0					1	1	1	1
+	080000	9	0	9	1	0	0	+	+			0	0	1	1
z	090000	0	0	0	0	1	0	z	z			0	0	1	1
+	0A0000	9	0	9	1	0	0	+	+	+		0	0	0	1
a	0B0000	0	0	0	0	1	0	T_1	T_1	T_1		0	0	0	1

a. Associative Reduction of '$\$a+b+c+b+z+a\$$'

| Token | SC | Before Reduction | | | | | | After Reduction | | | | | |
		Priority	Nest	Prec	opr	ID	Proc	Token			Proc		
a	010000	0	0	0	0	1	0	T_1	T_2	T_2	0	0	0
+	020000	9	0	9	1	0	0				1	1	1
b	030000	0	0	0	0	1	0				1	1	1
+	040000	9	0	9	1	0	0	+			0	1	1
b	050000	0	0	0	0	1	0	T_1			0	1	1
+	060000	9	0	9	1	0	0				1	1	1
a	070000	0	1	0	0	1	0				1	1	1
+	080000	9	1	9	1	0	0	+	+		0	0	1
a	090000	0	1	0	0	1	0	T_1	T_2		0	0	1
+	0A0000	9	0	9	1	0	0				1	1	1
b	0B0000	0	0	0	0	1	0				1	1	1
+	0C0000	9	0	9	1	0	0	+			0	1	1
b	0D0000	0	0	0	0	1	0	T_1			0	1	1
+	0E0000	9	0	9	1	0	0				1	1	1
a	0F0000	0	0	0	0	1	0				1	1	1

b. Associative Reduction of '$\$a+b+b+a+a+b+b+a\$$'

Figure 7. Associative reduction of expressions.

212

Example 1

Expression	No	quadruple
$a+b+c+b+z+a$	1	ADD a b T1
$T1+c+z+T1$	2	ADD T1 c T2
$T2+z+T1$	3	ADD T2 z T2
$T2+T1$	4	ADD T2 T1 T2
$T2$		

Example 2

Expression	No	quadruple
$a+b+b+a+a+b+b+a$	1	ADD a b T1
$T1+T1+T1+T1$	2	ADD T1 T1 T2
$T2+T2$	3	ADD T2 T2 T2
$T2$		

a. Quadruples Generated in the ACSEE Method

Example 1

Expression	No	quadruple
$a+b+c+b+z+a$	1	ADD a b T1
$T1+c+b+z+a$	2	ADD T1 c T2
$T2+b+z+a$	3	ADD T2 b T3
$T3+z+a$	4	ADD T3 z T4
$T4+a$	5	ADD T4 a T5
$T5$		

Example 2

Expression	No	quadruple
$a+b+b+a+a+b+b+a$	1	ADD a b T1
$T1+b+a+a+b+b+a$	2	ADD T1 b T2
$T2+a+a+b+b+a$	3	ADD T2 a T3
$T3+a+b+b+a$	4	ADD T3 a T4
$T4+b+b+a$	5	ADD T4 b T5
$T5+b+a$	6	ADD T5 b T6
$T6+a$	7	ADD T6 a T7
$T7$		

b. Quadruples Generated in Conventional Method

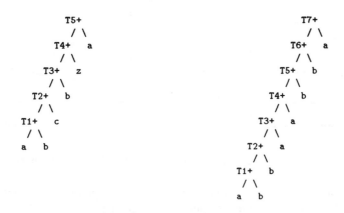

c. DAGs for the Quadruples from b

Figure 8. Examples of CSEs not detected in the DAG method.

Notice that there is no need to place the unprocessed tokens of the partially reduced expression in contiguous cells of an associative computer. All PEs with the processed tokens (Proc = 1) can be masked out. From the reduced expression (see Figure 7b), the '+' (its SC is 040000), with T_1 (its SC is 010000, it is physically three cells up but logically the immediate left neighbor to the cell with '+') as the left operand and another T_1 (its SC is 050000) as the right operand, is chosen for the second reduction resulting in the second CSE ($T_1 + T_1$) and the generation of the second quadruple 'ADD T_1 T_2 T_1' (Figure 8a). Thus, only three quadruples instead of seven are generated for the entire expression and the original CSE of length 7 is removed.

Note that conventional DAG methods cannot detect '$a + b$' (either contiguous or noncontiguous) as a

CSE. This is because quadruples for the consecutive operators are generated consecutively (Figure 8b) resulting in DAGs with no multiple labels on any node as shown in Figure 8c.

7   Efficiency of ACSEE

Figures 9 and 10 show that the ACSEE algorithm increases the execution efficiency as well as compilation efficiency. Expression evaluation without CSE removal (see the fourth column in Figure 9 and the NOCSE curve in Figure 10a) generates n quadruples (n is the number of input operators) and that with CSE removal (see the sixth column in Figure 9 and the CSE curve in Figure 10a) generates at most [log n] quadruples. The associative compilation with CSE elimination (see the fifth column in Figure 9 and the CSE

# of Tokens	# of CSEs	No CSE Removal		CSE removal	
		Compiling time in msec	# of Quadruples in the resulting code	Compiling time in msec	# of Quadruples in the resulting code
7	2	0.30	3	0.20	2
11	3	0.49	5	0.32	3
15	4	0.67	7	0.34	3
19	5	0.86	9	0.46	4
23	6	1.05	11	0.49	4
27	7	1.24	13	0.59	5
31	8	1.43	15	0.53	4
35	9	1.62	17	0.66	5

Figure 9. Efficiency of CSE removal in the ACSEE method.

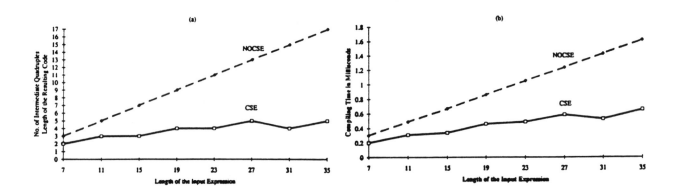

Figure 10. Graphs on efficiency of ACSEE method.

curve in Figure 10b) always takes much less time than the one without the CSE elimination (see the third column in Figure 9 and the NOCSE curve in Figure 10b). As the length of the expression increases, the time complexity of compilation with CSE removal increases more slowly than compilation without CSE removal, demonstrating the increased compilation efficiency of ACSEE. The increase in compilation efficiency is because ACSEE uses constant time-parallel associative operations to replace the CSEs in the source code with the result temporary without generating any quadruples for them.

8   Summary

The associative common subexpression elimination (ACSEE) algorithm presented here removes both contiguous and noncontiguous common subexpressions from an expression directly without needing a separate optimization pass. ACSEE uses constant time-associative operations to achieve the compilation efficiency. The authors believe that many other areas of compilation can also benefit from associative techniques.

References

[1] "ASPRO Programming Reference Manual," GER-16809, Goodyear Aerospace Corp., Apr. 1986.

[2] C. Asthagiri and J.L. Potter, "An Optimizing parallel Algorithm for Evaluating Infix Operator Expressions on an Associative SIMD Computer," Tech. Rep. CS-9010-30, Kent State Univ., 1990.

[3] C. Asthagiri, "An Associative Compiler for an Associative Computing Language," doctoral dissertation, Kent State Univ., 1991.

[4] K.E. Batcher, "STARAN Parallel Processor System Hardware," *Proc. Nat'l Computer Conf.*, 1974, pp. 406–410.

[5] C.A. Ellis, "Parallel Compiling Techniques," *Proc. ACM 16th Nat'l Conf.*, ACM Press, New York, N.Y., 1971, pp. 508–519.

[6] C.C. Foster, *Context Addressable Parallel Processors*, Van Nostrand Reinhold, New York, N.Y., 1976.

[7] W.D. Hillis and G.L. Steele Jr., "Data Parallel Algorithms," *Comm. ACM*, Vol. 29, No. 12, 1986, pp. 1,170–1,183.

[8] J.L. Potter, *Associative Computing: A Programming Paradigm for Massively Parallel Computers*, Plenum Press, 1992.

[9] *DTC Command Interface*, WaveTracer Inc., Jan. 28, 1991.

Section IV
Associative Processing
Applications

Database Mining and Matching in the Rutgers CAM

J. Storrs Hall, Donald E. Smith, and Saul Y. Levy
The Rutgers CAM Project,[1]
Laboratory for Computer Science Research
Hill Center, Busch Campus
Rutgers University
New Brunswick, NJ 08903
{josh, dsmith, Levy}@cs.rutgers.edu

Abstract

The Rutgers CAM architecture is an implementation of memory based on the set of operations that can be done with bit-serial, word-parallel algorithms on a classical content addressable memory. The design reduces the number of active elements, but increases speed and storage capacity compared with the original form. An expanded set of collective functions over the classic model drastically improves its flexibility in data representation, as well as increasing the number of parallel algorithms the architecture can execute.

Database mining and mass matching are applications that require performing simple operations on every element of large databases. Associative processors in general, and the Rutgers CAM in particular, are very efficient on tasks of this kind.

Classic CAM

In a conventional random access memory, each word has a fixed coordinate associated with it by the addressing hardware. "Pure" content-addressable memory (CAM) is a memory that, instead, lets the processor specify some partial pattern of bits that will identify the desired word by matching its contents.

It was understood by the early 1960s (see Falkoff[62]) that a CAM could be used for a form of parallel processing if the pattern could match and allow for writing into more than one word at the same time. We will refer to a CAM with this multiwrite capability as a "classic" CAM, and the form of parallel processing it allows, "associative processing." It has been called many things, including content-addressable parallel processing (Foster[76]) and associative computing (Potter[88]).

In a classic CAM, a broadcast value is compared with the stored data of each word (with a mask to pro-

vide "don't care" bit positions). The result of the comparison, rather than immediately causing a read or write of a matching word, is stored in an explicit "response bit." The bit is then used to control subsequent read/write operations; in particular, more than one word can be written into simultaneously. Boolean functions are then synthesized from sequences of tests, and bit-serial arithmetic can be performed on all words in parallel.

At a higher level, the model allows for logic, comparisons, and arithmetic between some global value and a local value stored in each word, or between local values in each word. Individual words may refrain from the operations based on locally determined conditions. This results in a model of computation that is equivalent to a SIMD star network, with the CPU as the hub and each word as a leaf processor. Since the hardware in the memory is only a few gates in addition to a flip-flop at each bit, classic CAM should, or so the theory goes, form the basis for massively parallel processors at densities near those of static RAMs.

Associative processors

CAMs useful for parallel processing require very wide words—256 bits is not unreasonable. Furthermore, each bit position requires a data line and a mask line in the bus, doubling its width. Requiring a 512-bit–wide bus is not impossible, but the CAM also requires a connection between each bit in any given word, which ordinary memory does not. Thus it is problematical to split CAM memories onto separate chips, requiring the pinouts of each chip to handle the entire bus width.

What is worse, in many CAM operations, particularly bit-serial arithmetic, most of the bus is wasted. An optimization can be performed: All the comparators at each bit can be removed, and in their place a one-bit ALU can be added to the word. The "match"

[1] Supported by DARPA and NASA under NASA-Ames grant NAG 2-668.

daisy chain and the read/write control lines can be replaced with a one-bit local bus running across the word. Now the (global) bus is much smaller: an opcode for the ALU, a bit address that can be decoded on-chip, a one-bit data bus. What is more, arithmetic is faster; single-bit arithmetic operations are built into the ALU rather than being synthesized from mask/test sequences. In practice, this has been the best trade-off point for CAM-like implementations, and it characterizes the CM-1, the DAP, and the MPP, among others.

Whatever their merits as parallel processors, these systems are not cost-effective as content-addressable memory; to our knowledge, there has been no cost-effective implementation of classic CAM.

Rutgers CAM architecture: Overview

The associative processing model, however, remains compelling. The Rutgers CAM Project is an attempt to find an implementation of the model that is cost-effective enough to be used as memory, replacing the RAM in a computer architecture.

The Rutgers CAM model starts with the operations of classic CAM, but we have designed an architecture that performs them directly. Instead of an original comparator-per-bit content-addressable memory model, it has proven more efficient to provide each cell with fixed-width fields, and an ALU and internal bus of that width. (We will henceforth refer to the fields as "words," but they are not to be confused with the original wide CAM words, which would correspond to the entire cell.) The architecture that results can be kept to within a given factor, in silicon per bit, of conventional DRAM by adjusting the ratio of ALU-to-DRAM area in each cell.

The Rutgers "CAM" is in actuality a fairly well-endowed associative processor, but is designed to be a more-or-less direct replacement for memory in an otherwise conventional computer architecture. Thus the term "CAM" is retained to suggest its intended use. The operations it implements are as follows:

- Activity control: All the following can be controlled on a per-cell, per-instruction basis. That is, we can add 17 to word 3 in each cell, or we can add 17 to word 3 only in those cells where word 10 is greater than 92.

- Parallel operations including addition, subtraction, comparison, and bitwise Boolean functions. They do *not* include multiplication, division, or floating point, although these can be done in software. These operations can be done only between words of the same cell.

- Broadcast: One of the operands in the above operations can be a "global" constant value (the same in each cell).

- Collective functions: Scalar-valued collective functions include the sum, max, and min of all the elements of a vector; vector-valued collective functions are parallel prefix (and suffix) forms of the scalar ones; and skip-shifting. This last moves a value from each active cell to the next active cell, no matter how far away, as a unit-time primitive.

- Segmentation: All of the collective functions and broadcasting can be done in segments, which, like the activity, are definable on the fly. Each segment can have a different "global" value that comes from some cell in the segment.

- Simple one-cell-at-a-time shifting that ignores activity and segment definitions can be done concurrently with other CAM operations; such shifting requires time proportional to distance shifted.

The following description of the design that implements the model above gives specific numbers for concreteness. However, the design itself is parameterized and is valid for CAMs of any desired word length. The Rutgers CAM memory architecture consists of three main parts (Figure 1), the tree, the leaf cells, and the memory. These operate concurrently under the influence of 3-opcode instructions from the CPU.

- Each leaf cell consists of an ALU with 16 registers and on the order of 10K words of DRAM. The ALU, register, memory, and all data paths are 32 bits wide. The first 4 registers are mapped into the tree (see below), the memory, the shifter, and the collection of one-bit registers that are the status, activity, segment, and so forth; the rest of the registers are general purpose. Each cell is like a very simple RISC with register-to-register operations and asynchronous load/store (but without the instruction sequencer).

- The cells are connected by a tree of simpler ALUs, each of which has one register. The tree is combinational—that is, each CAM cell presents it with a 32-bit value and two control bits, activity and segment. The tree forms a direct-wired circuit that produces the appropriate value at the root which is then stored into each tree node's latch. Tree functions take five times as long as local CAM operations.

In a scan or shift operation, the tree actually does two operations, one up and one down. Each phase is combinational internally.

- A (unidirectional) instruction bus, emanating from the CPU, which controls the cells and the tree nodes. Depending on chip size and process parameters, the bus may be pipelined: The bus is optimized for throughput, in contrast to the tree, which is optimized for latency.

- A shift register for overlapped I/O and data motion between CAM cells. Like the tree and the DRAM, the shift register operates asynchronously from the CAM cell. CAM efficiency is very dependent on its ability to move data. This is one of the reasons that the architecture has so much DRAM in each cell—loading and unloading of one problem's data while another problem is being worked on is crucial to CAM's efficiency. Thus the design calls for a separate data path for this function.

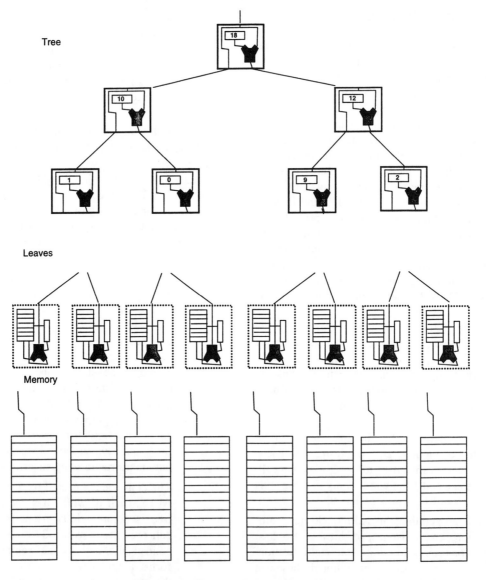

Figure 1. Rutgers CAM architecture.

Collective functions

The ALUs in the cells perform in constant time the arithmetic operations that a classic CAM did as bit-serial algorithms. The classic CAM is also capable of some operations that are functions of the memory as a whole, such as finding the maximum value, or counting the number of items that matched in a given search. These could also be done in a time independent of the number of words, with a bit-serial, word-parallel, algorithm. To include these operations in the model on an equal basis with the others, the Rutgers CAM design uses a binary tree of ALUs (whose leaves are the memory cells).

The most important feature of the tree is what it is not: It is not a tree-connected parallel processor. It is a single combinational logic circuit whose design is optimized to produce a value with latency comparable to a conventional DRAM. Thus its functionality is highly constrained. It is essentially a binary tree of 32-bit adders. It will produce from its root the sum of all the values presented at the leaves (that is, the value in the "tree" register of each CAM cell).

In the nomenclature of the Rutgers CAM (borrowed from APL) such a summation is called a *reduction*. The tree can do reduction using addition, min, max, bitwise AND, OR, or XOR as the function. Furthermore, the activity indication follows the data into the tree, so the circuit can take the sum, instantly, of only those values with an active bit set.

The ALU tree is capable of the collective functions that can be done bit-serially on a classic CAM, but it can also be used for another very interesting class of collective functions, the scans (also called parallel prefix operations). Scans are a very useful class of parallel operations, generally implemented in software on early associative processors.[2]

There are two definitions of scan, the inclusive and the exclusive.[3] Each transforms a string of values $[x_1, x_2, \ldots, x_n]$ using an associative scalar function $\Diamond$. The inclusive scan produces $[x_1, (x_1 \Diamond x_2), (x_1 \Diamond x_2 \Diamond x_3), \ldots, (x_1 \Diamond x_2 \ldots \Diamond x_n)]$, and the exclusive scan produces $[\phi, x_1, (x_1 \Diamond x_2), \ldots, (x_1 \Diamond x_2 \ldots \Diamond x_{n-1})]$, where ϕ is an inactive element. In other words each position receives the $\Diamond$-reduction of all the elements up to that point, either inclusive or exclusive of the element itself.

The collective function tree performs an exclusive scan; the inclusive version can be obtained by performing the scalar function in parallel between the scan result and the original string, but the opposite is not true. In particular, inclusive scans cannot be used for skip-shifting as described below.

A (left-to-right) scan consists of an up phase that is identical to a reduction, and a down phase that moves data from the root to the leaves. The phases are coupled through internal registers in each node. During the up phase, input is from the node's children, L and R respectively. L is gated into the internal register, and $L \Diamond R$, through the ALU, to its parent. After the entire tree settles, all registers are latched at once, and the down phase begins. During a down phase each node sends the value from its parent, P, down to the left child, and using the saved value from the register, which was L, sends $P \Diamond L$ to the right child.

For a right-to-left scan, exchange the words "left" and "right" in the above description. Other embellishments to the basic scan operation are the ability to extend activity control throughout the tree, summing or scanning only active elements, and the ability to segment the scans, essentially performing an independent scan in each segment. In the following, V is a vector, +\ means plus-scan, A?V is vector V with activity control A, and S!V is vector V with segmentation S.

Scans can form a rudimentary communication primitive. An (exclusive) scan provides, at each position, the reduction of all the elements in previous positions. If we scan using one of the identity functions $rt(x,y) = y$ or $lf(x,y) = x$.

Note that lf-scan is broadcast and rt-scan is shift. If we have hardware for scan, those functions come at the price of adding a mux function to the tree ALU. What is more, the motion scans interact quite usefully with activity and segmentation.

Shifting with activity skips over inactive elements, and broadcasting with segmentation does local broadcast. These capabilities combine fortuitously in communication algorithms.

A large class of algorithms can be done in parallel with the collective functions, which cannot be done without them. Foster [76] discusses them as "distributed hardware." Hall [81] gives algorithms for basic graph-theoretic algorithms using them. Blelloch's [90] "V-RAM" model of computation is based on them. The segmented operations are a one-dimensional version of what Weems and Herbordt [93] refer to as "multi-associative processing."

Conceptually, this CAM, which augments memory with a small amount of on-chip processing capability, is the dual of cache, which augments the processor with small amounts of on-chip memory. Both can serve to reduce the data flowing through the "von Neumann bottleneck."

---

[2] The use of scan as a general-purpose parallel operator has been popularized by Blelloch (see Blelloch [90]). Early implementations were software, for example, on the CM-1. An exception was the ITT CAPP, which could do scan in a ripple mode (see Fountain [87]). The CM-5 has provisions for hardware scan.

[3] APL's scan is inclusive; Blelloch's is exclusive.

	1	2	3	4	5	6	7	8	9	10	11	12	13	14	15	16	17	18	19
V =	1	9	0	8	9	3	2	3	8	9	6	4	2	6	8	3	5	1	9
+\V =	_	1	10	10	18	27	30	32	35	43	52	58	62	64	70	78	81	86	87
A?V =	1	9	–	–	–	–	2	–	8	–	–	–	–	6	8	3	–	–	9
+\A?V =	_	–	–	–	–	–	10	–	12	–	–	–	–	20	26	34	–	–	37
S!V =	1	9	0	8	9|	3	2	3	8	9|	6	4	2	6	8	3	5	1	9
+\S!V =	–	1	10	10	18|	–	3	5	8	16|	–	6	10	12	18	26|	–	5	6
V =	1	9	0	8	9	3	2	3	8	9	6	4	2	6	8	3	5	1	9
+\V =	_	1	10	10	18	27	30	32	35	43	52	58	62	64	70	78	81	86	87
lf\V =	_	1	1	1	1	1	1	1	1	1	1	1	1	1	1	1	1	1	1
rt\V =	_	1	9	0	8	9	3	2	3	8	9	6	4	2	6	8	3	5	1	
A?V =	1	9	_	_	_	_	2	_	8	_	_	_	_	6	8	3	_	_	9
rt\A?V =	_	1	_	_	_	_	9	_	2	_	_	_	_	8	6	8	_	_	3
S!V =	1	9	0	8	9|	3	2	3	8	9|	6	4	2	6	8	3|	5	1	9
lf\S!V =	_	1	1	1	1|	_	3	3	3	3|	_	6	6	6	6	6|	_	5	5

Furthermore, the two architectural enhancements are complementary in their areas of greatest efficiency; cache where relatively few data are accessed often, and CAM where relatively many data are accessed less frequently.

Database mining

Suppose you are the manager of a grocery store. You wish to place some items on sale to stimulate trade. You would prefer to place something on sale that is commonly bought along with other items, the more other items the better. It will do you little good to discount something that is usually bought alone. You might wish to place several items on sale to entice different groups of customers, but you don't want to discount *all* the items any given customer (or very many of them) is going to buy.

Suppose you have a database of all the transactions in your store for the past year. Each record is a list of bits, one for each item you sell, telling whether that item was bought in that transaction (that is, one record per customer per visit). The process of discovering regularities of the kind you are interested in is called *database mining*.[4]

Database mining is not, of course, limited to grocery stores. You could be a government considering taxes or tariffs with an eye to maximizing revenues and/or economic activity. You could be a football coach looking for weaknesses in an opposing team. You could be a programmer attempting to build an expert system in some area where there is no formally codified expertise in the field.

---

[4] See, for example, Agrawal, Imelinski, and Swami [93].

Database mining algorithms on Rutgers CAM

In the typical database mining algorithm, the primitives are a matching operation of some query with the records of the database, and the counting of matches (Figure 2). Each record is looked at exactly once in a given scan. Although the overall algorithm scans the database many times as it forms and revises its inductive hypotheses, there is no locality of reference at all. A conventional processor will gain very little performance from its cache on these algorithms. The Rutgers CAM architecture, however, seen as the dual of cache, finds a near-optimal application in the database mining problem.

The database mining algorithms all have as a core or "inner loop" a sequence of matching and counting operations. For example, suppose each record in a database is a bit vector indicating the presence or absence of a sequence of features. One probe would then consist of a comparison under mask of a given query set of features with each record in the database, accumulating a count of the number of matches.

This is exactly the basic operation supported by a classical content-addressable memory (with count-responders circuitry). The catch is that for the probe to be efficient, the CAM must be big enough to hold the entire database. Since leading current microprocessor systems would be able to perform a probe of a gigabit (one million 1,000-bit records) database in a few seconds at most, we must consider databases of at least this size. (A typical database of this configuration would be a record of supermarket transactions where each bit position denotes one type of item in the inventory.)

Simple form:

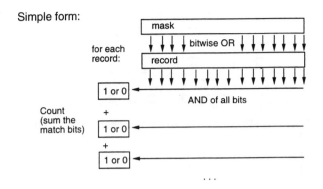

Complex form:

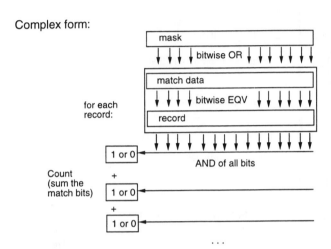

Figure 2. Database mining algorithm.

A gigabit conventional-design CAM could do the match extremely fast, probably in a few microseconds. However, a gigabit of conventional CAM would be prohibitively expensive. With the Rutgers-style hybrid memory scheme, a gigabit of memory is contained on, for example, twice the number of chips it would require for ordinary DRAM in the same technology. The Rutgers CAM would be able to do the probe in a few milliseconds.

It is a desideratum that a CAM should support parallel operations on the data in as many different layouts as possible. Consider the four layouts for the database shown in Figures 3-6. Each layout can be processed at a rate of 32 records per thousand cells each segmented-tree operation time (which is expected to be about equivalent to the DRAM load time). Thus the algorithm designer is more or less free to choose between representations depending on the constraints of other operations to be done on the database.

The memory maps in Figures 3-6 indicate how the bits of a given record are laid out. The solid area represents the bits of one record. The vertical charts indicate the overlapping timing of the instruction sequences for each of the three independent parts of the architecture. The memory access, leaf ALUs, and tree form effectively a three-stage pipeline. Each diagram contains a labeled sequence of instructions handling one batch of data, together with the previous and subsequent sequence in broken outlines.

In bit-row mode (Figure 3), 32 B-bit records are operated on in B cells. The mask is stored in leaf-node registers. Each line of memory is loaded and masked locally in the leaf. Then the bitwise ANDing across records is done in the tree. Each B-length segment ANDs 32 records in parallel, one at each bit position in the word. If B happens to equal the number of cells, this mode is slightly more efficient because it can be a reduction; otherwise, a segmented AND is done.

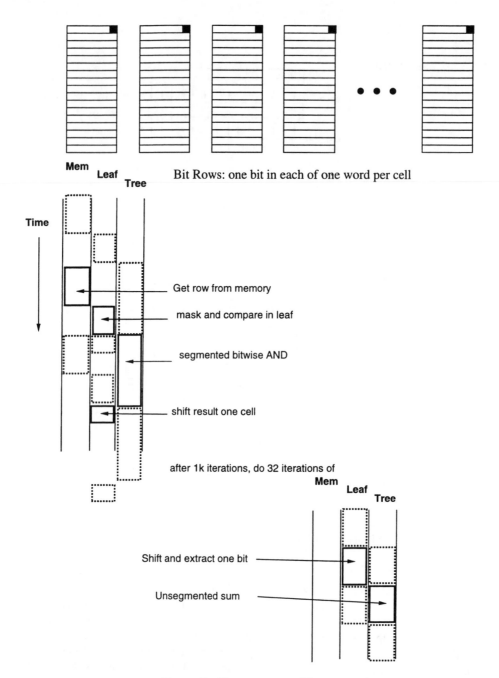

Figure 3. Memory map: Bit-row mode.

To count records, the results of the AND are broadcast across a segment of 32 words, each of which has a single-bit mask to pick out the corresponding bit. A 1 or 0 is selected in each word from this operation and the results summed in the tree.

In bit-column mode (Figure 4), 32 B-bit records occupy B words under each leaf. Again bitwise leaf operations are done for masking, but in this case the mask must be broadcast, or equivalently, encoded into the instruction stream by skipping the appropriate bit positions. The AND across the record is done by accumulation in a leaf register. Thus there is no ANDing to be done in the tree, but more counting. After B mask-accumulate steps, each bit position in the CAM holds the one-bit result of one match; they must be counted. We do this in 32 steps, shifting each bit into position, masking out the others, and doing a global sum across all cells.

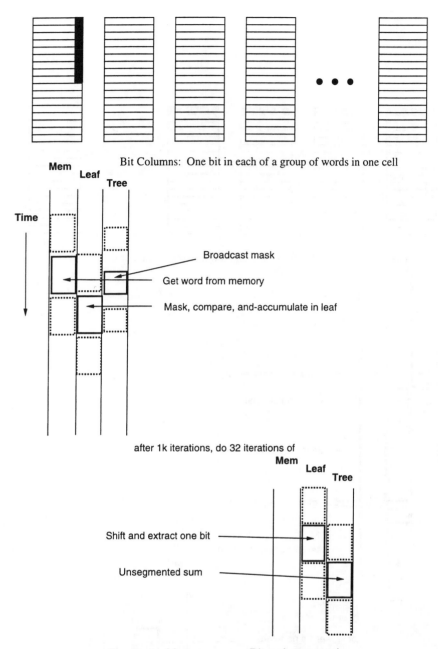

Bit Columns: One bit in each of a group of words in one cell

Broadcast mask

Get word from memory

Mask, compare, and-accumulate in leaf

after 1k iterations, do 32 iterations of

Shift and extract one bit

Unsegmented sum

Figure 4. Memory map: Bit-column mode.

Word-row mode (Figure 5) is similar to bit-row mode except that all the bits in a given word must be ANDed together after the masking. This can be done by inverting the sense of the bits and using the compare-to-zero operation. This can be done either before or after the segmented bitwise AND across the words of each record; a global sum with activity is the final stage in the count.

In word-column mode (Figure 6) bit mask and AND accumulation are done with bitwise operations in the words as in bit-column; then AND across the word is done as in word-row; and finally a global sum, no activity or segmentation required, counts the matches. In bit-column mode the mask could be implicitly "broadcast" by skipping bit positions, but in word-column mode it must be broadcast explicitly as a sequence of 32-bit values.

Each of these modes produces a sequence of values that the processor must accumulate, but the number of such values is reduced by a factor of the number of cells in the CAM. The overall speedup is thus proportional to number of cells and to the ratio between (conventional) DRAM time to CAM collective function time.

225

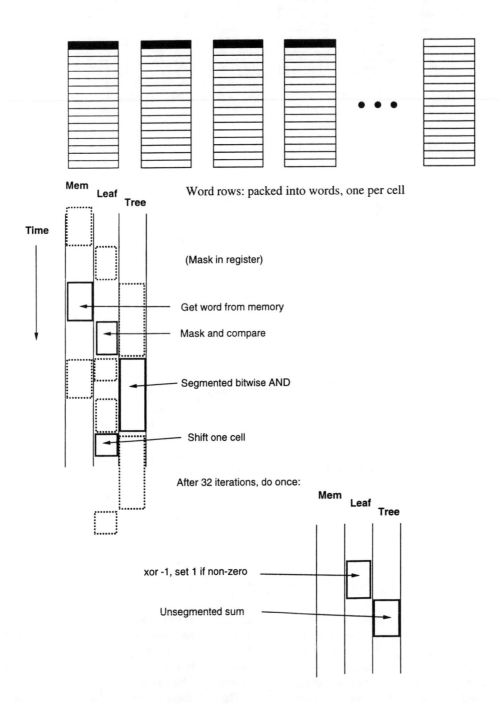

Figure 5. Memory map: Word-row mode.

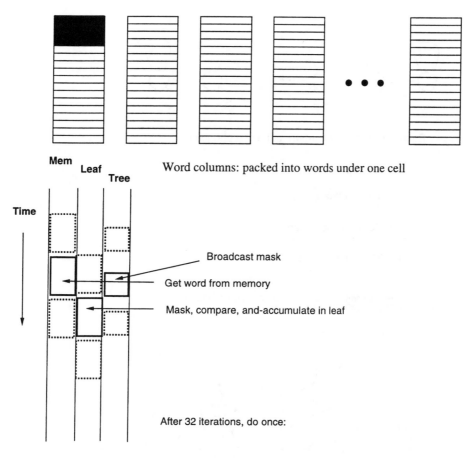

Word columns: packed into words under one cell

Mem Leaf Tree

Time

Broadcast mask

Get word from memory

Mask, compare, and-accumulate in leaf

After 32 iterations, do once:

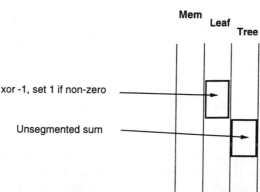

Mem Leaf Tree

xor -1, set 1 if non-zero

Unsegmented sum

Figure 6. Memory map: Word-column mode.

Match and search problems

A match operation that does impose constraints on the layout is a typical *numeric* feature vector. Consider a real-time speech recognition system (Figure 7). Vocabularies for these systems are commonly databases of hidden Markov models of the words the system is to recognize.[5] Current systems are limited because the most robust algorithms involve a brute-force matching of the input utterance with every word in the vocabulary.

The input sound is sampled in small segments, and each segment is classified using a numeric feature vector. A typical vector would have 20 features, which would be measures of various qualities of the sound such as distribution of energy with frequency. A typical word would have 10 states in its model, each characterized by a feature vector. A full vocabulary for English (much larger than current systems can handle) might contain 150,000 words.

---

[5] See Bristow[86].

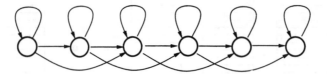

Each state represents (more or less) a phoneme

20 features per state

10 states per word

150,000 word vocabulary

30,000,000 word database

At each timestep, compute feature vector for input sound and match into EVERY WORD in the database.

State matching is by Euclidean distance.

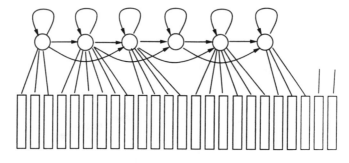

compute total match probability for each word in database.

Figure 7. Hidden Markov models for speech recognition.

At the core of the matching process is finding the Euclidean distance between a vector U from the utterance and a candidate vector C characterizing some state in some word model, $D = \Sigma(U_i-C_i)^2$.[2] Because the data are numeric, only word-mode layouts need be considered; otherwise the inner loop is similar to that for the database mining example (Figure 8). The time to do the multiplication dominates all the other steps in the algorithm, no matter which layout is used.

A big difference from the database mining example has to do with the comparison of the Rutgers CAM and classic CAM on the problems. Because the database mining example involved primarily bit manipulations, classic CAM was architecturally well suited to the task, the only problem being size. However, once the algorithms involve arithmetic, the classic CAM would not be significantly faster than the Rutgers CAM, even though it would require orders of magnitude more silicon area for the same problem size.

And finally, a word about layouts. The various row and column mode layouts we've been considering for the databases in the problems above tend to result in similar performance. This is not an accident. One major stumbling block for associative processing has always been that data layout critically impacted the amount of parallelism available. Whenever it was attempted to use an associative processor as a general-purpose computer, it would often be found that two ingenious parallel algorithms that performed successive steps in an overall task required the data in different formats. A linear-time reformatting step would not be a problem on a conventional machine, since the surrounding steps would tend to be at least linear anyway, but it would destroy the efficiency of the CAM.

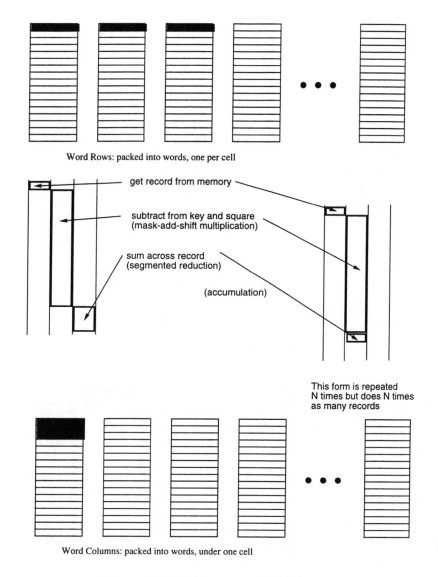

Word Rows: packed into words, one per cell

get record from memory

subtract from key and square
(mask-add-shift multiplication)

sum across record
(segmented reduction)

(accumulation)

This form is repeated
N times but does N times
as many records

Word Columns: packed into words, under one cell

Figure 8. Euclidean nearest neighbor.

The Rutgers CAM architecture is carefully balanced to alleviate this problem as much as possible. The tree has enough functionality so that the programmer often has the choice of layouts for any given operation. In the numeric matching problem the two layouts resulted in similar efficiencies. Classic CAM, lacking segmented collective functions, would be unable to use the equivalent of a word-row layout efficiently for this problem.

However, consider what happens if the problem is changed slightly. Assume the operation of interest is a best-match search. Now assume the database can be clustered and accessed by a tree search, using a Manhattan ($\Sigma|U_i-C_i|$) metric. Consider the case of one million 32-word records on a 4K-cell CAM (Figure 9). A word-column layout would provide a two-level tree with a compare time per level of 32, for a total of 64 times through the inner loop. A word-row layout would provide an arity-128 tree of three levels, but only one loop each for a total of 3. The flexibility of the Rutgers CAM allows it to take advantage of this algorithmic opportunity.

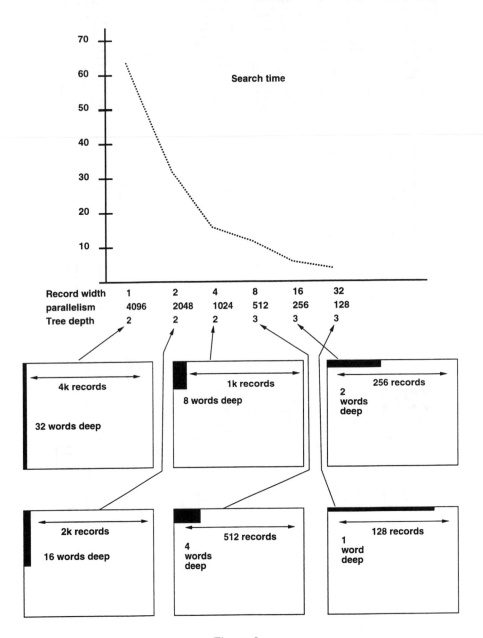

Figure 9.

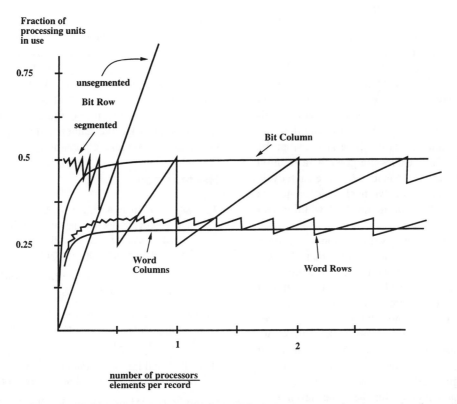

Figure 10. Database mining on the Rutgers CAM: Efficiency versus database size for various layouts.

Analytical and empirical results

We have implemented a rescheduling assembler that rearranges the micro-operations (for example, operations for tree, leaf cell, and memory) to achieve maximum overlap of the operations. It does this by using a data dependency model of the machine, and using time ratios of 1 cycle per operation in the leaf cell, 4 cycles per memory load/store, and 4 cycles in the tree per reduction, 8 for scan. It only reorders; every operation in the input program appears in the output program, even if a more clever optimizer might remove some of them.

The reordering assembler does a good job on the code for the database mining functions. The following table compares the times for database mining in the four data layout formats discussed above. The first column gives the time for code represented as a series of macro-operations (such as scan) expanded into micro-operations and run sequentially. The second column gives times for the same code, rescheduled. The third column gives times for the tightest hand-crafted code we could come up with, programming at the micro level ourselves. All times are in cycles for the inner loop.

It can be seen that the rescheduled code is a considerable improvement over the sequential times, closely approaching (equaling, half the time) the hand-coded versions that we feel are a good approximation to optimal.

Layout	Sequential	Rescheduled	Hand-coded
Bit rows	13	5	4
Bit columns	20	10	10
Word rows	15	10	10
Word columns	23	15	12

231

Speedups for the various layouts depend not only on the layout but on the interaction of the size of the database being searched with the size of the machine. If the database is just one record longer than some multiple of the machine size (counting by number of leaf cells—we're still assuming that it fits in memory beneath the leaves), the final iteration is mostly wasted; if it's an exact multiple, or just smaller, efficiency is much higher. This produces a sawtooth graph of efficiency as a function of database size, as can be seen in Figure 10. Efficiencies are given as a fraction of the functional units of the machine in use each cycle averaged over the algorithm (vertical scale); database size is given as a multiple of the machine width in leaf cells.

The line for bit rows has two overlapping versions for databases whose records are shorter than the machine (that is, from 0 to 1 on the horizontal scale). The straight line from (0,0) to (1,1) is for a layout that places only one record across and thus uses unsegmented tree operations; the sawtooth curve places more records across the machine when they are smaller and is thus more efficient; from 0.25 to 0.5 it represents doing two records at once but at half the rate (because segmented operations take twice as long) as the unsegmented version, for the same throughput; and at an exact fit, the unsegmented version achieves a remarkable 100 percent efficiency.

The other curves are more indicative of performance to be expected for the average application; they are still extremely good for SIMD style computation with as little communication hardware as the Rutgers CAM. They represent an extremely high utilization of active devices in the architecture.

Conclusion

The Rutgers CAM architecture is an implementation of memory based on the set of operations that can be done with bit-serial, word-parallel algorithms on a classical content addressable memory. The design gives up a bit comparator at every bit position in memory, gaining density, but replaces them with ALUs that make arithmetic much faster than the bit-serial version. It has hardware support for fast reduction and scan operations, which gives it the ability to

do substantial parallel processing in addition to the purely associative operations.

Database mining and mass matching are applications that require performing simple operations on every element of large databases. The classic CAM is architecturally well suited to database mining but is very expensive in the sizes that would be needed. The Rutgers CAM architecture could achieve thousandfold speedups on tasks like database mining over conventional machines with a comparable number of chips.

References

Agrawal, R., T. Imielinski, and A. Swami, "DataBase Mining: A Performance Perspective," *IEEE Trans. Knowledge and Data Eng.*, special issue on Learning and Discovery in Knowledge-based Databases, 1993.

Blelloch, G., *Vector Models for Data-Parallel Computing*, MIT Press, Cambridge, Mass., 1990.

Electronic Speech Recognition: Techniques, Technology, and Applications, G. Bristow, ed., McGraw-Hill, New York, N.Y., 1986.

Duda, R.O. and P.E. Hart, *Pattern Classification and Scene Analysis*, John Wiley and Sons, New York, N.Y., 1973.

Falkoff, A.D., "Algorithms for Parallel-Search Memories," *J. ACM*, Vol. 9, No. 10, Oct. 1962, pp. 488–511.

Foster, C.C., *Content Addressable Parallel Processors*, Van Nostrand Reinhold, New York, N.Y., 1976.

Fountain, T., *Processor Arrays: Architecture and Applications*, Academic Press, London, UK, 1987.

Hall, J.S., "A General-Purpose CAM-based System," in *VLSI Systems and Computations*, Kung, Sproull, and Steele, eds., Computer Science Press, Rockville, Md., 1981, pp. 379–388.

Hall, J.S., S. Levy, and D. Smith, *The Rutgers CAM Chip Architecture*, Tech. Report LCSR-TR-196, Rutgers University, New Brunswick, N.J., Apr. 1993.

Herbordt, M. and C. Weems, "Multiassociative Processing," presented at the 1993 Syracuse Associative Processing and Applications Workshop, New York, N.Y.

Potter, J.L., *Associative Computing: A Programming Paradigm for Massively Parallel Computers*, Plenum Press, New York, N.Y., 1992.

Prolog on the Associative String Processor

D.P. Rodohan, R.J. Glover, and I.P. Jalowiecki
Department of Electrical Engineering and Electronics
Brunel University
Uxbridge, Middx., UK
{Darren.Rodohan, Raymond.Glover, Ian.Jalowiecki}@brunel.ac.uk

1 Introduction

Associative implementations of Prolog have been investigated since 1987 with chips based on content-addressable memory (CAM) or with SIMD parallel computer architectures. The investigations have attempted to accelerate various stages in the execution of a Prolog program using associative processing techniques. In this paper we describe work that is currently being performed at Brunel University to implement Prolog on the Associative String Processor (ASP) [Lea88].

We first describe the ASP architecture and a general execution model for Prolog. We then describe how sequential Prolog programs can be executed on the ASP. The Prolog language is then extended to include a set processing mode so that we can further exploit the associative power of the ASP architecture. Finally, we present preliminary results obtained on a standard benchmark program for Prolog performance.

1.1 ASP Architecture

The ASP is a scalable architecture that can provide a very large number of processing elements. In fact, hybrid wafer scale [Hab93] and wafer scale integration will allow systems containing $O(10^6)$ processors to become feasible in the future. The current implementation of the architecture (Trax) has been optimized for image processing tasks, performing well in the DARPA image understanding benchmarks. The system, designed by Aspex Microsystems Ltd., contains 16K processors and has a clock frequency of 20 MHz.

The architecture, illustrated in figure 1, can be considered to consist of two parts: a set of bit serial processors plus a communication network. The bit-serial processors, known as Associative Processing Elements (APEs), consist of a one-bit arithmetic logic unit and 64 bits of local storage. An activity register of 6 bits is also associated with the local storage for each APE, both of which are implemented in content-

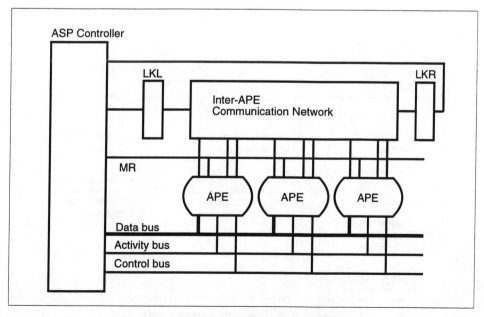

Figure 1. The Associative string processor.

addressable memory (CAM) cells, that can be addressed associatively in bit, byte, and word (32-bit) modes.

Two modes of communication are possible: synchronous bit-serial communication and asynchronous noninterleaved communication. The synchronous communication allows many-to-many mappings whereas the asynchronous communication allows one-to-many mappings. Bit-serial communication allows N APEs to shift data via a tag register to corresponding APEs, a distance D away. Asynchronous communication is possible by marking source and destination APEs, reading the source APE's data, and then broadcasting the data to the destination APE(s).

1.2   Prolog execution model

Prolog consists of two separate execution modes: forward and backward, as shown in Figure 2. The forward mode can be split into two further stages: clause invocation and variable instantiation. The clause invocation stage matches the query clause against the heads of the program clauses. The topmost matching program head clause is then selected for variable instantiation. The topmost match is always selected to ensure a depth-first search.

The variables in the clause head are then unified with those in the current query term. The unification process consists of searching for previous variable bindings and the actual binding of the variables to constant or other variable terms. If the unification fails, then a backtrack operation is required. The variable bindings made since the last choice point must be undone and the program restarted at the next alternative clause head. Selecting the next alternative clause head effectively changes the program execution sequence.

A crude implementation of the Prolog execution model relies on several stack structures. A global stack is required to keep track of the next clause term to be invoked. A stack structure is selected because it is a simple method to implement depth-first search. When a head term matches the current goal query, a pointer to the clause body terms is placed on the goal stack. If the clause head unifies successfully with the goal query then the goal stack is "popped" and the first term in the clause body is unified. A stack structure is also required for the variable bindings, so that if a unification fails a previous program state can be recovered. Finally, if more than one clause head can match a goal term, the address of the second clause head is stored for backtracking purposes. This is known as a *choice point* and is stored on the trail stack. Warren [War83] refined this crude model into an abstract machine for Prolog program execution, known as the Warren Abstract Machine or WAM.

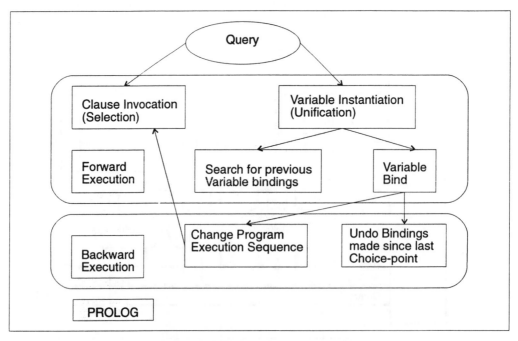

Figure 2. A Prolog execution model.

234

2   Sequential execution

The execution order of Prolog programs is determined by the textual order of the clauses in the program. However, many unnecessary unifications are performed when using a interpreted version of Prolog. Unification between clause heads containing mismatching types are often attempted, consuming a large amount of processing time. This can be avoided by associatively searching all of the clause head terms in parallel to remove all of the clauses that contain mismatching types or data. The topmost clause from the remaining clause heads should then be selected for unification. This concept, often referred to as clause filtering, was previously investigated by Robinson [Rob92] on the FAIM-1 (later to become the Mayfly project) using pattern-addressable memory. Naganuma [Nag88] and Oldfield [Old87] also used clause filtering in their systems by encrypting data type information with the clause head name to make up single or multiple word entries in CAM for each clause head in the program. When the interpreter is queried, a series of match operations are performed on the encrypted data to filter out clauses that cannot unify with the query clause, leaving only a few candidate head clauses that could possibly unify with the query. The possible matches that can be made are summarized in Table 1.

The second stage in the unification process is variable binding. This is performed in the WAM on a heap structure using pointers. A variable pointer that points to another memory location indicates that the variable is bound to a term or another variable. If the variable pointer points to its own memory location, it is a "free" or unbound variable. This leads to a large amount of time spent pointer following to determine if a variable is already bound, especially if a variable points to a variable that points to another variable, and so forth.

On the ASP, variable bindings are placed in an associative heap that can be searched in a one-step match operation. The variable bindings are stored together with their associated inference depth (ID). This

lets us search for variables by their ID as well as their name. The value of a variable can be obtained from the heap in single-step operation. Variables that are unbound are not stored on the heap; therefore, a simple match operation (that fails) is enough to show that a variable is unbound rather than the complex and time-consuming pointer following used in the WAM. Oldfield [Old87], Bacha [Bac91], and Naganuma [Nag91] also store their variable bindings in CAM together with the associated ID at which the binding was made.

When a backtracking operation is required in the WAM, the global heap pointer is reset and all "trailed" variables must be reset to *undefined*. Resetting the "trailed" variables can be a time-consuming process. However, we store all variable bindings with an associated ID. To backtrack, all bindings with an associated ID that is larger than the last choice point are set to garbage and reclaimed for future use. This can be performed in a few associative cycles and is independent of the number of variable binding to be reset. Again, a similar technique is used in the majority of CAM-based implementations of Prolog.

In this section we have outlined how the basic execution steps required for an associative implementation of Prolog can be supported. Next we will describe how we can map Prolog terms onto the ASP architecture so that we can exploit its associative capabilities.

3   Data representation

The representation of Prolog terms on the ASP must ensure that we can take full advantage of its ability to perform associative search. The representation should also try to prevent the ASP from performing a match resolution operation across its total string length. The time taken for this resolution is obviously proportional to the length of the string. The terms used in Prolog consist of structures, lists, constants, and variables as well as further combinations of these basic terms. The representation must also allow the processing of data sets, which will be discussed in section 4.

Table 1. Possible matches in Prolog.

Input Type	Output Type			
	Variable	**Constant**	**List**	**Structure**
Variable	Yes	Yes	Yes	Yes
Constant	Yes	Yes	No	No
List	Yes	No	Yes	No
Structure	Yes	No	No	Yes

Lists are known to be a sequential data structure. This is the case if we do not restrict the maximum length of a list. However, if the maximum length of a list is fixed, Bansal's [Ban92] left-justified structure representation can be used. The structure code implicitly denotes where brackets occur, that is, it signifies where a different structure or list starts. An example of the left-handed field code for the Prolog term $a(b(y(t), [1, 2]), [4, 5, 6], (Z, d))$ is shown in Table 2. The left-hand structure code lets the ASP perform "don't care" searches to select a whole subsection of a term. Figure 3 graphically illustrates the left-handed structure codes for the same example. All members of the list [4,5,6] could be selected using a match operation for all structure codes meeting the criteria 12**, (* refers to "don't care match"). This will allow operations, such as list membership, to be performed using associative search in one step. Vector arithmetic operations are also made feasible with this representation.

Table 2. Structure codes for Prolog term example.

Structure Code	Type	Name
1000 0000	functor	a
1100 0000	functor	b
1110 0000	functor	y
1111 0000	atom	t
1120 0000	list	.
1121 0000	integer	1
1122 0000	integer	2
1123 0000	nil	NIL
1200 0000	list	.
1210 0000	integer	4
1220 0000	integer	5
1230 0000	integer	6
1240 0000	nil	NIL
1300 0000	tuple	;
1310 0000	variable	Z
1320 0000	atom	d

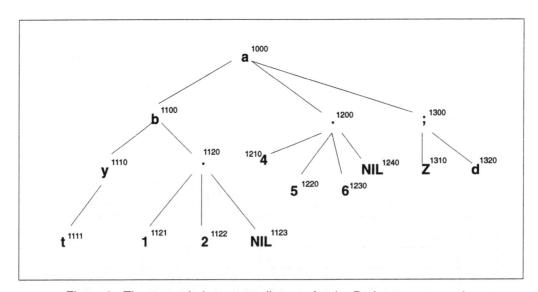

Figure 3. The expanded structure diagram for the Prolog term example.

The left-handed structure code representation also partially removes a problem inherent to a string architecture. When trying to locate the top (or leftmost) matching element in a structure, a multiple match resolution strategy must be employed over the entire length of the string. The time taken for this search is a function of the string length, which can be long, thus requiring a large amount of time. By employing a simple associative algorithm to find the least possible value in a structure code field, of one or more multiple bytes, the time taken for the resolution is constant and independent of the string length. However, if more than one structure matches the current search, a multiple-match resolution must again be performed.

An implementation of the left-hand–justified structure code with a field width of eight bits is shown in Figure 4. The structure code fields must be on the same APE rather than spread across multiple APEs. This is because structure codes are normalized when a structure is bound to a variable. The normalization process involves stripping out some of the most significant fields from the complete structure code and then shifting the data left to obtain the normalized code. It is the normalized code that is then placed on the associative heap together with the current inference depth (ID), as a variable binding.

Figure 4 also contains fields to represent the atomic value of a term: its type and arity. Temporary space fields are also included for numerical calculations. Finally, two fields are also reserved for set

binding. This allows a maximum of 80 (16 + 64) set bindings to be active at the same time. However, this value can be increased by allocating more APEs to the set binding fields. The use of the set binding fields will be discussed in more detail in section 5. The atomic value is represented by 32 bits to allow arithmetic operations. The term type can be represented using three bits (eight possible states), but eight bits have been allocated so that new types, such as floating-point numbers, can also be easily incorporated. The arity of a structure (term) is the maximum number of sub-structures it contains. The arity field width is eight bits, allowing a maximum arity of 255.

In the next section the extension of a set execution mode to the Prolog language is discussed, which lets us further exploit the associative power of the ASP architecture.

4   Incorporation of sets

Sets provide a high level of data abstraction for many problems [Dov91] and the opportunity for data-parallel operations on an associative computing architecture. Furthermore, the introduction of sets into Prolog can remove the need for shallow backtracking on an associative architecture. This in turn removes the requirement for multiple-match resolution between matching structures, as they are all selected as possible bindings.

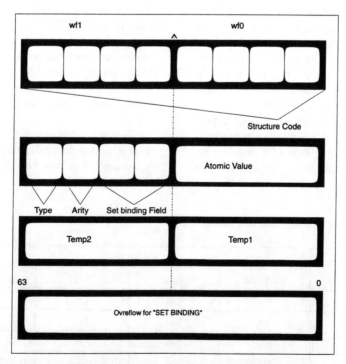

Figure 4. Mapping a Prolog term to the ASP architecture.

Sets can give a more natural expression of some problems. For example, in the program fragment below we require values for X that are four-sided shapes.

```
    five_sided (pentagon).
    four_sided (square).
    four_sided (rhombus).
    four_sided (rectangle).
?:- four_sided (X).
```

In a sequential implementation of Prolog, the system would sequentially return values for X by forcing a failure and backtracking to the next possible solution. The order of the solutions would be affected by the textual order of the clauses in the program: "square" would be returned first, then "rhombus" and finally "rectangle." The built-in Prolog predicates *setof* and *bagof* would return all of the solutions as a list, in the same order as above, by forcing the failure and backtrack operations. This effectively causes shallow backtracking to be performed. An associative architecture can effectively return all of the solutions in one time step as a set, that is, $X = \{$square, rhombus, rectangle$\}$, where "{ }" denotes a set of solutions.

Lists are currently used in Prolog rather than sets. This has mainly been influenced by the use of sequential architectures, where lists provide an efficient method for dynamic storage. An associative architecture instead provides an efficient mechanism to support sets through the use of "associative tags" rather than pointers. Dynamic data structures can therefore be supported by sets rather than lists on associative architectures, such as the ASP. A problem arises when the order of the list is important, but this can often be avoided. For instance, if a sorting algorithm is required, it is more efficient to use the architecture's associative capabilities to sort the data than to use a conventional pointer-based sort algorithm.

Kacsuk [Kac87] introduced five different set types: base, sibling, restricted, derived, and associated, which he manipulated during the execution of a Prolog program on the DAP. A new set that is related only to ground data terms is known as a base set. A sibling set is created during unification when two Prolog clauses contain the same variable name. For instance, given the Prolog fragment "parent (X, Y), parent (Y, Z)," two separate sets would be created for Y during unification. This effectively provides a link between the two clauses although they are semantically the same set. A restricted set is created if, during unification or a conditional expression, elements are removed from an existing set. A derived set is created to indicate that a new set is connected to a previous set by the "is" operator. For example, given the Prolog statement "X is f(Y)," X would be a derived set of Y. A set is said to be associated if it is contained in the same head clause as another set. For instance, in the clause "parent (X, Y)," X and Y are said to be associated sets.

5   Set-based execution

Prolog can be considered to consist of two modes: forward and backward. The forward mode consists of data process, unify, and restrict operations, and the backward mode consists of the backtracking operation. The fundamental operation for a set-based Prolog is set restriction.

In a set-based Prolog, the rule database should be separated from the fact database. This differs from most Prolog implementations as usually there is no distinction. However, the separation of the fact and rule databases allows a simplified unification algorithm. The execution of a program now consists of rules operating on a database of facts. If an associative processor is used, the facts can be manipulated in parallel, producing binding sets, if the fact clauses do not contain any variable terms. This results in no individual bindings being stored on the associative processor, thereby reducing memory requirements. The matches that are possible in this scheme are shown in Table 3.

The table differs from Table 1 in two ways. A fact variable cannot be used, and sets have replaced lists as the dynamic data type because they can be easily manipulated in parallel by an associative machine.

Table 3. Possible matches in a set-based Prolog.

Rule Type	Fact Type			
	Variable	**Constant**	**Set**	**Structure**
Variable	No	Yes	Yes	Yes
Constant	No	Yes	No	No
Set	No	No	Yes	No
Structure	No	No	No	Yes

A set variable corresponds to a particular bit in the set binding fields, as shown in Figure 4. Thus, if several data elements have bit 2 set in the set binding fields, they are all said to be bound to the variable corresponding to that bit position. This is a method similar to the bit-vector–basing techniques used in database management systems. The bit vector approach allows a data element to be a member of multiple sets and permits a simple backtracking scheme.

The ASP can bind multiple data elements to a set variable in one time step using the parallel-bit write operation. The number of elements involved in the operation is restricted only by the number of elements in the ASP string. By the same token, the backtrack operation can be performed over all data elements, so that all bindings made since the last choice point can be removed in one time step.

5.1 Unification

Unification can be broken into two distinct cases: those between variables in the same head clause, known as associated unifications, and those between variables in different clauses, known as independent unifications.

Associated unifications can be performed in parallel because the data elements are physically close to one another. For example, in the program below we are given some four-sided objects specified by their length and width, and we wish to find those that meet the rule defining a possible square.

```
four_sided (1,2).
four_sided (3,3).
four_sided (3,2).
four_sided (4,4).
possible_square (X) :-
four_sided (X,X).
```

This can be achieved by finding two distinct sets, X and X', and then performing pair-wise unification on the set elements. The unification would proceed as follows:

1. Find values for set X. ($X = \{ 1,3,3,4 \}$)

2. Perform pair-wise unification, that is, unify $(X, \{2,3,2,4\})$. (X now becomes the set $\{\_,3,\_,4\}$ as it has effectively been restricted by the unification .)

3. Restrict any associated or derived sets if necessary.

Prolog would generated the same set by backtracking to find the other solution.

Independent set unification is used between two sets that are neither associated nor derived. It is a more difficult operation than associated unification, as this is effectively the intersection of two sets through some joining value. For example, if we wanted to find which students are on a particular course from the program below, we use *CourseCode* as a joining value between the two clauses:

```
class(mathematics, 111)
class(french, 113)
student(fred, 111)
student(james, 117.

class(english, 112).
class(german, 114).
student(sarah, 113).
student(jan, 112).
```

Given the query:
```
?:- class(Subject, CourseCode),
student(Name, CourseCode)
```

This query corresponds to finding the *Subject* and the *CourseCode* sets that are members of a class and then finding the *Name* and the *CourseCode'* sets that are members of student. Semantically *CourseCode* and *CourseCode'* are the same set. The calls goal is satisfied by *CourseCode* = {111, 112, 113, 114}, and the student goal is satisfied by *CourseCode'* = {111, 113, 117, 112}. The intersection of *CourseCode* and *CourseCode'* gives *CourseCode* = {111, 112, 113} because these are the courses for which we have information. The associated sets *Subject* and *Name* are then restricted to give the final answer.

Prolog would return the answers above via the *setof* predicate by backtracking.

$$\left\langle \begin{array}{l} Subject \\ CourseCode \\ Name \end{array} \right\rangle = \left\langle \left\langle \begin{array}{l} maths \\ english \\ french \end{array} \right\rangle \left\langle \begin{array}{l} 111 \\ 112 \\ 113 \end{array} \right\rangle \left\langle \begin{array}{l} fred \\ jan \\ sarah \end{array} \right\rangle \right\rangle$$

5.2   Set restriction

Sets can be restricted by an implicit restriction, restriction condition, or by unification. The easiest case to deal with is explicit restriction or filter operation. An example of this is: Given a set $X = \{1,2,3,4,5\}$, restrict X to those elements less than 4, that is, $X < 4$. This results in a new set X', which consists of $X' = \{1,2,3\}$. An implicit restriction arises when the associated or derived set of Y of a set X is restricted in some way. In order to ensure data consistency, any sets that are related to the restricted set must also be restricted. As an example, consider the Prolog program fragment shown below

```
col(blue,3)           col(red, 4)
col (yellow, 5)       col(brown, 12)
?:-col(X,Y), Y<5
```

X unifies with the set {blue, red, yellow, brown} and then Y with the set {3,4,5,12}. The explicit restriction specified by "$Y < 5$" forces a new set to be created $Y' + \{3,4\}$. This in turn forces the corresponding elements, yellow and brown in set X, to be removed. This results in a new set X' consisting of {blue, red}. The new sets need to be formed so that backtracking is still possible. Implicit restriction can lead to a succession (chain) of restrictions taking place, which could be time-consuming.

5.3   Backtracking

A set-based execution scheme effectively removes the need for shallow (data) backtracking. This is because all data elements that can satisfy a particular goal are instantiated at the same time; this also removes the need to maintain data choice points. However, rule choice points must be maintained, and all variables that have been created after the last choice point must be removed. This can be performed in a manner similar to the sequential execution schemes wherein all new variables are tagged with their inference depth when they are instantiated. In order to backtrack, an associative search for all variables with an inference depth greater than that at the last choice point is made. All variables found in the search are then removed in one time step by resetting their associated bits in the set binding field.

6   Prolog performance on the ASP

The implementation of the set-based execution model for Prolog was tested on the N-queens problem, for 8 queens. This is a commonly used benchmark program and is thought to give a good indication of Prolog system performance. It was deliberately chosen so that it was not biased toward a set-oriented implementation, thereby allowing a fair comparison with other implementations. The performance obtained is comparable with many current implementations of Prolog as shown in Table 4. The implementations used for comparison are the Knowledge Crunching Machine (KCM), the Berkeley PLM, and Quintus Prolog 2.0. The comparative data for KCM, PLM, and Quintus Prolog was taken from Benker [Ben89]. The table contains two entries for the ASP implementation. The entry denoted by ASP-32 refers to an implementation that used full 32-bit arithmetic, which is performed bit serially on the ASP. Obviously, when using bit-serial arithmetic, the word length used can significantly affect performance. To account for this, a separate implementation that used 8-bit arithmetic on the program was also run. The performance of 8-bit implementation, denoted ASP-8, is significantly faster then the 32-bit version. The question now arises as to whether a compiler can detect such word width optimizations at compile time.

Table 4. Comparative results for the 8 queens problem.

Implementation	Time Taken (mS)
ASP-8	1.07
KCM	1.18
ASP-32	1.87
PLM	4.22
Quintus	9.01

7   Conclusions and future work

Associative processors combine CAM with closely coupled SIMD processors able to carry out data-parallel operations on marked sets of data. The introduction of sets into Prolog enables efficient exploitation of this data parallelism. Further, data structures to represent lists and sets on associative processors are described that allow list membership to be ascertained by associative search in one step. Vector arithmetic is also made possible by these data structures. List length and arity are determined by architectural constraints.

Sets provide a mechanism with which the underlying data parallelism of associative architectures can be exploited and offer a more natural way in which to describe many problems. The primitive instructions required to implement a set based Prolog were examined, and a mapping of a set-based interpreter to the ASP was discussed.

An implementation of Prolog for the ASP is shown to perform well against other high-performance implementations for the 8-queens problem. This is remarkable as the ASP hardware is not specifically designed for Prolog execution, having been previously applied to image processing.

It would be foolish to generalize as to the final appropriateness of the ASP for Prolog from a single benchmark, but we are proceeding with the implementation of Prolog for the ASP with heightened interest. A further investigation of a wide range of Prolog applications will be undertaken when the compiler is complete.

Future information systems will be required to work with subsymbolic information where it is not possible to write rules for the knowledge represented. Artificial neural networks are used in these situations, and we are currently investigating neurocomputing with the possibility of proposing hybrid subsymbolic/symbolic information systems employing associative processing.

Acknowledgment

It is a pleasure to acknowledge the help and support of the staff of Aspex Microsystems Ltd. and the department of Electrical Engineering and Electronics at Brunel University. This work is currently funded under the Science and Engineering Research Council (SERC) award entitled "An Investigation of a Distributed Parallel Associative Processor for the Execution of Logic Programs," reference number GR/H46893. It was previously funded under SERC studentship 89315132.

References

[Bac91] H. Bacha, "A Prolog Abstract Machine for Content-Addressable Memory," in *VLSI for Artificial Intelligence and Neural Networks*, J.G. Delgado-Frias and W.R. Moore, eds., Plenum Press, New York, N.Y., 1991, pp. 153–164.

[Ban92] A.K. Bansal and J.L. Potter, "An Associative Model to Minimize Matching and Backtracking Overhead in Logic Programs with Large Knowledge Bases," *Engineering Applications of Artificial Intelligence*, Vol. 5, No. 3, Pergamon Press, 1993, pp. 247–262.

[Ben89] H. Benker et al., "KCM: A Knowledge Crunching Machine," *Computer Architecture News*, Vol. 17, No. 3, June 1989, pp. 186–194.

[Dov91] A. Dovier et al., "{log}: A Logic Programming Language with Finite Sets," *Logic Programming: Proc. 8th Int'l Conf.*, The MIT Press, Cambridge, Mass., 1991, pp. 111–124.

[Hab93] C.M. Habiger and R.M. Lea, "Hybrid Wafer Scale Massively Parallel Computing Technology," *Computer*, special issue on multichip modules, Vol. 26, No. 4, Apr. 1993, pp. 50–61.

[Kac87] P. Kacsuk and A. Bale, "DAP Prolog: A Set-oriented Approach to Prolog," *The Computer J.*, Vol. 30, No. 5, 1987, pp. 393–403.

[Lea88] R.M. Lea, "The ASP: A Cost-Effective Parallel Microcomputer," *IEEE Micro*, Oct. 1988, pp. 10–29.

[Nag88] J. Naganuma et al., "High Speed CAM-Based Architecture for a Prolog Machine (ASCA)," *IEEE Trans. Computers*, Vol. 37, No. 11, Nov. 1988, pp. 1,375–1,383.

[Old87] J.V. Oldfield et al., "The Application of VLSI Content-addressable Memories to the Acceleration of Logic Programming Systems," *Proc. 1st Int'l Conf. Computer Technology Systems and Applications*, IEEE Press, Piscataway, N.J., 1987, pp. 27–30.

[Rob92] I.N. Robinson, "Pattern-Addressable Memory," *IEEE Micro*, June 1992, pp. 20–30.

[War83] D.H.D. Warren, "An Abstract Prolog Instruction Set," Tech. Note 309, SRI Int'l, 1983.

The IXM2 Parallel Associative Processor for AI

Tetsuya Higuchi, Kennichi Handa, and Naoto Takahashi
Electrotechnical Laboratory

Tatsumi Furuya, Toho University

Hitoshi Iida, Eiichiro Sumita, and Kozo Oi
ATR Interpreting Telecommunications Research Laboratories

Hiroaki Kitano, Sony Computer Science Laboratory

SIMD processing with large associative memories can support robust performance in speech applications. The IXM2 with 73 transputers has outclocked a Cray in some tasks.

Although researchers have been studying associative memory and associative processing for 30 years, the importance of associative memories as SIMD (single instruction, multiple data) devices has not been sufficiently recognized. Part of this is because large associative memories are difficult to develop, and the small associative memories available so far have allowed much less parallelism than needed to demonstrate effective SIMD processing on associative memories.

We describe the IXM2 associative processor and its main application in speech-to-speech translation. (IX stands for semantic memory system in Japanese, and the M stands for machine.) The IXM2 began as a faithful implementation of the NETL semantic network machine and grew into a massively parallel SIMD machine that demonstrated the power of large associative memories. In fact, it outperformed other significant machines in terms of language-translation tasks, which we discuss at the end of the article.

We selected speech-to-speech translation as our main application because it is one of the grand challenges of Massively Parallel Artificial Intelligence[1] (see the glossary on the next page). The social implications of successful automatic translation are enormous. Persons who speak different languages could communicate in real time by using interpreting telephony.

Speech-to-speech translation involves many computing operations because it requires such features as real-time response and a very large capacity for handling vocabulary and the corpus (see glossary for application terms). We focus on memory-based models of speech-to-speech translation that view episodic memory as the foundation of intelligence. This view naturally leads to implementing intelligent as-

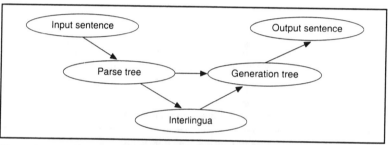

Figure 1. A traditional model of machine translation.

sociative memories. We first discuss the application as an illustration of associative processing and then shift to an exploration of the IXM2 itself.

Speech-to-speech translation issues

The traditional approach. The usual approach to natural language processing has been to rely on extensive rule application. This entails building an internal representation, such as a parse tree generated from an input sentence by using a set of rules. Figure 1 shows the main control flow in traditional models of translation.

Figure 2 is an example of traditional translation. First, the system inputs an English sentence for an analysis that uses grammar rules and a vocabulary dictionary. As the result, a parse tree is generated in which each node is a Japanese

phrase or word. Then, the system applies rules and dictionaries to transform the parse tree into a generation tree. Finally, a Japanese sentence is output when generation rules and dictionaries are applied. Systems based on this approach inevitably face a number of drawbacks.

- **Performance.** Most existing machine-translation systems are not sufficient for such real-time tasks as speech-to-speech translation.
- **Scalability.** Current machine-translation systems are difficult to scale up because their processing complexity makes system behavior almost intractable.
- **Quality.** The intractability of system behavior combines with other factors to lower the translation quality.
- **Grammar writing.** By the same token, writing grammar rules is very difficult, since a complex sentence has to be described by piecewise rules. It is time-consuming (partly

due to the intractability factor) to add these rules into the whole system.

Memory-based translation model. The alternative to the traditional approach is a memory-based model that uses examples for translation. This model was first proposed by Nagao[2] in 1984 and is the precursor of recent research on memory- and example-based translation models. Nagao argued that people translate sentences by using similar past examples of translation. This claim coincides with recent interest in memory- and case-based reasoning.[3]

Memory-based reasoning places memory at the foundation of intelligence. It assumes that numerous specific events are stored in people's memories and that they handle responses to new events by recalling similar events and invoking actions associated with them. This idea runs counter to most AI approaches, which make rules or heuristics the central thrust of reasoning.

The memory-based approach works well in machine translation, too. Figure 3 shows the control flow. At first, a sentence similar to the input sentence is retrieved. Then the retrieved sentence undergoes adaptation for generating an output sentence.

Let's consider the input sentence in Figure 2 again ("I would like to attend the party") and see how this sentence is translated into Japanese with a memory-based model. We used the ATR Interpreting Telecommunications Research Lab's corpus for conference registration as examples of translation. When the input sentence in Figure 2 is entered, the following sentences can be retrieved as the three most similar examples from the corpus. Each sentence is associated with a translated Japanese sentence.

- "I would like to register for the conference" becomes "Kaigi ni touroku shitainodesu."
- "I would like to take part in the conference" becomes "Kaigi ni sanka shitainodesu."
- "I would like to attend the conference" becomes "Kaigi ni sanka shitainodesu."

In the real system, each sentence will be assigned a similarity score. The next step is adaptation, in which differences between the input sentence and the example sentence are adjusted to create a translation. In this example, the difference is conference and party, so that the Japanese word for conference (kaigi) in the translation part of the example is replaced by the Japanese word for party (enkai).

Although at a glance this seems a naive approach, the method essentially is the same as or better than current MT (Machine Translation) systems. Given the fact that large-scale MT systems have a few thousand grammar rules for the exception handling of each specific case, memory-based translation is a straightforward and tractable approach to translation because it uniformly handles regular and irregular cases. In addition, there is a difference in the solution spaces of the two methods. Assuming that there is a set of grammar rules to cover a certain portion of natural language sentences, the grammar not only covers sentences that actually appear in the real world but also covers sentences that are grammatical but are never produced in reality. An empirical study revealed that only 0.53 percent of possible sentences considered to be grammatical are ever produced. The memory-based approach never generates implausible sentences because the memory contains only examples of actual sentences used in the past.

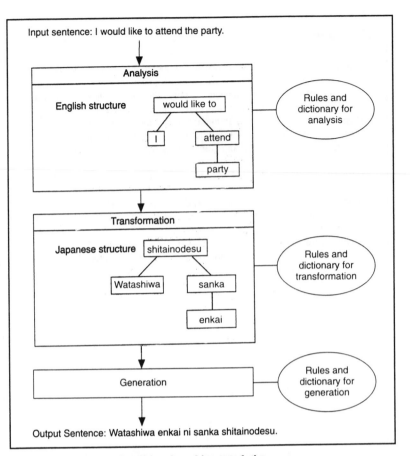

Figure 2. An example of traditional machine translation.

Parallel processing with associative memories

Apart from these linguistics discussions, the memory-based approach is well suited for data-parallel processing, as its performance is critical to search and retrieval of translation examples.

Associative memory as an inexpensive SIMD device. The most time-consuming aspect of memory-based translation is data retrieval from an example database, which can be done in a SIMD manner. Therefore, commercial SIMD parallel machines, such as ICL's Distributed Array Processor (DAP), Goodyear's Massively Parallel Processor (MPP), and Thinking Machine's Connection Machine 2 (CM-2), are promising as computing platforms. In memory-based translation operations, however, the dominant operation is to retrieve data that matches input data; scientific calculations are less frequent than in other problems to which commercial SIMD machines are applied. Therefore, associative memories repre-

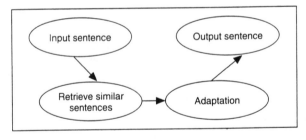

Figure 3. The control flow in memory-based machine translation.

sent the best candidate for speech-to-speech translation because they are both compact and inexpensive.

Let's examine why this is true. First, when we focus on associative search operations, the "parallelism per chip" is the largest among various LSI implementations. At all the bits of associative memory, comparisons with input data bits are done in parallel; the parallelism is 20,000 within a 20K-bit Nippon Telegraph and Telephone (NTT) associative memory (AM) chip, which is the type used in the IXM2. Thus, large parallelism within a

limited chip area can be obtained, since associative memory has regular cell structures suitable for LSI implementation, resulting in a compact and highly parallel device. Second, associative memories can be installed easily in a computer system; for example, they were installed in the IXM2 as ordinary memory devices. This leads to simple design and reduced cost. Third, no additional parallel software or software interface is required when using associative memories because they can be handled as ordinary memory devices. As described later, the associative

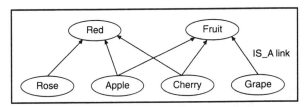

Figure 4. Network example.

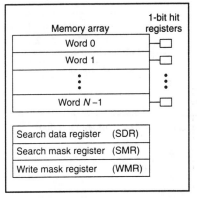

Figure 5. The architectural model of associative memory.

		Identifier			Marker bit field				Group identifier	
					0	1	2				
Red	0	0	0	0	...	...	...		0	0
Rose	1	0	0	1	...	...	...		1	0
Apple	2	0	1	0	...	...	...		1	1
Fruit	3	0	1	1	...	...	...		0	0
Cherry	4	1	0	0	...	...	...		1	1
Grape	5	1	0	1	...	...	...		0	1

Figure 6. Network representation of associative memory.

memory operations in the IXM2 can be directly specified in the high-level language Occam2.

We next describe parallel processing using associative memory. We have chosen network-structured data processing (such as a semantic network) because it is widely used in natural language processing.

Marker bit operations. In memory-based translation systems, a network data representation is often used to describe a knowledge base such as a thesaurus. In processing network-structured data, three fundamental operations are used intensively: *association*, *set intersection*, and *marker propagation*. Association locates a particular node in a network, set intersection finds common members of two sets, and marker propagation obtains members belonging to a set. These operations are performed efficiently when marker bits are assigned to each network node. A marker bit is a one-bit flag that contains processing results.[4] Processing with markers is suitable for implementations with associative memories because execution times become independent of the amount of data, that is, $O(1)$.

Figure 4 represents the marker bits. Suppose the network in the figure is asked which fruits are red. The solution will be the intersection of the set *fruit* and the set

red, obtained in the following manner.

First, an association operation is executed to set marker bit number 0 of the node red. Next, marker propagation sets marker bits 0 of all the nodes that belong to the hierarchy of node red along the links, descending from node red. These nodes represent set members of node red. Similarly, marker bits 1 for members of node fruit are set using association and marker propagation. Finally, a set operation is executed to find the intersection of set red and set fruit. This operation is performed in two steps: Find nodes where both marker bits 0 and 1 are set, and then set marker bit 2 on those nodes. In this case, the answers are the apple and cherry nodes.

Parallel processing with associative memories. We next describe how these operations are efficiently performed with associative memories.

Required functions. The architecture model of associative memory for network data processing consists of a memory array, one-bit hit registers, a search mask register (SMR), a search data register (SDR), and a write mask register (WMR), as shown in Figure 5. In the memory array, problem data is stored word-wise, and data contents are compared in parallel at every bit with data in the SDR. A one-bit hit register is associated with each word of the memory array. This register

is set when the word exactly matches the data in the SDR. The SMR is used when a part of each word (rather than the entire word) should match the corresponding part of the SDR. If a particular bit in SMR is 1, the search is conducted to the same bit position in the memory array. Otherwise, the search is disabled. A WMR is effective only when particular bits should be written; if a particular bit in a WMR is 1, the corresponding bit in the memory array is allowed to be written.

Representation for network data. Now we give data representations of this memory model for the network in Figure 4. The representation is node-based in that each network node occupies one word of associative memory. Each word has an identifier for its node, marker bits, and a group identifier for parallel marker propagation (described later), as shown in Figure 6. For example, the rose node occupies a word at address 1 of associative memory and its identifier is 001. Bit lengths in Figure 7 are chosen for this example. Information on connections between nodes is not kept in associative memory, but rather in RAM. (For clarity, this has been omitted from Figure 6.)

Set intersection in associative memory. At first, the red node is located by a search operation. Specifically, the SDR is loaded with the red's identifier, 000, at the leftmost position. The SMR is loaded to match only on the position of the node's identifier. The contents of the SDR and SMR are shown in Figure 7. After the search, word 0 is hit, and its one-bit flag register is set. Following this, a parallel-write operation is performed. This operation allows data writing only into those words whose one-bit hit registers are set. By this parallel-write operation, marker bit 0 of word 0 is set, though only word 0 is written in this case.

Second, members of the red node are obtained by marker propagations. Marker propagation can be done either sequentially or in parallel. Sequential marker propagation uses connection information stored in RAM, such as "Red is connected to the rose node with an IS_A link." (We use the term IS_A to indicate that a node belongs to another node conceptually.) Starting from a particular node like the red one, sequential marker propagation traverses a link and sets the marker bit of a node connected by that link. For example, executing sequential marker propagation three times

245

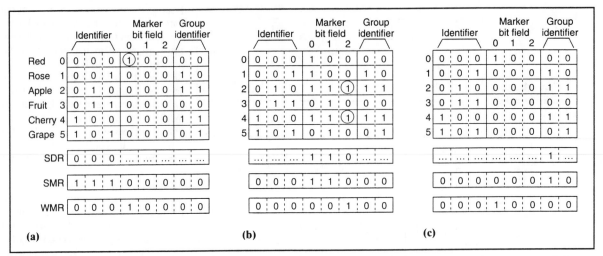

Figure 7. Register settings (SDR, SMR, and WMR) for marker bit processing: search (a), set intersection (b), and parallel marker propagation (c).

sets marker bits 0 of nodes rose, apple, and cherry. Figure 8a shows the result. Members of fruit are obtained in a similar manner; the fruit node is located by association and then its members, apple, cherry, and grape, are obtained by marker propagations (Figure 8b).

Finally, a set operation is performed to get the answer nodes; nodes where both marker bit 0 and 1 are set are located by a search operation, using SDR and SMR set as in Figure 7b. The search will locate words 2 and 4 (that is, the apple and cherry nodes) as the answer, followed by a parallel-write operation that writes marker bit 2 on those words (See Figure 7b).

While sequential marker propagation takes place in a time proportional to the number of links on which markers are propagated, parallel marker propagation can be done with constant times, regardless of the number of links. Parallel marker propagation is powerful in handling large network data where a node with many links (we call this a large fan-out node) often exists. In such a node, marker propagation has to be repeated as many times as the number of links connected to the node, resulting in an execution bottleneck.

In parallel marker propagation, a large fan-out node is referred to as a base node, and nodes connected to it are referred to as descendant nodes. For example, when members of the red node are obtained by marker propagation, the red node is a base node; and the rose, apple, and cherry nodes are descendants.

The basic idea of parallel marker propagation is to search descendant nodes by using a group identifier associated with each base node, and then write one particular bit at a time into each descendant node with a parallel-write operation. An allocator that encodes semantic networks into the representation on the IXM2's associative memories generates a group identifier for each group. A group consists of a base node, link type, and descendant nodes. For example, the network in Figure 4 has two groups: {RED, IS_A, {ROSE, APPLE, CHERRY}} and {FRUIT, IS_A, {APPLE, CHERRY, GRAPE}}. An associative memory word for each descendant node has a group identifier. Therefore, a base node can locate its descendant nodes by a search operation with the group identifier, and following this, a parallel-write operation sets each particular marker bit one at a time on each descendant node word. For example, via parallel marker propagation, descendant nodes of the red node can be located by a search operation with a value of 1, which is on the left bit of a group identifier in Figure 6, followed by a parallel-write operation. Figure 7c shows the register setting for those operations.

The IXM2

The IXM2 is the first massively parallel associative processor to clearly demonstrate the computing power of a large associative memory.[5] It attains 256K-fold

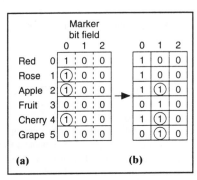

Figure 8. States of marker bit field: members of red (a) and fruit (b).

parallelism by using the NTT AM chip.

The system consists of 64 associative processors (APs) and nine network processors (NPs). The IXM2 is actually a co-processor under the control of a host SparcStation (see Figure 9 on the next page). Each AP has an associative memory of 4 Kwords of 40 bits, plus a 17.5-MHz IMS T800 transputer. The IXM2 also employs a complete connection scheme to speed up marker propagation among APs.

In an AP, eight AM chips are connected to the transputer bus via simple interface logic just as additional memories are connected to the bus. No independent AM controllers are required.

The NTT AM chip. The associative memory chip is an NTT 20-Kbit associative memory (512 words by 40 bits) designed by

Figure 9. The IXM2 and its host Sun SparcStation-2.

Ogura[6] and his colleagues. The chip is a processor rather than a memory, executing 26 instructions classified into four types: search, write, read, and garbage collection. This combination provides powerful functions, such as relational search and long-word data processing. The parallel-write instruction, which writes a pattern in parallel into all the words just selected by a previously executed search instruction, is extremely useful in SIMD processing, especially when intermediate results of problem solving are stored as marker bits, as described above.

Programming with a high-level language. Associative memory processing can be specified directly with Occam2. User-defined reserved words are used in programming statements directly corresponding to NTT AM instructions. For example, AM.Init is declared to be a literal with a particular value. When this address value appears on the transputer address bus, a part of this value is interpreted as the AM initialization instruction by the associative memory interface. Thus, IXM2 programming is simple and requires no software-interface routines, which can cause processing overhead.

Memory-based translation

There are two lines of research based on this idea. The first one is to use a mem-ory-based approach to identify top-level syntactic structures; the second is to use memory-based translation for translating phrases. These two approaches are complementary. Using sentence-structure matching in a memory-based approach lets the system segment phrases and identify macrostructures. The system can then decompose phrases and use memory-based translation to translate phrases at a high-quality level.

We describe three IXM2 memory-based systems: Astral[7] (Associative model of Translation of Language), the EBMT (Example-Based Machine Translation) and the TDMT (Transfer-Driven Machine Translation). Astral focuses on top-level tasks, and the EBMT focuses on phrase-level tasks. The TDMT is an effort to hybridize Astral and the EBMT.

Astral: An experimental system. This is an implementation of memory-based translation on the IXM2. Figure 10 shows the overall architecture. The memory consists of four layers: phoneme, phoneme sequence, lexical entry, abstraction hierarchies, and conceptual sequence.

- Phonemes represented as nodes in the network connect to each instance of a phoneme in the phoneme-sequence layer. Weights are associated with links that represent the likelihood of acoustic confusion between phonemes. The phoneme sequence of each word is represented in the form of a network (see Figure 11).
- The lexical (word) entry layer is a set of nodes. Each one represents a specific lexical entry.
- The class/subclass relation is represented using IS_A links. The highest (the most general) concept is *all, which entails all possible concepts in the network. Subclasses are linked under the *all node, and each subclass node has its own subclasses.
- Concept sequences that represent patterns of input sentences are represented in the form of a network. Concept sequences capture linguistic knowledge (syntax) with semantic restrictions.

Figure 11 shows a part of the network. The figure shows a node for the word "about," and how the phoneme sequence is represented. The left side of the figure shows how the network on the right side is represented in the IXL program-

ming language.[8] (Refer to Kitano and Higuchi[7] for details of the mapping of semantic networks to IXM2.) We have encoded a network including *phonemes, phoneme sequences, lexical entries, abstraction hierarchies,* and *concept sequences* that cover the entire task of the ATR conference registration domain.

The vocabulary size is 405 words in one language, and more than 300 sentences in the corpus have been covered. The average fan-out of the network is 40.6. We did not set the weight in this experiment so that we could compare the performance with other parsers that do not handle stochastic inputs. (In real operation, however, a fully tuned weight is used.) We also used a hierarchical memory network to attain a wider coverage with smaller memory requirements.

The host computer contains the table for templates of the target language. The system creates the binding table between each concept and concept sequence, and specific substrings by using the corpus. When parsing is complete, the generation process is invoked on the host. It is also possible to perform distributed computing on 64 T800 transputers. The generation process is computationally cheap, since it only retrieves and concatenates substrings in the target language. These substrings are bound to conceptual nodes in patterns that mimic the concept sequence in the target language.

Algorithm. The parsing algorithm is simple. Activation markers (A-markers) and prediction markers (P-markers) control the parsing process. A-markers are propagated through the memory network from the lexical items, which are activated by the input. P-markers designate the next possible elements to be activated. When an A-marker collides with a P-marker, the A-marker is moved to the next element of the sequence. We have implemented several mechanisms to attain robust processing. These include tolerances against noisy phoneme insertion, phoneme misrecognition, and missing phonemes. This algorithm is similar to the basic framework of the ΦDM-Dialog speech-to-speech translation system.[9] (Refer to Kitano[10] for details.)

System performance. We carried out several experiments to measure system performance. The system attained parsing on the order of milliseconds. PLR is a parallel version of Tomita's LR parser. Its performance provides only a general idea of the speed of traditional parsing models. Since PLR machines and grammars differ from those in our experiments, we cannot directly compare the two processes. However, the total time required and the exponential increase of parsing time in the case of PLR clearly demonstrate the problems inherent in the traditional approach.

The memory-based approach on the IXM2 (with the MBT) shows an order-of-magnitude faster parsing performance. Also, the parsing time increases almost linearly to the length of the input sentences, as opposed to the exponential increase seen in traditional parsing algorithms. The CM-2 runs at a slow speed but exhibits similar characteristics to those of the IXM2. The CM-2's speed is due to the processing element capabilities and the machine architecture. The fact that the CM-2 shows a similar curvature indicates the benefits of the MBT. The Sun-4 implementation that the performance degrades drastically as the size of the knowledge base (KB) grows, as discussed below.

We have also tested scalability by increasing KB size. This size is measured by the number of nodes in the network. Performance degradation grows more slowly than a linear function of the grammar KB, due to the local activation of the algorithm. This trend is the opposite of the traditional parser, in which parsing time grows faster than a linear function of the grammar KB size (which generally grows as the square of the size of grammar rules), due to a combinatorial explosion of serial rule applications. The CM-2 shows a performance trend similar to that of the IXM2, but is much slower due to the slow processing capability of 1-bit PEs. The Sun-4 has a disadvantage in a scaled-up KB due to its serial architecture. Particularly, the MBT algorithm involves extensive use of set operations to find nodes with an A-marker, P-marker collision, which is suitable for SIMD machines. Serial machines search the entire KB, which leads to the undesirable performance.

Example-Based Machine Translation. While Astral focuses on identifying entire syntactic structures, the EBMT focuses on producing translation at the phrase level. The EBMT

(1) prepares a database consisting of translation examples,
(2) retrieves examples whose source

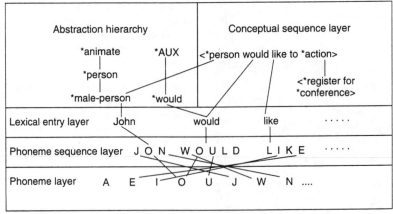

Figure 10. Astral's overall architecture.

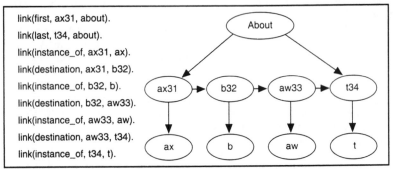

Figure 11. Network for the word "about" and its phoneme sequence.

part is most similar to the input phrase or sentence from the example database, and

(3) obtains the translation based on retrieved examples.

By focusing the task at the phrase level, we can collect a larger effective dataset to produce translation. This is a critical issue in attaining high-quality translation. One of the key issues in the EBMT is semantic distance calculation, and the IXM2 has been proven to be computationally effective for this task.

The other key issue in the EBMT is to determine a set of examples with minimum semantic distance from the input. In other words, the EBMT involves the full retrieval of the most similar examples from the example array.

Experiments. Suppose Input I and Example E are composed of n words. Our semantic distance measure is the summation of the distance, $d(I_k, E_k)$ at the k-

th word, multiplied by the weight of the k-th word, w_k.

$$\sum_{k=1}^{n} d(I_k, E_k) \times w_k$$

The distance $d(I_k, E_k)$ is determined by a method we devised using a thesaurus. Each word corresponds to its concept in the thesaurus. The distance between words is reduced to the distance between concepts. The distance between concepts is determined according to their positions in the thesaurus hierarchy. The distance varies from 0 to 1. When the thesaurus is $(n+1)$ layered, the distance, (k/n) is given to the concepts in the k-th layer from the bottom ($0 \leq k \leq n$). The weight w_k is the degree to which the word influences the selection of the translation. For example, the Japanese words "kaigi" (conference) and "kaisetsu" (commentary) have a distance of 1/3 because a minimal common node in the thesaurus hierarchy can be found at 1/3 of the total hierarchy layer.

But, the Japanese words "kaigi" (conference) and "soudan" (meetings) have a distance of 0, since the words are subsumed by a concept at the bottom layer. This is a very crude way of determining the distance, but our experiments demonstrate that such methods work reasonably well in the domain.

In fact, it has been demonstrated[11] that the EBMT outperforms traditional machine translation in the accuracy of target word selection in function words (for example, Japanese particles and English prepositions).

In the experiments, we translated the Japanese noun phrases of the form "A no B" into English. (A and B are nouns, and "no" represents an adnominal particle.) They are translated into various English noun phrases such as "B̃ of Ã," "B̃ in Ã," "B̃ for Ã," "B̃ at Ã" and so on (Ã and B̃ are English translations of A and B.) They are representative because the examples are composed of three variables, or words (two or three variables is typical), and they are difficult in traditional machine translation, although the EBMT can handle them well. The "A no B" examples were collected from the ATR corpus, which consists of Japanese sentences and their English translations concerning the conference registration task.

Experimental results. We have experimented with 1,000 examples. The processing time was 270 milliseconds on the SparcStation-2 and 21 milliseconds on the IXM2. The IXM2 attains a speed almost 13 times greater than that of the SparcStation-2. A fully equipped IXM2 (with 64 associative processors) loads 64,000 examples. For this set size, the IXM2 can attain a speed $13 \times 64 = 832$ times greater than the SparcStation-2 if communication overhead is not considered.

The IXM2 can perform in this manner because it carries out matching processes by using parallel search and parallel-write operations for the AM chip. Distance calculations are triggered in constant time and are executed in linear time by the transputer.

On the other hand, another massively parallel machine, the CM-2, took 240 milliseconds. Although the CM-2 conducts matching processes in constant time, the example collection process is executed linearly by the host machine, a SparcStation-2. Unfortunately, the communication between CM-2 and SparcStation-2 occurs through the VMEbus, which is very slow. Thus, the advantage of a data-

parallel search was completely lost in the communication bottleneck of data collection by the host.

Transfer-Driven Machine Translation. The TDMT is an effort to design and develop a novel machine-translation architecture based on our previous experiments with Astral and the EBMT.[12,13] the TDMT is essentially a combination of two processes: sentence pattern identification and phrase-level translation. Af-

---

The TDMT approaches translation by determining how concepts expressed in one language should be converted to another.

---

ter the sentence pattern is identified, phrase translation proceeds concurrently.

Although most machine-translation models consider translation as a pipelined process of parsing-transfer-generation, the TDMT approaches translation as a problem of determining how concepts expressed in one language should be converted into another. The TDMT discards the notion of pipelined processing and adopts a transfer-driven view. This approach resulted in vastly different machine-translation architectures. Translation is performed by the transfer module using stored empirical transfer knowledge. Other modules, such as lexical processing, analysis, generation, and contextual processing, help the transfer module apply transfer knowledge and produce correct translation results.

In the TDMT, transfer knowledge is the primary knowledge used to solve translation problems. Most of the knowledge is described by an example-based framework. Transfer knowledge describes the correspondence between source-language expressions (SEs) and target-language expressions (TEs) in certain meaningful units, preserving the translational equivalence.

The TDMT uses the EBMT's semantic distance-calculation method to determine the most plausible target expression and structure in a transfer. The semantic distance between words is reduced to the dis-

tance between concepts in a thesaurus.[8,9]

Transfer knowledge in an example-based framework is described as follows:

$$SE \quad => \quad TE1 \quad (E11, E12, \ldots),$$
$$: \quad :$$
$$TEn \quad (En1, En2, \ldots)$$

Each TE is associated with examples. E_{ij} indicates the j-th example of TE_i. To select a TE, the input sentence is matched against all examples in the memory base using an extended version of the semantic distance calculation adopted in the EBMT. An example with the smallest distance from the input is chosen, and the TE of that example is extracted to make the most plausible target sentence.

Massively parallel TDMT. The most important consideration in implementing the TDMT strategy on a massively parallel machine is to maximize parallelism. Since semantic distance calculation is the most computationally demanding step in the TDMT, our successful implementation of this calculation on the IXM2 was significant. Careful analysis of the computational cost in the sequential version of the TDMT reveals that the semantic distance calculation for the top 10 patterns accounts for nearly 94 percent of the whole semantic distance-calculation time.

Accordingly, we have decided to implement the semantic distance calculation of the top 10 patterns on the IXM2 to substantially reduce the computing time. Each pattern of the top 10 is assigned to each associative processor. Examples of each form are stored in one associative processor. Thus, examples of the top 10 patterns are stored in 10 APs.

Performance analysis of sequential vs. massively parallel TDMTs. To attain real-time performance for spoken language translation, we assume that the translation time per sentence must be a few seconds, at most.

In a test run of 746 sentences with sequential TDMT,

(1) half were translated in less than 2 seconds,
(2) most of the rest were translated in more than 2 but less than 10 seconds, and
(3) 25 were translated in more than 10 seconds.

In terms of the experiment mentioned in the EBMT section, the semantic distance calculation time is reduced to about 1/13 when using the IXM2. As a result, the total translation time per sentence is reduced by half on average and is a maximum of 2.5 seconds for 97 percent of the test sentences (Figure 12). Therefore, the massively parallel TDMT will attain a speed sufficient for spoken language translation.

Discussion

The most salient feature of memory-based translation is that matching input with an example database can be performed with fine-grained parallelism, but example collections cannot be parallelized after the matching procedure. Execution time for the example collection is influenced heavily by differences in computer architecture. To examine this, let's look at the EBMT results again.

The CM-2 has a serious communication-overhead problem. The VMEbus bottleneck is between the host and the CM-2. The CM-2 took only 9 milliseconds to calculate each semantic distance. The data-parallel nature of the EBMT makes this a quick process. This computing time is constant up to 64K examples because one processor has only one example to calculate. Despite this high performance in distance computing, the CM-2's overall response time is 240 milliseconds, indicating the significant impact of the communication overhead.

Intel's iPSC/2 loosely coupled multiprocessor system took 328 milliseconds for 1,000 examples with a 16-PE configuration, though this is slower than the 270 milliseconds achieved by a SparcStation-2. Interprocessor communication absorbs 110 milliseconds of the 328 milliseconds. Based on our experiments, a 256-PE iPSC/2 would require 220 milliseconds for communication, whereas semantic distance calculation is completed in about 14 milliseconds (for the 1,000 examples). Thus, communication overhead is also a serious problem in a loosely coupled multiprocessor.

Nor is the Cray X-MP 216 a good choice; it was slower than more recent workstations such as the 99-MHz HP735: 101 milliseconds for the Cray and 90 milliseconds for the HP with 1,000 examples. The main reason for this is that translation does not involve many floating-point operations. In addition, the average vector length was about 60, which is not suitable for a vector supercomputer.

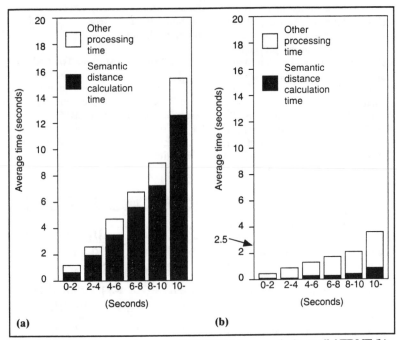

Figure 12. Translation time for sequential TDMT (a) vs. massively parallel TDMT (b).

The IXM2 architecture was superior to other machines because of high-performance example search by associative memory and minimum communication overhead due to the use of the transputer for collection examples. In fact, the interprocessor communication required for the EBMT is simply the transmission of the chosen examples to the host. Experimental data indicates that the IXM2 took 14 milliseconds for matching and 7 milliseconds for collection. Though execution time only for IXM2 distance calculation is slower than that for the CM-2 (9 milliseconds), the IXM2's overall performance is better.

Requirements for associative memory as a SIMD parallel device. Because of our experiences in using associative memories for massively parallel computing, we believe three functions are required for associative memories: (1) partial writing, (2) parallel writing, and (3) a multiword function.

In marker bit processing implemented on associative memories, as we described, each marker bit is used as temporary storage of intermediate processing results, just as a microprocessor uses register files to store intermediate results. This usage of associative memory is inevitable for SIMD parallel processing on associative memories. To realize this usage, partial

writing capability that permits bits to be written selectively is required.

The parallel-write operation is second only to the search function in terms of contributing the most to parallel processing on associative memories. As previously described, this function reduces the algorithmic complexity of the problem; for example, set intersection on a sequential machine takes $O(N)$, where N is the number of data, whereas it takes $O(1)$ on the IXM2. Set intersection with associative memory is very powerful, outperforming a Cray by two orders of magnitude for 64K data.[5]

A key issue in using associative memories is how to represent (or encode) necessary information on associative memory in the most compact form; however, multiple words are usually required. A multiple-word function is needed to represent information that cannot be represented with one word. To implement a multiword function, the search result of one word (that is, the content of a hit register) should be propagated to an adjacent word. This function is implemented in the NTT AM chip to represent one EBMT example with four words.

Though the IXM2 attains better performance in memory-based translation than other computers

Status report

The IXM2 is the successor of the IXM1, which began in 1987 as an implementation of the NETL semantic network machine proposed by S. Fahlman. By 1990, the IXM2 grew into a massively parallel SIMD machine with large associative memories. Research was mainly performed by T. Higuchi in collaboration with Carnegie Mellon University and ATR with the overall goal of developing a machine that could answer one of the Grand Challenges — automatic real-time speech translation between languages.

The IXM2 uses 64 associative processing transputers and nine communications transputers, having a total of 256 Kwords of associative memory (one of the largest associative memories developed). It can outperform a Cray supercomputer by an order of two magnitudes in set-intersection operations, which are heavily used in such AI applications as speech translation and knowledge-base processing.

The IXM2 is being upgraded with faster transputers and memories, and a TDMT that uses 5,000 examples. Initial experiments show that the IXM2 can maintain its current level of response while processing this increase in examples.

do, there is much room for performance improvement. The first area is the associative memory. The NTT AM chip used for the IXM2 was made in 1988 with a 1.2-micron VLSI design rule, whereas a 0.5 micron design rule is now common. The chip operates at 4.4 MHz, which is quite slow compared with the current technology standard VLSI implementation. In addition, the silicon chip size of the NTT AM is almost one fourth of today's VLSI standard. Considering recent progress, there is no doubt that we can make much more powerful AM chips. Ogura, who designed the NTT AM chip, estimates that were the NTT AM chip to be designed again with current technology; a 256-Kbit, 40-MHz AM chip would be feasible. This means roughly a ten-fold increase in both speed and density is possible with current technology, resulting in a desktop associative processor with a database of at least one million examples.

The transputer can also be improved. The type used for the IXM2 is slow compared with current RISC chips, both in the MIPS value and the communication speed. Recently, intercommunication for multiple computers employing wormhole routing has achieved much higher performance in communication than the transputers in the IXM2.

Considering these potential improvements, memory-based translation supported by an associative multicomputer system seems the most promising choice for real-time speech-to-speech translation. ∎

References

1. *Massively Parallel Artificial Intelligence*, H. Kitano and J. Hendler, eds., AAAI Press/MIT Press, 1994.

2. M. Nagao, "A Framework of a Mechanical Translation between Japanese and English by Analogy Principle," *Artificial and Human Intelligence*, A. Elithorn and R. Banerji, eds., Elsevier Science Publishers, B.V., Amsterdam, 1984, pp. 173-180.

3. C. Stanfill and D. Waltz, "Toward Memory-Based Reasoning," *CACM*, ACM, New York, Vol. 29, No. 12, Dec. 1986, pp. 1,213-1,228.

4. S. Fahlman, *NETL: A System for Representing and Using Real-World Knowledge*, MIT Press, Cambridge, Mass., 1979.

5. T. Higuchi et al., "IXM2: A Parallel Associative Processor," *Proc. 18th Int'l Symp. Computer Architecture*, ACM, New York, 1991, pp. 22-31.

6. T. Ogura et al., "A 20-Kbit Associative Memory LSI for Artificial Intelligence Machines," *IEEE J. Solid-State Circuits*, Vol. 24, No. 4, 1989, pp. 1,014-1,020.

7. H. Kitano and T. Higuchi, "High-Performance Memory-Based Translation on IXM2 Massively Parallel Associative Memory Processor," *Proc. AAAI-91*, American Assn. for AI, Menlo Park, Calif., 1991, pp. 149-154.

8. K. Handa, "Flexible Semantic Network for Knowledge Representation," *J. Information Japan*, Vol. 10, No. 1, 1986, pp. 13-19.

9. H. Kitano, "ΦDM-Dialog: An Experimental Speech-to-Speech Dialog Translation System," *Computer*, Vol. 24, No. 6, June, 1991, pp. 36-50.

10. H. Kitano, *Speech-to-Speech Translation: A Massively Parallel Memory-Based Approach*, Kluwer Academic Publishers, Boston, 1994.

11. M. Sumita et al., "Example-Based Machine Translation on Massively Parallel Processors," *Proc. IJCAI-93*, Morgan Kaufmann Publishers, San Mateo, Calif., 1993, pp. 1,283-1,288.

12. O. Furuse and H. Iida, "Cooperation Between Transfer and Analysis in Example-Based Framework," *Proc. Fifteenth In'l Conf. Computational Linguistics*, Assoc. Computational Linguistics, Bernardsville, N.J., 1992, pp. 645-651.

13. K. Oi et al., "Toward Massively Parallel Spoken Language Translation," *Parallel Processing for Artificial Intelligence 2*, H. Kitano, V. Kumar, and C.B. Suttner, eds., Elsevier Science Publishers, B.V., Amsterdam, 1994, pp. 177-184.

Image Rendering with Content-Addressable Parallel Processors

Richard Storer

Department of Computing and Information Systems
University of Paisley
Paisley PA1 2BE, UK
Richard.Storer@paisley.ac.uk

Abstract

Associative processors based on content-addressable memory (CAM) often have a simple CPU attached to each memory word. The associative behavior of the CAM is used to select a subset of processors that perform the next associative or arithmetic operation.

As the operation can be applied to all memory words simultaneously, these processors can be classed as SIMD parallel processors. Like other SIMD machines, associative processors are most efficient when used for processing large quantities of data, each of which requires an identical sequence of operations.

As many computer graphics and image-processing operations have this characteristic, an associative processor can be used as an intelligent frame store, where each pixel is processed by its own processing element.

Existing, favored computer graphics algorithms tend not to work well when recoded for SIMD implementation because the criteria for optimizing an algorithm for a sequential, or MIMD, machine are different from those for a SIMD machine.

In this paper, I examine the requirements for suitable SIMD algorithms for image rendering in an intelligent, associative frame store. SIMD algorithms are described for producing antialiased circles, lines, and two- and three-dimensional polygons.

I describe a practical scheme for implementing these algorithms on an array of associative rendering engines and outline performance predictions for this scheme, using the GLiTCH associative processor.

1 Content-addressable parallel processors

This paper describes algorithms developed for a class of associative processor that is based on content-addressable memory (CAM) with an arithmetic and logic unit (ALU) attached to each CAM word. Caxton

Foster coined the term *content-addressable parallel processor* (CAPP) [1] for computers based on such enhanced CAM. They are also termed associative processors or associative processor arrays. A typical construction for a CAPP is shown in Figure 1.

Binary data are stored in a memory array of one-bit CAM cells and can be manipulated by three types of associative operation: search, read, and write. The CAM words may be divided into several fields that hold the various attributes of the data stored in that word. To search for all the data with a particular attribute, the pattern corresponding to that attribute is loaded into the corresponding field position in the comparand register, and mask register bits are set to exclude the other fields from the search. All CAM words compare their contents with the comparand simultaneously, usually in a single machine cycle, and record the results, say, 1 if they are identical and 0 if not, in a one-bit register in each ALU called the *match* or *activity* register.

The results of a search on the CAM data can be used to identify a set of CAM words for reading by an external device or, more usually, to identify those processing elements that will perform some further operation on their CAM data fields. New data can be written into the activated CAM words. The new data is loaded into the comparand register in the position of the field to be overwritten and other fields are masked out. As with the search, all CAM words are written simultaneously. Data can also be read from the activated CAM words, but this must be done serially, one word at a time.

The ALU attached to each CAM word is used for arithmetic, logic, and comparison operations between CAM fields and for processing the responses to associative searches. Each CAM word with its ALU is termed a processing element (PE); each is a simple computer without a control unit.

A communications network lets processing elements exchange CAM data and ALU register data.

data and control signals to/from controller

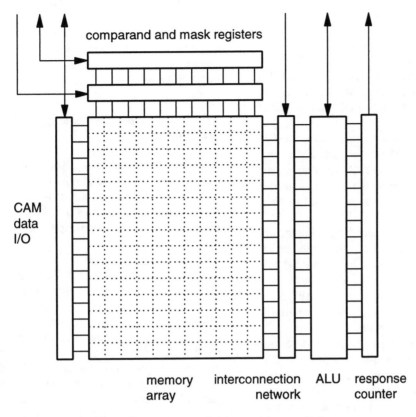

Figure 1. A bit-parallel content-addressable parallel processor.

Array, hyper cube, and perfect shuffle network topologies are commonly used. For the CAPP image-rendering algorithms I will describe, there is so little inter-PE communication that the nature of the network used is immaterial.

The processing elements and interconnection network are controlled by instructions broadcast from a host controller. Instructions may come from a simple microsequencer or they may be interpreted from commands issued by a host computer. The host is often a conventional computer that provides mass storage, input and output devices, and a user interface for the CAPP. Bulk, processed data held in the CAM may be extracted by the host for further serial processing, for storage, or for output. In the case of image rendering, pixel data generated in the PEs must be output to a digital frame store.

2   Processing modes available in a CAPP

The combination of content-addressable memory and a one-bit processor allows the programmer to choose

different modes of processing as appropriate to the problem. The CAPP may be used as a pattern-matching machine, an array processor, or an arithmetic lookup table, and all these modes may be used on the same data.

2.1   Pattern matching

Using the word-parallel matching capabilities of the CAM to find and replace individual data values is the simplest use of a CAPP's associativity. This operation takes just two machine cycles: one to find and activate all the PEs containing all the relevant patterns and a second to write new data to the activated PEs. Estrin and Fuller described various applications of CAM pattern matching in 1963 [2], including dynamic programming, pattern recognition, and convolution. Pattern matching can often be used as a shortcut in part of an arithmetic operation. For example, to find all the fields containing a value less a given power of two, a search for zeros in the higher bit positions can be used, which very often can be performed as a single machine cycle operation.

2.2 Arithmetic

CAPP ALUs usually support bit-serial arithmetic, logic, and comparison between data CAM fields; some provide a fully parallel integer or even floating-point ALU in each PE. Otherwise, each bit of a bit-serial arithmetic and logic operation will complete in all PEs simultaneously, and multiplication and division must be achieved by repeated bit-serial addition and subtraction.

In some CAPPs, the associative match mechanism is used to address the CAM bits in such a way that both operand bits are sent to the ALU simultaneously, and an addition is completed within a single machine cycle [3]. A second machine cycle is needed to write the result bit back to CAM.

Adding two 16-bit integer fields, for example, will take 33 machine cycles; multiplying them, about 500 machine cycles. If there are 1,000 PEs in a CAPP with a 33-MHz clock, this is a rate of 10^9 additions per second and 66×10^6 multiplications per second. Additional time for interprocessor communication is required if the operands are not in the same PE.

All the bit-serial rendering calculations described here are implemented with fixed-point arithmetic. The size and radix point position of each CAM field is chosen to satisfy the precision required of the calculations by means of arithmetic routines that can handle arguments of varying size and precision.

2.3 Lookup table processing

An alternative to direct computation on CAM word fields is to use the pattern matching of the data CAM as an inverted lookup table (LUT). For this, the array controller issues a search instruction for all possible values of the operands and, for each operand or operand pair, the corresponding result value is written into the PEs that have matching operand fields.

This differs from a conventional LUT where the data is processed sequentially by a table lookup for each item. Here the LUT itself is processed sequentially, each LUT entry replacing all matching data entries in parallel. Typically, this requires two machine cycles per LUT entry.

In general, a LUT operation on an n-bit operand (or n-bit word that combines a number of smaller operands) requires 2^{n+1} cycles, the equivalent of $2^{n+1}/2r^2$ r-bit, bit-serial additions per bit of an r-bit result field. When $n=8$, for example, a LUT operation is equivalent to one 16-bit addition for each bit of a 16-bit result. This makes it a useful technique only where several bit-serial operations would be required to calculate each bit of the result, as in successive approximation or summation of a series. For example, to calculate the 16-bit square root of an 8-bit field by successive approximation requires 760 machine cycles whereas to search for all 256 possible 8-bit values and write their corresponding 16 bit results requires only 512 cycles. In addition, work space CAM, to hold intermediate results, is required by the bit-serial algorithm but not by the LUT version.

2.4 Associativity means parallel processing

Associative processing is often thought of as useful only for searching operations in pattern matching or database query applications. It is important to realize that it can also be used as a mechanism for bringing parallelism to array arithmetic through the techniques described above.

As arithmetic operations in a CAPP can be applied to all stored data simultaneously, it can be classed as a single instruction stream, multiple data stream (SIMD) parallel processor, in Flynn's taxonomy [4]. Like other SIMD machines, CAPP are most efficient when used for processing large quantities of data, each of which requires an identical sequence of operations. Many computer graphics operations have this characteristic. A large number of pixels may be affected by each object to be rendered; each pixel will be processed with the same series of operations.

3 Image generation

Computer generation of images generally follows a fixed sequence of processes:

- Each object to be displayed is represented by a numerical model in an object database, along with attributes concerning its current color and position in the modeled universe.

- Geometrical transformations, on the objects, scale and position them in this universe.

- To display the models as seen from a given viewpoint in the universe, a viewing transformation produces their coordinates relative to the viewpoint. For 3D models, this may also involve perspective calculations.

- A windowing algorithm distinguishes which objects are visible (or partially visible) from the viewpoint to eliminate unnecessary processing on those that cannot be seen.

- A clipping algorithm redefines those objects that are partially visible so that only their visible parts are modeled.

- The objects, each now expressed in suitable coordinates, must be combined into a 2D image, usually in a digital frame store for a raster display device. The image is often calculated for each raster scan line in turn, a process known as scan conversion.

- During scan conversion, each image pixel must determine which part of which object it represents and be lit accordingly. This involves two algorithms.

  (1) Where objects overlap, as seen from the viewpoint, hidden surface removal decides which object surface will be visible at a given pixel. The pixel must then be rendered with the color of that surface. For 3D images, one of a number of shading algorithms is used to determine the intensity of the light reflected from the object.

  (2) If the object database has not had excess detail removed, an antialiasing filter removes high spatial frequencies from the displayed image.

3.1 Parallel rendering

These tasks form a pipeline of processes. High-performance hardware for image generation is usually based on a corresponding pipeline of processors specialized for each task. General-purpose parallel computers are also increasingly used for image generation. Depending on the type of parallel processors, they process either several objects or several pixels in parallel.

In the object-parallel approach, multiple processors are each assigned some of the objects in the model database. During scan conversion, each object processor reports the visibility of its objects at the current pixel. The pixel is rendered by the object that appears closest to the viewpoint. In this approach, more objects can be accommodated by adding more processors, but higher pixel resolution requires faster processors. It is most suitable for MIMD architectures [5].

In the pixel-parallel approach, multiple processors are each assigned part of the image frame store. Each object is considered serially and its effect on multiple image pixels calculated in parallel. Image resolution can be increased by adding more processors, but to display more objects, processor speed must be increased.

This approach is most suited to SIMD machines, like CAPP, with a large number of processors, ideally one for each image pixel, and is often known as the "intelligent frame store" approach. Much work on this approach has been done with the University of North Carolina's series of Pixel-Planes architectures [6,7].

We have used many of the algorithms that they have adopted and extended them to include antialiasing calculations

In order to achieve the processing speed required for both the modeling operations and the pixel-rendering operations, some parallelism is required in both. A solution is to make use of both object- and pixel-parallel approaches in different parts of the image generation pipeline.

4 Using a CAPP for image rendering

Fine grain, SIMD parallelism makes a CAPP most suitable for use as an intelligent frame store performing the last stages (windowing, clipping, and scan conversion) of the image generation pipeline. Other processors, probably MIMD parallel processors, would perform the object transformations required to generate a particular view.

Rather than have one PE per pixel of a high-resolution image, it is more practical, and affordable, to divide the image into smaller windows that are each rendered separately. This is also the approach adopted in Pixel-Planes 5 [7]. For example, a 1,280×1,024 image can be divided into 80 windows of 128×128 pixels each. For each image window, a list is constructed of the transformed objects that appear in it. As each list is completed, a rendering array comprising a CAPP and its host is assigned to that window to produce that part of the final image. When a renderer has finished its task, it copies its image to the corresponding window of an output frame store and renders the next, waiting image window. Assuming that the transformation part of the pipeline is able to produce objects at least as fast as they can be rendered, the speed of the complete operation will depend on the number of parallel renderers and the distribution of the scene complexity across the image.

4.1 Full-color images

When generating full-color images, the color of a pixel is commonly stored in 24 bits: 8 bits for the intensity of each of the red, green, and blue color components. As a result, many of the rendering calculations must be repeated three times. This is achieved by storing three intensity fields in each PE or, for faster rendering, by using three PEs for each image pixel.

As the depth buffer algorithms used for 3D rendering use some of the same equations as the shading calculations, some extra parallelism can be exploited by calculating all three colors and the depth buffer values at the same time. This requires four PEs for each image pixel.

5 Designing graphics algorithms for a CAPP

A pixel-parallel approach, and the limited memory of most CAPPs, requires a careful choice of algorithm. Commonly used computer graphics algorithms are designed to be fast on a sequential computer. They tend not to work well when simply recoded for SIMD implementation because the criteria for optimizing an algorithm for a sequential, or MIMD, machine are different from those for a SIMD machine.

Consider calculating an array, S, containing the square root of every element in the array X. In a serial computer this is achieved by a simple iteration:

```
for (i ...) S[i] = sqrt(X[i])
```

In a CAPP where each element is stored in a separate PE, all the elements are processed simultaneously. This can be expressed simply as:

```
S = sqrt(X)
```

In the serial case, considerable time can be saved by identifying special cases where the calculation could be simplified. For example, if you know that many of the elements have the value 4, you could use:

```
for (i ...) if (X[i] == 4) S[i] = 2
else S[i] = sqrt(X[i])
```

In a CAPP there is often an equivalent "where–elsewhere" instruction:

```
where (X == 4) S = 2 elsewhere S =
sqrt(X)
```

To execute this instruction, a search operation first identifies and activates those PEs holding X elements with value 4. A write instruction writes the value 2 into S in the activated PEs. The activity bit of all PEs is then inverted before applying the square root operation to the remainder of the array. Unlike the serial case, this instruction takes longer than simply calculating the square root for every element.

When optimizing a serial, image generation algorithm the emphasis is on making decisions that reduce the number of operations required on the huge amount of pixel data or that reduce the amount of data to be processed. The programmer will try to identify the special cases of data that need only minimum processing.

The fine-grain, large-scale parallelism of a SIMD processor array is more efficiently used for data-parallel operations than for serial decisions. The emphasis when programming this kind of architecture must be on choosing operations to apply to all the data that will give optimum results without the need to process special cases. For this reason, many standard image generation must be rethought for CAPP implementation.

5.1 Suitable algorithms

To perform the calculations described in this section and those that follow, each processor must know the coordinates of the pixel it is generating. A unique address must be written into two fields, x and y, of every processing element's data CAM. Once these values are in place, the various calculations are performed with a mixture of bit-serial arithmetic and pattern matching.

As each PE will have only a small amount of data, CAM algorithms are favored that do not require intermediate results to be stored. In particular, calculations of the form $ax + by + c$ are particularly economical to implement. In a CAPP that uses bit-serial arithmetic, the result of this expression can be calculated in two multiplications:

1. The constant value c is written into an accumulator field in all the processing elements. This rarely requires more than a single machine cycle.
2. The constant b is loaded into a controller register and used as a multiplier for the y field in each PE. For each '1' in b, a shifted copy of y will be added to the accumulator field in each PE.
3. The product ax is added to the accumulator in the same way.

On a bit-parallel ALU, tests such as $y - mx - c < 0$ are often considered efficient because only the sign bit of the result must be examined. However, bit-serial comparison is faster than bit-serial subtraction, as no result needs to be written, so the test is best performed as, $y < mx + c$.

In the algorithms discussed next, the CAPP host broadcasts the parameters of the object to be displayed and each pixel calculates some local attribute using these parameters and its address in the frame store. Two calculations form the basis for all the shapes: the distance of a pixel from a line through the image, and the distance of a pixel from a point in the image. These calculations allow the pixel to decide whether or not it is within the object to be plotted. Those that are take part in the rendering calculations. Furthermore, by calculating these distances to subpixel accuracy, they yield antialiasing information that can be used when the object is plotted.

6   Windows and clipping

When generating an image from an object database, objects that are not visible in the current view are normally excluded from the processing pipeline to save processing time. Those that are partially visible are normally clipped, their definition temporarily changed so that they have no parts outside the current view.

With the techniques described here it is not necessary to clip—in the *x-y* plane—lines, polygons, and so on that are partly off the screen. As pixels are mapped to physical processing elements, only pixels that actually exist take part in the calculations. This means that only the plotting objects that are completely outside the displayed screen area have to be removed from the display list. As all pixels are processed in parallel, reducing the size of a polygon by clipping does not reduce the processing time. Clipping of 3D objects in the *z* plane is still required.

If required, any object can easily be confined to a screen window by deactivating all pixels outside the window. Simple rectangular windows are achieved by broadcasting the coordinates of opposite corners. Each processor compares its address with these and decides if it is inside or outside the window. Those outside do not take part in any further processing until reactivated. Membership of more complex polygonal or circular windows is calculated in exactly the way as described in following sections for generating those shapes.

7   Antialiasing

To ensure that there are no aliasing artifacts in an image, all high spatial frequencies must be removed from it. The displayed image must be considered as a set of discreet point samples of the real continuous image that it represents. These point samples are at the centers of the displayed pixels, which our eyes blend into a continuous image.

If the true image contained no spatial frequencies above half the sampling rate (the Nyquist limit), the displayed image can, theoretically, be a perfect representation of it, with no aliasing artifacts. There are two approaches used in practical methods for achieving the low pass filtering required for this process. The most accurate method, according to Franklin Crow's original analysis [8], is to produce each image sample by convolution of a smoothing filter directly over the object space representation of the image. The accuracy of the filter is limited only by the accuracy of the stored model. Practical limits on the time available for antialiasing calculations means that a second, more approximate method is often used.

In this second method, displayed image samples are derived by averaging several pixels from a higher resolution image. No filtering is used in deriving the high-resolution image from the object representation. Typically, four times oversampling is used for visually acceptable results. This means the image is generated with four times the pixel frequency at which it is displayed. That is, the high-resolution image contains 16 times as many pixels as the final displayed image. Each pixel in the displayed image can be generated by a simple average of 16 high-resolution pixels to approximate a low-pass filter.

Although this second method is quicker when using the usual, sequential object-sampling algorithms, the distance calculations suggested here can provide antialiasing information that removes the need for oversampling and average filters. Kenneth Turkowski [9] has shown how distance calculations and a lookup table can give antialiasing that is equivalent to object space prefiltering, without the need for convolution. Lookup tables are easily implemented on a CAPP, as described above, so this method can add high-quality antialiasing to images without much extra processing.

8   Straight lines

Most methods for drawing straight lines are descended from Jack Bresenham's algorithm for X-Y plotters [10]. This algorithm calculates each pixel position in the line sequentially, and yet it is still adapted and used in parallel forms on SIMD machines [11], which would benefit more from a pixel-parallel approach.

8.1   Narrow lines with antialiasing

The perpendicular distance d of a point (x_p, y_p) from a straight line is given by

$$d = y_p \cos\theta - x_p \sin\theta + r \qquad (1)$$

where θ is the angle the line makes with the x axis, such that $-\pi/2 \leq \theta \leq \pi/2$ and r is the perpendicular distance from the line to the origin. Note that points on the clockwise side of this ray (decreasing θ) will appear to have negative distances. To generate a line between two points (x_0, y_0) and (x_1, y_1), the CAPP host calculates:

$$h = \sqrt{(x_1 - x_0)^2 + (y_1 - y_0)^2} \qquad (2)$$

$$r = (x_0 y_1 - x_1 y_0)/h \qquad (3)$$

$$cos\theta = (x_1 - x_0)/h \qquad (4)$$

$$sin\theta = (y_1 - y_0)/h \qquad (5)$$

It then broadcasts the values of r to an accumulator in each PE into which the product $-sin\theta \times x_p$ and $cos\theta \times y_p$ are then added, so that each pixel calculates the perpendicular distance of its center from the true line.

To avoid aliasing, the line must be filtered to remove all spatial frequencies above one half the pixel interval. If a given pixel has a background intensity i_b, its new intensity, i_p, will be a blend of this and a contribution from the filtered line,

$$i_p = i_b + (i - i_b)H_l(d) \qquad (6)$$

where $H_l(d)$ is the contribution factor, between 0 and 1, of the filtered line at a distance d from the pixel center. It is equivalent to the convolution of the true line with the filter kernel centered on the pixel. To find this contribution factor, the distance d is calculated to the nearest 0.25 pixel and used as an index into a lookup table of previously calculated values. For a radially symmetric, Gaussian filter, G,

$$G(d) = \frac{1}{\sqrt{2\pi\sigma}} exp\left(\frac{-d^2}{2\sigma^2}\right) \qquad (7)$$

$$H_l(d) = exp\left(\frac{-d^2}{2\sigma^2}\right) \qquad (8)$$

where σ controls the degree of smoothing of the filter.

The Gaussian filter is not a perfect antialiasing filter, but it has the advantage that it can be approximated to have a finite impulse response. This means that only a finite range of pixels close to the true line are influenced by it. For $\sigma = 0.5$, the filter has a radius of about 1.25 pixel and removes almost all the frequency components above one half the pixel frequency.

The lookup table is the same for positive and negative distances, so there are 6 possible values of $|d|$, between 0 and 1.25, which must be included in the table, as shown in Table 1.

Three CAPP cycles are needed for each lookup. Two match operations identify all the pixel distances having a particular value of d and $-d$, and a write operation writes the corresponding contribution factor into a field in those processing elements. For $d=0$, only one match operation is needed, making a total of 17 cycles to find the antialiased intensity contribution factors along the entire length of the line. All the filtered pixels then use Equation 6 to calculate their final intensity.

Line segments can be produced by disabling processing elements beyond the end points of the line. This gives an abrupt end to the line, which may be undesirable. Antialiasing at the ends can be achieved by superimposing a Gaussian-filtered point circle over each end point.

8.2   Wide lines with antialiasing

The apparent width of the displayed line can be varied somewhat by altering the value of σ, but for line widths of more than one or two pixels, another method is used.

For a line of width w, the perpendicular distance d (Equation 1) is used to give the distance from the edge of the line, d_e:

$$d_e = w/2 - |d| \qquad (9)$$

Table 1. The intensity contribution factor lookup table for narrow straight lines.

| Distance From Pixel | | Intensity Contribution Factor | |
Decimal	Binary	Decimal	Binary
0.00	0.00	1.0000	1.0000
0.25	0.01	0.8750	0.1110
0.50	0.10	0.6250	0.1010
0.75	0.11	0.3125	0.0101
1.00	1.00	0.1250	0.0010
1.25	1.01	0.0625	0.0001

Pixels whose centers are within the boundary of the line edges have positive values of d_e. Those with $d_e > r_H$, where r_H is the radius of the antialiasing filter, are considered completely covered by the line and take on its intensity, i, as shown in Figure 2. Those with $d_e < -r_H$ are far enough away from the line to remain at their original intensity i_b, and pixels with $-r_H \leq d_e \leq r_H$ are partly covered by the filtered line edge and calculate their intensity, i_p, according to a blending equation,

$$i_p = i_b + (i - i_b)H_p(d_e) \qquad (10)$$

Provided that the line is wider than the diameter of the filter, a suitable contribution factor, H_p, for a Gaussian-filtered line edge is given by

$$H_p(d_e) = 2\int_{-d_e}^{\infty} G(\rho)arccos\left(\frac{-d_e}{\rho}\right)\rho d\rho \qquad (11)$$

Using the same Gaussian filter as for thin lines, Equation 7, this integral is evaluated numerically to create a lookup table of intensity contribution factors for d_e between -1.25 and $+1.25$. The intensity contribution factors, calculated to the nearest 1/16 turn out to be 1 for $d_e > 0$ and 0 for $d_e < -1$. As a result, only five entries are needed in the lookup table, Table 2. Each pixel can then calculate its new intensity, using Equation 10. This technique can be extended to render any polygon composed of pairs of parallel sides.

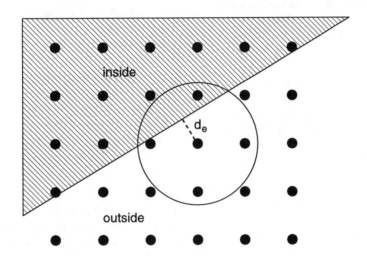

At each pixel, the intensity contribution of the edge is given by the convolution of the circular filter, centred on the pixel, with the edge.
The perpendicular distance of the pixel from the edge is used to index a look-up table of pre-computed convolution results.

Figure 2. The distance of pixel centers from the edges of a thick line.

Table 2. The intensity contribution lookup table for straight edges.

Distance From Pixel		Intensity Contribution Factor	
Decimal	Binary	Decimal	Binary
0.00	0.00	0.8125	0.1101
-0.25	1.11	0.5000	0.1000
-0.50	1.10	0.2500	0.0100
-0.75	1.01	0.1250	0.0010
-1.00	1.00	0.0625	0.0001

259

9   Polygons with antialiasing

General polygons can be generated from a list of their vertices. Taking two adjacent vertices, (x_0, y_0) and (x_1, y_1), in anticlockwise order, the methods introduced in Section 8 can be applied to find which side of the edge a pixel is on. Repeating this for each edge, the polygon covers those pixels found to be on the inside, anticlockwise side, of all the edges.

If the perpendicular distance of each pixel from a polygon edge is calculated, using two vertices taken in anticlockwise order in Equation 1, then those pixels outside the polygon will have a negative result, those inside a positive result, and those on the edge a zero result. After all the edges have been treated in this way, all the pixels are identified as being inside, outside, or on the edge of the polygon. Calculating each distance to the nearest 0.25 pixel gives the index into the lookup table for straight edges, Table 2. This table provides the intensity contribution factors for antialiasing.

Pixels found to be near two edges lie within a filter radius of the polygon's vertices. Their precise, antialiased intensity is complex to calculate, but as an approximation, the lesser of the two edge intensities is taken.

The order of operations is as follows:

```
Classify all pixels as "inside" with
contribution factor 1.

For each polygon edge
    CAPP host calculates cosθ and sinθ
(Eqs. 4,5).
    Pixels not classed "outside"
calculate distance d from line (Eq. 1)
    Pixels are classified as outside,
vertex, or edge:
        Where d has an entry in the
lookup table, Table 2
        Where pixel is classed "edge"
classify as 'vertex'
        Elsewhere classify as "edge"
    Where pixel is classed "inside" and
d<0 classify as "outside"
```

All pixels still classed as "inside," "edge," or "vertex" calculate their intensity according to the blending equation, Equation 10.

Concave polygons can be generated by combining information about two or more convex polygons. Polygons with polygonal holes can be generated by traversing the vertices of the hole in a clockwise order and applying similar inclusion tests.

10   Circles

Two methods are used to plot circles; both calculate each pixel's distance from the center of the circle. In the first method, each pixel substitutes its address into the equation of the circle. In the second, all pixels calculate their distance from the circle center by coordinate rotation.

The square of the distance, d^2, of a pixel at (x_p, y_p) from the center of a circle (x_c, y_c) is given by

$$d^2 = (x_p - x_c)^2 + (y_p - y_c)^2 \qquad (12)$$

and this is sufficient for determining membership of the circle or disc. To find the true distance, we have found CORDIC rotation to be quicker than a square-root calculation. This method is used for antialiased circles and discs. Figure 3 shows two circles drawn by these methods, using the GLiTCH simulator.

10.1   Circles without antialiasing

If all pixels calculate their value of d^2, a disc without antialiasing is generated by illuminating all the pixels that satisfy:

$$d^2 \leq r^2 \qquad (13)$$

This can be achieved by a bit-serial comparison in each processing element. Similarly, an annulus is generated by comparing the squared distance with an inner and an outer radius, $r_i^2 \leq d^2 \leq r_o^2$.

10.2   Circles with antialiasing

For antialiased circles, the pixels whose centers are within one filter radius of the true circle must perform antialiasing calculations. If we assume that the circle's edge is almost a straight line across the span of one filter diameter, we can use the distance of the center of these pixels to the edge of the circle as an index into a contribution factor, lookup table, as for lines and polygons.

For thin circular lines, the distance from the edge will be $| r-d |$, and the thin line lookup table, Table 1, is used. For solid discs, the distance from the edge is $r-d$ and the edge lookup table, Table 2, is used. This lookup table is also used to generate an annulus of width w, where the edge distance is taken to be $w/2 - | r-d |$. Unfortunately, all these cases would require a square-root calculation to find d from Equation 12, a costly operation in terms of both execution time and data CAM space.

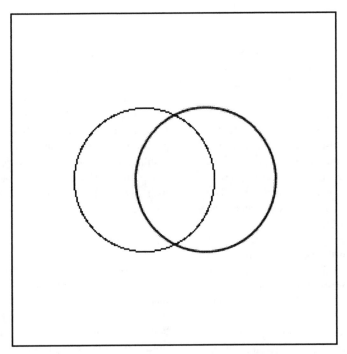

Figure 3. Two circles of radius 50 pixels drawn with (right) and without (left) antialiasing.

The CORDIC algorithm [12] is a commonly used technique for calculating square roots bit serially. This algorithm evaluates functions by mapping them into coordinate transformations in a suitable coordinate system. We can find d directly from the pixel coordinates, using a CORDIC coordinate rotation, as described by Turkowski [9].

Every point in the image is translated so that the center of the circle is at the origin: $x'_p = x_p - x_c$ and $y'_p = y_p - y_c$. The CORDIC rotation is then used to rotate all the points, incrementally, about the new origin until their y coordinate is zero. This effectively converts each pixel's coordinates from a Cartesian to a polar coordinate system, with the circle center as origin. At iteration i, the pixels where $y'_{i-1} \geq 0$ are rotated:

$$x'_i = x'_{i-1} + (y'_{i-1} >> i)$$

$$y'_i = y'_{i-1} - (x'_{i-1} >> i)$$

where $>>i$ represents a right shift of i bit positions. In pixels where $y'_{i-1} < 0$, the rotation increment is:

$$x'_i = x'_{i-1} - (y'_{i-1} >> i)$$

$$y'_i = y'_{i-1} + (x'_{i-1} >> i)$$

Eventually, the points lie along the x' axis with coordinate, x''_p, proportional to the radius of the point from the origin,

$$x'' = k\sqrt{{x'_p}^2 + {y'_p}^2} \qquad (14)$$

$$= k\sqrt{(x_p - x_c)^2 + (y_p - y_c)^2} \qquad (15)$$

$$= kd \qquad (16)$$

where k is a known constant, introduced by the algorithm, which is always the same for a given number of iterations.

Special versions of the two intensity contribution tables, scaled by a factor k, are used to produce the antialiased circles. The indexes will now be calculated from $|\,kr-kd\,|$, $kr-kd$ or $kw/2 - |\,kr-kd\,|$, depending on whether a thin, solid, or annular circle is required.

11   Rendering 3D solids with polygonal facets

A common method of rendering 3D surfaces is the use of polygonal facets. Solid objects are represented by a list of 3D coordinates of points on their surface. The points are chosen so that they divide the surface into almost flat, polygonal surface patches. The larger the curvature of the surface, the more polygons are required to represent it.

11.1 Visibility

When displaying the surface from a chosen viewpoint, those facets that are totally or partly hidden by others must be displayed accordingly. The CAPP architecture is particularly suited to implementing the z-buffer, or depth buffer, solution to this problem [13]. The depth in the scene of each point in the polygon is interpolated from the known depth at three of its vertices (it is assumed that all the vertices are coplanar). A data field in each processing element, z, the depth buffer, stores the depth of the pixel it is currently displaying. The new polygon is displayed only at pixels where its depth is less than the pixel's current depth.

The CAPP host will have calculated the x, y, and z coordinates of the vertices of the polygon by applying the viewing transformation to the object model to be displayed. Pixels can be classified as inside, outside, edge, or vertex of this polygon, in the x,y plane, one edge at a time, as above.

If antialiasing is required, the intensity contribution factors are looked up for each class along each edge. Meanwhile, the host solves the plane equation, $ax + by + cz + d = 0$, for any three vertices of the polygon.

The values, $-d/c$, $-b/c$ and $-a/c$ are broadcast to the array so that each pixel (x_p, y_p) classified as inside, edge, or vertex can calculate the z coordinate of the polygon at its center:

$$z_{poly} = -(a/c)x_p - (b/c)y_p - (d/c) \qquad (17)$$

Where this value is closer to the viewer than the existing value z_p, the pixel updates its depth buffer value, $z_p = z_{poly}$, and its intensity value.

If antialiasing is required, the intensity contribution factors are used in the blending equation, Equation 10. Note that if c is zero or very small, all the points in the polygon can be considered colinear in the plane of the display. The view of the polygon is infinitely thin and not plotted. The host must trap such cases to avoid overflow in the limited, fixed-point arithmetic of the CAPP.

11.2 Shading

If the polygon being displayed represents a flat surface, it will generally have a uniform intensity over its inside pixels, known as Lambert shading. The intensity is found by the CAPP host by calculating the angle between the surface normal, given by the plane equation, and a unit vector pointing toward the light source. The contributions of several light sources can be included. This is the intensity, i, in Equation 10, used to update the edge and inside pixel values. Figure 4 shows a GLiTCH-generated "tree" constructed of 14 depth-buffered, Lambert-shaded polygons. The object is superimposed on a background, by GLiTCH, for comparison with Figure 5.

Figure 4. Depth-buffered, lambert-shaded polygons used for representing 3D objects.

Figure 5. Depth-buffered, Gouraud-shaded, antialiased polygons used for representing 3D objects.

If the polygon is one facet of an approximation to a smooth surface, the gradual change in intensity over that surface can be approximated using Henri Gouraud's technique.

The intensities at the vertices of the polygon are calculated from the average surface normals of the connected polygons. These intensities are interpolated across the polygon in exactly the same way as the depth buffer values in Equation 17; the values of $-d/c$, $-b/c$ and $-a/c$ are found from the x, y, and intensity values of three vertices. To find the final, shaded-pixel values, each pixel uses its own, interpolated value of i in Equation 10. This method makes the assumption that the polygon vertices are coplanar in color space. Figure 5 shows the 14 polygons of Figure 4 with Gouraud shading and antialiased edges. Antialiasing takes place at all the polygon boundaries, taking account of the intensity of the background or a previously plotted object. The object is superimposed on a background loaded into the GLiTCH array from a digital frame store. When displayed on a computer monitor, this shows the effectiveness of the antialiasing at the object boundaries.

11.3 Rendering other solids

Just as the depth buffer allows polygons to be extended into three dimensions, it also allows spheres and other regular solids in the object space to be plot-

ted directly into the image space. Any 3D shape that can be described or approximated by an equation in x, y, and z, such as cylinders, ellipsoids, or cones, and so forth, can be plotted directly into the intelligent frame store without the need for first converting them into a network of surface polygons. Ultimately it may be desirable to generate the images directly from a model described with Constructive Solid Geometry (CSG) [14].

12   Evaluating the algorithms

Using a CAPP simulator [15], the accuracy and speed of a number of image generation algorithms have been found for a variety of differently sized image windows. From the results, the performance of a CAPP-based image renderer can be predicted.

12.1   GLiTCH

GLiTCH is a CAPP processor designed at Bristol University [3]. In the prototype design there are 64 PEs on each GLiTCH chip, each with 64 bits of data CAM and a 1-bit ALU. Extra RAM for each processor and an interchip routing network are provided by a supporting chip set. GLiTCH has been designed with image processing and graphics processing in mind and so includes a video shift register with an 8-bit cell in each PE. This is used to transfer pixel data between the data CAM and a full-frame digital frame store. A high-resolution image frame can be processed as a sequence of possibly overlapping windows. The array of GLiTCH chips extracts a rectangular window from an input frame store, processes it, and shifts it out to an output frame store as the next input window is shifted in.

The GLiTCH host is an Inmos transputer that carries out serial calculations, calls GLiTCH subroutines, and communicates with other, transputer-hosted modules. The GLiTCH subroutines are stored, precompiled, in a 96-bit–wide instruction memory and delivered to the array of GLiTCH chips by a microsequencer.

From a programmer's point of view, the GLiTCH array can be considered a coprocessor for the transputer, which provides it with fast array processing and pattern matching. Programs for the whole module are written in C; a special structure type is used for declaring array variables and all array operations are invoked from a library of dedicated C functions. On compilation, the array processing functions generate GLiTCH object code, which is transferred to the GLiTCH instruction memory.

Each of the shapes described in the previous sections, and a number of others, has been generated on a simulation of a GLiTCH array. The simulations were used to check the accuracy of the algorithms and investigate their speed of execution on differently sized GLiTCH renderers. As the width of the rendered image increases, so will the number of bits required for the x and y fields in the data CAM. All bit-serial arithmetic involving these values will, accordingly, take longer. Balancing this, of course, is the increased parallelism achieved.

12.2 Plotting speeds

As an example, times for some of the calculations fundamental to the image generation algorithms are given in Table 3, and times for plotting various shapes are given in Table 4. All the calculations use large enough bit fields to allow antialiasing equivalent to four times oversampling. The calculations in Table 3 are as follows:

t_{window}	A rectangular window of pixels can be defined with four bit-serial comparisons against the x and y coordinates of opposite corners of the window.
t_{dline}	Every pixel calculates its perpendicular distance from a thin line, Equation 1.
t_{dedge}	The distance from a thin line is modified to give the distance from the edge of a thick line, Equation 9.
t_{CORDIC}	Conversion from Cartesian to polar coordinates, using CORDIC rotation.
$t_{LUTline}$	Every pixel within one filter radius of a thin line looks up one of 6 intensity contribution factors for antialiasing.
$t_{LUTcircle}$	Scaled lookup table of 17 intensity contribution factors for pixels near thin circles.
t_{blend}	All pixels calculate their antialiased intensity according to their intensity contribution factor, Equations 6 and 10.
t_{depth}	The new depth buffer values for all pixels are calculated.
$t_{Gouraud}$	Smooth shading values are interpolated across a 3D polygon.

Table 3. Execution times, in machine cycles, for image generation calculations.

Execution Times	Image Width in Pixels					
	32	64	128	256	512	1024
t_{window}	32	36	40	44	48	52
t_{dline}	343	422	508	602	704	814
t_{dedge}	18	20	22	24	26	28
t_{CORDIC}	296	430	470	636	684	882
$t_{LUTline}$	18	18	18	18	18	18
$t_{LUTcircle}$	51	51	51	51	51	51
t_{blend}	176	176	176	176	176	176
t_{depth}	243	243	243	243	243	243
$t_{Gouraud}$	207	207	207	207	207	207

Table 4. Execution times, in machine cycles, for plotting graphics objects in various sizes of image window.

Plotting Tasks	Image Width in Pixels					
	32	64	128	256	512	1024
Thin line segments	112	128	178	200	260	286
Antialiased, thin line segments	554	634	722	818	921	1034
Filled parallelograms	192	226	316	254	472	508
Antialiased filled parallelograms	970	1136	1316	1512	1724	1952
Filled polygons, per vertex	96	114	158	178	236	260
Antialiased filled polygons, per vertex +176	374	454	540	634	736	846
Filled discs	372	484	612	760	924	1104
Antialiased filled discs	544	684	730	902	956	1156
Filled ellipses	686	968	1064	1410	1522	1944
Antialiased filled ellipses	894	1176	1270	1616	1726	2136
Flat-shaded 3D polygons, per vertex +244	96	114	158	178	236	260
Gouraud-shaded, antialiased, 3D polygons, per vertex +626	382	462	548	642	744	854

These figures provide a guide to the performance of any typical CAPP with bit-parallel search capability and a bit-serial ALU.

A CAPP of 64K PEs can render a 128×128, 24-bit color image with 4 PEs per pixel. Applying the performance figures from the GLiTCH simulator, a CAPP with a 100-MHz clock would be capable of rendering 44,050 full-color, antialiased, depth-buffered, Gouraud-shaded triangles per second. Sixteen of these renderers could produce a maximum of 704,800 triangles per second by rendering 16 image windows in parallel. We can expect that some of the triangles, say 20 percent, will overlap more than one window, so a reasonable estimate of their performance might be about 500,000 triangles per second.

Although this performance may not equal that of the best specialized graphics processors, CAPPs are programmable in a more general sense than specialized processors and are not limited to performing a particular calculation built into hardware. CAPPs can be used for a wide variety of image generation and image processing calculations such as resampling, nonlinear filtering and character recognition [16, 3], which may make them a useful component in general-purpose graphics workstations.

13   Summary

In a typical image generation pipeline, a content-addressable parallel processor can perform parallel object clipping, scan conversion, hidden surface removal, shading, and antialiasing. Each CAPP processing element stores the intensity and virtual depth of a display pixel, forming an intelligent frame store that renders all the pixels in parallel. The transformations on the model database must be calculated by some other supporting processor.

Image generation algorithms must be carefully chosen to suit the limited memory of the CAPP processing elements and the need to process all pixels identically. We have identified efficient algorithms for drawing straight lines, parallelograms, general polygons, circles, ellipses, and depth-buffered polygonal facets. Accurate antialiasing for these shapes is achieved by calculating their positions in the image to subpixel accuracy and using lookup tables to give their low-pass, filtered intensity at nearby pixel centers. The use of CAM speeds up many of the calculations by adding a pattern-matching facility as well as speeding up the bit-serial arithmetic mechanism itself.

With the GLiTCH simulator, we have tested the accuracy and speed of the algorithms for a variety of differently sized image windows and have predicted the performance of a CAPP-based image renderer. This performance compares favorably with that of special-purpose image rendering engines.

History has repeatedly shown that fast general-purpose hardware is better than hardware designed to accelerate the execution of one particular algorithm. The latter is usually produced as the only way to achieve a target application and is abandoned when standard computing components become available with sufficient power to fulfill the application in software. We feel that the content-addressable parallel processor has capabilities beyond a more conventional SIMD design, which make it a candidate for a general-purpose array processor with the power to execute image rendering and similar tasks in software rather than hardware.

Content-addressable parallel processors have been proposed as general-purpose, SIMD computers repeatedly over the past 30 years. There have been successful examples built for particular applications, but they have not become accepted components of general-purpose computers. Two problems have prevented this from happening. The large silicon area and input/output bandwidth of content-addressable memory makes them expensive and difficult to incorporate into standard systems. This problem is being partially relieved by the increasing density available in VLSI circuits, but CAM will always be less dense than RAM and will be adopted only where there are clear advantages for its use.

The second problem is the unusual programming style that must be adopted to make effective use of these machines. This problem will remain until data-parallel algorithms are better understood by programmers and can be more easily incorporated into standard programming languages.

Acknowledgment

This work was carried out while the author was a research fellow at the University of Bristol, as part of the SERC-funded GLiTCH project led by Prof. E.L. Dagless.

References

[1] C.C. Foster, *Content-Addressable Parallel Processors,* Van Nostrand Reinhold, New York, N.Y., 1976.

[2] G. Estrin and R.H. Fuller, "Some Applications for Content-Addressable Memories," *Proc. AFIPS Fall Joint Computer Conference,* Vol. 24, 1963, pp. 495–508.

[3] R.H. Storer et al., "An Associative Processing Module for a Heterogeneous Vision Architecture," *IEEE Micro,* June 1992, pp. 42–55.

[4] M.J. Flynn, "Some Computer Organizations and Their Effectiveness," *IEEE Trans. Computers,* Vol. C-21, No. 9, Sept. 1972, pp. 948–960.

[5] S. Green, *Parallel Processing for Computer Graphics.* Pitman Publishing, London, UK, 1991.

[6] H. Fuchs et al., "Fast Spheres, Shadows, Textures, Transparencies and Image Enhancements in Pixel-Planes," *Computer Graphics,* Vol. 19, No. 3, 1985, pp. 111–120.

[7] H. Fuchs et al., "Pixel-Planes 5: A Heterogeneous Graphics System Using Processor-Enhanced Memories," *ACM Computer Graphics,* Vol. 23, No. 4, May 1989.

[8] F.C. Crow, "A Comparison of Antialiasing Techniques," *IEEE Computer Graphics and Applications,* Vol. 1, No. 1, Jan. 1981, pp. 40–49.

[9] K. Turkowski, "Antialiasing Through the Use of Coordinate Transformations," *ACM Trans. Graphics,* Vol. 1, No. 3, July 1982, pp. 215–234.

[10] J.E. Bresenham, "Algorithm for Computer Control of a Digital Plotter," *IBM Systems J.,* Vol. 4, No. 1, 1965, pp. 25-30.

[11] W.E. Wright, "Parallelization of Bresenham's Line and Circle Algorithms," *IEEE Computer Graphics and Applications,* Vol. 10, No. 5, Sept. 1990, pp. 60–67.

[12] J.S. Walther, "A Unified Algorithm for Elementary Functions," *Proc. AFIPS Spring Joint Computer Conference,* Vol. 38, 1971, pp. 379–385.

[13] D.F. Rogers, *"Procedural Elements for Computer Graphics*, McGraw-Hill, New York, N.Y., 1985.

[14] J. Goldfeather et al., "Near Real-Time CSG Rendering Using Tree Normalization and Geometric Pruning," *IEEE Computer Graphics and Applications,* Vol. 9, No. 3, May 1989, pp. 20-28.

[15] A.W.G. Duller and R. Storer, "Fast and Accurate Simulation of Associative Processor Arrays," *Proc. European Workshops on Parallel Processing,* 1992, ESPRIT-sponsored workshops, Barcelona.

[16] A.W.G. Duller et al., "Image Processing Applications Using an Associative Processor Array," *Proc. 5th Alvey Vision Conf.*, 1989, pp. 289–292.

Ray Tracing Acceleration Using Content-Addressable Memories

Heng Wang
Computer Laboratory
University of Cambridge
Pembroke Street
Cambridge CB2 3QG, UK
hw@cl.cam.ac.uk

George A. Betzos
Department of Electrical Engineering
Colorado State University
Fort Collins, CO 80523
betzos@lance.colostate.edu

John V. Oldfield
Department of Electrical and Computer Engineering
Syracuse University
Syracuse, NY 13244
oldfield@cat.syr.edu

Neil E. Wiseman

Abstract

Ray tracing is a technique used primarily for generating realistic synthetic images. It is simple, elegant, but computationally intensive. Uniform grids and octrees speed up ray tracing by partitioning an object space uniformly and dynamically, and by sorting objects in a spatial order. The main problems in ray tracing acceleration with conventional grid and octree structures concern memory management and data structure traversal. The overhead time of these operations affects the choice of the optimal level of space subdivisions and the efficiency of acceleration algorithms. A content-addressable memory (CAM) with ternary storage can be used to store octree nodes and to search, in a single cycle, a node when the coordinates of a point inside the node are known.

This paper describes trial experiments using associative processing to improve data structure traversal and management for ray tracing. First, two efficient ray traversal algorithms are studied, one suitable for a uniform grid and one suitable for an octree, as they apply to the intervisibility problem, a special case of ray tracing. Storing the data structure in a CAM can improve the performance of both algorithms, but both have disadvantages. The uniform grid algorithm traverses the structure in small steps that require little computation, but time is wasted traversing vast empty space. The octree algorithm requires more computation to traverse each octant, but it can skip large pieces of empty space fast.

A new ray traversal method named adaptive 3D-DDA (three-dimensional digital differential analyzer) is presented that is based on the CAM architecture. This method combines the qualities of the uniform grid and octree algorithms and, in addition, takes advantage of the possible associative processing. It is shown that the adaptive 3D-DDA can remove ray-octant intersection operations and allow efficient octree traversal and empty space skipping.

1 Introduction

Ray tracing has been widely used in realistic image generation [1]. The original ray tracing algorithm was computationally intensive due to the time-consuming calculation of ray-object intersections. Several techniques have been developed to accelerate ray tracing by reducing the number of intersection tests using bounding volumes of objects, space subdivisions, and ray classifications. In these approaches, space subdivisions have shown advantages in ray tracing all kinds of objects including Brep, CSG-defined objects, and primitive-instancing schemes. Moreover, the regularity of space subdivisions are also more suitable for hardware implementation and parallel processing.

Space subdivision techniques for optimizing ray tracing include hierarchical subdivisions—octrees [2, 3] and nonhierarchical uniform subdivisions [4, 5, 6]. Subdivisions can be either in image space or in object space. Glassner [2] used modified linear octrees, a hash table, and linked lists to store octrees. The inner loop for locating an octant for a given point is slow as it requires computing the hash name of the octant. In octree methods, overheads of traversing an octree come from two sources. The first one is to locate an octant that encloses a given point. The second one is to construct the point used to locate the next octant. Finding the point involves a ray-octant intersection test that intersects the ray with each of the current octant's six faces to obtain the exit point of the ray. When a ray passes through many octants before it hits any object or exits the object space, overheads in locating octants and ray-octant intersections become significantly large.

Recently, Spackman and Willis [3] improved on Glassner's technique by storing the octree in a breadth-first list, which allows faster access. Also, they did away with the time-consuming ray-octant intersections by proposing a technique that navigates the ray inside the octree using fast incremental operations and therefore avoids costly multiplications and divisions. Their technique can be implemented in many cases using only integer arithmetic, which makes it quite fast.

A uniform subdivision method was proposed by Fujimoto et al. [4] as a spatially enumerated auxiliary data structure (SEADS). With SEADS, the space is subdivided into a 3D array using a uniform subdivision. A ray is traced through this 3D array using a 3D-DDA (3D digital differential analyzer) method. Other researchers [5, 6] use different voxel traversal algorithms for similar data structures.

Uniform subdivision algorithms have been favored in some studies [5, 6] for several reasons. First, voxel traversal for a uniform-sized grid is very fast. For example, it requires fewer than 10 integer operations to move to the next cell [5]. Second, it is a nonhierarchical structure so that locating a cell containing a ray origin can be done, in theory, in constant time. However, for the uniform subdivision scheme to be effi-cient it should use a large enough grid. This requires a large amount of memory, most of which will be empty. To deal with this problem, Cleary and Wyvill [5] use hashing. The scheme is also sensitive to the distribution of objects and to the variation in the object's size. Many objects may concentrate in a few grid cells and leave most cells empty.

In summary, hierarchical subdivisions are suitable for ray tracing of highly complex and unstructured environments; nonhierarchical subdivisions are best for scenes with many objects homogeneously distributed in spaces. But for most environments, neither technique is a clear-cut a priori winner. A better way to compare the two techniques arises when, for a given environment, the level of subdivision is fixed and the same for both. In this case the main difference between the two techniques comes down to how fast they can skip empty space.

In the following, we first compare the Spackman and Willis [3] and the Cleary and Wyvill [5] techniques, as they apply to the intervisibility problem, to find out which one skips empty space faster. Since both Glassner's and Cleary and Wyvill's scheme use hashing to deal with memory management, we show how the use of a CAM can benefit both. Then we propose a new scheme that is based on associative processing and which combines the best features of both techniques.

2   The CAM hardware

Content-addressable memories (CAMs) are generally described as a collection of elements that have data storage capabilities and can be accessed simultaneously on the basis of data contents instead of specific addresses.

The major advantages of CAMs over conventional memories are that a CAM supports an effective and natural way of organizing and retrieving data, reduces software complexity, and increases computing speed and power. During the early years of research, however, the use of CAMs has been restricted by the cost and the technology. In recent years we have seen rapid advances in VLSI technology, along with renewed interest in CAMs and their potential applications [7]. New commercial products [8] give us more chances to test new ideas and develop new application systems.

In the field of image processing, Oldfield et al. [9] have discussed the use of a ternary CAM in quadtree-based images and operations. Octrees can be stored in a similar way [10] as quadtrees by means of locational codes that are derived by interleaving bit patterns of x, y, and z coordinates, then indicating sizes of octants by replacing the rightmost m (determined by octant size) bits of x, y, and z with "don't cares." The resulting locational codes are trit words to be stored in ternary CAMs.

We implemented our trial experiment on the Coherent Processor of Coherent Research Inc. (CRiCP) [8], which allows for binary (4K words 32 bits) and ternary (2K words 32 trits) storage. Its logic/multiple response resolver unit incorporates 3 response registers, a Boolean logic unit and a shift register, which make it capable of some associative processing of the stored data (that is, it is more powerful than a common CAM). Also, each CAM word has 4 tag bits/trits attached to it. More details about the CRiCP can be found in [8]. It should be noted that our experience with the PS/2–CRiCP configuration indicates that accessing the CAM is a quite costly operation. We have measured an overhead of about 6 μsec to perform a 0.5–1.5 μsec operation on the CAM, which greatly compromises the speedups we actually obtained but which, if taken into account, indicates the advantage of using associative processing. Of course, we are certain that a better configuration can be easily arranged.

3   Complexity analysis of two intervisibility algorithms

Of the several algorithms that have been proposed for tracing a ray through an octree and through a uniform grid, the SMART algorithm [3] and the Cleary-Wyvill algorithm[1] [5] were chosen to be compared because they can be implemented using integer arithmetic. The algorithms are given an $n \times n$ array of elevation values between 0 and n-1 and a viewpoint, $v = (v_x, v_y, v_z)$ and produce an $n \times n$ array of bits indicating which surface voxels are visible from the viewpoint and which are not. A voxel is considered visible if, at least, half of its upper face is visible. To find out whether a surface voxel is visible from the viewpoint, rays are traced from the midpoint of its upper surface to the viewpoint. This ensures that at least half of the voxel's upper surface is out of sight. Voxels (and octants respectively) intersected by the ray are visited in proper order. If a visited voxel (octant) belongs to the terrain, then that voxel obscures the view from the viewpoint and the tracing stops. Therefore, both algorithms trace $n2$ rays, but they differ in the way they trace the rays. The first traces the rays through a uniform grid, which has the advantage of using a very fast next-voxel calculation and the disadvantage of taking many steps to skip empty space. The second method converts the terrain data to an octree representation, during a preprocessing step, and then uses the octree to trace the rays. It has the advantage of being able to skip empty

---

[1] This is the name we will use to refer to the algorithm they analyze in their paper.

space using very few steps and the disadvantage of having to perform a slower next-octant calculation, as well as a much slower ray tracing initialization.

3.1   Complexity analysis of the Cleary-Wyvill algorithm

The running time of the algorithm will depend, among other factors, on the characteristics of the terrain and the position of the viewpoint. Also, the number of voxels out of sight must be taken into account, because for those voxels the rays will not be traced in all of their length. In [5] the authors show that the average time it takes to trace a ray through the uniform grid is:

$$\frac{3}{2}\rho t + t_i$$

where ρ is the mean length of the rays (in the above expression we consider a voxel to be the same size as a unit cube), t is the time it takes to perform the next voxel calculation, and t_i is the time it takes to set up and initialize the next-voxel calculations.

In the intervisibility case, ρ depends on the position of the viewpoint and the relief of the terrain. We can calculate a close approximation of ρ by considering a flat terrain positioned at the mean elevation of the actual terrain. The mean length of the traced rays will be the sum of the lengths of the line segments with, as endpoints, the viewpoint and a point on the flat surface, divided by the area of the surface. Therefore ρ can be computed by the next double integral:

$$\rho = \frac{1}{n^2} \sum_{i=0}^{n} \sum_{j=0}^{n} \sqrt{(v_x - x_{ij})^2 + (v_y - y_{ij})^2 + (v_z - z_{ij})^2}$$

$$\approx \frac{1}{n^2} \int_0^n \int_0^n \sqrt{(v_x - x)^2 + (v_y - y)^2 + (v_z - z_{av})^2} \, dx dy$$

The exact result of the above double integral is a very long expression, which we omit here. For our purposes we will approximate this result by

$$\rho \approx C(v, z_{av}) \cdot n$$

where $0 < C(v, z_{av}) < {}^3\sqrt{3}$, which is a function of the location of the viewpoint, v, and the average elevation of the terrain, z_{av}. Given that k surface voxels will be out of sight, $0 \leq k \leq n^2$, and therefore the tracing of k rays will terminate before they reach the viewpoint very near the voxel, the overall average time, T_{CW}, it takes this algorithm to trace all the rays will be approximately

$$T_{cw} \approx (n^2 - k)\frac{3}{2}C(v, z_{av})nt^{cw} + n^2 t_i^{cw}$$

where t^{cw} is the average time it takes the Cleary-Wyvill algorithm to calculate the next voxel and t_i^{cw} is the average ray initialization time. Although k is an important factor in the above expression for T_{cw} (t^{cw} and t_i^{cw} are constants and C can be treated as such), the overall running time of the algorithm is primarily dependent on n. Therefore this is an $O(n^3)$ algorithm.

3.2 Complexity analysis of the SMART algorithm

We base our analysis of the SMART algorithm on the analysis of the uniform algorithm. The main difference in this case is the fact that the ray will traverse fewer cubic volumes but of different sizes. We define the following quantity, which is terrain dependent:

$$r = \frac{octants}{n^3}$$

We call this quantity the *measure of coherence* of the terrain. It is the inverse of the average number of voxels per octant. The smaller it is, the more flat the terrain. Because r is dependent on the input data, we introduce the following approximation: The average of the total number of octants the SMART algorithm traverses would be approximately equal to the number of voxels it would have traversed if it were given a uniform grid with a number of voxels equal to the number of octants. Let ρ' be the average length of rays in such a grid. Since the position of the viewpoint and the terrain remain the same, the only change is in the units where ρ' is measured. In this case

$$C(v, z_{av}) = \frac{\rho}{n} = \frac{\rho'}{n'}$$

where $n' = \sqrt[3]{octants}$ and therefore,

$$\rho' = C(v, z_{av})n' = C(v, z_{av})\sqrt[3]{octants} = C(v, z_{av})n\sqrt[3]{r}$$

So the average time, T_S, it takes for the SMART algorithm to trace all rays will be approximately

$$T_s \approx (n^2 - k)\frac{3}{2}C(v, z_{av})n\sqrt[3]{r}t^s + n^2 t_i^s$$

where t^s is the average time it takes the SMART algorithm to propagate the ray horizontally or vertically,

and t_i^s is the time it takes to initialize the traversal of the octree. Assuming that the number of octants will be a multiple of n^2, the measure of coherence, r, will be a multiple, greater than 1, of n^{-1} and the complexity of this algorithm will be $O(n^2)$. This means that the octree algorithm can be potentially faster than the uniform grid algorithm. But if r is close to 1, as it would be, for example, in the case of a "bumpy" terrain with very high peaks and very low valleys, the algorithm becomes $O(n^3)$.

Next we compare the two algorithms and the above theoretical approximations with actual results. We assume that r is a multiple, greater than 1, of n^{-1}. This is a very approximate estimation of the SMART's algorithm timings; the actual results may differ significantly from the estimates because of peculiarities of the terrain, the position of the viewpoint, and the particular structure of the octree.

3.3 Complexity comparison

We have shown that the Cleary-Wyvill algorithm is an $O(n^3)$ algorithm and that the SMART algorithm can be an $O(n^2)$ algorithm. This indicates that the SMART algorithm can be faster, but for actual implementations we must consider the other factors in the expressions for T_{cw} and T_s. Of those factors, t^{cw} and t_i^{cw} are important to the first algorithm; r, t^s, and t_i^s are important to the second. The rest are common to both expressions.

From experimental implementations we can deduce some relationship between t^{cw} and t^s, and between t_i^{cw} and t_i^s. From the implementation of the Cleary-Wyvill algorithm on a PS/2, we have

$$t_i^{cw} \approx 4.476 \times 10^{-5} sec$$

and

$$t^{cw} \approx 1.535 \times 10^{-5} sec$$

and from the implementation of the SMART algorithm on the same platform we have

$$t_i^s \approx 2.116 \times 10^{-5} sec$$

and

$$t^s \approx 3.227 \times 10^{-5} sec$$

Therefore

$$t_i^s \approx 4.7 t_i^{cw}, \quad t^s \approx 2.1 t^{cw} \quad and \quad t_i^{cw} \approx 2.92 t^{cw}$$

The factor r depends on the terrain data and n and $\sqrt[3]{r} = \dfrac{\sqrt[3]{octants}}{n}$. Therefore,

$$D = T_{CW} - T_S =$$

$$= \left[(n^2 - k)\frac{3}{2} C(v, z_{av}) n t^{cw} + n^2 t_i^{cw} \right] - \left[(n^2 - k)\frac{3}{2} C(v, z_{av}) n\sqrt[3]{rt}^{\,\sigma} + n^2 t_i^{s} \right] =$$

$$= \left[\frac{3}{2} C(v, z_{av})(n - 2.1\sqrt[3]{octants}) - 10.8 \right] t^{cw} n^2 - \frac{3}{2} C(v, z_{av})(n - 2.1\sqrt[3]{octants}) t^{cw} k$$

and if we factor out t^{cw} we get

$$D' = \frac{D}{t^{cw}} = \left[\frac{3}{2} C(v, z_{av})(n - 2.1\sqrt[3]{octants}) - 10.8 \right] n^2 - \frac{3}{2} C(v, z_{av})(n - 2.1\sqrt[3]{octants}) k$$

Where D' is positive, the Cleary-Wyvill algorithm is slower than the SMART algorithm, and where it is negative, the Cleary-Wyvill algorithm is expected to be faster than the SMART algorithm. Figures 1, 2, and 3 show how these two algorithms compare with each other. We plot D' as a function of $C(v, z_{av})$ and k, for $n = 32$, $n = 64$, and $n = 128$. The resulting surfaces appear similar but what differs is the range of values D' takes. We note that for small n the Cleary-Wyvill algorithm is faster, but for large n and $C(v, z_{av})$ and small k, the SMART algorithm is faster. Therefore, the SMART (octree subdivision) algorithm is very well suited for large terrains, viewpoints located at a large average distance from the terrain, and relatively flat terrains, although it is still faster even if half or more of the surface voxels are out of sight. The Cleary-

Wyvill (uniform subdivision) algorithm is expected to be faster when most of the terrain will be out of sight, the average length of the rays is small, and/or when the size of the terrain is small.

3.4 The use of a CAM

The efficiency of both algorithms can be improved by the use of a CAM to store the terrain data. A CAM that can search for ranges of integer values will provide quite compact storage for the elevation data for the Cleary-Wyvill algorithm because we will need to store just $O(n^2)$ values. A ternary CAM can be used instead, and the terrain data can be stored as either an octree or as just the surface voxels. The idea is that when the search is successful, the ray has intersected the terrain and is therefore blocked.

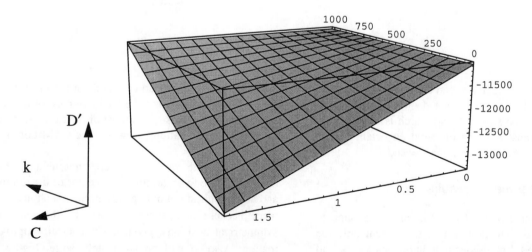

Figure 1. Plot of D' for $n = 32$.

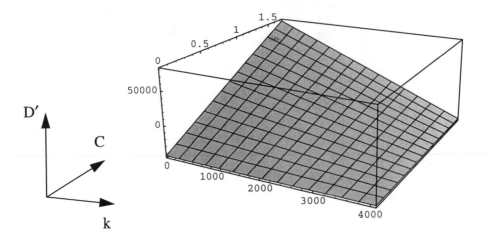

Figure 2. Plot of *D′* for *n* = 64.

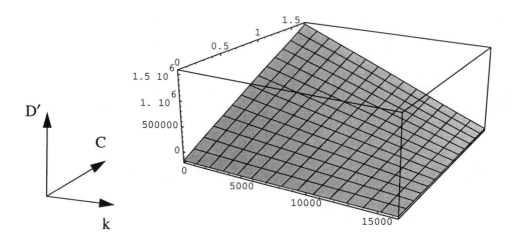

Figure 3. Plot of *D′* for *n* = 128.

The SMART algorithm can store the octree in the CAM, but only the leaves that do not belong to the terrain need to be stored. If the search is not successful, the ray must have encountered an octant that is part of the terrain; therefore, it is blocked.

3.5 Experimental results

Because the size of the CRiCP is not big enough to hold all but the smallest octree, we present only the times obtained from sequential implementations and compare them with the theoretical approximations. Using the CAM as cache is a solution, but it imposes the considerable overhead of searching the memory to find the data to load into the CAM in case of a miss. Also, both algorithms spend most of their time in next-voxel/octant calculations, in which the CAM does not participate.

The sampling viewpoints were chosen in the 6th octant, relative to an origin at the center of the terrain, and at the highest possible position. Such a choice was made because of symmetry: ρ will be the same, at symmetrical positions, given the flat terrain approximation. Also, ρ will be adequately large. Figure 4 shows an orthogonal projection of the location of the sampling viewpoints.

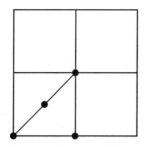

Figure 4. Sample viewpoints.

Tables 1, 2, and 3 present results obtained using test terrain data for $n = 32$, $n = 64$, and $n = 128$. The terrain for $n = 32$ is a scaling of the terrain for $n = 64$, and that terrain is a scaled portion (a quarter) of the terrain for $n = 128$. The estimates are presented alongside for comparison. Table 1 shows the average length of the rays and the average number of voxels per ray for the Cleary-Wyvill algorithm. Actual and approximate estimated values are provided for four viewpoints for each of the three terrains. The number k of voxels that are out of sight, for each viewpoint, and the average height of the terrain are also provided. Note that the estimated values are close to the actual values.

Table 2 shows the actual average number of leaf, and the average number of leaf and nonleaf octants, per ray, for the SMART algorithm. The same viewpoints and terrain data as in Table 1 are used. It also shows the estimated average number of octants per

ray. Note that for $n = 32$ the estimates are close to the actual values, but for $n = 64$ and $n = 128$ the estimates are somewhat far from the actual values. Nevertheless, Table 3 supports the conclusions made based on Figures 1, 2, and 3, which themselves are based on the theoretical approximations. In fact, the theoretical approximations overestimate the running time of the SMART algorithm. This further supports the advantage of a CAM-octree implementation.

Table 3 compares the running times obtained on a PS/2 by the two algorithms using the same test data and the same viewpoints as before. All times are in seconds. Note that, overall, the running times conform to the predictions made by observing the behavior of D', despite the approximate nature of the theoretical approach. As the size of the terrain data and the average length of the rays increase, the SMART algorithm outperforms the Cleary-Wyvill algorithm.

Table 1. Cleary-Wyvill algorithm statistics.

Viewpoint			Average Length of Rays		Average Number of Voxels/Ray		k
v_x	v_y	v_z	Actual	ρ	Actual	$\dfrac{3\rho(n^2-k)}{2n^2}$	
$n = 32, z_{av} = 11.28$							
16	16	31	24.17	23.55	29.07	31.46	112
0	0	31	32.21	32.05	41.06	39.30	187
8	8	31	26.95	25.85	33.59	35.14	96
0	16	31	29.47	28.04	36.31	37.50	111
$n = 64, z_{av} = 22.6$							
32	32	63	49.10	47.91	59.69	62.78	518
0	0	63	66.99	64.73	83.53	78.27	794
16	16	63	54.58	52.47	68.74	69.96	455
0	32	63	59.58	56.79	73.09	73.81	547
$n = 128, z_{av} = 60.9$							
64	64	127	86.13	83.65	68.41	65.98	7,768
0	0	127	126.35	120.36	106.07	104.80	6,873
32	32	127	99.08	93.70	89.49	91.21	5,752
0	64	127	110.47	103.18	110.38	107.89	4,965

Table 2. SMART algorithm statistics.

Viewpoint			Average Number of Octants/Ray		
			Actual		Estimated Total
v_x	v_y	v_z	Leaf	Total	$\dfrac{\sqrt[3]{\rho^3 r}(n^2 - k)}{2n}$
n = 32, r ≈ 0.12, air = 1,996, terrain = 1,820					
16	16	31	8.10	16.50	15.52
0	0	31	9.01	17.94	19.38
8	8	31	8.67	17.15	17.33
0	16	31	7.35	14.64	18.50
n = 64, r ≈ 0.06, air = 7,826, terrain = 7,687					
32	32	63	9.44	19.79	24.58
0	0	63	10.43	21.37	30.64
16	16	63	9.95	20.29	28.49
0	32	63	8.38	17.29	28.90
n = 128, r ≈ 0.03, air = 36,357, terrain = 36,353					
64	64	127	11.80	26.52	21.52
0	0	127	7.12	22.78	34.18
32	32	127	10.57	23.21	29.74
0	64	127	9.53	21.17	37.67

Table 3. Running times.

Viewpoint			Cleary-Wyvill	SMART
v_x	v_y	v_z	$n = 32$	
16	16	31	0.52	0.83
0	0	31	0.67	0.95
8	8	31	0.57	0.82
0	16	31	0.60	0.72
			$n = 64$	
32	32	63	4.00	3.67
0	0	63	5.27	4.05
16	16	63	4.52	4.05
0	32	63	4.65	3.40
			$n = 128$	
64	64	127	17.72	19.25
0	0	127	26.18	17.35
32	32	127	22.87	17.43
0	64	127	27.35	16.38

3.6   Comparison conclusions

We have analyzed two of the fastest algorithms for tracing a ray through a subdivided space as they apply to the intervisibility problem. Each algorithm has advantages and disadvantages. The Cleary-Wyvill algorithm is faster when the terrain size is small or the average length of the rays is small or when most of the surface voxels are obscured. The SMART algorithm is faster when the terrain size is big or the average length of the rays is big and when most of the rays have to be traced in their full length.

We have provided a way to accurately estimate the running time of the Cleary-Wyvill algorithm and a way to estimate the running time of the SMART algorithm. We have also indicated that both algorithms spend most of their time in calculating the next-voxel/octant and very little time accessing the data structure that holds the terrain data. The use of a CAM can certainly provide faster access to this data structure and will require less memory in the case of the octree.

4.   A new scheme

The new scheme we propose here (Figure 5c) combines several advantageous features of uniform and octree subdivisions. These features are the tight voxels of uniform subdivisions and the dynamic subdivisions of octrees. It can be seen that the new scheme is a variation of octree subdivisions with two major improvements. First, empty cells are deleted. Second, each cell tightly binds objects with which it intersects. Memory is saved by having variously sized cells and ignoring empty cells. At the same resolution (depth 3 in this example), the uniform subdivision scheme has 64 cells, the octree scheme has only 16 octants, and the new scheme has the least number of nodes, which is 9.

Table 4 shows the number of voxels (or octants) visited and the number of ray-object intersection tests involved for each sample ray in Figure 5. A uniform subdivision has a small number of ray-object intersection tests (7) and a large number of voxel traversals (48). An octree subdivision has a large number of ray-object intersection tests (13) and a relatively small number of octant traversals (23). However, it's more

expensive to locate an octant for a given point in a conventional octree than to locate a voxel in a uniform subdivision scheme. An octree-accelerated ray tracer is slowed down not only by expensive octant traversals but also by the remaining large number of ray-object intersection tests caused by large octants that bind objects loosely. Many rays that hit the octant miss objects in it, thus tests are wasted, for example, the ray number 7 in Figure 5b.

With the new scheme, the number of visited voxels is reduced to 7, which is far smaller compared to the corresponding numbers in the uniform subdivision and octree subdivision schemes. The number of ray-object intersections is the same as that of uniform subdivision. Therefore, the new scheme can be faster due to its small number of voxel traversals and ray-object intersection tests.

How can a ray quickly traverse the space shown in Figure 5c? With conventional architectures, traversing such a space organization may be complex. Peng et al. [11] have tried to use conventional linear octrees to store a similar spatial organization. To find the next octant, they used binary searches. They also tried to skip empty regions more efficiently using a heuristic method that finds the ray exit point for a given octant. However, the procedures of binary searches and ray-octant intersection tests remain the primary sources of overheads.

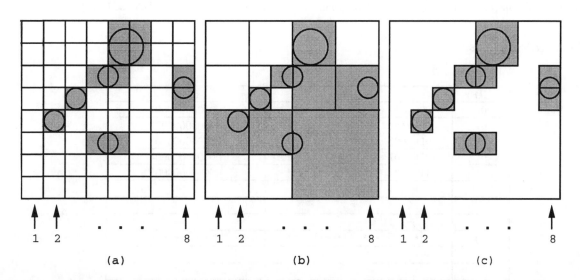

Figure 5. Comparison of different space subdivision schemes: (a) uniform subdivision; (b) octree subdivision; (c) proposed scheme.

Table 4. Analysis of space subdivision algorithms used for accelerating ray tracing.

Ray No.	Uniform		Octree		New	
	Voxels Visited	Inter-section Tests	Voxels Visited	Inter-section Tests	Voxels Visited	Inter-section Tests
1	8	0	4	1	0	0
2	4	1	2	1	1	1
3	5	1	3	2	1	1
4	8	2	5	2	2	2
5	3	1	1	1	1	1
6	7	1	3	3	1	1
7	8	0	3	2	0	0
8	5	1	2	1	1	1
Total	48	7	23	13	7	7

To overcome problems encountered in conventional octree-accelerated ray tracers and to improve their performance, we have developed an algorithm using CAM octrees. Our aims are:

- to simplify memory management;
- to speed up the octree node access process by

  1. using CAM searches to locate an octant for a given point;
  2. removing ray-octant intersections.

5 Ray tracing using CAM octrees

A CAM octree is constructed with a two-pass preprocessing method. In the first pass, the space is recursively subdivided into eight subspaces (octants) until the number of objects in an octant is less than some criteria (for example, six objects). In the second pass, we check the tightness of those octants that are larger than the smallest octant from the first pass. The tightness of an octant around its associated objects is tested by further subdividing the octant and examining whether there are more than four empty suboctants. The nontight octant is replaced by its nonempty children. The second pass improves the efficiency of bounding octants and at the same time prevents the space from being subdivided too finely on crowded areas.

Only the nonempty octants are stored in the CAM. CAM contents contain nonempty octants' locational codes and indices (Table 5). Each index points to the memory address of a group of objects associated with each octant. Traversal of a ray through the octree space is implemented using an *adaptive 3D-DDA* algorithm, described later. The traversing technique includes two parts: adaptive 3D-DDA and CAM operations.

Table 5. CAM contents.

ID	Location						Index
01	000	***	***	***	***	***	000000000001
01	001	***	***	***	***	***	000000000002
01	011	001	***	***	***	***	000000000003
01	011	101	***	***	***	***	000000000004
01	110	***	***	***	***	***	000000000005
.			.				
.			.				
.			.				
00	***	***	***	***	***	***	***********
.			.				
.			.				
.			.				

5.1 Adaptive 3D digital differential analyzer

Fujimoto et al. [4] were the first to use a 3D-DDA for space traversal. The 3D-DDA algorithm is a 3D extension and modification of DDA, which evaluates some functions incrementally. The 3D-DDA algorithms examines the ray path voxel by voxel while our adaptive 3D-DDA algorithm examines a group of voxels in a single step. A ray is split into a series of segments, each segment has a cross section that is the unit square of a voxel (that is, an octant at the lowest level of the octree subdivision). The position and the length of a segment is calculated from the parameters that are determined by the ray origin and direction. Figure 6 two-dimensionally illustrates the ray segments of our adaptive 3D-DDA in several typical cases.

Because some ray segments do not fit the constraint of the octree space subdivision, they are further broken into fragments. These fragments (separated by dotted lines) can be seen in Figures 6b and 6c. In relation to Figure 6, Table 6 compares the number of voxels visited by the 3D-DDA method and the number of fragments examined for the same ray in our adaptive 3D-DDA method. In the best case, the ray can be tested against the object space in one step with a single segment. In general situations, the number of fragments is about one third of the number of voxels visited by the ray. Even in the worst case, the number of fragments is less than two thirds of the number of voxels.

Calculation of each ray segment is implemented by simple comparison, addition, and subtraction. Each ray segment has a position indicated by coordinates and a length. A ray segment position is determined by its left-bottom-back corner. Ray segment width and height are unit size. Each ray segment is updated from the previous segment. The first segment is calculated from the ray origin if it is inside the boundary of the octree space, or from the point where the given ray enters the octree space. The tests for intersecting a ray with objects involves CAM operations and standard ray-object intersection tests.

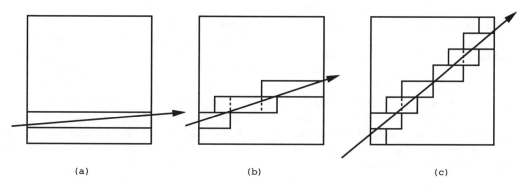

| (a) | (b) | (c) |

Figure 6. Two-dimensional illustrations of adaptive 3D-DDA for rays of different orientations: (a) the best situation where the ray is nearly parallel to one axis (for example, the horizontal axis); (b) general situation; (c) the worst case where the ray enters from one corner of the world space and leaves at the opposite corner.

Table 6. Comparisons of traversal steps for 3D-DDA and for adaptive 3D-DDA.

Traversal Step	3D-DDA	Adaptive 3D-DDA
(a) Best case	8	1
(b) General case	10	3
(c) Worst case	14	8
Total	32	12

5.2 CAM operations

The task of a CAM is to find, in the right order, the octants intersecting with the ray currently being traced. To compare a ray segment with a CAM octree, a search pattern must be constructed whose locational code comes from the parallelepiped corresponding to the ray segment. Then a CAM search operation is called with the search pattern. For example, a line in full length of the space has a pattern of *00 *01 *00. However, the ray segment computed from the adaptive 3D-DDA method does not always fit into octree subdivision (see Figures 6b and 6c.) It is therefore necessary to break each unfit ray segment further into a group of fitted fragments, then to compare each fragment with the CAM octree.

Segment splitting is a key operation. Its function is to split one-dimensional orthogonal lines (ray segments) into several parts that fit the octree subdivisions. It generates a list of integers from the bit patterns of the coordinates and length of a ray segment. Each integer gives the position of a part of the ray segment. Its length can be derived from the position of its subsequent part. All parts are fitted into the spatial restriction of octrees (that is, powers of 2—see Figure 7).

A fragment has some features that are used to determine where we can split the original ray segment. For a fragment at level i of an octree subdivision, we know that it has a length of $2^{(D-i)}$ (where D is the maximum depth of the octree) and a start coordinate divisible by the length. The number of fragments varies for different ray segments, but the maximum number is determined by the depth of octrees.

$$MaximumNumberofSegments = \begin{cases} 1 & , \text{ if } Depth = 0 \\ 2 \times DEPTH, & otherwise \end{cases}$$

Since all the nodes in CAM are nonempty octants, the inquiry may yield zero, one, or many responders. This means that the ray intersects zero, one, or many octants, respectively. If a search returns no responders, then the ray fragment hits nothing in space. The program continues for the next ray fragment. If a search returns one responder, the ray fragment intersects one octant. This octant could either be the same as the octant hit by the previous fragment or be a new octant that has not been tested before. In the first case, the program jumps to the next fragment and continues. Otherwise, all objects in the octant are tested in turn against the ray, and the control returns to the main program if the ray intersects an object. If there are multiple responders, the current ray fragment must be divided into two parts of equal size. The CAM search process is repeated for each half in turn. As a result, the intersected octants can be visited in the right order.

6. Results and discussions

Experiments were carried out to test the performance of our CAM octree ray tracer. Haines [12] proposed a standard procedural database (SPD) package for testing rendering algorithms. In that database, he selected six scenes that are familiar to many graphics researchers and users. Among the six scenes, the recursive tetrahedral pyramid and the sphereflake are most widely cited. The pyramid scene was introduced by Glassner [2]. Here, we choose the pyramid and sphereflakes.

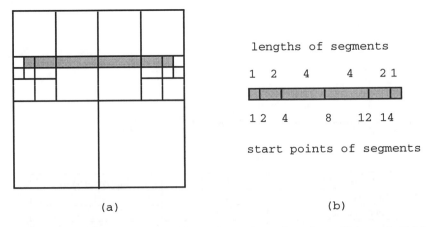

(a)   (b)

Figure 7. Generating a RunList from a ray: (a) a ray in a 2D region of quadtree subdivision; (b) the same ray is split into maximal segments.

In the pyramid example, the eye rays are not parallel to any of the three axes of the object space. This example is used to measure the algorithm for arbitrarily oriented rays. In this case, the eye rays are entering the object space from one corner and leaving from its opposite corner. This is nearly the worst case for adaptive 3D-DDA. Objects of the pyramid database are the same size and are distributed regularly in space. Such object distribution is relatively rare in reality. The scenes of sphereflakes have the characteristics that objects differ significantly in size and objects' distribution is uneven in space. There are three light sources. In sphereflake scenes, parallel eye rays were used that represent the best case of adaptive 3D-DDA. Shadow rays from three light sources represent general cases of adaptive 3D-DDA.

Our experiments were carried out with a CAM simulator under a Unix environment at Cambridge University Computer Laboratory in the UK and with the CRiCP hardware running on a PS/2 at Syracuse University in New York. Both systems use a CAM with words of 32 trits in width. We can only test up to a depth of six space subdivisions. Therefore, the root of an octree is a cube with a size of 64. To make calculations of adaptive 3D-DDA simpler, all objects are scaled in preprocessing to a cubic space corresponding to the octree root. The eye position and lights' positions are scaled in the same way. The simulator has 8,000 words while the CRiCP has 2,048 ternary words for storing octants.

We estimate the execution time of the algorithm on the simulated CAM by profiling the program and subtracting the time used for hardware functions. Such time estimates represent the idealized situation where the process of constructing CAM words (for example, encoding/decoding of leafcodes, combining/splitting of logical fields, and so forth) is run by hardware.

Several factors may strongly influence the direct comparison of different accelerating algorithms. First, the published timing data are based on different machines that have different architectures, speeds, and floating-point coprocessors. Second, programming languages may be different. Although most ray tracers are implemented in C, some of them use an assembler program to improve execution of heavily used procedures, and other systems exist in Fortran 77 [5]. Third,

the code organization is important for the execution efficiency. It depends on whether the data structure is a linked list or an array, and on whether the program is object oriented or is optimized by removing most procedure calls. Finally, the test scene complexity must be considered. Different models tend to work best for different scenes. Thus it would be more meaningful to compare the features of algorithms rather than simply the execution times. The timing results are listed in Table 7 only to serve as an outline of the speed of using CAM octrees to speed up ray tracing.

6.1   CAM simulator

Table 7 compares our simulated CAM octree ray tracer with Glassner's conventional octree based ray tracers for the pyramid scene. Our simulator and ray tracer algorithm ran on Digital Equipment Corporation's MIPS machine. The scene has 1,024 polygons. The speedup factor in the table is derived by dividing the time of the naive ray tracer by the time of the accelerated ray tracer. The naive ray tracer has not applied any acceleration algorithm. With the CAM octree accelerated ray tracer, the average number of intersections per ray is reduced to 1.35. All intersection tests consume 29 percent of the total execution time. The time for octant traversal is 48 percent of the total time. The rest of the execution time is spent on shading and other calculations. In comparison, the corresponding statistics for Glassner's octree ray tracer [2] gives an average of 25 ray-object intersections per ray. In his case, with such a large number of intersections per ray, the intersections used less than 10 percent of the total time. The overheads in octree traversal took up about 90 percent of total execution time. From the results in Table 7, we can see that the speed of the simulated CAM-based algorithm is about 20 times as fast as Glassner's algorithm in this example.

We ran three models of sphereflakes, each with different numbers of objects in the scene. The timing of these scenes is listed in Table 8, which shows that the execution time varies almost linearly with the number of objects in the scene. Therefore, it may be expected that the more objects exist in a scene, the more significant the speedup is.

Table 7. Statistics of Glassner's and simulated CAM octree ray tracers for the tetrahedral pyramid scene.

Algorithm	Resolution of Eye Rays	Number of Octants	Average Intersections Per Ray	Time (Sec.)	Speedup
Glassner	(512,512)	473	25.60	NA	7.3
CAM	(512,512)	256	1.35	82	152.0

Table 8. Statistics of the simulated CAM octree ray tracer for several sphereflake scenes.

Sphereflake	Resolution of Eye Rays	Level of Subdivision	No. of Octants	Time (Sec.)	Speedup
Balls91	(100,100)	2	38	4.8	9.3
Balls820	(100,100)	4	341	12.2	42.0
Balls7381	(100,100)	5	2,956	32.8	157.0

6.2   CRiCP

Table 9 lists the results of the MTV ray tracer and the CAM octree ray tracer on the real CAM card, with the CRiCP running on a PS/2 model 70, which is rather slow compared to RISC processor-based Unix machines. The PS/2 has a math coprocessor. The MTV ray tracer is a public domain program that uses bounding plane sets. Table 10 gives the results of another public domain ray tracer (Rayshade) using a uniform grid subdivision scheme for two different grid sizes. Because CRiCP is a general-purpose binary/ternary CAM, all special interface functions for octrees are in software. These include encoding/decoding operations of leafcodes, construction of CAM words for storing octrees and searching the CAM, and so on.

We mentioned previously that there are significant overheads in using the CRiCP. In addition, the high-level interface to the CAM—used both with the simulator and in the CRiCP implementation—increases the overhead of a CAM operation by a considerable number of function calls. The above timings would be improved, as suggested in our results from the CAM simulator, if a highly coupled CAM interface existed. The ideal situation is to use special-purpose ternary CAM that is dedicated to octree operations and ray tracing.

The improvement of our CAM octree ray tracer in comparison to the conventional octree accelerated ray tracers [2] is mainly due to the constant CAM searches, special CAM pattern matching capabilities, and the simple adaptive 3D-DDA algorithm. Because of the parallel CAM searching capability, the time to locate the octant that encloses a given point is $O(1)$ instead of $\log(n)$ as for conventional octrees. By using pattern matching and adaptive 3D-DDA, we avoid calculating the point used for locating the next octant.

Table 9. Comparisons of ray tracers using Kay and Kajiya's method (MTV) and using CAM octrees (time in seconds on a PS/2).

	Resolution	MTV	CRiCP	MTV/CRiCP
Tetra1024	(512,512)	1,246	875	1.43
Balls91	(512,512)	6,711	2,345	2.86
Balls820	(512,512)	11,528	3,934	2.93

Table 10. Comparisons of ray tracers using a uniform grid method and using CAM octrees (time in seconds on a PS/2).

	Resolution	Grid1 (11,11,11)	Grid2 (20,20,20)	Grid1/CRiCP	Grid2/CRiCP
Tetra1024	(512,512)	1,106	1,145	1.26	1.31
Balls91	(512,512)	4,586	4,777	1.96	2.04
Balls820	(512,512)	10,952	7,434	2.78	1.89

7. Summary

The new ray tracing acceleration algorithm using CAM octrees has the following major features.

- It uses an adaptive space subdivision.

- It keeps nonempty octants only, and each octant binds tightly to its associated objects.

- No ray-octant intersection tests are necessary.

- The next nonempty octant to be visited for testing ray-object intersections is found by simple searches in CAM.

- The use of adaptive 3D-DDA allows, in general, a small number of steps for a ray to traverse the object space. The empty spaces are skipped quickly for arbitrary rays.

- The space traversals of rays that are parallel to any of the three axes of the object space can be handled very efficiently.

The underlying benefits of employing CAM are that we can accommodate dynamic and fine-space subdivisions without too much increase in memory or a significant decrease in speed. In our current implementation of the CAM octree ray tracer, we have experimented with object models of Breps and pure primitive instancing schemes. Our algorithm can be extended straightforwardly to speed up ray tracing of CSG models.

Neil Wiseman died in 1995 after a brave struggle with cancer. His leadership of the Cambridge Rainbow Group inspired many developments in computer graphics, as well as the lives and careers of his research students and colleagues. A fuller tribute can be found on the World Wide Web. See http://www.cl.cam.ac.uk:80/Research/Rainbow/people/neilw.html for more information. He is sorely missed.

Acknowledgments

We acknowledge the contributions to this work made by Richard Williams while he was at Cambridge. For sponsoring this research, Heng Wang thanks Cambridge University Commonwealth Trust, the ORS Award Scheme, St. John's College, Cambridge Philosophical Society. Part of this research was funded by IBM-FSC, Owego, New York, under contract 417557-DC.

References

[1] A.S. Glassner, *An Introduction to Ray Tracing*, Academic Press, London, 1989.

[2] A.S. Glassner, "Space Subdivision for Fast Ray Tracing," *IEEE Computer Graphics and Applications*, Vol. 4, No. 10, 1984, pp. 15–22.

[3] J. Spackman and P. Willis, "The SMART Navigation of a Ray Through an Oct-Tree," *Computers & Graphics*, Vol. 15, No. 2, 1991, pp. 185–194.

[4] A. Fujimoto, T. Tanaka, and K. Iwata, "Arts: Accelerated Ray-Tracing System," *IEEE Computer Graphics and Applications*, Vol. 6, No. 4, 1986, pp. 17–26.

[5] J.G. Cleary and G. Wyvill, "Analysis of an Algorithm for Fast Ray Tracing Using Uniform Space Subdivision," *The Visual Computer*, Vol. 4, No. 2, 1988, pp. 65–83.

[6] J. Amanatides and A. Woo, "A Fast Voxel Traversal Algorithm for Ray Tracing," *Proc. EUROGRAPHICS '87*, 1987, pp. 3–10.

[7] T. Kohonen, *Content-Addressable Memories*, Springer-Verlag, New York, second edition, 1987.

[8] C.D. Stormon et al., "A General-Purpose CMOS Associative Processor IC and System," *IEEE Micro*, Vol. 12, No. 6, 1992, pp. 68–78.

[9] J.V. Oldfield, R.D. Williams, and N.E. Wiseman, "Content-Addressable Memories for Storing and Processing Recursively Subdivided Images and Trees," *Electronic Letters*, Vol. 23, No. 6, 1987, pp. 262–263.

[10] H. Wang, "Modelling and Image Generation," Tech. Report No. 235, Computer Laboratory, Univ. of Cambridge, UK, 1991.

[11] Q.S. Peng, Y.N. Zhu, and Y.D. Liang, "A Fast Ray Tracing Algorithm Using Space Indexing Techniques," *Proc. EUROGRAPHICS '87*, 1987, pp. 11–23.

[12] E.A. Haines, "A Proposal for Standard Graphics Environments," *IEEE Computer Graphics and Applications*, Vol. 7, No. 11, 1987, pp. 3–5.

Section V
Associative Processing and Neural Computation

The Cellular Neural Network Associative Processor (C-NNAP)

Jim Austin, Stephen Buckle, John Kennedy, Anthony Moulds, Rick Pack, and Aaron Turner
Advanced Computer Architecture Group
Department of Computer Science
University of York
York, YO1 5DD
United Kingdom
austin@minster.york.ac.uk

Abstract

This paper describes a novel associative processor that uses neural associative memories as its processing elements. The machine has been designed to tackle problems in AI and computer vision, with nodes that allow rapid search using inexact information over very large data sets. The associative processor is ideally suited as a pattern processing machine, which is where most of the application work has been centered. This is because it is capable of taking large subsections of images and performing matching and comparisons on these.

Each processing element of the associative processor is an advanced distributed associative memory (ADAM) that is capable of storing large numbers of pattern associations yet allows rapid access. As a neural network, the memory performs associative match, not by conventional CAM (content-addressable memory) approaches but by forming a mapping between the patterns to be associated. The benefits are rapid access, fault tolerance, and an ability to match on inexact data. These abilities arise due to the distributed storage used in the memory, which also allows for high capacity storage in the memory. The memory is designed to work on large data word sizes, that is, matching can take place on data items as small as 64 bits or as large as megabytes.

The paper describes the cellular neural network associative processor, C-NNAP, which supports a number of ADAM systems operating in parallel. The ADAM memory is particularly simple to implement in dedicated hardware, requiring a small amount of custom logic to allow operation at high speed. However, large amounts of memory are required for implementing any practical problems. The design of the processor card within C-NNAP is described, which consists of an FPGA logic-based device (SAT) to support the ADAM evaluation, a DSP processor for control, and local memory for the ADAM associations.

1   Introduction

In this paper we describe an associative processor based on a neural associative memory. The architecture of the processor is basically an array of *advanced distributed associative memories* (ADAM). These differ from conventional associative memories in that the associative recall is performed using a high-speed correlation matrix memory where data is forced into a smaller space, resulting in faster search times compared to conventional listing associative memories.

The machine is primarily aimed at solving problems in image recognition and analysis, although applications in general image processing problems have been considered. The machine is currently in use in our group where its limitations and extensions are under investigation.

Section 2 describes the motivation for the work. Section 3 describes the neural associative memory used in the machine and why it is preferable to more conventional associative devices. Section 4 describes the abilities of the neural associative memory compared with conventional memories. Section 5 describes the architecture of the C-NNAP machine and how it provides a view of the machine that is easy for a programmer to understand and use. Section 6 describes our current implementation and describes the hardware trade-offs that we have had to deal with. Section 7 outlines the software support and describes how the machine is currently programmed. Finally, section 8 shows how the machine is being used to solve image processing problems.

2   Motivation

This work has been motivated by the need to construct architectures that support processing of pattern data rather than numeric data for applications where the data is inexact. "Inexact" means similar to data seen previously but not exactly like it, that is, belonging to a previously known class or set. In image processing, for example, raw image data is expressed as a set of pixel values that map onto some domain that may represent an edge or some other feature. In document processing, the pixels may map onto a letter in the alphabet or a feature of a letter. In more commercial applications, one may want to see if a data set is in some sense "typical," that is, does this person's characteristics fit the type of person that would buy our product? Our particular motivation for constructing such a machine comes from our study of image processing problems.

All these problems require a classification process. The process requires a system to identify whether X belongs to class Y. Unfortunately, X will be unlikely to exist exactly in Y, and could exist in two or more classes. Any system that performs this operation must have a model of the classes and have a means by which an unknown example is seen as belonging to the classes.

This classification process is fundamental to many problems, and many inexact matching processes have been developed (from Bayes' theory to fuzzy sets). The present work has investigated the use of neural networks to perform the classification process. We have been keen to implement systems that operate at high speed both in the process of learning classifications and in the process of recognizing unknown examples. This is required if the machine is to be used on realistically sized examples. Unfortunately, many neural network methods suffer from long learning times for even small sets of data. The ADAM memory does not suffer from these problems: It can acquire new classes very rapidly and scales well as the problem size grows. The memory implements a classifier and an associative recall process, that is, the memory is capable of matching an unknown example to a class and then recalling a "typical" example, or stored label, for that class.

The use of this type of memory in image processing has been explored at many levels of the problem [1]. For example, in low-level image processing it may be necessary to identify line segments, textures, and so forth. At this level, individual ADAM systems are trained (that is, associations stored) on typical examples of lines and textures, then the image is convolved using the memory to identify the possible features. The memory is able to output a label at each point to indicate the feature found. This operation can be achieved by using an array of ADAM systems operating in parallel over the image. Later stages in the process may require memories to communicate their outputs to each other. Our work has investigated an algorithm for extracting lines from images, that is, labeling a set of colinear line segments as belonging to the same line.

This requires iteration between the memories and is described in more detail in section 8.2.

These image processing examples lead to the design of the cellular neural network associative processor (C-NNAP). The machine supports arrays of ADAMs working in parallel and lets memories communicate with each other in a cellular (local neighborhood) fashion.

3   The associative memory element

As described in section 2, the C-NNAP machine uses an associative neural network, ADAM, for its processing elements. This associative memory differs from conventional memories used in associative processors (for example, see [2] and other chapters in this book) in that it performs associative lookup through a mapping process rather than a listing process. Consider the problem of identifying if an item X is similar to any stored items and, if it is, to recall an associated item X′ (this is the class of the item). The simplest way to do this is to match the input item X to all the stored items (listing approach), and select the most similar pattern as the best match. The "class" this pattern belongs to is then reported. The similarity measure used between the input and all those stored can be the Hamming distance (when using binary patterns) or Euclidean distance (when using continuous patterns). The major problem with this approach is the time taken to perform the operation on large data sets. Very long processing times can result when millions of examples are to be matched, which can limit the usefulness of the approach. The speed problem can be overcome by dedicated implementations of associative memories, but unfortunately these types of memory are expensive.

To overcome this problem, the mapping memory does not store all the examples to be matched separately, but instead it stores a compact representation of each of the examples. It can be seen as forming a "function" that, given any input pattern X, calculates the possible class, X′, that X belongs to. The function is formed through "training." Many neural networks operate in this way, which allows very rapid recall of associations as the function is quite small and can be evaluated quickly. Unfortunately, nearly all techniques take a long time to find this compact function (train.) This is because the network must search for a compact function that optimally maps the patterns to be associated with each other. Our approach, used in the ADAM memory, does not need to search for an optimal solution but "builds" a mapping function through a set-based operation using a correlation matrix memory.

An ADAM memory is made up of a number of stages: an N-tuple preprocessor, a correlation matrix memory, an intermediate class, and a second stage correlation matrix. We describe its operation and the rationale for its design next.

Figure 1 shows the correlation stage of the memory; this is the section of the memory that effectively stores associations. The input pattern and output pattern to be associated are placed in the buffers A and B. Both patterns are binary. The memory can be viewed as a single-layer neural network but is best seen as a matrix, M, of binary digits, $A_{max} \times B_{max}$ in size, where A_{max}, B_{max} are the size of the arrays "A" and "B." During training, each weight records if a bit in the input pattern at logical 1 matched a bit in the output pattern at logical 1. If they do, the weight is set to logical one. (All weights are binary 0 to start with). This is the same as taking the outer product (or tensor product) of A and B to produce M. Each subsequent pair of patterns results in another matrix, which is ORed on top of the original. Equation (1) describes this operation

$$M = \bigcup_{alli} A_i \otimes B_i \qquad (1)$$

which is used to train the network, where $\cup$ represents a logical OR, and $\otimes$ represents a tensor product (that is, the outer product) of two binary vectors, and where A_i and B_i are two example patterns to be trained. To recall from the memory an unknown pattern "A," a matrix vector multiplication is applied to M. This results in a real-valued vector, C, as shown in Equation (2).

$$C = A^T M \qquad (2)$$

This operation is also illustrated in Figure 2. The next stage is to threshold the result, C, to recover the original binary pattern. ADAM uses a special K-point thresholding method [3] (sometimes termed L-max [4]). In order to use this thresholding approach, every C pattern used in associations must have K bits set to one. If this is done, then the recalled array, "C," can be thresholded by selecting the highest N values from the array, setting them to one, and setting all others to zero. Typically, this will result in the recovery of the original pattern associated with A_i, that is, B_i. It has been shown [3] that this representation of data allows reliable recall of data.

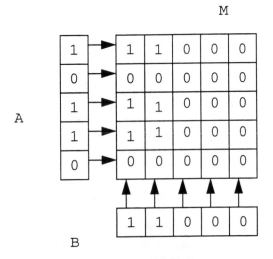

Figure 1. A correlation matrix trained on two patterns, A and B. The matrix, M, represents the outer product of A and B.

286

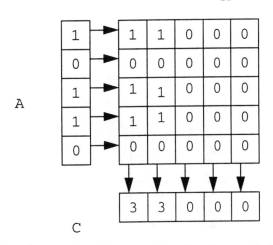

Figure 2. The recall of a previously associated pattern, A, using the matrix M, resulting in the class array C.

Although the simple correlation matrix described above can be used to store associations, it suffers from poor capacity, that is, the number of patterns it can store—before recall results in an error—is low. This is because (1) the memory suffers from excessive cross talk between associations stored, and (2) the size of the memory is bounded by the input and output array sizes. In the small example above, two 5-bit patterns are associated. The maximum number of patterns that can be stored in these memories is quite small [5]. To overcome these problems, the following steps are taken. First, an orthogonalizing preprocessor ensures that the input patterns are sufficiently separated (in pattern terms) to allow the storage and recall to be more reliable. Second, a two-stage correlation memory allows the size of the memory to be independent of the size of the patterns to be associated. These two stages are illustrated in Figure 3, which now shows the full ADAM system.

In this example of the memory, the input preprocessor consists of a set of binary decoders. These decoders each take a unique set of N bits from the input data (a tuple) and assign a unique state. The state can be determined in many ways. In this example, the tuple is put through a 1-in-N decoder (Figure 4 shows the state assignments to each pattern).

This is a fast and effective way to ensure all possible 2^N states of a tuple are given a unique state. Every bit in the input data is passed uniquely to a tuple. The result of this operation is an array of states, 2^N states for each tuple. This operation acts to make the possible set of patterns presented to the correlation matrix more sparse and thus more different from each other. This "orthogonalization" process reduces the possibility of pattern recall failure. The effect is most notice-

able if the tuple size, N, is equal to the size of the data array. This would result in a state being defined for every possible input pattern to be assigned by the decoder. The memory would then be a simple lookup device. Unfortunately, this approach is not feasible for pattern sizes involved in most tasks including image processing. Furthermore, the system would not generalize, that is, be able to recognize patterns that were not exactly like those taught into the associative memory. In practice, setting the tuple size to a value between 4 and 8 results in good orthogonalization between the input patterns while maintaining an ability to generalize. This technique is described in [6], which presents an analysis of the N-tuple size against generalization.

The next stage, shown in Figure 3, is to pass the state assignments to the correlation matrix. The array of tuple states forms an access list to the rows of the correlation matrix. The correlation matrix is taught and tested as described by Equations (1) and (2).

Figure 3 shows two correlation matrices with an intermediate class pattern. The aim of this arrangement is to allow control of the storage in the memories. If two data arrays were associated in one matrix, the size of the matrix (assuming no N-tuple preprocessing) would be $A_{max} \times B_{max}$, where A_{max} and B_{max} are the size of the arrays to be associated. Unfortunately, this results in a fixed size of memory determined solely by the size of the data arrays to be associated and not by the number of associations to be stored. As a result, the number of associations that can be stored is fixed. By using a two-stage memory, the number of associations becomes independent of the size of the input and output arrays. It now depends on the size of the intermediate class array, which can be large or small, as required by the problem.

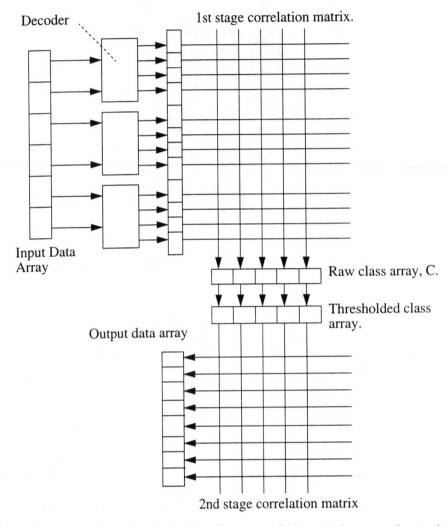

Figure 3. The ADAM memory showing the use of two correlation matrix memories and the N-tuple pre-processing.

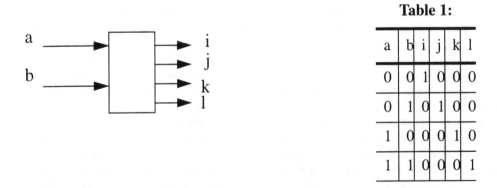

Table 1:

a	b	i	j	k	l
0	0	1	0	0	0
0	1	0	1	0	0
1	0	0	0	1	0
1	1	0	0	0	1

Figure 4. The N-tuple decoder state assignments for the decoders shown in Figure 3.

288

The operation of the two-stage memory is simple. During associative storage, the two patterns to be trained are presented and a unique class is selected. The class pattern is an N-point pattern, and the data is associated by training the correlation memories. Recall is also straightforward. The key pattern is presented into buffer A, then the N-tuple process prepares an expanded version of the data. This is then presented to the first correlation matrix, and the first memory is tested. The raw class, C, is recalled and K-point thresholded. This pattern is then presented to the second memory, and this part of the memory is tested to recall the data associated with the key. The thresholding used on the data recalled from the second stage is a simple Wilshaw threshold [5]. This involves setting any element set to K to 1 and the rest to 0, where K is the number of bits set in the class.

The number of patterns that can be stored in the associative memory is approximately given by Equation (3).

$$T \approx \frac{ln\left(1-\dfrac{1}{C_{max}^{\left(\frac{1}{V}\right)}}\right)}{ln\left(1-\dfrac{K \times V}{C_{max} \times I}\right)} \qquad (3)$$

K is the number of bits set in the class, C_{max} is the size of the class, I is the input array size to the correlation matrix, and V is the number of bits set to one in the input array. It includes the number of patterns that can be stored in the correlation matrix used in the first stage and the second stage of the ADAM memory. The full derivation can be found in [3].

The structure of the memory described here is the original ADAM described in [3]. There have been many enhancements to this structure since then. These include the use of nonbinary input data, the use of continuous weights, the use of an optimizing process for class selection, and the use of an optimizing preprocessor (for the last of these see [7]).

4 Recall reliability versus speed in the processor node

The most important aspect of the memory is how it allows faster associative recall than conventional listing memories (that is, classical content-addressable memories), while coping with inexact input data. The

memory trades off speed against recall reliability. For example, to store a fixed number of associations, the ADAM memory may be made small and fast but with a high probability of recall failure; conversely, it may be made large with a slower recall time but with a lower probability of recall failure. The approximate relationship between probability of recall failure and size is given by Equation (4),

$$P \approx 1 - \left(1 - \left(1 - \left(\frac{K \times V}{C_{max} \times I}\right)^T\right)^V\right)^{C_{max}} \qquad (4)$$

which gives the probability of successfully recalling a data item from a correlation matrix (from [3]). This relates to the first- or second-stage correlation matrix. The fact that the memory may fail can be of concern in applications; however, in many real-time applications, it is better to get any answer in a given time than no answer at all, as long as you can tell if the answer is correct or not. For example, consider a listing memory that takes a fixed time T to recall data, but the memory recalls data that is always correct. The mapping memory takes time Q to recall, where Q << T. An application requires a result less than time P to meet a hard real-time deadline. It may be the case that T > P but Q < P. The listing memory cannot be altered to achieve this deadline, but the mapping memory can, at the cost of a lower possibility of recall success (it is explained later how this probability of recall failure can be improved). Typical applications that require this behavior are in aircraft tactical systems, which must make a decision before an obvious real time deadline. This is also found in the nuclear industry, in chemical plants, or other applications where any result will be better than none at all.

The ADAM memory can detect a recall when using exact input data (noiseless) through the K point threshold mechanism. If the class cannot be thresholded so that exactly K elements are set to 1, the recall has failed (that is, if more than K bits have the same value). Most recall failures are of this type. However, it is possible that patterns taught to the memory cause a "ghost" pattern to be recalled. This is a result of unintended internal correlations in the memory where two or more patterns coincide to produce a third pattern that is incorrect. Both cases of recall failure can be completely detected and removed by validating the memory after training by comparing the data recalled against what was trained. Any recall failures or ghosts can be identified and the memory retrained to remove them. Without validation, there remains a small probability that failures cannot be detected.

A simple comparison will show the recall speed and accuracy of a correlation matrix against a listing memory. Consider performing recall on one pattern against M data items of I bits in size. A listing memory would require M amounts of I-bit matches, where a match would be a Hamming distance comparison. Assuming the Hamming distance calculation took H(I) time to compute, the operation would take in the order of M×H(I) operations to perform. A correlation matrix, as used in the first-stage memory of ADAM, would take the input pattern (I bits in size) and associate it with a class of Cmax bits in size (assuming no N-tuple preprocessing). If the operation of the correlation matrix is examined, the raw class recovery is equivalent to C_{max} number of I-bit Hamming measures. Each element of the raw class is the result of performing a Hamming distance measure between the input data and the column in the matrix.[1] Thus the computation time is in the order of C_{max}×H(I) operations. As long as C_{max} < M, the recall speed of the correlation matrix will be faster than the listing memory. Unfortunately, as shown above, the correlation matrices are inflexible and error prone on their own.

The ADAM memory uses two correlation matrix memories for its computation, as well as a constant time overhead to do the N-tuple preprocessing and class thresholding. However, to fully compare the two methods, the listing method requires some means of recalling the pattern associated with the input data. For this reason, we ignore the time to compute the second ADAM correlation matrix in this analysis.

The N-tuple preprocessing has the effect of increasing the array size of the input data prior to its application to the correlation matrix. The subsequent computation is not increased by this operation. This is because the number of bits set in the data pattern after N-tuple preprocessing are less than or equal to the number of bits set to one in the original input data (inspection of the N-tuple method will make this clear). The number of bits set to one in the data array applied to the correlation matrix is equal to the number, V, of N-tuple samples taken from the input data, as can be seen from the architecture in Figure 3 and the use of the decoders as laid out in Figure 4. For each active bit on the input to a correlation matrix, a row of the correlation matrix is added into the raw class. Thus, V rows of the correlation matrix are summed into the class. Hence, the computation is in the order of V × A(C_{max}), where A() is the time to add one bit in the correlation matrix into a raw class element. If we assume that the computation required for a bit comparison in a Hamming distance calculation is equal to the time to add, then A() = H().

These results suggest a ratio of computation of ADAM:Listing memory given by:

$$V \times H(C_{max}): M \times H(I),$$

Where V = Number of N-tuple samples = number of bits set to one in data presented to the first correlation matrix in ADAM;

C_{max} = The number of elements in the class in ADAM;

I = The size of the input data array in the listing approach;

M = The number of patterns to be stored in the listing memory.

Note that V << I always holds. In ADAM, for perfect recall the class size is made equal to the number of data items to be stored (M), using a K point size of 1, that is, C_{max} = M. Thus, the correlation matrix method is faster by a factor I/V. This speedup is entirely due to the use of the N-tuple preprocessing. In practice, I/V is between 4 and 8. Unfortunately, the gain is offset by the need to perform N-tuple preprocessing, which adds to the computation time. As this depends on implementation, under these conditions (where C_{max} = M) we can assume that the ADAM approach is as fast if not faster than the listing memory approach. It will be noted that large N-tuple sizes will result in a smaller value for V and thus a corresponding speedup. However, it can result in unacceptably high memory use. The memory used, U, by the first stage correlation memory in ADAM is given by

$$U = \frac{I}{N} \times 2^N x C_{max} \tag{5}$$

where C_{max} is the size of the class array, I is the input data array size, and N is the tuple size.

The interesting case is when the size of the class is made smaller than M. In this case the class has more than one bit set. If K bits are set, then the number of unique class patterns are $\left(\frac{K}{R}\right)$, which is the maximum number of patterns that can be stored (note that typically the memory would be saturated long before this maximum is reached). When the class array size C_{max} is less than the number of stored examples, M, the probability of recall becomes less than 1 (see Equation (4)).

---

[1] Note that, in the Hamming distance measure, all the elements that are different between two binary patterns are counted, whereas in the correlation matrix memory only the elements that are at logic 1 in the input data are compared and counted

The main application of the memory has been in image processing where fast lookup is required. In this application the data presented to the memory is different from the training data. The memory is able to identify the closest stored association to the input data and recall the associated pattern.

5 The processor architecture

Our interest in the ADAM system, of course, has been for image processing. For our problem, we require an array of associative memories, each inspecting a small part of the image [1]. To let us build a machine that would be easily programmable, we have defined a simple high-level architecture that is generic enough to allow us to specify a wide range of specific architectures for particular problems. From this, we have defined the programming interface and constructed a machine to let a user easily build and execute a given architecture.

The simple model we use has two major components: ADAM units and input/ output memories. The ADAM units can be connected to the input/output memory by a mapping function that defines where each data bit of the input to ADAM is connected in the input/output memory (io-memory). The io-memory is logically a one-dimensional array of 8-bit bytes. Any number of ADAM units can be connected to an io-memory, and a system can have as many io-memories as required (see Figure 5). The ADAM units consist of a number of stages of processing, which are controlled by these functions:

1. Map in: force the data in the io-memory onto the input of an ADAM by using the mapping function defined for the memory.

2. Group the data in the ADAM input buffer into tuples.

3. For each tuple, find the state assigned to it (using a decoder as shown in Figure 4).

4. Recall, using the tuple state assignments, from the first-stage correlation matrix to obtain the raw class.

5. Threshold the raw class to produce the class pattern.

6. Recall using the class array. Produce the raw recalled data item.

7. Threshold the recalled data pattern.

8. Map the thresholded data pattern back onto the io-memory using a stored mapping function.

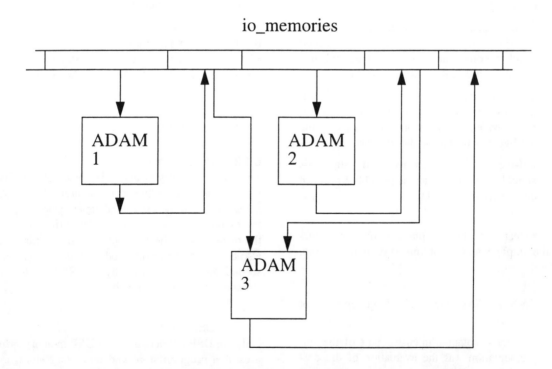

Figure 5. A C-NNAP's architecture using io_memories and ADAMS.

The software that allows the manipulation of the C-NNAP machine also allows specification of the N-tuple mapping function, that is, any individual bit of a binary N tuple can be mapped anywhere in a particular io_memory space.

The handling of ADAM units and io_memories is by a single "handle," which is a name given to these units by a programmer. The construction of a system takes place by (1) defining and creating the required number of ADAM memories and io_memories, (2) connecting the ADAMs to the io_memories, and (3) specifying the order in which the memories are evaluated and outputs and inputs mapped onto the io_memories. It is left open to the programmer how data arrives into the io_memory and is read from it, as this depends widely on the application of the system.

6   The current implementation

From the simple architecture definition just given, the physical implementation of the machine was considered. Our major constraints in achieving the implementation were these:

- The system should be made available on a network via a workstation.

- The system should be extensible to allow a large number of ADAM systems to be physically implemented.

- System speed was not as important as how the system could be physically implemented to allow constraints to be examined and projected speedup calculations to be done.

- Software support, allowing execution without the physical system being available, should be provided to let work continue on the hardware as well as on the software.

- Off-the-shelf components and standards should be used as much as possible to reduce construction cost and time.

It was clear from the start that a number of factors made the implementation of this system interesting, including;

- Each ADAM may use a large amount of memory.

- The most compute-intensive part of the implementation was the evaluation of the correlation memories.

Expertise in our group existed in VME bus system design and support, digital signal processors, and PCB technology. We did not have support for VLSI facilities but did for FPGAs.

From these considerations the system was designed and is now into its third revision.

The block diagram for C-NNAP is that of Figure 6. The host workstation is connected to the Supervisor node (S node) via an Ethernet link. The S node controls the C-NNAP nodes (C nodes) by providing them with address information and control programs. The I/O memory is used by the data acquisition system as a data store from which the C-NNAP cards read in the input data.

6.1   The C node

This contains a dedicated peripheral process, the Sum And Threshold (SAT) processor [8], which has been designed to implement the compute-intensive part of the ADAM implementation.

Each C node consists of a SAT processor daughterboard (see Figure 7). The SAT processor uses an Actel A1280XL FPGA, an Actel A1425A FPGA, and a DSP daughterboard that currently hosts an AT&T DSP32C. Along with this are three memory systems and connection to the VME via a set of VIC and VAC devices that allow bus master capability.

The following sections describe the operation of the various subcomponents of the C node card.

6.1.1   Weights memory
The weights memory uses 25ns static RAM that is accessible by either the DSP or the SAT processor. The memory is used by the DSP to store the weights after their calculation and by the SAT processor during the recall operation.

6.1.2   Buffer memory
The buffer memory is also 25ns static RAM, divided into two independently accessible areas. The first area is used to store the nontupled image prior to processing by the DSP and the tupled data prior to switching the memory into the SAT address area. This area can also be accessed by other nodes on the VME bus. The second area is also used by the SAT as temporary storage and for storing results.

6.1.3   DSP memory
Only the DSP has access to the DSP memory, which it uses as a program store and temporary storage. This memory is also 25ns static RAM.

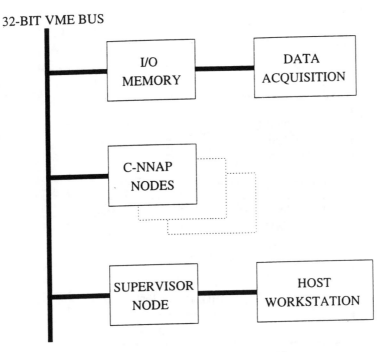

Figure 6. The high-level architecture of the machine.

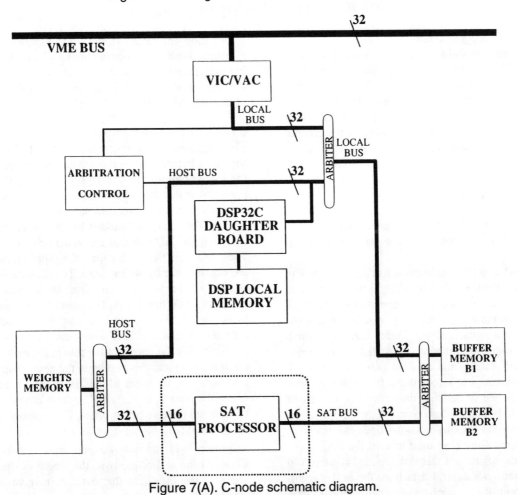

Figure 7(A). C-node schematic diagram.

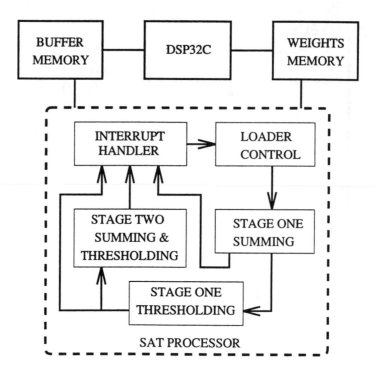

Figure 7(B). Sum and threshold block diagram.

6.1.4   DSP daughterboard

The DSP daughterboard uses a microcontroller to load in the DSP's program from EPROM into the DSP memory. The DSP is an AT &T DSP32C clocked at 50 MHz. The DSP32C is economical in cost and of relatively low performance, but the processing power required of the DSP is not as extensive as the computationally intensive work done by the SAT processor.

6.2   The SAT processor

This section describes the SAT processor that performs all of the operations within the dotted box of Figure 7b.

The SAT is a peripheral processor that operates in parallel with the DSP, thus releasing it to perform preprocessing and data movement operations. The SAT has access to the weights memory, which contains the correlation matrices, and the buffer memory, which holds the control information, the states of the decoders, summed values, and recalled patterns. The SAT has 16 16-bit registers (counters) for summing. The counters operate in parallel, thus allowing 16 bits of the matrix to be summed in one clock cycle.

The interrupt handler acknowledges the interrupt from the controlling DSP used to start the SAT processor. On completion of this task, control is passed to a loader that reads control data from the buffer memory. The control data consists of location of matrices,

information for result storage, the number of rows, threshold levels, and operations required. Once loading is completed, control is passed to the main state machines that perform the summing and thresholding of the ADAM matrices.

6.2.1   Stage-one summing

The stage-one binary matrix is stored as 16-bit rows as shown in Figure 8 so that the data can be accessed in the format required by the 16 summing counters. Figure 8 shows that the SAT needs to know which lines of the stage-one matrix require summing. These are the lines of the matrix addressed by the decoders in the first stage of ADAM that are generated by the DSP. The addressed lines are called the tuple pointers and are stored in the buffer memory. To calculate the exact address of the weights, an offset is provided in the control data. When the tuple pointer values are added to the offset, the correct row and line of weights is accessed. When the SAT sums the next row of the matrix it adds the length of the row in the matrix to the original offset and this results in the new offset for the next row. An example of this is shown in Figure 8 where the lines 1, 3, 6, 8, and so forth are the lines to be summed relative to the offset, for example, the first set of weights to be summed are at location 0×2001 (the offset + 1), the next weights are at 0×2003, and so on. At the end of the row, the length of the row is added to the offset, in this case M, to give the new start location.

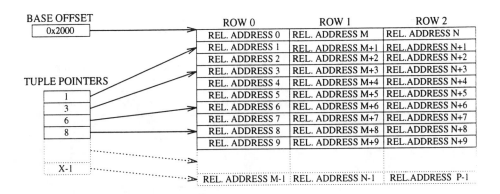

	ROW 0	ROW 1	ROW 2
BASE OFFSET 0x2000	REL. ADDRESS 0	REL. ADDRESS M	REL. ADDRESS N
	REL. ADDRESS 1	REL. ADDRESS M+1	REL.ADDRESS N+1
	REL. ADDRESS 2	REL. ADDRESS M+2	REL.ADDRESS N+2
	REL. ADDRESS 3	REL. ADDRESS M+3	REL.ADDRESS N+3
	REL. ADDRESS 4	REL. ADDRESS M+4	REL.ADDRESS N+4
	REL. ADDRESS 5	REL. ADDRESS M+5	REL.ADDRESS N+5
	REL. ADDRESS 6	REL. ADDRESS M+6	REL.ADDRESS N+6
	REL. ADDRESS 7	REL. ADDRESS M+7	REL.ADDRESS N+7
	REL. ADDRESS 8	REL. ADDRESS M+8	REL.ADDRESS N+8
	REL. ADDRESS 9	REL. ADDRESS M+9	REL.ADDRESS N+9
	REL. ADDRESS M-1	REL. ADDRESS N-1	REL.ADDRESS P-1

TUPLE POINTERS

| 1 |
| 3 |
| 6 |
| 8 |
| X-1 |

Figure 8. Weights address calculation in SAT.

Figure 9 shows the hardware used to perform weights addressing and its relationship with the two memories. The weights address calculation has the longest propagation delay of the SAT operations and has a propagation delay of 125ns. In the evaluation section (section 6.3) this is referred to as a LONG cycle.

Figure 10 shows the block diagram for the summing hardware. The controller uses two counters called the Run Length and the Class Size counters. These act as internal variables to count the size of data the SAT has operated on. When the required weights in the weights memory have been accessed, the summing counters are clocked. This has the effect of incrementing those counters whose input has an active weight. When all the active lines in a row have been summed, the 16 summed values are stored in the buffer memory.

6.2.2 Stage-one thresholding

When all the summed values have been written to the buffer memory, L-max thresholding (section 3) is applied to them. The hardware used for this is shown in Figure 11.

Thresholding begins by inspecting all the summed values to find the maximum value stored, and this becomes the current threshold value. All of the summed values are then checked, and where a summed value equals the current threshold value, this indicates that the corresponding class bit should be stored for use by the stage-two summing controller. If insufficient class bits were found after the first thresholding iteration, then the operation is repeated by finding the next highest summed value and using this as the new threshold value. This is repeated until all K class bits have been recovered.

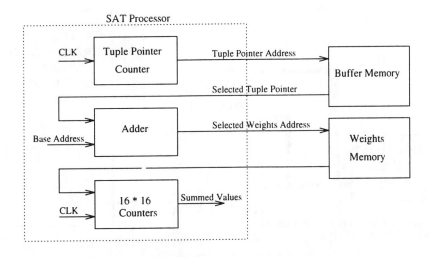

Figure 9. The weights address selection path.

295

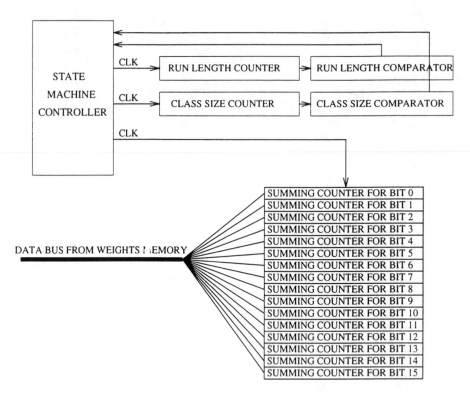

Figure 10. The summing block diagram.

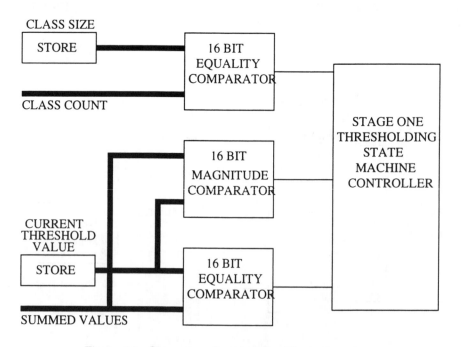

Figure 11. Stage-one thresholding block diagram.

6.2.3 Stage-two summing and thresholding

The basic hardware for stage two is the same as that used for the stage-one summing. The primary difference between the two operations is that the summed values are not written to the buffer memory unless the user specifically requests it.

The thresholding required is an equality comparison, that is, does the summed value equal the number of class bits set?

6.3 SAT performance evaluation

The timing evaluation has been done using the state machine behavior to produce Equations (6), (7), and (8). These equations can be used to determine the execution time for any input data size. The slowest operation in the SAT processor is the weights address calculation and is called a LONG (l) clock cycle. All the other clock cycles are called a NORMAL cycle (N). l and N are used in the following equations:

Stage-one summing equation: S1IS is the stage-one input image size, SITS is the stage 1 tuple size and CS is the class size.

$$S1 = \frac{CS}{16}\left(\frac{S1IS}{S1TS} \times (N+1)\right) \qquad (6)$$

Stage-one thresholding equation: CS is the class size and SVEQTV is the number of times that a summed value is equal to the stored threshold value in an iteration. I is the number of iterations required to find all l bits of the class pattern.

$$S1T = I\left(4 \times CS \times N + 2 \times SVEQTV \times N\right) \qquad (7)$$

Stage-two sum and threshold equation: S2IS is the stage-two input image size and S2TS is the stage-two tuple size. BS is the number of bits set in the class pattern (usually BS = l).

$$S2 = \left(\left(S2IS / (S2TS) \times^{S2TS}\right)/16\right) \times$$
$$\left(34 \times N + BS \times (N+1)\right) \qquad (8)$$

Overall SAT performance equation: Equations (6), (7), and (8) give the total execution time for all the SAT operations; this is Equation (9).

$$SAT execution time = S1 + S1T + S2 \qquad (9)$$

6.3.1 SAT analysis

Equation (9) was used to produce the graph in Figure 12. A tuple size of four was used (a typical size used in most applications), and the number of iterations for the stage one thresholding was limited to one iteration. It was originally estimated that a LONG cycle would be 125ns and a NORMAL clock cycle, 50ns. These timings have been shown to be true in practice. The graph shows that the SAT processor is 20 times faster than the DSP, which has a dedicated FPGA coprocessor, and 450 times faster than the DSP without the assistance of its dedicated coprocessor. The graph also shows that the SAT processor can process an ADAM network for an input image of 220 × 220 black-and-white pixels with a class size of 32 bits at 25-Hz frame rates.

7 Software and tool support

Good software support is essential for the practical use of any machine. The programming model given in section 5 lets users quickly grasp the machine's capabilities. For efficient and practical use, it has been our aim from the outset to provide a software emulation of the machine. In fact, the software was developed first, while the first version of the hardware was being developed. The software consists of a library of routines written in C, to be compatible with the host Unix operating system and because C supports bit manipulation. The software has been written in three layers: low-, medium-, and high-level functions. These layers let the programmer interact with the machine at the most suitable level of abstraction for a task. The lowest level contains the functions to perform the correlation matrix multiplication, N-tupling, and so on. The second level provides functions that group these into practical operations, such as training and testing a memory, saving weights to a disk and retrieving it, and clearing memory. These exist as C-level functions. The highest level provides a Unix-level interface to the software which allows the machine to be used on the command line. The hardware replaces the level-one functions. The pipeline support will eventually replace the software at the second level but maintain the C function interface.

Any program written using the machine emulation can be recompiled to use the C- NNAPs machine. If a user accesses the low-level functions, each function call will execute on the hardware. The medium-level functions are built out of these low-level functions. To allow efficient operation when a medium level function is called, all the low-level functions it executes are run on the C-NNAP machine (separate calls to the machine are not made from the host).

The software provides basic functions for displaying image data on an X windows system and basic functions for displaying data structures in the machine.

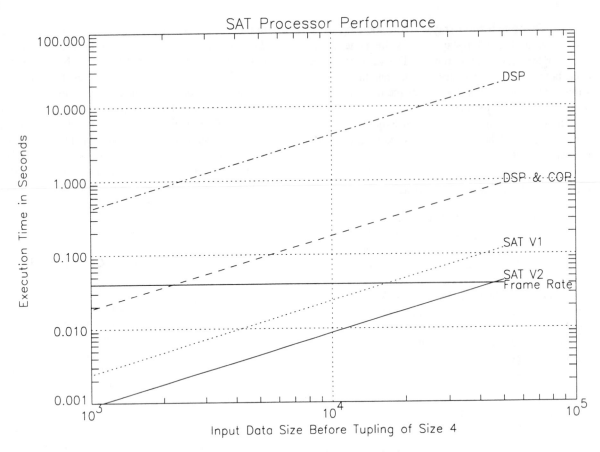

Figure 12. SAT execution timing analysis.

8 Example application in image processing

The C-NNAP system is designed to be flexible, capable of implementing both simple and complex image processing tasks. To illustrate this, we explain how the architecture can implement a simple image segmentation operation. Although the system is useful for these types of operations, our current research is aimed at the system's use in complex image analysis. In particular, it is aimed at recognizing a potentially large number of objects in large images. We also explain how we intend to tackle this problem.

8.1 Simple image analysis tasks on C-NNAP

The types of operations that can be run on C-NNAP are convolutions that segment an image based on texture or that find features. Our work [1] [10] has demonstrated the effectiveness of the ADAM memory for both operations. For segmentation, the ADAM is

The software library (Version 3.1) is fully described in [9].

trained to recognize small image regions as belonging to the required texture classes. For example, the image shown in Figure 13 contains urban and rural areas that can be separated using the processor. To do this, the ADAM was trained and tested to produce the image shown in Figure 14. The ADAM memory was constructed with an input image window of 16×16 pixels (to process grey-scale images we used the grey-scale N-tuple method described in [11]). Two ADAM class patterns were used; one to represent urban areas and one to represent rural areas. The class patterns were very simple, (01) was used for urban and (10) used for rural. Samples for both urban and rural areas were taken from the image and to train the network [11]. These two classes were trained into the network. To segment the image into rural and urban areas, the trained ADAM memory was, in effect, scanned over the image at 16,16 pixel intervals. At each point the memory was tested and the class pattern recovered (the second stage of ADAM was not used in this problem). If the class pattern represented an urban area, then a white dot was placed in a result array at the same position at which the ADAM was tested in the image array. A black dot was used if the class was for a rural area.

Figure 13. The raw image processed with an ADAM network.

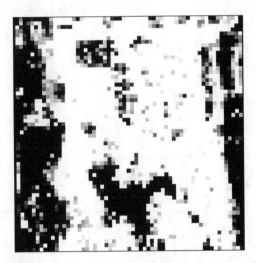

Figure 14. The urban areas found using ADAM.

The process of feature recognition can be achieved in the same way. In the result shown in Figure 15, the road features have been recognized. The ADAM memory was trained to recognize four orientations of road and recall a small image segment representing the road (See [1] for details). The convolution of the image was the same as in the previous example, but in this case the second stage of the ADAM memory was used to recall the image feature and place it in the result image.

8.2 Complex object recognition using C-NNAP

The problem of mapping complex image analysis tasks onto C-NNAP is currently being researched. The ar-

chitecture has been designed to implement a number of object recognition methods. For example [12] describes how an array of ADAM memories can be used to implement the generalized Hough transform and explains its use in document analysis. Although not yet ported to the C-NNAP system, the approach is ideally suited to such an implementation.

Our research is motivated by the need to produce an object recognition system that is capable of recognizing a potentially large number of objects, anywhere in an image. Although the research is ongoing, it is useful to show how the C-NNAP architecture can be used to build complex image analysis systems. We next explain the motivation for our research and present a simple architecture based on C-NNAP.

Figure 15. Road features found using ADAM.

Our approach is based on a hierarchy of feature recognizers, although we do not physically build a hierarchy. The aim is to allow the lowest level of the hierarchy to recognize basic image features (lines and edges, for example) and later processing layers to recognize more complex features, until the highest layer recognizes the whole object. The process of recognizing an image primitive from a set of features is a *grouping process*.

To illustrate, consider Figure 16, which shows an image of a square, made up of four lines, each with four noisy edge segments.

Suppose the image were covered with an 8 × 8 grid of feature recognizers, where each can recognize eight edge orientations (see Figure 17).

The problem for each 3 × 3 sampling array is to find what larger feature the image features within the grid belong to. In this example we have a nine-dimensional input, with a maximum of three edge features present that belong to the shape. To recognize the shapes in this space, it is necessary to train the neural network to find all the possible combinations of the three low-level features that represent known larger features, typically lines and corners.

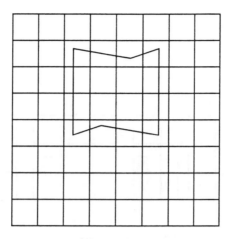

Figure 16. The simple image classification problem showing a square in a 8 × 8 grid.

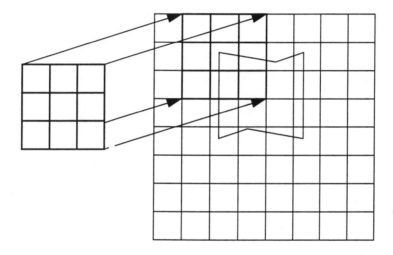

Figure 17. The local feature grouping process. This shows one 3 × 3 feature grouping window that contains three features. The same size window is used to compute features over the whole image.

The problem at this stage is how to deal with the many possible interpretations of the group features in the 3 × 3 array. It is important to maintain the minimum possible set of interpretations of the features in the 3 × 3 array. If each unique group of features is given a different label, then during recognition there is likely to be a large number of feature groups suggested at each image location. This is because many featurecombinations will be similar to the input, especially when noise is present. For example, if one of the features is assumed to be in error within the 3 × 3 array (due to the noise process in the image), this will lead to a large number of possible groupings and thus a large number of potential feature labels. Moving to the next level in the hierarchy, this leads to more feature combinations, leading to an expo-

nential generation of labels higher in the hierarchy.

To overcome this problem our approach is to minimize the number of groupings that can be recognized. This is achieved by careful labeling of *clusters* of feature groups, instead of labeling each individual feature combination.

Figure 18 illustrates this. Typical feature combinations that could have generated the input image are shown, given a probability of a 1-feature-in-9 error rate. By clustering these possible features and assigning the grouping a single label, the recognizer will generate only a small number of interpretations of the input image. If the clustering process is also used at later levels in the hierarchy, the exponential growth in feature groups can be contained.

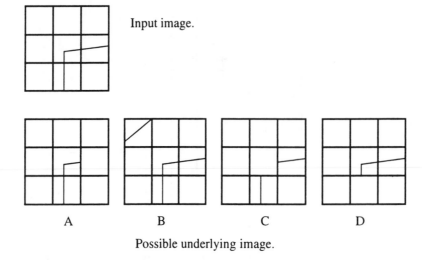

Input image.

A   B   C   D

Possible underlying image.

Figure 18. An illustration of some of the features groups that could have generated the input image, given that one feature recognizer, on average, is incorrect.

With this approach, it may be possible to build hierarchical descriptions of the image, maintaining a good computational load at each stage in the feature grouping and labeling process. Any objects of interest will survive up through the hierarchy. Noise will be grouped early on and then fail to be grouped at later stages because the label combinations will not be recognized.

Although the approach is elegant, the depth of the hierarchy depends on image size. This makes construction in parallel hardware expensive. To overcome this problem, a "flat" architecture is adopted in the C-NNAP architecture, which allows any depth of processing to be achieved as well as allowing spatially distant features to be grouped early on in the recognition process.

8.3   Implementing hierarchical grouping on C-NNAP

The approach we take is to use a 2D array of recognizers that (1) spreads information laterally in an array so that feature labels can meet together and be grouped, and (2) feeds the output of the array back to the input so that a "virtual" hierarchy can be built. This lets us reuse recognizers at different levels.

We first expect the image to be preprocessed using an ADAM array so that the image is broken into its individual features as described in section 8.1. This converts the image to a set of image feature labels.

Our experimental architecture is based on an array of communicating ADAMs that act as the feature recognizers that identify groups of features. The main element of the architecture is shown in Figure 19.

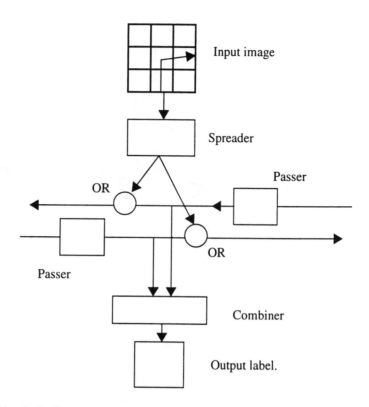

Figure 19. A single processing unit for implementing feature grouping.

Image feature information is taken by a spreader unit (an ADAM), which identifies the feature on its input and spreads labels in all directions away from itself. The aim here is to provide different labels for each direction, so that any ADAM receiving a label will know which direction it has come from and what the feature is.

This information is picked up by an array of passer units, which propagate the labels laterally in the array. As they do so, they translate the labels, allowing the system to note how far a label has been passed. This is so that receiving (combiner) units know how far away a particular feature is, thus preserving the topological information about features in the image.

Another set of ADAMs, the combiner units, monitor labels being sent over the array and output a new label whenever a group of labels that they recognize appear on the inputs. Thus, these units are capable of recognizing the location and type of features at any point in the image.

At every feature position in a 2D array, there is a combiner, a spreader, and a set of passer units. In practice, there is only one implementation of each of these units, as the information in every spreader, combiner, and passer is exactly the same. This allows position-independent recognition.

To illustrate how the architecture works, consider a simple 1D problem consisting of a line of features representing an edge, E, with a corner, C, at each end given in Figure 20. This shows the state of the system after four iterations.

303

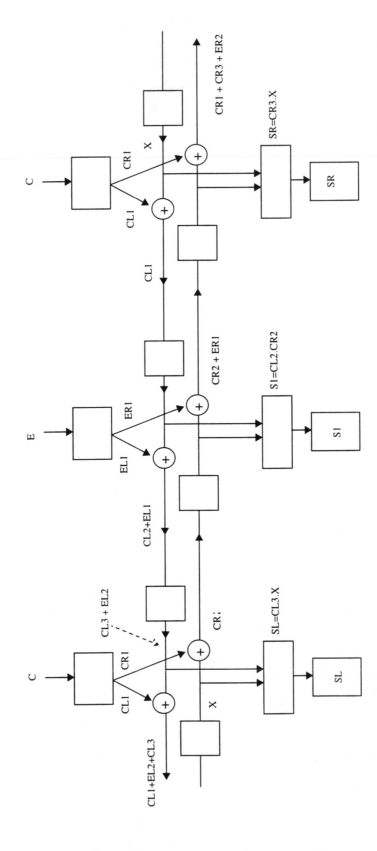

Figure 20. This illustrates the action of the 1D array when seeing three features of the top of a square. C = corner, E = edge, thus the input is C, E, C. This is passed into the spreader units that spread these labels left and right to produce the labels: edge right 1, ER1, to indicate one step right; edge right 2, ER2, to indicate two steps; CR for corner right; and X indicates a blank area off the edge of the diagram. The "+" indicates multiple labels are present. The combiner units observe these labels and, as shown, recognize when the group of labels are present that represent the top of the square (S1 is the top of the middle line of the square; SR is the top right-hand corner, SL the top left-hand corner). The rules known by the combiner to recognize these are shown next to each combiner.

304

Input E has been converted to a set of labels, EL (edge left) and ER (edge right), and C to CR and CL by the spreader units. These are then picked up by the passer units, which pass the labels on, and as they do they translate the symbols to indicate the distance the feature has been passed.

When the two labels coming from both directions meet, the combiner units recognize the group and output a label indicating which one it is. In this case, the groups are for the center top of the square and the left and right top corners. The center of the line is found first, and, as the labels pass to either end, the whole line is identified.

All the features have been recognized at this level of the virtual hierarchy once the array has stopped producing new labels on the output of the combiner units.

Next, the combiner outputs are passed back into the input to the spreaders, and the next level of grouping takes place by the same process. A copy of the spreader output is saved to indicate the feature labels at that level of grouping.

This process continues until all the image is labeled with the object level labels.

It will be evident from the architecture that the combiner units will receive multiple overlapped patterns to recognize. Furthermore, the combiner units will be trying to recognize combinations of labels that appear on the outputs of the passer units. The ability of the ADAM network to deal with these overlapped inputs as if they were individually presented for recognition is a particularly useful feature for the problem given here.

To limit the amount of information being passed by the spreaders between the units in the array, they are trained so that the labels can be propagated only a limited distance.

Because the capacity of the ADAMs is very high, a large number of feature group combinations can be recognized. Without the ADAM's ability to recognize patterns and look up an associated label, the process shown here could not be achieved.

Obviously, the power of the system depends on the rules that are trained into the ADAM memories and on the ability of the memories to recognize patterns as being similar to patterns previously trained. These aspects of the architecture are currently under investigation.

It will be apparent that the process shown here is not unlike a cellular automata. However, in the C-NNAP approach, the system uses an associative memory at each grid position and not a simple logic function. It is from this similarity that the system gains its name.

Conclusion

We have described the first steps in the design of a machine that uses associative mapping memories as computing elements and its use in computer vision. Although a great deal of research remains to be done, we are satisfied that the machine we built is a valuable tool in our research on the application of the ADAM memory. This work represents the first steps in producing an associative processor that uses a fast, efficient, and flexible associative memory.

Acknowledgments

Portions of this work were carried out as a part of a joint Science and Engineering Research Council/Department of Trade and Industry project "Vision by Associative Reasoning," Grant number GR/F 36330 (IED 1936). The hardware design and implementation was partly supported through funds provided by the Dept. of Computer Science, University of York, UK.

References

[1] J. Austin et al., "ADAM Neural Networks for Parallel Vision" *Proc. JFIT Technical Conf.*, 1993, pp. 173–180.

[2] J.L. Potter, *Associative Computing*, Plenum Press, New York, N.Y., 1992.

[3] J. Austin and T.J. Stonham, "An Associative Memory for use in Image Recognition and Occlusion Analysis," *Image and Vision Computing*, Vol. 5, No. 4, Nov. 1987, pp. 251–261.

[4] D. Casasent and B. Telfer, "High Capacity Pattern Recognition Associative Processors," *Neural Networks*, Vol. 4, No. 5, 1992, pp. 687–698.

[5] D.J. Wilshaw, O.P. Buneman, and H.C. Longuet-Higgins, "Non-Holographic Associative Memory," *Nature*, Vol. 9, June 7, 1969, p. 222.

[6] I. Aleksander, *Advanced Digital Information Systems*, Prentice-Hall, Englewood Cliffs, N.J., 1985.

[7] G. Bolt, J. Austin, and G. Morgan, "Uniform tuple storage in ADAM," *Pattern Recognition Letters*, Vol. 13, North-Holland, Amsterdam, 1992, pp. 339-344.

[8] J.V. Kennedy et al., "C-NNAP: A Parallel P–ocessing Architecture for Binary Neural Networks," *Proc. Int'l Conf. Neural Networks '95*, 1995.

[9] J. Austin et al., "The ADAM software manual Version 3.1," Computer Architecture Group Internal Report, Univ. of York, UK, Oct. 1993.

[10] J. Austin and S. Buckle, "Segmentation and Matching in Infra-Red Airborne Images Using a Binary Neural Network," *Neural Networks*, J. Taylor and A. Waller, eds., 1995, pp. 95–117.

[11] J. Austin, "Grey Scale N-tuple Processing," *Proc. Pattern Recognition: 4th Int'l Conf.*, Lecture Notes in Computer Sci., Vol. 301, Springer-Verlag, Berlin, 1988, pp. 110–120.

[12] J. Austin and S.E.M. O'Keefe, "Application of an Associative Memory to the Analysis of Document Fax Images," *Proc. The British Machine Vision Conf.*, 1994, pp. 315–325.

Neural Associative Memories

Günther Palm, Friedhelm Schwenker, Friedrich T. Sommer, and Alfred Strey

Department of Neural Information Processing
University of Ulm
D-89069 Ulm, Germany
{palm, schwenker, sommer, strey}@neuro.informatik.uni-ulm.de

Abstract

Despite processing elements that are thousands of times faster than neurons in the human brain, modern computers still cannot match many of the brain's processing capabilities, even those we consider trivial (such as recognizing faces or voices, or following a conversation). A common principle for those capabilities involves correlations between patterns to identify pattern similarities. Regarding the brain as an information processing mechanism with associative processing capabilities while viewing, conversely, associative memories as artificial neural networks revealed to us a number of interesting results. These ranged from theoretical considerations to insights in the functioning of neurons, as well as parallel hardware implementations of neural associative memories.

This paper discusses three main aspects of neural associative memories:

- *theoretical investigations, for example, on the information storage capacity, local learning rules, effective retrieval strategies, and encoding schemes;*

- *implementation aspects, in particular for parallel hardware; and*

- *applications*

One important outcome of our analysis is that the combination of binary synaptic weights, sparsely encoded memory patterns, and local learning rules—in particular Hebbian learning—leads to favorable representation and access schemes.

Based on these considerations, several parallel hardware architectures have been developed in the past decade; the current one is the PAN IV (Parallel Associative Network), which uses the special-purpose Bacchus chips and standard memory for realizing 4,096 neurons, and which has 128 Mbytes of storage capacity.

1 Introduction

From a theoretical point of view, an artificial neural network realizes a mapping F between an input space X and an output space Y. Neural networks provide a mapping F that is approximative in some sense (see below) and that can be specified by learning from (a finite set of) examples. Three different kinds of mappings can be distinguished, corresponding to different applications:

1. Both the input and output space are continuous spaces (function approximation or interpolation)

2. F is a mapping from a continuous set into a finite set (classification, recognition)

3. Both the input and output space are discrete (classification, memory)

Applications like control, navigation, robotics, or prediction of time series typically require mappings between continuous inputs and outputs (1). Neural networks for this kind of application have to be *approximative* or interpolative, which means $F(x^\mu + \varepsilon) = y^\mu + \delta$ for small ε and δ, if (x^μ, y^μ) is an input-output relation from the *training set*, for which $F(x^\mu,) = y^\mu$ is known.

Neural networks for classification or pattern recognition realize a mapping F into a set of finite elements (class labels). If the input space is continuous (2), this space is divided by F into a finite number of labeled regions (pattern recognition). The mapping F is required to be approximative in the following sense: A new input pattern $x^\mu + \varepsilon$ close to an input x^μ from the learning set should be classified to $y^\mu = F(x^\mu) = F(x^\mu + \varepsilon)$, which is the desired output corresponding to the input x^μ.

Neural networks establishing a mapping between discrete input and output spaces (3) are what we are concerned with here. Such discrete mappings describe, for example, the function of computer memory where a content string can be accessed by an address string and they have been extensively studied in computer science [Kohonen 1979, Kohonen 1983, Kanerva 1988]. A mapping $x \rightarrow y$ is called *heteroassociation* or pattern mapping if the content y is addressed by a key or address x where address and content are different strings. The special case of equal content and address is called *autoassociation*. Such mappings realize fault-tolerant self-addressing or pattern completion if the approximative property of the mapping F is guaranteed—now in the sense that $\tilde{x} \rightarrow x$ for all $\tilde{x}$ that are close to x with respect to a defined metric in X.

In neural network applications, the execution of the mapping F is viewed as retrieval or performance while establishing F on the basis of examples is referred to as training or learning. We will concentrate on the storage and retrieval of binary learning patterns in a *neural associative memory* (NAM) consisting of threshold neurons. A NAM is a single-layer neural network (see Figure 1) that maps a set of input patterns $X = \{x^1, \ldots, x^M\}$ into a set of output patterns $Y = \{y^1, \ldots, y^M\}$, in such a way that each input pattern x^μ is associated with one output pattern y^μ. The typical representation of a NAM is a matrix. The rows, or horizontal wires, correspond to axons, the columns (vertical wires) to dendrites, and the cross points to modifiable synapses. The output is computed by summing up the weights of the synapses in a column and comparing the sum against a threshold, which corresponds to the computation of the activation function in the soma of a neuron. The idea of Steinbuch's Lern-

matrix network was to implement a mapping that associates binary input patterns with binary output patterns by a Hebbian learning process that produces binary synaptic weights [Steinbuch 1961]. The performance of this associative memory network has been studied by D. Willshaw [Willshaw 1969] and G. Palm [Palm 1980] in terms of the number of storable patterns, error probability of retrieved output patterns, and memory capacity.

One possible categorization of NAMs is into feedforward and feedback networks. In a feedforward network, as shown in Figure 1, an input vector x is presented to a single layer of n neurons. In a single processing step, an output vector y is evaluated.

In a feedback associative memory, the output signals of the neurons are fed back to the input. When the current output pattern is again presented as a new input, the network computes a new activity pattern at the output. The idea of feedback associative memory is that the sequence of output patterns generated by iterating one-step retrieval converges to a stable state, which represents the final output of the memory. It was W.A. Little [Little 1974] who introduced the analogy between Ising spin systems in physics and neural network models. An Ising spin system consists of a set of feedback-coupled basic elements, each able to take the two states "up" or "down," corresponding to states "active" and "silent" of a binary neuron. Methods developed in statistical physics for such systems could be adapted to analyze the behavior of the feedback retrieval process in large NAMs [Hopfield 1982, Amit 1987].

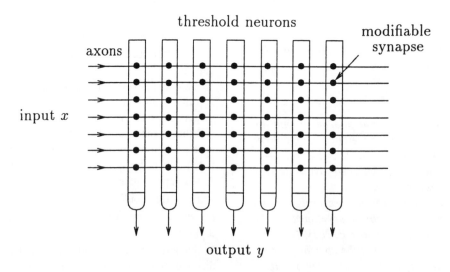

Figure 1. The architecture of a NAM consisting of threshold neurons with modifiable synapses.

We assign the two neural states the real numbers "a" and "1" with $a \in [-1, 0]$. The total number of "1" elements in a pattern will be called the pattern activity. We distinguish *distributed patterns* where the activity in a pattern is larger than one from *singular* or *local patterns* where exactly one component is set to "1" and the others are set to "a." We call the pairs of associations (x^μ, y^μ) to be stored in a NAM the set of *learning* or *memory patterns*:

$$S = \left\{ (x^\mu, y^\mu) \mid \mu = 1, \cdots, M \right\} \qquad (1)$$

The introduction of the constant a assigning the silent neural state is important for the subsequent discussion: Biologically inspired models use $a = 0$, Ising spin models use $a = 1$, and generally it is optimal to adjust this value according to the pattern activity.

2 Learning and retrieval in associative memory

In the learning process, each pair $(x^\mu, y^\mu) \in S$ is presented to the NAM: the address pattern x^μ at the input, and the corresponding content pattern y^μ at the output. If the neurons simply conduct these learning signals back to the synapses, this provides a pre- and postsynaptic signal at every synapse (see Figure 1). According to these two signals the synaptic weight is changed. A prescription that determines the synaptic change by the post- and presynaptic signals we call *local learning rule* or *local two-term rule*. A local learning rule R can be described by a 2×2 matrix, or a vector $R = (r_{aa}, r_{a1}, r_{1a}, r_{11})$, where r_{xy} determines the amount of synaptic modification for presynaptic signal x and postsynaptic signal y. We focus on local learning rules and use one-step learning for synaptic modification, in which each pattern is presented only once, whereas network models with more flexible retrieval behavior often need time-consuming learning procedures presenting the learning set many times. The following local learning rules are very common in the literature of NAMs:

- The Hebb rule or asymmetric coincidence rule $H := (0, 0, 0, 1)$ increases the synaptic value for pre- and postsynaptic activity, corresponding to "1." This rule for synaptic modification was postulated by D.O. Hebb between pairs of firing nervous cells [Hebb 1949]. For $a = 0$ it corresponds to the product of x and y and to the Boolean AND.

- The agreement rule or symmetric coincidence rule $A := (1, -1, -1, 1)$ increases the synaptic

value for agreeing pre- and postsynaptic signals and decreases the synaptic value for disagreeing states. This rule is used in the Hopfield model; therefore, it may be called the Hopfield rule [Hopfield 1982]. For $a = -1$, it corresponds to the product of x and y and to the Boolean equivalence.

- The correlation rule $C := (pq, -p(1-q), -(1-p)q, (1-p)(1-q))$ builds up the correlation between activity states of the pre- and postsynaptic neurons over the set of learning patterns. It depends on the probabilities

$$P = prob\left[x_i^\mu = 1 \right] \text{ and } q = prob\left[y_i^\mu = 1 \right]$$

of having a "1" as pre- and postsynaptic signal, respectively [Palm 1988, Willshaw 1990].

In heteroassociation the set of learning patterns $S = \{(x^\mu, y^\mu) \mid \mu = 1, \ldots, M\}$ is stored by forming the synaptic connectivity matrix W with a two-term learning rule R:

$$W = \left(w_{ij} \right) = \left(\sum_{\mu=1}^{M} R\left(x_i^\mu, y_j^\mu \right) \right). \qquad (2)$$

The connectivity matrix in autoassociation, where a learning set $S = \{(x^\mu, x^\mu) : \mu = 1, \ldots, M\}$ is stored, becomes

$$W = \left(w_{ij} \right) = \left(\sum_{\mu=1}^{M} R\left(x_i^\mu, x_j^\mu \right) \right). \qquad (3)$$

Basically, we distinguish between additive and binary learning rules in NAMs. If the final synaptic strength is reached by M single updates we call this an additive learning rule. In binary learning the synaptic weight matrix $\overline{W}$ is obtained by a nonlinear operation called clipping,

$$\overline{w}_{ij} = sgn \, w_{ij}, \qquad (4)$$

with the convention sgn $0 := 0$. For the Hebbian learning rule A with the choice $a = 0$, the binary weight matrix $\overline{W}$ can efficiently be implemented by a Boolean OR:

$$\overline{w}_{ij} = \bigvee_{\mu=1}^{M} \left(x_i^\mu y_j^\mu \right) \qquad (5)$$

In the retrieval phase of a NAM, an address or input pattern x is applied to the input of the network. The values of the input components are propagated through the synaptic connections to all neurons at the same time. Each neuron j transforms the input signals into its *dendritic potential* s_j, which is the sum of inputs x_i weighted by the corresponding synaptic strength w_{ij}:

$$s_j := \sum_i w_{ij} x_i. \qquad (6)$$

In the neural update the new activity y_j of neuron j is determined by a nonlinear operation:

$$\hat{y}_j = f_j(s_j - \theta_j) \qquad (7)$$

Usually, in neural network models, the function f_j is a monotonously increasing function, the transfer function. In our models it is $f_j = f$ for all neurons, and the threshold value θ_j is also adjusted globally to $\theta_j = \theta$ (see [Buckingham 1995] as an example for neuron-specific threshold setting in NAM). For binary output patterns, f is a binary-valued transfer function with $f(x) = 1$, for $x \geq 0$ and $f(x) = a$ for $x < 0$, corresponding to the neural states "active" and "silent," respectively.

In one-step retrieval, the output pattern is determined from the incoming address pattern by a single synchronous update step of all neurons in parallel. For iterative retrieval, two different neural update schedules are distinguished: The spin glass literature on autoassociation typically considers asynchronous updating where feedback is preceded by the computation of a new output activity in only one randomly selected neuron. In synchronous updating, feedback is preceded by a complete processing step by all neurons as in one-step retrieval.

3 Analysis of neural associative memory

3.1 Evaluation criteria

As a consequence of the NAM's approximative behavior, noisy address patterns can be used to retrieve the desired content. Not surprisingly, a memory device that allows errors in the addressing may also exhibit some errors in the output pattern $\hat{y}$. With binary learning patterns, two types of retrieval errors are possible. These are characterized by the conditional error probabilities

$$e_1 = prob[\hat{y}_j^\mu = a | y_j^\mu = 1],$$
$$e_a = prob[\hat{y}_j^\mu = 1 | y_j^\mu = a]. \qquad (8)$$

In this context a few questions arise, which we try to answer subsequently:

- How many patterns can be stored and retrieved with a small number of errors?

- With how many wrong bits in the address pattern can the desired content pattern still be retrieved?

- How many components per pattern should be set to "1"?

- What is the best local learning rule?

- Does additive learning improve binary learning?

- Does iterative retrieval outperform one-step retrieval?

Answering these questions requires evaluation criteria for the evaluation and comparison of different learning rules and retrieval procedures. To compare the performance on different memory and coding schemes, it's most natural to base evaluation criteria based on the information content of the stored and retrieved data sets.

We consider a set of randomly generated learning patterns $S = \{(x^\mu, y^\mu) \mid x^\mu \in \{a, 1\}^n, y^\mu \in \{a, 1\}^m, \mu = 1, \ldots, M\}$. All components of x^μ and y^μ are generated independently with the same probability

$$p := prob\left[x_i^\mu = 1\right]$$

for all input patterns, and with probability

$$q := \left[y_i^\mu = 1\right]$$

for all output patterns.

In this setting, a single component y_i^μ of a content pattern y^μ can be considered a binary random variable, taking the value $y_i^\mu = 1$ with probability q. Thus, the information content in a single component can be measured by the Shannon information

$$i(q) := -q \, ld \, q - (1-q) \, ld \, (1-q). \qquad (9)$$

Because the components and patterns are independently generated, the *mean information* contained in a single content pattern y^μ is given by the product

$$I(y^\mu) := m \, i(q). \qquad (10)$$

and the mean information of the whole set of content patterns $S^C := \{ y^\mu \mid \mu = 1, \dots, M \}$ is

$$I(S^C) := M\, m\, i(q). \tag{11}$$

The amount of information that can be stored in a NAM is measured by the pattern capacity P. It compares the mean information of the content pattern set S^C with the size of the weight matrix W and is defined by

$$P := max \frac{I(S^C)}{nm} = \frac{M^*}{n} i(q). \tag{12}$$

Here, the maximum is taken over all possible learning sets S (corresponding to different parameter settings M, p, and q). In addition, an error bound for the retrieved output patterns can be required limiting the number of maximal storable patterns to M^*. The pattern capacity P does not account for the information loss due to errors in the retrieved patterns.

The stored information is read out by addressing the content pattern $y^\mu \in S^C$ with its corresponding address pattern $x^\mu \in S^A := \{ x^\mu \mid \mu = 1, \dots, M \}$. The result is an output pattern $\hat{y} \in \hat{S}^C := \{ \hat{y}^\mu \mid \mu = 1, \dots, M \}$. Probably, a retrieved content pattern $\hat{y}$ contains some errors as defined in Equation (8). To measure the information obtained from a NAM, the information necessary to correct the errors of the retrieved output pattern should be subtracted from the information of the original content pattern y^μ. In information theory, this capacity measure is named the *transinformation* $T(\hat{S}^C, S^C)$. It measures the information of $\hat{S}^C$ in comparison to S^C and is defined by

$$T(\hat{S}^C, S^C) = I S^C) - I(S^C \mid \hat{S}^C). \tag{13}$$

Here the conditional information $I(S^C \mid \hat{S}^C)$ denotes the amount of information necessary to correct the errors in the patterns of $\hat{S}^C$ with respect to the correct output patterns. These considerations lead to the definition of the memory capacity or association capacity A of a NAM as

$$A := max \frac{T(\hat{S}^C, S^C)}{nm} = \frac{M^*}{n} \left[i(q) - I y_i^k \mid \hat{y}_i^k) \right]. \tag{14}$$

The conditional information $I(y_i^\mu \mid \hat{y}_i^\mu)$ per vector component is given by

$$I(y_i^\mu \mid \hat{y}_i^\mu) := prob[\hat{y}_i^\mu = 1] \cdot i(prob[y_i^\mu = a \mid \hat{y}_i^\mu = 1]) + prob[\hat{y}_i^\mu = a] \cdot i(prob[y_i^\mu = 1 \mid \hat{y}_i^\mu = a]) \cdot \tag{15}$$

Again, the maximum is taken over all possible learning sets S. M^* is the maximum number of patterns for a predefined error criterion on the retrieval results $\hat{S}^C$.

In an autoassociative memory, the performance of a pattern completion task can be measured by the *completion capacity C*. The information of the initial input patterns $\tilde{x}$ about the stored content pattern x is also taken into account. This can be achieved by the transinformation $T(\tilde{S}^C, S^C)$, where $\hat{S}^C$ is the set of initial input patterns $\tilde{x}^\mu$, which are noisy versions of the patterns $x^\mu \in S^C$. If we assume that the patterns $\tilde{x}^\mu$ are derived from x^μ according to the distortion probabilities

$$\tilde{e}_1 = prob\left[\tilde{x}_j^\mu = a \mid x_j^\mu = 1 \right],$$
$$\tilde{e}_a = prob\left[\tilde{x}_j^\mu = 1 \mid x_j^\mu = a \right], \tag{16}$$

this simplifies the definition of the completion capacity to

$$C := max_{p,n,M} \frac{T(\hat{S}^C, S^C) - T(\hat{S}^C, S^C)}{n^2} =$$
$$\frac{M^*}{n} \left[I(x_i^k \mid \hat{x}_i^k) - I(x_i^k \mid \tilde{x}_i^k) \right]. \tag{17}$$

As already demonstrated in Equation 15, C can be expressed in terms of the parameters p,n,M and the probabilities $\tilde{e}_1, \tilde{e}_a, e_1, e_a$. In the following sections we use the association capacity A in heteroassociation and the completion capacity C to evaluate storage and retrieval performance in NAMs.

3.2 Asymptotic results

First we consider the special case of binary Hebbian learning with $a = 0$ in a heteroassociative memory [Palm 1980]. After the storage of a set containing M randomly generated patterns (x^μ, y^μ), the probability for an arbitrary synaptic weight w_{ij} to stay at $w_{ij} = 0$ is

$$p_0 = (1 - pq)^M \approx exp(- Mpq). \tag{18}$$

Thus a fraction $p1 = 1 - p_0$ of synaptic weights w_{ij} have switched from 0 to 1.

311

Starting the retrieval process with a part $\tilde{x}^\mu$ of the memory pattern x^μ as input, and setting the threshold to $\theta = \sum_i \tilde{x}_i^\mu$, the retrieved output $\hat{y}^\mu$ contains all ones of the content pattern y^μ and some additional ones. Thus $e_1 = 0$, whereas $e_0 \neq 0$. The error probability e_0 strongly depends on the density of ones in the synaptic weight matrix W. Provided that W is randomly filled with ones with probability $p_1 = prob[w_{ij} = 1]$, the error probability e_0 is approximately $e_0 = p_1^\theta$. Thus e_0 increases with the density p_1. In order to achieve a high memory capacity, the entries of the synaptic weight matrix W should be balanced, which means $p_1 = p_0 = 0.5$. To achieve $p_1 \leq 0.5$, that is,

$$M pq = -ln\, p_0 \leq ln\, 2, \qquad (19)$$

the product M_{pq} must be kept low. This can be achieved by using sparsely coded address and content patterns. We call a binary pattern x sparsely coded if only a few components are $x_i = 1$. If the number of ones per pattern is of the order $\log n$, the optimal asymptotic association capacity of $ln\, 2 \approx 0.69$ is obtained [Willshaw 1969]. In this case it is possible to store $M \gg n$ patterns in a NAM with very small error probability e_0.

In an autoassociative memory and pattern completion by means of a one-step retrieval procedure, the completion capacity $C = ln2/4 \approx 0.173$ can be achieved with sparse content patterns by addressing with distorted content patterns where half of the "1"-components are deleted, that is, set to "0". In [Palm 1992] an upper bound for the completion capacity for fixed-point retrieval has been determined as $ln\, 2\, /2 \approx 0.346$. As we will see in section 3.3, this bound cannot be reached with iterative retrieval strategies starting from an incomplete or noisy version of the content pattern.

For additive learning rules with threshold detection retrieval, a signal-to-noise analysis [Palm 1988, Willshaw 1990] shows that for heteroassociation the optimal association capacity of $A = 1/(2\, ln\, 2) \approx 0.72$ can be achieved with the correlation rule $C := (pq, -p\,(1-q), -(1-p)q, (1-p)(1-q))$. For any local learning rule R, the best choice of the probability $p = prob\left[x_i^\mu = 1\right]$ is determined through the zero average input condition: $p + (1 - p)a = 0$. This determines the optimal relation between a and p in the address pattern.

If this zero average input condition is not fulfilled for a learning rule R $\neq$ C, it can be shown that the asymptotic memory capacity for this learning rule is equal to zero. For $p = 1/2$ the zero average input con-

dition implies $a = -1$, and for sparse input patterns, that is, $p \to 0$ asymptotically, the zero input activity is approximately fulfilled for $a = 0$ in the limit $n \to \infty$. For the best possible choice of parameters, that is, the correlation rule and $p = -a/(1 - a)$, the highest capacity values and the lowest error probabilities are obtained for $q \to 0$, that is, for sparse output patterns. The Hebbian scheme ($p,q \to 0$, $a = 0$, rule H) is thus clearly superior to the Hopfield scheme ($p,q = 1/2$, $a = -1$, rule A). In the latter case the correlation rule becomes $(1/4, -1/4, -1/4, 1/4)$, which is equivalent to the Hopfield rule A. This shows that in the Ising spin model the Hopfield rule is optimal.

Furthermore, it turns out that retrieval with a high fidelity requirement for the retrieval result

$$e_1 \to 0 \quad e_a\, /q \to 0, \qquad (20)$$

can be obtained only for sparse content patterns (for $q \to 0$ in the limit $n \to \infty$). For small p and q, the correlation rule is very similar to the Hebbian learning rule. Therefore, the asymptotic capacities of the correlation rule and the Hebb rule for sparse learning patterns are identical. For sparse address and content patterns ($p,q \to 0$), and using the Hebbian learning rule, a memory capacity of $A = 1/(2\, ln\, 2)$ can be achieved with high retrieval accuracy.

For additive learning autoassociation and pattern completion with sparsely coded patterns, a completion capacity of $C = 1/(8ln\, 2) \approx 0.18$ can be achieved with one-step retrieval. For fixed-point retrieval, an upper bound for the completion capacity has been determined as $1/(4\, ln\, 2)$ [Palm 1992]. As already mentioned in the case of binary learning, this capacity value cannot be achieved by iterative retrieval strategies starting from a part of stored patterns.

3.3 Iterative retrieval procedures

In this section we focus on the storage by Hebbian learning and retrieval of sparsely coded binary memory patterns (with $a = 0$) from an autoassociative memory (see, for example, Gardner-Medwin 1976, Amari 1989, Gibson 1992). One-step and iterative retrieval procedures are discussed subsequently. We assume that the NAM contains n binary threshold neurons with feedback connections from the output to the input. The learning patterns x^μ, $\mu = 1, \ldots, M$ are assumed to be sparsely coded binary patterns each with exactly k ones:

$$S \subset B_{n,k} := \left\{ x \in \{0,1\}^n \mid \sum_{i=1}^n x_i = k \right\}. \qquad (21)$$

312

In iterative retrieval, the threshold θ has to be adjusted in each retrieval step, and the end of the iteration loop must be determined by a threshold control strategy. In [Schwenker 1995] three different threshold control strategies have been proposed for iterative retrieval in autoassociative memory. One of these is strategy CA.

Strategy CA (Constant Activity)

Because all learning patterns $x^\mu \in S$ contain exactly k ones, the threshold $\theta(t)$—here t counts the number of iterations of the NAM—can be adjusted in such a way that in each iteration step the number of ones $\hat{k}_\theta$ of the retrieved pattern $\hat{x}^\mu(t)$ is close to the expected activity k. This can be achieved by testing different threshold values θ and taking that threshold, which minimizes the absolute value of the difference between k and $\hat{k}_\theta$:

$$D(\theta) \quad := \left| \hat{k}_\theta - k \right|. \qquad (22)$$

In general, there may be more than one threshold value θ minimizing this difference $D(\theta)$. In this case, $\theta(t)$ is set to be the smallest among these values. Typically, with this choice the whole learning pattern x^μ (or at least a large portion of it) is part of the retrieved pattern $\hat{x}^\mu(t+1)$. We say that a binary pattern x is part of another binary pattern y, iff $\{i \mid x_i = 1\} \subset \{i \mid y_i = 1\}$. The iteration process can be stopped if a fixed point or a cycle in the sequence of output patterns $\hat{x}^\mu(t)$ is detected.

The results presented for one-step and two-step retrieval are obtained by computer simulation and theoretical treatment as well, whereas for iterative retrieval, simulation results are shown.

In computer simulations, binary Hebbian learning always performs better than additive Hebbian learning; Figure 2 shows the simulation results for an associative memory with $n = 1,900$ neurons. Additive learning achieves a completion capacity C of approximately 7 percent for one-step and 9 percent for iterative retrieval, whereas with binary Hebbian learning, 14.5 percent and 18 percent can be obtained.

It can be observed in Figure 2 that the capacity for iterative retrieval decreases to the capacity values for one-step retrieval if only a few or many patterns were stored in the memory. Only in an intermediate range does iterative retrieval yield higher capacity values. In Figure 2, these effective storage ranges for iterative retrieval are $2,000 \leq M \leq 7,000$ for additive, and $5,000 \leq M \leq 14,000$ for binary Hebbian learning. This effective storage range is a typical property of iterative retrieval.

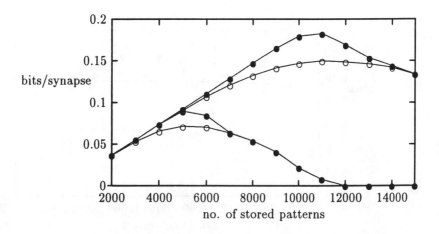

Figure 2. The completion capacity C of the additive and binary learning rule for one-step retrieval (o) and for iterative retrieval (•). The activity is $k = 13$ in the memory patterns and $l = 6$ of the initial input address patterns.

For additive Hebbian learning, the completion capacity values that can be achieved with realistic memory sizes (up to $n \approx 10^4$) are far below the asymptotic bound of $C = 1/(8\ln2)$. The rate of convergence to the asymptotic completion capacity seems to be much faster for the binary Hebbian learning rule, so that it is possible to achieve reasonably high completion capacities with memory sizes in the range of $n = 10^3$ to $n = 10^4$. With binary Hebbian learning, we have obtained completion capacities exceeding the asymptotic capacity of $C = \ln2/4 \approx 0.173$, both with iterative and with two-step retrieval (see Figure 3). For an associative memory with 20,000 neurons, we achieved 17.9 percent for two-step and about 19 percent for iterative retrieval. In this simulation more than 600,000 patterns with a constant activity of $k = 19$ had been stored.

Theoretical analysis shows that the optimal completion capacity for two-step retrieval reaches its absolute maximum (which is slightly larger than the capacity value for $n = 20,000$) for a matrix containing about $n = 200,000$ threshold neurons and then decreases toward the asymptotic value of $\ln2/4$. It appears that this is also true for iterative retrieval.

The optimal completion capacity values for one-step, two-step, and iterative retrieval in Figure 3 have been reached by using half of the learning pattern as address pattern. These completion capacities were reached with a very small number of errors (for example, for the simulation with $n = 20,000$ neurons, the error ratio e_0/p is less than one percent for iterative retrieval) and the retrieval process takes a very short time (fewer than 5 iteration steps in the mean). These properties, together with the fact that only one bit per synapse is needed for the storage matrix, suggest that the autoassociative memory with the binary Hebbian learning rule is most suitable for applications.

4   Sparse similarity-preserving codes

Fault-tolerance is a crucial aspect of neural memories [Buckingham 1995]. The optimization of NAMs as we described earlier led us to the requirement of sparse input and output patterns. To take advantage of the NAM's high capacity and fault tolerance, coding techniques are required that translate actual data points or symbol strings, as they appear in particular applications, in a similarity-preserving way into sparse binary vectors. More formally, this coding is a mapping between nonbinary, multidimensional data points and sparse binary patterns with the constraint that similarities between original data points should be preserved in the distances between the sparse patterns.

Neural memory retrieval is based on the number of agreeing 1-components between the stored and the input pattern. Therefore, this quantity, called *overlap* is the relevant similarity measure between representations. The most common distance definition in a space of binary vectors is the Hamming distance counting the total number of disagreeing components. For two representations c^i and c^j with activities l_i, and l_j respectively, the overlap o_{ij} is related to the Hamming distance d_{ij} by

$$d_{ij} = l_i + l_j - 2 \cdot o_{ij} \qquad (23)$$

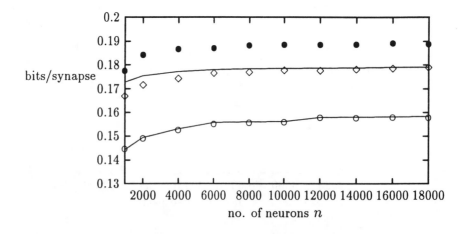

Figure 3. Optimal completion capacities (*M* and *k* are optimized) for one-step (o) and two-step retrieval (◊) simulation and theoretical results (curves), and the simulation results for iterative retrieval (•).

To represent different degrees of similarity by different overlap values, let us say at least v degrees (including equalness), distributed representations must be used where the activities satisfy $l_i \geq v - 1\ \forall i$. Because the definition of similarity between original data points depends entirely on the application the coding problem cannot be generally solved. For two examples of common data structures, we will briefly describe simple techniques to construct similarity-preserving sparsely coded binary patterns.

To represent k-strings of symbols from an alphabet of length l (for example, words), the idea is to describe each word with a small set of occuring features in a large set of possible features and to represent each feature by one coding component. Similarity preservation is then provided for items with agreeing features. For instance, simple letters as features would map all words with the same letters on the same coding vector, entirely disregarding their order. On the other hand, to take all possible k-strings as features would perfectly preserve the letter structure in the word but would produce local 1-of-l^k coding vectors. As already discussed, this local coding could not be similarity-preserving because the overlap can take only the two values 0 for dissimiliar coding vectors and 1 for identity. A coding between these extremes should use as features parts of a word that already bear some structural information like n-grams of letters, that is, substrings in the word of length n. Some redundancy can be introduced by coding all occuring n-grams instead of only the disjunct n-letter building blocks of the word; for $n = 2$ the features present in the word "pattern," would be $\{pa,at,tt,te,er,rn\}$. This provides some information about the order between the n-grams to be represented in the code. A coding using n-gram features with fixed n generates $(k - n + 1)$-of-l^n vectors—increasing length n in the features enhances the sparseness of the representation.

As a second example, numerical values with a certain precision and range (for example, temperatures) are to be represented. A local coding would simply represent each section in the interval with one component: The interval [0,10] with a precision of 0.1 would be represented in a 1-of-100 coding, setting the first bit for $x = 0.0$, the second for $x = 0.1$, and so on. If we use a few ones to indicate the value, we achieve the desired similarity preserving coding: 1111000 … 00 has overlap 3 to 0111100 … 00, but overlap 0 to 00 … 0111100. The component i in a pattern can be interpreted as the feature "$[x = i/10] \wedge [x = (i - 1)/10] \wedge [x = (I - 2)/10] \wedge [x = (i - 3)/10]$." Thus, each pattern with four adjacent 1-components represents a unique number.

Another requirement for good NAM exploitation concerns the feature distribution in the data: Each feature should occur with equal probability, and the number of features present in each item should be almost the same. In the case of stored words, we will discuss these points in section 9.

4.1 Data analysis and similarity-preserving coding

Applications where the data can be described in a high-dimensional continuous and metric space X are often analyzed by vector quantization or cluster analysis. Such procedures extract a set of representative points or cluster centers $\{v^1, \dots, v^K\} \subset X$. The coding should be based on the properties of these points that are given by their $K \times K$ distance matrix $D = (d(vi, vj))$. Of course, the distances $d(vi, vj)$ are real-valued, whereas the overlap between two binary patterns is an integer value. Therefore, it will be impossible to preserve the exact distances by the binary coding procedure.

The distance matrix $D = (d(v^i, v^j))$ can be used to determine distance classes by collecting similar entries of the distance matrix into the same distance class. These classes can be labeled by integer-valued distance numbers d_{ij} without destroying the order provided by the order relation $>=$ in the original distances. If only even numbers d_{ij} are assigned, they can be transformed to an integer-valued $K \times K$ overlap matrix $O = (o_{ij})$ by Equation (23). For a given overlap matrix O, a similarity-preserving coding algorithm (SPC algorithm) developed in our group [Stellmann 1992] generates a set of binary code vectors $c^1, \dots, c^K$, reflecting the distance structure of the data points in the input space.

The basic SPC concept algorithm is quite straightforward: The initial code sequences are arranged line by line into a matrix with n rows. In the beginning, these code sequences contain "0" elements. They are successively "filled" with "1" elements, column by column, from left to right. Adding the column vector $e_i + e_j$ to the already existing code sequences leads to an overlap of 1 for the code vectors c^i and c^j and does not change all other overlaps. Here e_i denotes the i–th unit vector. Proceeding in this way one is able to generate code sequences $c^1, \dots, c^K$, which have the same overlaps as given by the overlap matrix O. Sometimes these code vectors can become very long. Generating the code vectors as described before, the length L of each code vector is

$$L = \sum_i \sum_{j>i} o_{ij}. \tag{24}$$

In each of the code vectors c^i there are

$$Z_i = \sum_{j \neq i} o_{ij} \qquad (25)$$

components set to 1. It is often possible to achieve shorter code vectors; for example, by adding the column $e_i + e_j + e_k$. This column gives overlaps between the code vectors c^i and c^j, c^j and c^k, and c^i and c^k, so we get three overlaps instead of only one. This idea leads to a minimization problem concerning the length of the code vectors, which is computationally hard, but reasonable suboptimal solutions can be found by heuristic strategies.

The explained similarity-preserving coding procedure is demonstrated for a distance matrix of $K=5$ data points:

$$D = \begin{pmatrix} 0.0 & 30.0 & 29.0 & 17.3 & 14.1 \\ 30.0 & 0.0 & 31.3 & 43.1 & 29.1 \\ 29.0 & 31.3 & 0.0 & 32.0 & 30.0 \\ 17.3 & 43.1 & 32.0 & 0.0 & 20.0 \\ 14.1 & 29.1 & 30.0 & 20.0 & 0.0 \end{pmatrix}$$

The data points $\{v^1, \ldots, v^5\}$ are cluster centers that are the result of a k-means clustering procedure of a set of data vectors in IR^{11}. In a first step, these real-valued distances are grouped into the distance classes

$$D^0 = \{0.0\} \; D^1 = \{14.1\} \; D^2 = \{17.3\} \; D^3 = \{20.0\}$$
$$D^4 = \{29.0, 29.1, 30.0, 31.3, 32.0\} \; D^5 = \{43.1\}$$

On the basis of these classes, an (even) integer-valued distance matrix $D_{classes}$ is defined, which can be transformed into an overlap matrix $O_{classes}$

$$D_{classes} = \begin{pmatrix} 0 & 8 & 8 & 4 & 2 \\ 8 & 0 & 8 & 10 & 8 \\ 8 & 8 & 0 & 8 & 8 \\ 4 & 10 & 8 & 0 & 6 \\ 2 & 8 & 8 & 6 & 0 \end{pmatrix} \qquad \Rightarrow$$

$$O_{classes} = \begin{pmatrix} l_1 & 1 & 1 & 3 & 4 \\ 1 & l_2 & 1 & 0 & 1 \\ 1 & 1 & l_3 & 1 & 1 \\ 3 & 0 & 1 & l_4 & 2 \\ 4 & 1 & 1 & 2 & l_5 \end{pmatrix}$$

Starting the SPC algorithm with this overlap matrix

$O_{classes}$ results in a set of 5 binary code vectors $\in \{0,1\}^{15}$:

$$c^1 = (1,1,1,1,1,1,1,1,1,0,0,0,0,0,0)$$
$$c^2 = (1,0,0,0,0,0,0,0,0,1,1,0,0,0,0)$$
$$c^3 = (0,1,0,0,0,0,0,0,0,0,1,0,1,1,0,0)$$
$$c^4 = (0,0,1,1,1,0,0,0,0,0,0,1,0,1,1)$$
$$c^5 = (0,0,0,0,0,1,1,1,1,0,1,0,1,1,1)$$

This set of binary code vectors can serve as a code book for the whole input space X. For a data point $x \in X$, a sparse binary code vector can for example be determined as follows: Calculate the distance $d(x, v^j)$ for $j = 1, \ldots, 5$, detect the two closest neighbors v^{j1}, v^{j2} to x, and calculate the binary code vector $c(x)$ of $x \in X$ by the Cartesian product of c^{j1} and c^{j2}: $c^{j1} \times c^{j2} =: c(x) \in \{0,1\}^{225}$.

5 Comparison of content-addressable and neural associative memory

In many computer applications, an enormous amount of information must be stored in memory for later retrieval. All data elements are stored at certain addresses in a conventional computer memory; any stored information can be accessed again only if the corresponding memory address is known.

However, in a content-addressable memory (CAM), often also called an associative memory, some additional memory logic is provided that allows fast access of any stored information by using only the contents of a supplied input keyword (see [Kohonen 1979]). Figure 4a shows the typical structure of a CAM. The information set S is composed of the two subsets X and Y. Each information entry to be stored in the CAM can be represented as the pair (x,y) with $x \in X$ and $y \in Y$. The element x contains the part of the information that can be used for identification during a search operation. The corresponding part y contains additional information belonging to the data element x.

As an example, in a typical database application of a CAM, the set X contains the name and birth date of all company employees whereas the set Y contains some personal information like salary or education. For retrieving any information, a keyword and a key mask must be supplied to the CAM. The keyword contains the already known information of a searched CAM entry, the key mask describes the position of the known information in a stored word x. By using both keyword and key mask, a parallel search in all rows of

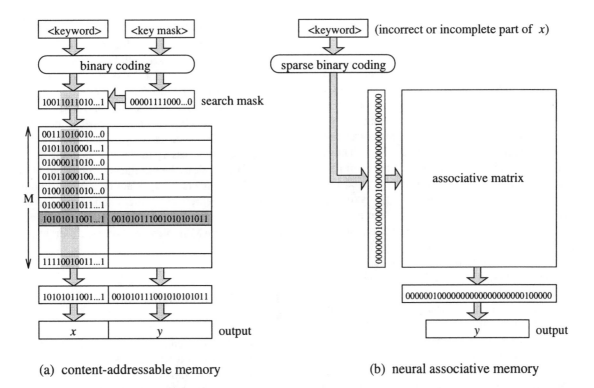

(a) content-addressable memory   (b) neural associative memory

Figure 4. Comparison of CAM and NAM: (a) content-addressable memory, (b) neural associative memory.

the matrix can be performed by the CAM's hardware. In case of a match, the stored word (x,y) is presented at the output. If several matches occur, a special resolution logic controls the sequential presentation of all matching words at the output.

A basic difference between CAMs and NAMs is the kind of fault tolerance provided for noisy queries. With the key mask, some unreliable, uncertain, or unimportant components can be disregarded in the search, but such components must be specified explicitly by generating the key mask. In NAMs, noisy patterns can be processed without explicitly deciding which components are unreliable.

The most striking comparison of CAMs and NAMs lies in the storage capacity. All M elements of the information set S are stored in random order in consecutive rows of the CAM by using a simple binary coding. Let x be a word of length k from an input alphabet with a elements, and y a word of length l from an output alphabet consisting of b different elements. Then, in each memory row of the CAM, at least k ld $a + l$ ld b one-bit storage elements are required, the total capacity for storing all M elements of the set S is $M \cdot (k$ ld $a + l$ ld $b)$. In NAMs the information set S is considered as the pattern mapping problem $x \in X \rightarrow y \in Y$ (see Figure 4b). This is a heteroassociation problem that can be implemented by using the binary Hebbian learning rule A with the choice $a = 0$ as described in

section 2. To achieve a large storage capacity, the patterns $x \in X$ and $y \in Y$ must be coded into sparse binary sequences. If, in addition, the coding procedure is similarity preserving, the associative memory can efficiently be used for fault-tolerant retrieval (see section 4).

Storage, with the binary Hebbian learning rule, needs a matrix with about $m \times n$ one-bit storage elements, where $m = ka$ and $n = lb$. In section 3.2, we saw that this memory does not work well for all possible parameters $l,k,a,b,$ and M. A set of parameters for which the memory capacity is reasonably close to the asymptotic memory capacity value $A = \ln 2 \approx 0.69$ is determined by Equations (14), (18), and (19). For example, if $a = 2,800$, $k = 9$, $b = 33$, $l = 3$, and $M = 62,500$, the memory works with a memory capacity of about 0.4 or, in other words, with an efficiency of 40 percent per matrix element. The information contained in the whole pattern set is $M \cdot l \cdot$ ld $b = 945,800$ bit and the size of the hetero-associative memory is $k \cdot a \cdot l \cdot b = 2,494,000$. For CAM storage (see above), the memory matrix size is $M (k$ ld $a + l$ ld $b) = 7,387,100$ bit, which is much less effective.

The matrix size in this example is quite large because a large amount of information, about 10^6 bits, has to be stored in the memory. With fewer bits to be stored, the example would have been less favorable for the NAM, because NAMs work more efficiently when they get larger.

6 The Parallel Associative Network (PAN) system

The operation principle of a NAM is rather simple. Binary weight values should be used for achieving a large storage capacity (see section 3.2), and only simple operations on binary values are necessary in the learning and retrieval phases. However, the correlation matrices used in applications can be very large. Thus a parallel implementation of a NAM is highly desirable. Each associative retrieval step must be computed in a very short time, especially for real-time applications.

Most state-of-the-art microprocessors are not specialized for simple Boolean operations and have a very complex internal architecture (containing, for example, floating-point arithmetic units and caches) that cannot be used efficiently when simulating NAMs. A more practical implementation possibility for NAMs has simple PEs operating in parallel on different parts of the correlation matrix, combined with enormous numbers of cheap dynamic memory chips (DRAMs). This approach is also the basis for the PAN system architecture.

Other important aspects of the PAN system design are as follows:

- balance between parallel computing power and the maximal system throughput,
- system scalability,
- parallel addressing scheme for accessing many memory chips simultaneously.

Four different versions of the PAN system have been realized. In PAN I and PAN II, a small number of 8-bit microprocessors (Zilog Z80) was used; each of them simulates a fixed number of neurons and the corresponding columns of the storage matrix (see Figures 1 and 4b). Instead of using modern, complex 32-bit microprocessors for PAN III and PAN IV, an alternative approach was chosen. Special-purpose ICs (Bacchus) have been developed that perform exactly the operations necessary to simulate NAMs.

Before we describe the Bacchus chip and the latest PAN IV architecture, we examine a NAM implementation on a theoretical parallel computer model and its performance. See [Strey 1993] for a more detailed analysis of NAM implementation on different parallel architectures.

6.1 The underlying parallel computer model

The parallel computer model used as a basis for the implementation is a typical SIMD (single instruction, multiple data) model. It consists of n PEs, indexed 0 through $n - 1$. Each PE has a simple arithmetical processing unit, some registers, and a sufficient amount of local memory. All PEs are controlled by a special control processor (CP) that broadcasts instructions, addresses, and data to the PEs and performs operations on scalar data. The PEs can be enabled/disabled by a mask, and all enabled PEs perform the same instruction synchronously on (different) data. Each PE has a special register containing the unique index $id \in \{0, \ldots, n - 1\}$.

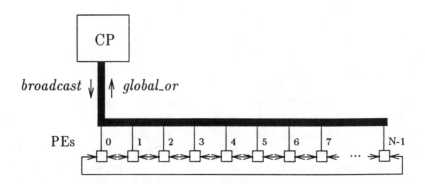

Figure 5. The underlying parallel computer model.

The global bus is the main communication medium of the parallel computer model and has a data path width of at least $\log n$ bits. Only the CP is allowed to broadcast data via the global bus to all PEs. The bus can also be used for gathering data from the PEs by a *global_or* operation. All active PEs put some local data on the bus, and the CP receives a scalar value that represents the bitwise logical disjunction of all data values. If all but one PE are disabled by a mask, the CP can read the data of a single processing element. Furthermore all processing elements are connected by an additional ring network that has a 1-bit wide data path. Each of the n PEs at location $A(x)$, $x \in \{0, \dots, n - 1\}$ is connected to the left and right neighbor PEs at locations $A(x \pm 1 \bmod n)$. In one time step, all PEs can transmit some local data only to their nearest neighbor in the same direction. This operation is called a *cyclic shift* to the left or right.

6.2 Parallel implementation

Due to the sparse coding of the binary input vector x, only a few vector elements x_i have the value one. We call these elements relevant input vector elements and we call the corresponding vector indices addresses. An input vector x with p relevant elements can shortly be described by an address vector a_x containing only the p addresses in ascending order. This vector represents a request for an association to be performed by the NAM.

It is assumed that, at the beginning of the request phase, the p addresses of the active vector elements x_i are stored in the CP memory. During the NAM's simulation the following operations must be realized on the parallel computer model:

1. Distributing the p addresses of the active input vector elements x_i to all those PEs where the corresponding synapses w_{ij} are stored.

2. Multiplying the input values x_i with all nonzero synapse values w_{ij} for all relevant input vector elements x_i and all neurons j in parallel (due to the binary data type of x_i, the multiplication is a simple logical AND operation).

3. Summing the products $x_i w_{ij}$ of all relevant input vector elements x_i and all nonzero weights w_{ij} for all neurons j in parallel.

4. Comparing the sums s_j with the threshold θ for all neurons j in parallel.

5. Collecting the q addresses of the newly active neurons (that is, of those neurons j for which $s_j \geq \theta$).

The q new addresses are returned to the CP and may be used again for a further association in the case of heteroassociation or for a further iteration in the case of autoassociation.

Figure 6 illustrates the parallel implementation for an associative memory with 31 neurons on a computer model with 32 PEs. In Figure 6a the starting configuration is shown. Each neuron j is mapped to PE j according to the unique PE index *id*. The PE with the highest index 31 is not used in this example. The distribution of the p addresses of active input vector elements x_i is realized by the CP, which broadcasts the p addresses via the global bus. Figure 6b illustrates the storage of the synapses w_{ij} in the local memory of each PE j. All weight values w_{ij} that belong to neuron j are stored in the local memory of PE j at consecutive addresses starting at some address α. So w_{ij} is stored in the local memory of PE j at address $\alpha + i$ and the CP can address a row i of the matrix W by broadcasting the corresponding physical address $\alpha + i$. In addition to the column j of the matrix W, the neuron index j and the threshold value θ must be available in each PE.

The addressed weight values w_{ij} are summed in PE j in p time steps (see Figure 6c). Due to the binary weight values the summing operation can be considered a counting operation: All ones contained in the addressed elements of each column of W are counted. The distributing phase can be overlapped with the summing phase, thus avoiding a local storage of the broadcasted addresses in each PE. All PEs j compare their calculated sums s_j with the threshold values θ and generate a Boolean value y_j, which is true only if $s_j \geq \theta$. All values y_j together represent a Boolean mask y that marks all active neurons. The gathering of the q addresses of the active neurons with $y_j = 1$ is shown in Figure 6d. It represents a big problem in a synchronous parallel computer model because the PEs have no capability to put some data onto the bus (except for the case that the CP issues a global_or command). In the following, three different algorithms that solve this problem are described.

Algorithm A1: The CP broadcasts in order the indices $0, 1, \dots, n - 1$ of all PEs via the global bus. After the broadcast of each index i, all PEs in parallel compare the received value i with their locally stored index *id* and generate a logical mask, which is true only in that one PE where $i = id$. The CP disables all PEs where the computed mask bit is false and executes a *global_or* command. So in step i the CP receives y_i and i is considered as the address of the next active neuron only if $y_i = 1$. This algorithm takes $3n$ time steps ($2n$ bus operations and n comparisons).

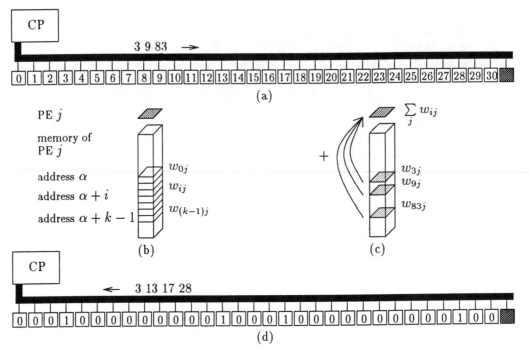

Figure 6. Parallel implementation of an associative memory with 31 neurons on a computer model with 32 processing elements.

Algorithm A2: It is assumed that at the beginning in all PEs a logical mask is available, which is true for the PE with index $id = 0$ and false for all other PEs. This mask is used for enabling/disabling the PEs, and it is shifted in n steps through all PEs of the array processor by using the *shift_right* operation of the ring network. Thus, after each vector shift by a distance of 1 to the right another PE is enabled. If $y_i = 1$, the enabled PE puts its neuron index i on the global bus that is read by the CP by using a global_or command. The algorithm takes n elementary vector shifts on the ring, n bus operations, and n comparison steps.

Algorithm A3: Only the PEs j with $y_j = 1$ are considered active PEs. It is assumed that a fast algorithm exists for finding out the PE with the minimal index of all active PEs. Only this one PEs puts its index $j_{\min}$ on the global bus and sets subsequently its local vector element y_j to 0 by which it becomes disabled. Thereafter the PE with the next minimal index is determined, and its index is read again by the CP by a *global_or* command. These steps are repeated until the active set of PEs is empty and the CP reads an invalid value (for example, –1).

The search for the PE with the minimal index can be done in parallel by using the global bus. A fast $O(\log n)$ algorithm has been proposed by Falkoff [Falkoff 1962]. The minimum of some distributed integer data values in the range from 1 to n can be found in $\log n$ steps by only using the *global_or* and *broadcast* bus operations.

6.3   Analysis

For the analysis, only the retrieval phase is considered, which is the most frequent system operation and which produces the highest system throughput.

The following table summarizes the total counts of computation steps t_{op} and communication steps t_{comm} needed for the different phases of the implementation (with n = number of PEs, k = number of active input vector elements, and l = number of active output neurons). The last column of the table above shows the time complexity of each basic operation if k and l are of order $O(\log n)$ which is necessary for achieving a large storage capacity (see section 3.2).

The most time-consuming operation of the parallel implementation of the neural associative memory on the presented computer model is the collection of the addresses of the active neurons. Whereas the distributing and summing phases can be realized in $O(\log n)$ steps, the collecting phase requires at least $O(\log^2 n)$ steps. Thus, a further acceleration of the implementation is only possible by using a faster (hardware) mechanism for collecting the addresses of the active neurons. Therefore, a special logic has been developed for the Bacchus chip and the PAN system, which are described next.

320

Operation	t_{op}	t_{comm}	Order
Distribute	–	k	$O(\log n)$
Sum	k	–	$O(\log n)$
Compare	1	–	$O(1)$
Collect A1	n	$2n$	$O(n)$
Collect A2	n	$2n$	$O(n)$
Collect A3	$4(l+1)$	$(2\,\mathrm{ld}\,n+1)\cdot(l+1)$	$O(\log^2 n)$

7   The Bacchus chip

For the realization of the PAN system concept several VLSI standard cell designs (Bacchus I to III) have been developed in a joint project at the Institute for Microelectronics in Darmstadt [Huch 1990]. Each Bacchus chip contains 32 binary neurons, the corresponding weights are stored offchip in standard DRAM memory chips. Thus the maximal number of weights per neuron is limited only by the capacity of available memory chips. According to the SIMD operation principle, the memories' addresses are generated by the control processor.

Figure 7 shows the detailed architecture of the Bacchus III chip. It is connected by 32 inputs/outputs (at the top of Figure 7) to the data ports of the memory chips and by 8 inputs/outputs (at the bottom of Figure 7) to the global data bus of the CP.

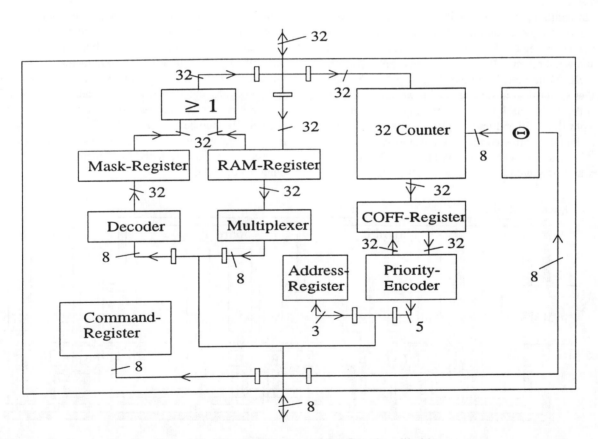

Figure 7. The architecture of the Bacchus III chip.

321

Each of the 32 neurons is essentially realized by an 8-bit counter, which performs the summing and the threshold comparison. In the retrieval phase the counter is first preloaded from an 8-bit data register with a threshold value θ, which has previously been written into the register by the CP. Then the CP addresses a row of the weight matrix W stored in the DRAM and the Bacchus chip reads 32 binary weights in parallel. If the weight value belonging to neuron i is "1" the i-th counter is decremented; if the weight value is "0" the i-th counter is not modified. If all rows of W that correspond to active elements of the input vector x have been addressed, the 32-bit COFF-register represents the result y of the retrieval step. The i-th bit of the register is set to "1" if the counter of neuron i has reached zero, for all other neurons it is set to "0." For the address generation, the algorithm A3 described in the last section is used. The priority-encoding logic generates the index (0, ..., 31) of the first active neuron that is encoded by a 5-bit binary value and combined with a preloaded 3-bit address to an 8-bit address. If this 8-bit address is read by the CP, the priority-encoding logic switches the currently active neuron to inactive and generates the index of the next active neuron that can again be read by the CP, and so on.

In addition, the Bacchus chips provides a special write logic for the learning phase, which is shown in the upper left part of Figure 7. The CP addresses a row of the weight matrix W and the contents are read from the DRAM into the 32-bit RAM-FF register. The new output vector that must be learned is written by the CP into the 32-bit mask register. The bitwise disjunction of both RAM-FF and mask register contents is written back into the addressed row of the memory.

The Bacchus chip contains about 26,000 transistors and runs with a clock rate of 10 MHz, which is sufficient for today's DRAM memory chips: One address can be processed per cycle. Because the counter logic is independent of the address generation logic, pipelining is possible. While one input vector is processed by conditional counting, the addresses of the previous output vector can be generated and read by the CP.

The PAN III was built in Darmstadt, based on our PAN concept using 16 Bacchus I chips. These are controlled by a specially designed circuit board mounted in a PC. This configuration is used as a demonstrator running an image recognition application.

8   The PAN IV

The PAN IV represents a system design that is particularly applicable to large networks and which is easily extensible by using more Bacchus ICs and more DRAM chips. The overall architecture of the PAN IV is shown in Figure 8. One printed circuit board contains 8 Bacchus chips (designated as B0 to B7 in Figure 8) each equipped with 1 Mbyte of local DRAM memory (M0 to M7). The prototype of the PAN IV consists of 16 boards physically located in a VME-bus rack. Thus, the overall number of neurons is 4,096 with a total memory of 128 Mbytes. The control processor (called AMMU: associative memory management unit) resides on an additional board and is based on a 68030 CPU. It provides communication with a Unix SPARCstation via a bidirectional FIFO interface and generates the instructions and addresses for all memory boards. If the number of required neurons exceeds the number of available PEs, a simple partitioning strategy is used. All address modifications necessary for the partitioned implementation are computed by the AMMU.

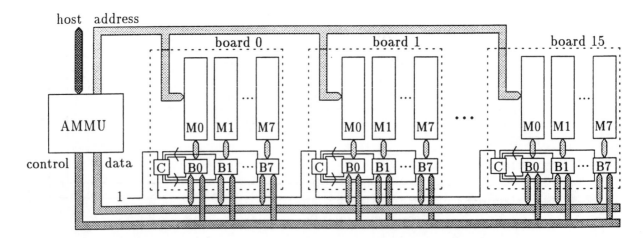

Figure 8. The system architecture of the PAN IV system.

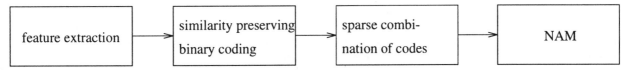

Figure 9. The architecture of an information retrieval system composed of a feature extraction module (for example, vector quantization), a similarity preserving binary coding algorithm (see section 4), an algorithm to construct sparse binary codes (for example, Cartesian product of different code vectors) and a NAM.

A special hardware acceleration has been developed for the time-consuming collection of active neurons' addresses after a retrieval phase. Basically, the algorithm A2 explained in section 6.2 is used, with the shift of a mask bit implemented only between different boards. Each board is provided with a controller (designated as C in Figure 8) that receives a special signal from all Bacchus chips indicating whether they contain active neurons. Depending on this information, either some Bacchus chips are allowed to put the addresses of the active neurons in order on the data bus, or the mask bit is shifted to the next board. Thus, the number of time steps required in the collecting phase could be reduced drastically. A more detailed description of the PAN IV hardware and system software can be found in [Palm 1991].

9 Information retrieval with neural associative memories

The use of a NAM is attractive for applications with strong demands on two issues: fast response to queries in large databases, and similarity-based fault-tolerant access to stored patterns. Such applications can be as diverse as the recognition of faces, the retrieval of words from large lexica or the search in genetic databases. In each case the associative memory identifies the most similar pattern in basically constant time, largely independent of the query properties and the number of items stored.

For each of these applications an appropriate sparse feature representation is necessary. An autoassociative memory scheme can be used to map the incomplete request pattern to the original stored pattern, selected according to the similarity measure. Alternatively, a heteroassociative memory scheme can be used to establish a mapping between patterns in different representations (for example, the face in a pixel representation and a feature-based representation), or between patterns representing different objects, like a face, an utterance, and the name of its owner. Another important difference—which requires different codes and therefore heteroassociation—lies in the use of syntactical similarity versus semantical similarity. This could be used to represent a thesaurus, where words

are considered similar if their meaning, not their spelling, is similar.

Usually, a query in retrieval applications should arouse not one item but a list of items, ordered with regard to their relevance to the query. This can be achieved by iterative retrieval: After one item is retrieved, it is used for suppression in the retrieval of a second item, and so on. Also, heteroassociation could be realized with iterative retrieval, if a bidirectional associative memory model is used [Kosko 1988]. The first cycle in a bidirectional memory can be analyzed with our methods as described in section 3.

A straightforward application of NAMs in information retrieval is the access of words in a large dictionary [Bentz 1989]. The following results are obtained with a dictionary of approximately 300,000 German word forms. Experiments with NAMs on this database have been performed both in our group and elsewhere.

In [Heimann 1994, Ekeberg 1988] the trigram encoding described in section 4 yielded a little more than 3 million trigrams in total; 7,561 features occur in the data, which is a low fraction of the set of $l^3 = 17,576$ possible trigrams. A systematic test regarding the fault tolerance had been carried out for some typical typing errors—for example, exchange of two characters at the beginning, in the middle, and at the end of a word, or deletion of a character in the middle. The most severe effects happen when characters in the middle of the words are exchanged, since this error changes the largest number of trigrams. Furthermore, errors in short words can be catastrophic: The number of remaining correct trigrams may not be sufficient to identify the original word, or the error may yield another existing word. Nevertheless, the correct word was in the set of answers in 90 percent of the cases for all types of errors.

The PAN IV system described in section 6 has been used to handle the dictionary data prototype system that was presented by our group at the CeBit exposition in Hannover in 1994. From linguistic research on written words, the n-gram features are known to obey a hyperbolic distribution (Zipfs law), that is, to be far away from an even feature distribution, which was mentioned in section 4 as another important requirement on the coding. To meet this requirement, we used a dynamic feature extraction scheme generating n-gram features of different length depending on the occurrence frequencies in the data: If the frequency of an n-gram feature is too high, it is replaced by several (n + 1)-gram features containing it—rare combinations of letters may be represented as pairs, frequent combinations as parts of quadruples, and the rest as triplets. This procedure extracted a set of 15,000 different features from the dictionary where the statistics are much closer to an even distribution, as can be seen in Figure 10.

The heteroassociative memory should map such sparse feature representations to binary output patterns that represent the address numbers of the dictionary entries. In the hexadecimal address number, upper and lower digits are separated into number strings of the same length. Each of these numbers is coded in a 1-of-n pattern (as described in the example of section 4). These patterns are concatenated to a representation vector containing two "1"-components. For distributed output representations it is difficult to decompose a memory output that contains several items. In this case, representation redundancy can be introduced by

splitting the hexadecimal address into two overlapping number strings. Then, in a superposed output pattern, pairs of 1-entries belonging to valid addresses can be selected by checking the match between the overlapping digits in the number strings.

Our coding prescriptions led to input patterns of the length of 15,000, which was far below the limit of 64K in the PAN IV system, and to output patterns with 4,096 components corresponding to the available neurons in the realization of the PAN system. We used 30 Mbytes of PAN memory, resulting in a storage efficiency of 11 percent in comparison to the 3.2 Mbytes of storage space for the original dictionary. However, there was no storage optimization, that is, the density of 1-entries in the connection matrix p_1 was low, see equation (18). The response time virtually does not vary for different words, for input errors, or for the correctness of the result: Even with a software-simulated associative memory, it was always around 1.2 seconds on a Sun SPARCStation 2. The PAN IV can deliver one association result in approximately 1 ms. This would become important if the retrieval system were to be simultaneously accessed by many users.

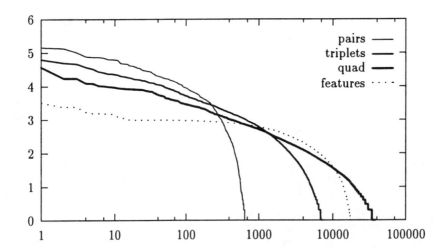

Figure 10. The curves display-ordered feature histograms on the dictionary of 300,000 German words for different coding features. On the y-axis, the logarithmic number of occurrences of features is plotted. On the x-axis, the features occurring in the data are ordered with respect to decreasing occurrence frequencies. The dotted line shows the histogram of the coding with a feature set dynamically generated on the data. The feature set contains n-grams with $n = 2,3,4$.

In another application we used a NAM to access FFT data files by different cues. The members of our research group concerned with speech processing must handle large databases with utterances, for example, a database of 19 consonant-vowel combinations spoken by 8 different speakers (several versions per speaker). The FFT spectra were analyzed by a k-means clustering algorithm and extracted prototypes were coded into binary patterns by the similarity-preserving coding (SPC) algorithm as presented in section 4.1. A confusion matrix of these 19 consonant-vowel utterances had been determined from different psychophysical experiments. This confusion matrix C, more precisely the symmetric version $C + C^T$ of the confusion matrix, served as a similarity matrix of these utterances. On the basis of this similarity matrix, the binary codes of the 19 consonant-vowel combinations were calculated by using the SPC algorithm. The speakers' names were represented by the dynamic n-tuple extraction described above. For each FFT data file the binary codes of the FFT spectra, the consonant-vocal utterance, and the speaker's name were concatenated and stored in the NAM by using 2-of-n output code vectors for the file names. Such a coding scheme allows different parts and information combinations to access subsets of files of the whole database for use in different speech recognition or psychophysical experiments.

Acknowledgment

This work has been supported by the German Ministry for Research and Technology under project number 413-4001-01 IN 103 E/9 (WINA).

References

[Amari 1989] S.I. Amari, "Characteristics of Sparsely Encoded Associative Memory, *Neural Networks*, 1989, pp. 451–457.

[Amit 1987] D. Amit, H. Gutfreund, and H. Sompolinsky, "Statistical Mechanics of Neural Networks Near Saturation, *Annals of Physics*, Vol. 173, 1987, pp. 30–67.

[Buckingham 1995] B. Buckingham and D. Willshaw, "Improving Recall from an Associative Memory, *Biological Cybernetics*, Vol. 72, 1995, pp. 337–346.

[Ekeberg 1988] Ö. Ekeberg, "Robust Dictionary Lookup Using Associative Networks," *Int'l J. Man-Machine Studies*, Vol. 28, 1988, pp. 29–43.

[Falkoff 1962] A. Falkoff, "Algorithms for Parallel-Search Memories," *J. ACM*, Vol. 9, 1962, pp. 488–511.

[Gardner-Medwin 1976] A. Gardner-Medwin, "The Recall of Events Through the Learning of Associations Between Their Pairs," *Proc. Royal Society of London B*, Vol. 194, 1976, pp. 375–402.

[Gibson 1992) W. Gibson and J. Robinson, "Statistical Analysis of the Dynamics of a Sparse Associative Memory," *Neural Networks*, Vol. 5, 1992, pp. 645–662.

[Hebb 1949] D.O. Hebb, *The Organization of Behavior*, John Wiley and Sons, New York, N.Y., 1949.

[Heimann 1994] D. Heimann, "Information Retrieval auf der Basis Neuronaler Assoziativspeicher [German]," PhD thesis, Technical University of Hamburg-Harburg, Germany, 1994.

[Bentz 1989] H.J. Bentz, "Information Storage and Effective Data Retrieval in Sparse Matrices," *Neural Networks*, Vol. 2, 1989, pp. 289–293.

[Hopfield 1982] J. Hopfield, "Neural Networks and Physical Systems with Emergent Collective Computational Abilities," *Proc. Nat'l Academy of Sciences*, USA, 1982, p. 79.

[Huch 1990] M. Huch, W. Pöchmueller, and M. Glesner, "BACCHUS: A VLSI Architecture for a Large Binary Associative Memory," *Proc. Int'l Neural Network Conf.*, Kluwer Academic Publishers, Boston, Mass., 1990.

[Kanerva 1988] P. Kanerva, *Sparse Distributed Memory*, MIT Press, Bradford, UK, 1988.

[Kohonen 1979] T. Kohonen, *Content-Addressable Memories*, Springer-Verlag, Berlin, 1979.

[Kohonen 1983] T. Kohonen, *Self-Organization and Associative Memory*, Springer-Verlag, Berlin, 1983.

[Kosko 1988] B. Kosko, "Bidirectional Associative Memories," *IEEE Trans. Systems, Man, and Cybernetics*, Vol. 18, 1988, pp. 49–60.

[Little 1974] W. Little, "The Existence of Persistent States in the Brain," *Mathematical Biosciences*, Vol. 19, 1974, pp. 101–120.

[Palm 1980] G. Palm, "On Associative Memory," *Biological Cybernetics*, Vol. 36, 1980, pp. 19–31.

[Palm 1988] G. Palm, "On the Asymptotic Storage Capacity on Neural Networks," Vol. F41 of *NATA ASI Series*, Springer-Verlag, Berlin, 1988, pp. 271–280.

[Palm 1991] G. Palm and M. Palm, "Parallel Associative Networks: The PAN-System and the Bacchus-Chip," *Proc. 2nd Int'l Conf. Microelectronics for Neural Networks*, Kyrill & Method Verlag, Munich, 1991.

[Palm 1992] G. Palm and F.T. Summer, "Information Capacity in Recurrent McCulloch-Pitts Networks with Sparsely Coded Memory States," *Network*, Vol. 3, 1992, pp. 1–10.

[Schwenker 1995] F. Schwenker, F.T. Sommer, and G. Palm, "Iterative Retrieval of Sparsely Coded Associative Memory Patterns, *Neural Networks*, (accepted for publication).

[Steinbuch 1961] K. Steinbuch, "Die Lernmatrix," *Kyber-netik*, [German], Vol. 1, 1961, p. 36.

[Stellmann 1992 U. Stellmann, "Ähnlichkeitserhaltende Codierung," PhD thesis, [German], Univ. of Ulm, Germany, 1992.

[Strey 1993] A. Strey, "Implementation of Large Neural Associative Memories by Massively Parallel Array Processors," *Proc. Int'l Conf. Application-Specific Array Processors*, IEEE CS Press, Los Alamitos, Calif., 1993, pp. 357–368.

[Willshaw 1969] D.J. Willshaw, O.P. Buneman, and H.C. Longuet-Higgins, "Nonholographic Associative Memory," *Nature*, Vol. 222, 1969, pp. 960–962.

[Willshaw 1990] D.J. Willshaw and P. Dayan, "Optimal Plasticity from Matrix Memories: What Goes Up Must Come Down," *Neural Computation*, Vol. 2, 1990, pp. 85–93.

Mapping Sigma-Pi Neural Networks and The Associative Reward-Penalty Training Regime to The Associative String Processor

Richard Stuart Neville, Ray Glover, and Thomas John Stonham
Department of Electrical Engineering
Brunel University
Uxbridge, Middlesex
UB8 3PH, ENGLAND
r.s.neville@herts.ac.uk, {Raymond.Glover, John.Stonham}@brunel.ac.uk

Abstract

This article presents a methodology for training and mapping sigma-pi neural networks onto a massively parallel processing (MPP) system. The implementation uses a sigma-pi neuron model that can be viewed as an associative element which enables one to easily map the model to an MPP Associative String Processor (ASP) structure. The novelty of this article is that it utilizes the associative nature of the sigma-pi neuron model and their bounded quantized site values (weights) to facilitate quick training of these types of neurocomputing systems. We use three methods to enable us to do this: The first method utilizes precalculated constrained lookup tables to train a network; in the second, we pipeline the input vectors; the third utilizes data-parallel methodology to further increase the efficiency of training sigma-pi networks with the associative reward-penalty (A_{R-P}) training regime.

1   Introduction

Massively parallel processing machines let us implement large neural systems and speed up training of such structures [1]. In our research we use the sigma-pi neuron model [2] [3] [17]–[23] [61] as it utilizes quantized integer variables to store the "weights" of the artificial neural network. We utilize an associative processing MPP system that lets us utilize precalculated constrained lookup tables as constrained parametric space. These are calculated prior to runtime, once the constants for the training phase have been defined.

In this article we give a brief review of the Associative String Processor. Then we present logical neural networks and the sigma-pi neuron model, followed by a description of the associative reward-penalty training methodology. We next describe how to map the sigma-pi model and associative reward-penalty to the Associative String Processor (ASP), give our results, and end with concluding remarks.

2   The Associative String Processor

The ASP [5] is a homogeneous, fine-grain SIMD (single instruction, multiple data) machine, made up of thousands of processing elements (see Figure 1). The ASP system lets us perform tera-ops (operations per second) and giga-flops (floating-point ops) with low-MIMD/high-SIMD second generation massively parallel processor systems.

The ASP can implement computer vision tasks [6] and works in real-time environments [7], which require diverse computational analysis of real-time data.

The ASP may be viewed as a large processing and associative lookup table, where precalculated equations corresponding to multidimensional variables (which are constrained in parametric space), and which are calculated prior to the runtime of the system once the constants in the equations have been initialized. In contrast to the more traditional parallel computer architectures, the ASP uses scalar-vector "content-matching" rather than "location-addressing" techniques. The ASP may be thought of as an associative matching process for selective set-based operations (that is, a sequence of scalar-vector and vector-vector processes).

A single program controller manages the common processing flow of large numbers of identical associative processing elements (APEs), arranged in a linear string, each made up of 64 data bits and 6 activity bits. Each APE has four flags. Two indicate a match TR1 (M match flag) and TR2 (secondary match flag). The others are a carry flag C and an activation flag A, which points out those APEs that are ready to execute an instruction. The technique the ASP uses is: APEs are selected for subsequent parallel processing by

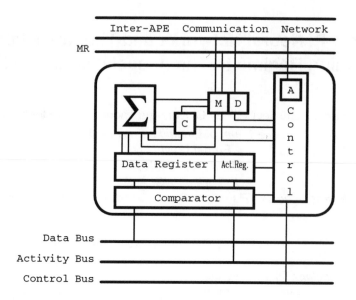

Figure 1. The Associative Processing Element.

comparing or matching their data and activity contents with the states of the corresponding data and activity buses broadcast by the program controller. More simply, the ASP works by first tagging selected data items in the string and then operating on these tagged APEs in parallel. Hence the algorithmics the ASP performs are of an associative nature. This lets us utilize the selective set-based structure of the ASP, where set-based processing enables us to operate only on a subset of all the data items in the APE string.

3 Introduction to logical neural networks

Most artificial neural network researchers utilize neuron models that implement a linear sum of the weights times their input stimuli. This sum is then passed through an activation-output function, which is normally a sigmoidal transfer function. These units are termed *semilinear* as the shape or linearity of the transfer function is defined by ρ (for example, Equation (16)), which is a positive parameter that defines the shape of the curve. This may be set to a hard limiter if $\rho \to 0$ or with $\rho \to 0.4$ the curve becomes semilinear, where both the input and output of these units are real-valued.

Some researchers [2]–[4] [8]–[43] have a different perspective—they use what may be called "digital networks" as they can implement the node functionality in hardware using random access memories (RAMs). The initial research on digital neural net-

works has been attributed to Aleksander and his colleagues. The breakthrough of these researchers was to realize a hardware implementation of the *n*-tuple pattern recognition technique of Bledsoe and colleagues [44] [45]. The driving force behind their research derives from the fact that the mainstay of computational devices today are digital in nature. These digital computational devices process analog information by first digitizing the input (for example, coding the analog signal using an analog-to-digital (A/D) converter), processing the signal, and converting the digital signal back to analog (for example, with a digital-to-analog (D/A) converter).

The whole ethos of these RAM-based units is that they enable Boolean functions to be implemented as lookup tables in a RAM. Hence logic nodes of this type have inputs and outputs that are binary or bivalent.

The basic difference between the semilinear neuron model, which sums the product of the inputs and their weights and the simple logical node, is that logical nodes [8] [9] [11] respond to their input patterns in addressable locations, S_μ; the locations contain either a logical "1" or "0" (for example, $S_\mu \in \{0, 1\}$ then $Y = 1 \big| S_{\mu=1}$).

3.1 Introduction to sigma-pi (probabilistic) neural networks

The generalization of the logical node to the multilevel probabilistic unit [25] is now presented.

328

The diagram in Figure 2 shows a simple 3-state *probabilistic logic node* (PLN) [10] [13] [18] [19]. Figure 2 introduces the concept of a site containing a probability value that defines the output $P(Y = 1|_\mu) = S_\mu$. For a 3-state unit ("state implies the number of discrete states the site value of a unit may take) the site values are $S_\mu \in \{0, u, 1\}$ where

$$P(Y = 1|_{S_{\mu=0}}) = 0$$
$$P(Y = 1_{S_{\mu=u}}) = 0.5 \qquad (1)$$
$$P(Y = 1|_{S_{\mu=1}}) = 1$$

defines the three possible states per site of the basic probabilistic logic node.

This may be represented in hardware terms as a storage location (in the case of the 3-state unit) in a RAM that stores the site value S_μ. Then $S_\mu \in \{0, 0.5, 1\}$ in binary representation is $S_{\mu binary} \in \{00_2, 01_2, 10_2\}$, that is, 3 values (later in the article we term this the machine-quantized representation and designate it S_{m-q}).

We can now generalize the 3-state unit to a multi-level logical node, for example, for a 5-state unit the site value S_μ takes on the following probabilities $\{0, 0.25, 0.5, 0.75, 1\}$ of outputting a logical "1" if the output function is linear. If we interpret the site value as ranging over a set of discrete levels $S_m \in \{-2, ..., +2\}$, where S_m is represented in polarized notation, we arrive at the output functions for the linear and sigmoidal cases that are depicted in Figure 3.

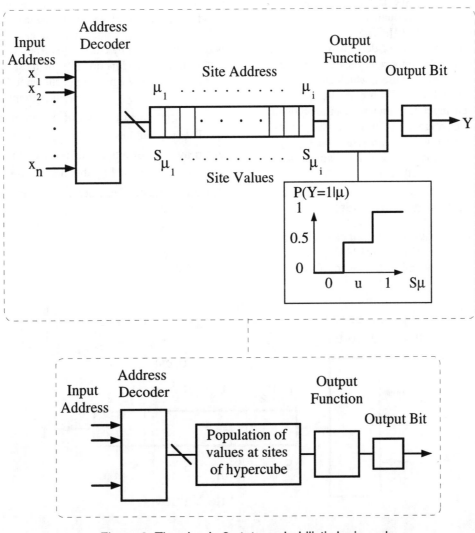

Figure 2. The simple 3-state probabilistic logic node.

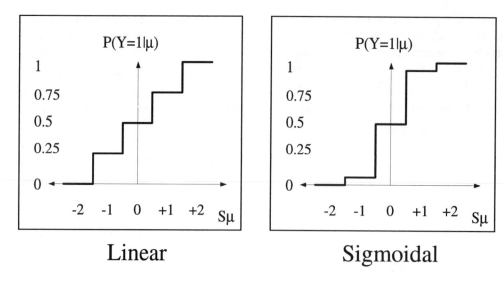

Linear   Sigmoidal

Figure 3. Output function 5-state multilevel logic node.

The more important issue is that these multilevel units have had their functionality described mathematically by Gurney [4] [14]. They are then called sigma-pi units (the notation is described in the following paragraphs). The important aspect of presenting a mathematical representation, which can deal with real-valued inputs and outputs (for example, analog or continuous-valued inputs), is that we can analytically prove learning convergence in a supervised regime, such as *associative reward-penalty* and *back propagation of error*. The mathematical foundations of the sigma-pi model is addressed next.

3.2   The sigma-pi neuron model

The neuron model we utilize has been called a sigma-pi unit, first defined by Gurney [4] [14]–[16]. These units are similar to the pRAM units of Gorse and

Taylor and colleagues [30]–[33], and as they are RAM based, they may be placed in the same category as the PLN units of Aleksander and colleagues [10]. The model was derived by Gurney [4] from a mathematical description of the functionality of these devices. We start by visualizing a basic unit, shown in Figure 4.

Here $x \in \{x_1, x_2, ..., x_i\}$ is a binary input vector that may be represented as a set of bits in positions x_1 to x_i. The site address $\mu \in \{\mu_1, \mu_2, ..., \mu_i\}$ is represented by a set of bits in positions μ_1 to μ_i. The site value S_μ is addressed by the binary string μ. Gurney [4] mathematically described the functionality of these sigma-pi units as

$$y = \frac{1}{2^n} \sum_\mu S_\mu \prod_{i=1}^{i=n} (1 + \overline{\mu}_i \overline{x}_i) \qquad (2)$$

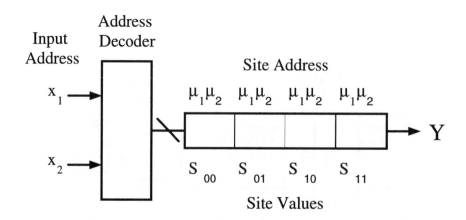

Figure 4. Simplistic structural details of a sigma-pi cell, for analytical visualization.

where $\overline{x}$ denotes polarized notation $\overline{x} \in \{-1, 1\}$, $\overline{\mu} \in \{-1, 1\}$ and $\underline{S}_\mu$ denotes unpolarized notation, that is, in binary $\underline{S}_{\mu binary} \in \{0, 1\}$. The output $\underline{y}$ is in unpolarized notation, giving a binary representation $\underline{y} \in \{0, 1\}$.

This may be cast in the more normal form of an activation (which in the semilinear case is a linear sum-of-weights function) and an output function. The activation is:

$$a = \frac{1}{2^n} \sum_\mu \overline{S}_\mu \prod_{i=1}^{i=n} (1 + \overline{\mu}_i \, \overline{x}_i) \qquad (3)$$

where $a = \overline{y}$, hence

$$\underline{y} = \frac{1}{2}(a + 1) \qquad (4)$$

Note that the site value is represented in its polarized form $\overline{S}_\mu$ and $\overline{y}$, which take the values $\{-1, 1\}$. We now present the sigma-pi models, which in our research has taken the form of stochastic models as the site values are interpreted as probabilities. The input x_i may also be interpreted as the probability of a "1" appearing at the ith input to the node. The output y is defined by a probabilistic process, which is presented in the following paragraphs.

The first model is a *time integration node* (TIN), as stated by Gurney [4], and contains a hypercube of sites that feeds a bit stream or activation stream, which is then interpolated through an output function. The TIN is shown in Figure 5.

A time integration node stores site values in a hypercube, which is addressed by an i bit input vector. The input vector addresses a site μ, which contains a site value S_μ that stores a value $S_\mu \in \{-S_m, \ldots, S_m\}$ and which we interpret as a quantized number for reasons of hardware implementation, but which may also be a real number. The site value is passed through a bit generator function, which fills the activation stream with a bit b. The stream is then used to estimate an activation value, which is then passed through an output function (which may be linear or sigmoidal) in order to produce the output.

The TIN's activation may be defined as

$$a = \frac{1}{S_m} \sum_\mu S_\mu P_\mu = \frac{\langle S_\mu \rangle}{S_m} \qquad (5)$$

when

$$P(\mu) = \frac{1}{2^n} \prod_{i=1}^{i-n} (1 + \underline{\mu}_i \, z_i) \qquad (6)$$

given

$$P_{\underline{\mu}}(\underline{x}_i) = \frac{1}{2}(1 + \underline{\mu}_i \, z_i) \qquad (7)$$

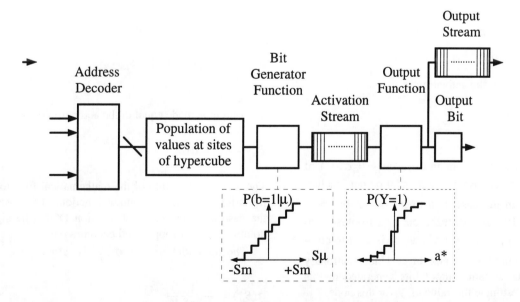

Figure 5. The time integration sigma-pi unit.

where a is the activation found by summation of all the addressed sites times the probability that the site address was visited, $((S_\mu \times P(\mu)))$. The new input address is formed from a set of Boolean variables $\{X_i\}$. These are defined via a set of probability distributions determined by z_i.

$$P_1(\underline{x}_i) = \frac{1}{2}(1+z_i) \text{ and } P_0(\underline{x}_i) = \frac{1}{2}(1-z_i) \qquad (8)$$

where z_i, the input probability distribution, defines the probability of the input x_i. Hence the probability $P_\mu(\underline{x}_i)$ that $\underline{x}_i$ is equal to the ith component of the site address μ is given, where $P(\mu)$ gives the probability that the current input address locates site μ. Noting that, if we define the current input address as η, then use S_η to generate a, the new activation stream bit is given by

$$P(\underline{b} = 1 | \eta) = \frac{1}{2}(\frac{S_n}{S_m}+1) \qquad (9)$$

Over many time steps, if the input vector is held constant

$$\langle \underline{b} \rangle = P_1(\underline{b}) = \frac{1}{2}(\frac{\langle S_n \rangle}{S_m}-1) \qquad (10)$$

then

$$a = 2\langle \underline{b} \rangle - 1 = \langle \overline{b} \rangle \qquad (11)$$

If N_1 is the number of 1's in the activation stream, which is L bits long, then an estimate for $\langle \underline{b} \rangle$ is $\frac{N_1}{L}$. An estimate a^* for the activation is

$$a^* = 2\frac{N_1}{L} - 1 \qquad (12)$$

This is then used to obtain an estimate $y^* = \sigma(a^*)$ of the output y in the case of a sigmoidal output function or $y^* = (a^*)$ in the case of a linear output function. This in turn defines a distribution on a Boolean random variable y, by $P_1(y) = y^*$, which is used to communicate the output to the next layer. Under stationary conditions, the streams output bits generated in this manner, then estimate the value of y for this node.

The TIN may be utilized for continuous-valued in-puts where the real-valued input defines the probability (z_i) of entering a "1" onto an input x_i of a node. In our depiction of the TIN, the site values are quantized, hence the linear bit generator is quantized into multi-levels as is the sigmoidal output function, but this is due to quantization of a^* to allow these models to be realized in hardware. This method has been generalized to enable the sigma-pi units to operate with real-valued site values, which are termed an "analog model." In fact, we utilize a unit known as a "stochastic model."

When the TIN sigma-pi unit is configured into a multilayered net topology, a change in the input probabilities means that the new outputs at the final layer will be estimated after mL time steps, where m is the number of layers in the network.

A training regime (reward-penalty) requires correlations between short-term fluctuations in the output of the nodes in subsequent layers to provide information for training; we utilize the nonlinearity $\sigma(\cdot)$ in the output stream bit generator for this reason. The sigmoidal function may not be required if, for example, we were using a TIN to perform an approximation to a function, for example, a polynomial function, and obviously if we required a linear unit we would utilize a linear output function.

Another type of model exists that we will call the *direct output node* (DON) (see Figure 6), as it does not utilize the bit stream to provide an output. With this, the activation in the analog model is

$$a = \frac{1}{2^n} \sum_\mu \sigma(S_\mu) \prod_{i=1}^{i=n}(1+\overline{\mu_i}\, z_i) \qquad (13)$$

so that in the stochastic model

$$a = \sum_\mu \sigma(S_\mu)P(\mu) = \langle \sigma(S_\mu) \rangle \qquad (14)$$

The output is made equal to the activation a and

$$P(\underline{y} = 1 | \eta) = \sigma(S_\mu) \qquad (15)$$

The above description of the mathematical functionality is for the sigmoidal output function DON case. In the case of a linear output function DON, the sigma notation $\sigma(\cdot)$ is dropped and becomes $f(\cdot)$.

The sigmoidal function $\sigma(S_\mu)$ is defined as

$$\sigma(S_\mu) = \frac{1}{1+e^{-S_\mu/\rho}} \qquad (16)$$

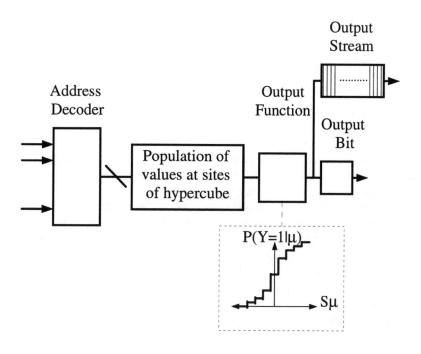

Figure 6. The direct output node (DON) sigma-pi unit.

where ρ is a positive valued parameter that determines the shape of the curve. The DON is a simplified version of a TIN with no activation stream, so the site values are only processed through the output functions to any subsequent layers and output streams. The site values in the DON are quantized, and if the output stream is not required as a stochastic representation of the nodes' output (activation), then the resultant model is the same as the multilevel probabilistic logic node (MPLN) of Myers [24].

In our research we utilize the stochastic model direct output node (DON). The output behavior of these units is similar to that of the Boltzmann units of Hinton and colleagues [46] [47]. The DON is so called as it produces an output directly from the site value stored at the site address defined by the input vector and not from an activation stream that the TIN utilizes to obtain an output.

3.3   The quantized sigma-pi model

For our implementation, all site values are quantized. Hence the site value is divided into D discrete levels, where

$$S_{\mu_q} \in \{-S_m, \ldots, +S_m\} \qquad (17)$$

and, hence, there are

$$D = (2S_m + 1) \qquad (18)$$

levels. This leads to the interpretation of S_μ as equal to

$$S_\mu = \frac{S_{\mu_q}}{S_m} \qquad (19)$$

then

$$S_{\mu_q} = \{n \mid n = -S_m, \ldots, -1, 0, +1, \ldots, +S_m\} \qquad (20)$$

hence if $S_m = 5$ then

$$S_{\mu_q} = \{n \mid n = -5, \ldots, -1, 0, +1, \ldots, +5\} \qquad (21)$$

giving

$$S_\mu = (\frac{S_{\mu_q}}{S_m}) = \{n' \mid n' = -1, \ldots, -0.2, 0, +0.2, \ldots, +1\} \qquad (22)$$

This may be represented in hardware as

$$S_{\mu_{m-q}} = \{n'' \mid n'' = 0, \ldots, S_m, \ldots, 2S_m\} \qquad (23)$$

which we term the machine-quantized representation, normally stored in a binary form, which for $S_m = 5$, is

$$S_{\mu_{m-q}} = \{n'' \mid n'' = 0000_2, \ldots, 0101_2, \ldots, 1010_2\} \qquad (24)$$

333

4 Associative reward-penalty training

4.1 Historical overview of associative reward-penalty

The term *reinforcement* comes from experiments in psychology on animal learning. Reinforcement refers to the occurrence of an event, given the correct relation to a response, that is, liable to increase the probability of the occurrence of the same response. Barto [48] states that the basic premise has root in the classical *law of effect* of Thorndike [50]. The associative reward-penalty (A_{R-P}) learning rule was derived from research by Barto and Jordan in 1987, [48]. Barto's work entailed using associative reward-penalty applied to a task; for example, where nonlinear associative mappings are to be learned by a feedforward network. Barto and Jordan's [48] work of 1987 on A_{R-P} followed research by Williams [51]–[53] on reinforcement-training methodologies.

The initial research on RAM-based digital sigma-pi networks utilizing the associative reward-penalty paradigm was carried out by Gurney [4] [14]. Complementary work on similar models (that is, pRAMs) was done by Gorse and Taylor and colleagues [30]–[33], who also apply the reward-penalty methodology.

A unification of the sigma-pi model and the reward-penalty algorithm has been presented formally by Gurney [4] [14]. Investigations by Neville [17] into the use of reward-penalty—for on-board training of VLSI hardware implementation of sigma-pi networks—initiated the work of Hui and colleagues [35]–[43] into cascadable sigma-pi nets. Complementary work in this area has been carried out by Clarkson and colleagues [26]–[29], using the pRAM units of Gorse and Taylor [30]–[33].

4.2 Associative reward-penalty for sigma-pi units

In order to define a reward-penalty signal for sigma-pi units, we define the mean-squared output error term:

$$e_o = \frac{1}{N_v} \sum_{i=1}^{i=I_v} [Y_t^i - \sigma(S_\mu^i)]^2 \qquad (25)$$

where $[\cdot]^2$ is the square error per input stimuli, defined on the output: This is summed over all N_v output units or visible units. The sum is over the set I_v of these output units. The error is the difference between the target response, Y_t^i, of a stated output for a given input/output pattern pair and the sigmoidal value of the

site $\sigma(S_\mu^i)$, where μ specifies an address on unit i 's input lines. The scalar reward is defined probabilistically. The net is given a debit or penalized if its output is wrong [54]. The initial research of Barto [48] defines the reward signal $r \in \{0,1\}$ in his P-model as

$$r_{(t)} = \begin{cases} 1, with\ probability\ 1 - e_{o(t)} \\ 0, with\ probability\ e_{o(t)} \end{cases} \qquad (26)$$

where the error e_0 is the mean-square output error of the net. This means the reinforcement is deduced solely as a function of the output error and the present input stimuli, which we call *primary* information.

The site values of the sigma-pi units are adapted depending on the reinforcement value r, for each node j, for input address μ then

$$\Delta S_\mu^j = \begin{cases} \alpha[Y^j - \sigma(S_\mu^j)] & if\quad r = 1 \\ \alpha\lambda[1 - Y^j - \sigma(S_\mu^j)] & if\quad r = 0 \end{cases} \qquad (27)$$

where $\alpha > 0$ is the learning rate and $0 \le \lambda \le 1$ is the penalty coefficient.

4.3 Training output units

The output units are trained using a delta "δ" rule, where the addressed site μ of output node i is updated with

$$\Delta S_\mu^i = \begin{cases} \alpha[Y^i - \sigma(S_\mu^i)] & if\quad r^i = 1 \\ \alpha\lambda[1 - Y_t^i - \sigma(S_\mu^i)] & if\quad r^i = 0 \end{cases} \qquad (28)$$

where the reward signal "r^i" for each output unit i is derived from the units' output error given by:

$$e_o^i = [Y_t^i - \sigma(S_\mu^i)]^2 \qquad (29)$$

A different approach is to use the delta "δ" rule of Widrow and Hoff [55], where the output units are adapted with

$$\Delta S_\mu^i = \alpha\rho\frac{2}{N_v}\sigma'(S_\mu^i)[Y_t^i - \sigma(S_\mu^i)] \qquad (30)$$

The adaption technique above is a symmetrical learning rule, our methodology utilizes a nonsymmetrical learning rule for updating of visible and hidden units, as the noise term λ is then utilized to avoid absorption in suboptimal states. This philosophy is also followed by Gorse and Taylor [30]–[32], but they utilize separate independent reward and penalty signals.

4.4 Quantized sigma-pi model training and noise

To approximate the expectation of ΔS_μ over time, the fractional component of ΔS_μ is interpreted as a probabilistic component. Then the site changes in the quantized model are:

$$\Delta_q S_\mu = I_\mu + F_\mu \qquad (31)$$

where I_μ is the integral part of the left-hand side (LHS), formed by truncating the Δ change in the site value. F_μ is the remaining fractional part.
Then

$$\Delta_q S_\mu = I_\mu + \delta S_\mu \qquad (32)$$

where δS_μ is a unit increment or decrement made stochastically with probability $|F_\mu|$. That is

$$
\begin{aligned}
P(\delta S_\mu = +1) &= \frac{1}{2}[1 + sgn(\Delta S_\mu)]\,|F| \\
P(\delta S_\mu = -1) &= \frac{1}{2}[1 - sgn(\Delta S_\mu)]\,|F|
\end{aligned}
\qquad (33)
$$

while $\delta S_\mu = 0$ otherwise (that is, if $\Delta S_\mu = 1.25$ then $sgn(\Delta S_\mu) = +1$ and if $\Delta S_\mu = -1.6$ then $sgn(\Delta S_\mu) = -1$. This gives the required expectation

$$\langle \Delta_q S_\mu \rangle = \Delta S_\mu \quad or \quad \Delta S_\mu + n_q \qquad (34)$$

where n_q is a noise term with zero expectation. We observe that the effective noise n_q may be increased or decreased dependent on the value of S_m and ρ, (that is, Equation (16)). When $S_m \to \infty$ the noise term $n_q \to 0$, but by selection of an $S_m \leq 10$, say, we may obtain beneficial results from the noise term.

We may also set the slope of the sigmoid, which previous researchers have set to a high slope $\rho = 0.04$ [34], to a semilinear curve, that is, $\rho = 0.3$, and hence more noise may also be introduced into the incremental learning regime. This hypothesis has been extended in the light of Gullapalli's [49] work: He postulates that by keeping the values of the units output, Y, from saturating (that is, going to their maximum values, as in the case of Y pertaining to a real number)

we can enhance learning efficiency. In our case by using $\rho = 0.3$ one does not allow the $\sigma(\cdot)$ to asymptotically reach its maximum/minimum values, hence the difference term $[Y - \sigma(S_\mu)]$ never goes to zero, (which it would do if $\rho = 0.04$, where it has a very narrow nonasymptotic region). By setting $\rho \geq 0.3$, we obtain a probabilistic output even when the site value reaches its extreme asymptotic values. This may also be another reason why we obtain more efficient learning when $\rho = 0.3$ [2]. Note that the site value update function (defined in Equations (27) and (28)) will be clipped at its extreme values due to the nature of $S_\mu \in \{-S_m, ..., S_m\}$, although we could train the quantized sigma-pi model with a modified A_{R-P} rule that is multiplied by $\sigma'(S_\mu)$, and then it would not be necessary to check that S_μ does not go out of bounds, as in Equation (30). Initial studies of the variation of S_m and ρ were carried out by Myers [25], where a value of $S_m = 5 (D = 11)$, gave optimal results when tested on 7-bit parity and simple 16-pattern generalization tests.

4.5 Algorithmics of A_{R-P} training

The algorithm presented in pseudocode for associative reward-penalty training of sigma-pi units is detailed below:

```
clamp training vector
for each layer do {
   latch addresses
   generate new site values
   generate new output bits
} od
calculate error e_o
generate reinforcement bit r
for each unit in each layer do {
   calculate ΔS_μ
} od
update site values
```

The algorithm is computing error estimates with Equation (25), on the assent of r (Equation (26)), then is using Equation (27) for the hidden units and Equation (28) to update the visible or output units. Note that this is a *sequential* training method. Where each vector is presented, delta changes in the site values ΔS_μ are made, then the next vector is presented. This differs from the methodology used by Rumelhart and colleagues [56] who use a *batched* training update method, whereas we require errors only on a per-pattern basis, which is a *sequential* method.

5   Training sigma-pi units on the ASP

The method usually used to implement a neural net on a sequential computer is to first set up an array for the weights, then randomly initialize the weights sequentially, and finally train the net by adapting each of the weights in the net sequentially using a regime such as back propagation of error. This is not the case in an MPP system where the majority of the sequential operations may be carried out in parallel.

The method we use to train the neural network utilizes constrained lookup tables [59] [60]. This lets us precalculate the variables for the feedforward (FF) phase, and while we are carrying out the FF operation, we can download the precalculated delta changes ΔS_μ, at the same time, for each node in parallel. This can be done because the sigma-pi neuron model may view its site values in the polarized notation as $\overline{S}_\mu \in \{-1, \ldots, 1\}$, and these may be interpreted in turn as a set of integer elements $S_{\mu_q} \in \{-S_m, \ldots, S_m\}$ that are represented in the machine as a set of integer elements denoted by "m–q" the machine-quantized representation $S_{\mu_{m-q}} \in \{0, \ldots, S_m, \ldots, 2S_m\}$, for example, for $S_m = 5$ then $S_{\mu_{m-q}} \in \{0, \ldots, 5, \ldots, 10\}$. This lets us precalculate constrained lookup tables that the net requires for the FF phase and the training phase. This may be best described as follows. Given $r = 1$, then $\alpha[Y^j - f(S_\mu^j)]$, where the constant $0 < \alpha$ is the learning rate, which is initialized prior to the training phase. The output variable $Y^j \in \{0, 1\}$ is the binary output of the jth sigma-pi unit. The only other variable is $f(S_\mu^j)$, which takes on one of $D = 2S_m + 1$ discrete values. An example of a precalculated FF and training constrained lookup table is depicted in Table 1.

In Table 1, $S_m = 2$, $\alpha = 2.0$, $\lambda = 0.5$, and $f(S_{\mu_{m-q}}) = S_{\mu_{m-q}} / (2S_m)$ for the linear output case. Note

that we must download all four $\Delta S_{\mu_{m-q}}$'s in the FF phase. At the end of the FF phase, one $\Delta S_{\mu_{m-q}}$ is used to update $S_{\mu_{m-q}}$, as r is calculated after the FF phase and each node's output Y^j is known after the FF phase. Also note that the output (visible) units use $Y^j = Y_t^j$ to update, where Y_t^j is the target output, as defined in Equation (28).

To download the $f(S_{\mu_{m-q}})$'s and the $\Delta S_{\mu_{m-q}}$'s using the constrained lookup table methodology with the above predefined constants takes 30 instructions on the ASP, while to carry out the mathematic calculations for $f(S_{\mu_{m-q}})$'s and the $\Delta S_{\mu_{m-q}}$'s would take 200 instructions (for the linear case) on the ASP, using 5 bits in order to quantize to $0.25_{10} = 000.01_2$. This is the simpler case, but for "$r = 0$," we would be required to calculate $\Delta S_{\mu_{m-q}}|_{r-0} = \alpha\lambda[1 - Y^j - f(S_\mu^j)]$ on the ASP. This would require 395 instructions, which is more than 13 times that required for the lookup table method. The precalculated lookup table approach depends on the number of discrete site value states, $D = 2S_m + 1$.

6   Mapping sigma-pi units on to the ASP

In the following sections we relate how we map sigma-pi neural networks on to the ASP to take advantage of the ASP's associative nature and to fully utilize the parallelism that is encapsulated in the associative reward-penalty training regime. We deal with the mapping in two stages: Stage 1 relates how the sigma-pi model and A_{R-P} is mapped to the ASP to maximize its parallel processing capabilities. Stage 2 states how we pipeline input vectors for the two-layer feedforward neural networks that utilize the sigma-pi model and A_{R-P}. The final method we use is the data-parallel

Table 1. Visualization of lookup table of $f(S_{\mu_{m-q}})$ and $\Delta S_{\mu_{m-q}}$ values for A_{R-P} training of sigma-pi networks.

Binary $S_{\mu_{m-q}}$	$S_{\mu_{m-q}}$	$f(S_{\mu_{m-q}})$	$\Delta S_{\mu_{m-q}}|_{r=1}[Y^j=0]$	$\Delta S_{\mu_{m-q}}|_{r=1}[Y^j=1]$	$\Delta S_{\mu_{m-q}}|_{r=0}[Y^j=0]$	$\Delta S_{\mu_{m-q}}|_{r=0}[Y^j=1]$
000_2	0	0.00	0.00	+2.00	+1.00	0.00
001_2	1	0.25	−0.50	+1.50	+0.75	−0.25
010_2	2	0.50	−1.00	+1.00	+0.50	−0.50
011_2	3	0.75	−1.50	+0.50	+0.25	−0.75
100_2	4	1.00	−2.00	0.00	0.00	−1.00

methodology where one places a number of complete copies of the network nodes in a number of substrings. Then a set of patterns are presented to the set of networks in parallel. This means that patterns are associated with copies of the neural network and are processed independently and hence, simultaneously. The data-parallel methodology can be applied with both Stage 1 and Stage 2 mapping techniques.

6.1 Mapping sigma-pi units onto the ASP: Stage 1

The ASP is a linear string of fine-grain processors that, for the sake of simplicity, we will consider a stack of PE elements. Each processing element in the stack, for mapping purposes, is composed of 6 activity bits and a 64-bit data register. Before we elaborate how to map to the MPP, note that the ASP can be partitioned into virtual APEs. Each virtual APE is made up of a set of processing elements, that is, one virtual APE may be a substack (substrings) of 8, 16, 32 and so forth PEs; these are then termed segments.

To map the sigma-pi neuron model and the A_{R-P} learning regime to the MPP machine, we must consider the memory requirements. Then we can define the segment size (virtual PE size) of the ASP. We map each sigma-pi neuron to a single virtual PE substack (substring). The virtual PE substack stores all the site values S_μ for each separate neuron and all the other variables required to carry out local training of the sigma-pi neuron utilizing the A_{R-P} training regime.

In view of the fact that the ASP is an associative MPP, that is, each processing element in the stack is in fact a content-addressable memory (CAM), we have assigned space for each site address μ and its site value S_μ to make optimal use of the ASP's associative matching capabilities. This overcomes the problem we would have of selecting a site value S_η given a site address η that would otherwise require us to index from the first site $\mu = 0$ in the node to the required site $\mu = \eta$, which would be time-consuming. With our method, we *match* the present input site-address μ_{IN} and then *tag* the site value μ (for example, $\mu = \mu_{IN}$) that correlates to the site-address, μ, and then operates on the *tagged* site value, S_μ, as and when required. Because there are four columns of combined site addresses and site values (see Figure 7) we actually carry out the match and tag operation four times to select the correct site value. Figure 7 shows how we map the sigma-pi neural model and the local learning regime to a virtual ASP substack.

Activity Bits						wf1				wf0			
a1	a2	a3	a4	a5	a6	bf7	bf6	bf5	bf4	bf3	bf2	bf1	bf0
						63...56	55...48	47...40	39...32	31...24	23...16	15...8	7...0
X	X	X	1	0	0	μ_0	S_{μ_0}	μ_l	S_{μ_l}	μ_m	S_{μ_m}	μ_n	S_{μ_n}
.	.	.	.	.	.	μ_1	S_{μ_1}	μ_{l+1}	$S_{\mu_{l+1}}$	μ_{m+1}	$S_{\mu_{m+1}}$	μ_{n+1}	$S_{\mu_{n+1}}$
.	.	.	.	.	.	.	.	.	.	.	.	.	.
.	.	.	.	.	.	μ_{k-1}	$S_{\mu_{k-1}}$	μ_{l+k-1}	$S_{\mu_{l+k-1}}$	μ_{m+k-1}	$S_{\mu_{m+k-1}}$	μ_{n+k-1}	$S_{\mu_{n+k-1}}$
X	X	X	1	0	0	μ_k	S_{μ_k}	μ_{l+k}	$S_{\mu_{l+k}}$	μ_{m+k}	$S_{\mu_{m+k}}$	μ_{n+k}	$S_{\mu_{n+k}}$
X	X	X	0	1	0	Y	REFCol	μ_{IN}			TEMP RAND		RAND-NUMB
X	X	X	0	0	1	$e_o(S_\mu)$				$f(S_\mu)$			
X	X	X	1	0	1	$\Delta S_\mu \mid_{r=0 \text{ and } y=0}$				$\Delta S_\mu \mid_{r=0 \text{ and } y=1}$			
X	X	X	1	1	1	$\Delta S_\mu \mid_{r=1 \text{ and } y=0}$				$\Delta S_\mu \mid_{r=1 \text{ and } y=1}$			

Figure 7. Mapping a sigma-pi node and the A_{R-P} training regime to an ASP substack: Stage 1.

In Figure 7, $a_1, \ldots, a_6$ are the activity bits that tag the different memory variables, *wf* 0 & *wf* 1 are 32-bit word fields, and *bf* 0, K , *bf* 7 are 8-byte fields. The sigma-pi's site address $\mu_o, \text{K} , \mu_{n+k}$ and site values $S_{\mu_o}, \text{K} , S_{\mu_{n+k}}$ are laid out side by side to utilize the ASP's fast tag and operate processes. The Y variable stores the present output bit. The REFCol variable stores which of the four columns the selected site is positioned in, μ_{IN} is the present input site address. RANDNUMB is the pseudorandom variable used by the sigma-pi neuron to define its output bit probabilistically, that is, $P(\underline{y} = 1 \big| \mu) = f(S_\mu)$ and TEMP RAND is used when RANDNUMB is updated.

The $e_o(S_\mu)$ variable is the visible nodes output error, and the output-function value $f(S_\mu)$ is the variable used for output bit generation (for example, if $f(S_\mu > RANDNUMB \quad then \quad Y = 1\, else\, Y = 0))$. The last four variables are the delta changes ΔS_μ, which are utilized by the A_{R-P} learning regime. The six variables at the bottom of the virtual APE substack are all precalculated prior to training of the net and are downloaded during the FF phase. During the FF phase each node utilized $f(S_\mu)$ to generate an output bit Y, and all the nodes on a given layer, calculate their output in parallel. Once the FF phase has been carried out, the reward signal r is calculated using Equations (25) and (26). Then, in the training phase, we can select one of the delta changes ΔS_μ^j, given r the reward signal and Y^j each nodes output, to update S_μ^j the site value selected in each node j.

6.2 Algorithmics of A_{R-P} training on the ASP

The algorithm presented below in pseudocode is for the FF phase of the neurocomputer system mapped to the ASP:

(PROCESS HIDDEN LAYER)

```
clamp training vector/s (down-
load μ_IN^HIDDEN values).
Down-load Variables.

if ((f(S_μ) > RANDNUMB))
        Y^HIDDEN = 1
else
        Y^HIDDEN = 0
endif
```

(PROCESS OUTPUT LAYER)

```
clamp μ_IN^OUTPUT = {Y_0^HIDDEN, K , Y_n^HIDDEN}
Down-load Variables.

if ((f(S_μ) > RANDNUMB))
        Y^OUTPUT = 1
else
        Y^OUTPUT = 0
endif
```

Procedure (Down-load Variables)

```
for (count:=0 to D-1) do {
    REFCol_count = 0.
        Tag and write
variables.
    INC REFCol_count
        Tag and write
variables.
    INC REFCol_count
        Tag and write
variables.
    INC REFCol_count
        Tag and write
variables.
} od
```

Procedure (Tag and write variables)

```
Tag μ if equal to μ_IN in
column defined by REFCol_count
(Tag TR2).

Tag site value if S_μ = count
(Tag TR1) if TR2 set.

Write f(S_μ), ΔS_μ's and e_o(S_μ) if
output layer to TR1 tagged
nodes.
if Tag TR1 set. Tag REFCOL
with TR2.

Write REFCol = REFCol_counter
to TR2 tagged nodes.
```

In training the sigma-pi net, the four ΔS_μ's are downloaded at the same time as $f(S_\mu)$'s and $e_o(S_\mu)$. All the nodes in a layer are operated on in parallel for the FF phase. The delta changes are downloaded in the FF phase, and the training phase has only to carry out the update of the site value, $S_{\mu_{(t)}} = S_{\mu_{(t-1)}} + \Delta S_{\mu_{(t)}}$, which is a simple addition carried out on a per node (virtual APE) basis in parallel for all the nodes in the net/s.

6.3 Mapping sigma-pi units onto the ASP: Stage 2

In this section we relate how we pipeline the input

vectors of two-layer feedforward neural networks that utilize the sigma-pi model and A_{R-P}. The above mapping has the problem that we process only one layer at a time. In Stage 1 mapping we may not process both the output layer and the hidden layer of the network in parallel; Stage 1 is a step-by-step methodology of processing only one layer at a time. The two-layer networks we use in our experimental work may be more efficiently mapped onto an MPP structure if one processes the layers in parallel, as other researchers have done [57].

In Stage 2 mapping we pipeline the input vectors. Then the two-layer nets process both layers in parallel. This is carried out by first clamping input vector $x_{i_{(t+1)}}$ to the input layer, then processing the hidden layer to calculate the hidden layer output, which becomes the input vector to the output layer. Finally, processing the output layer derived from input $x_{i_{(t+1)}}$ also processes the hidden layer utilizing the next input vector $x_{i_{(t+1)}}$, which is now clamped to the input nodes.

To let us utilize the methodology we used in Stage 1 mapping, we must now consider two sets of deltas ΔS_μ, and hence the virtual ASP substack now has to retain one set of deltas relating to $x_{i_{(t)}}$ and another relating to $x_{i_{(t+1)}}$. We must also store the previous site address $\mu_{IN_{(t)}}$, $Y_{(t)}$, and $r_{(t)}$ to enable the update process utilized by the training regime to work correctly. The Stage 2 mapping is presented in Figure 8, which shows how we map the sigma-pi neural model and the A_{R-P} training regime and utilize pipelined input vectors.

The only difference between Stage 1 and Stage 2 mapping is that we now require eight more variable locations in the ASP substack. Two of these variables store $REFCol_{(t+1)}$ and $\mu_{IN(t+1)}$: One is used to store the input vector's address, one to store the value of Y, and the remaining four store the next vector's delta changes (that is, $\Delta_{(t+1)}$). Note that the modification to the substack layout is carried out only on the hidden layer.

Activity Bits						wf1				wf0			
a1	a2	a3	a4	a5	a6	bf7	bf6	bf5	bf4	bf3	bf2	bf1	bf0
						63...56	55...48	47...40	39...32	31...24	23...16	15...8	7...0
X	X	X	1	0	0	μ_0	S_{μ_0}	μ_l	S_{μ_l}	μ_m	S_{μ_m}	μ_n	S_{μ_n}
.	.	.	.	.	.	μ_1	S_{μ_1}	μ_{l+1}	$S_{\mu_{l+1}}$	μ_{m+1}	$S_{\mu_{m+1}}$	μ_{n+1}	$S_{\mu_{n+1}}$
.	.	.	.	.	.	.	.	.	.	.	.	.	.
.	.	.	.	.	.	μ_{k-1}	$S_{\mu_{k-1}}$	μ_{l+k-1}	$S_{\mu_{l+k-1}}$	μ_{m+k-1}	$S_{\mu_{m+k-1}}$	μ_{n+k-1}	$S_{\mu_{n+k-1}}$
X	X	X	1	0	0	μ_k	S_{μ_k}	μ_{l+k}	$S_{\mu_{l+k}}$	μ_{m+k}	$S_{\mu_{m+k}}$	μ_{n+k}	$S_{\mu_{n+k}}$
X	X	X	0	1	0	$Y_{(t)}$ and $Y_{(t+1)}$	$REFCol_{(t)}$	$\mu_{IN_{(t)}}$	$REFCol_{(t+1)}$	$\mu_{IN_{(t+1)}}$	TEMP RAND	$r_{(t)}$	RAND-NUMB
X	X	X	0	0	1	$e_o(S_\mu)$				$f(S_\mu)$			
X	X	X	1	0	1	$\Delta S_{\mu_{(t)}} \mid r=0$ and $y=0$				$\Delta S_{\mu_{(t)}} \mid r=0$ and $y=1$			
X	X	X	1	1	1	$\Delta S_{\mu_{(t)}} \mid r=1$ and $y=0$				$\Delta S_{\mu_{(t)}} \mid r=1$ and $y=1$			
X	X	X	0	1	1	$\Delta S_{\mu_{(t+1)}} \mid r=0$ and $y=0$				$\Delta S_{\mu_{(t+1)}} \mid r=0$ and $y=1$			
X	X	X	1	1	0	$\Delta S_{\mu_{(t+1)}} \mid r=1$ and $y=0$				$\Delta S_{\mu_{(t+1)}} \mid r=1$ and $y=1$			

Figure 8. Mapping a sigma-pi node and the A_{R-P} training regime to an ASP substack: Stage 2.

The algorithmics of A_{R-P} training also requires modification as we now download the next delta changes $\Delta_{(t+1)}$ prior to calculating the present updated site value $S_{\mu_{(t)}} = S_{\mu_{(t-1)}} + \Delta S_{\mu_{(t)}}$. Hence before downloading $\Delta_{(t+1)}$, the previous delta changes in these locations are shifted to the variable position, which stores $\Delta_{(t)}$ changes. This adds two tag operations and four WordRead, WordWrite operations to the FF phase of the feedforward networks' algorithmics. We must also copy the old $REFCol_{(t+1)}$ and $\mu_{IN_{(t+1)}}$ to $REFCol_{(t)}$, and $\mu_{IN_{(t)}}$ and $Y_{(t+1)}$ is copied to $Y_{(t)}$, which requires one tag operation and three ByteRead, ByteWrite operations. This adds an extra 17 operations to the A_{R-P} algorithmics described in section 6.2. We now require only one process layer routine. It is however very important to note that if we are just carrying out an FF operation and not an FF and download of deltas, we require no extra ASP code, and the speedup for the FF phase is twice as fast when we utilize pipelined input vectors for our two layer networks when compared to nonpipelined. Once these transfers are completed, the next delta changes $\Delta_{(t+1)}$ are downloaded. The updating was similar to that used in Stage 1 mapping to the ASP in section 6.2.

7   Multicube feedforward structures of sigma-pi units

One of the problems with fully connected networks of logical nodes that require each unit to cover a large input retina is that these units suffer from the problem of an exponential rise in resources as the number of inputs increases. For example, a 3-tuple requires $2^3 \rightarrow 8$ sites in the cube. But for a fully connected net to cover an input retina of 25 inputs, we require a 25-tuple, giving $2^{25} \rightarrow$ approx. 33×10^6 sites in the cube. Note that a single-cube node's functionality may contain thousands more functions than required.

If we consider the standard sigma-pi unit with a single cube (hypercube) of site values followed by an output function, a linear extension of this type of structure would be to sum the site values from several cubes [4] [14] [15] [19]–[21], and then pass this through an output function. This is depicted in Figure 9. The next extension to this type of structure would be to utilize linear weights on connections from other inputs or units to the summation unit of the multicube unit to enable these units to be configured into competitive networks (that is, in competitive nets, the units compete for the opportunity to respond to the input stimuli).

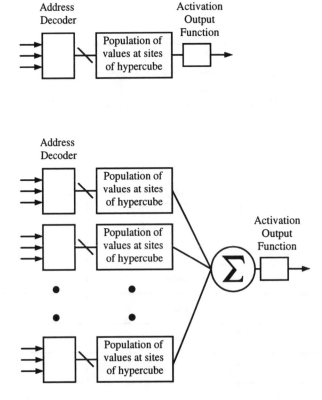

Figure 9. A single-cube sigma-pi unit (top) and a multicube sigma-pi unit (bottom).

The multicube structure with no output function but with an integer output is the same structure as the WISARD system [9] [12] whereas if we configure the multicube unit with a hard limiting (or threshold) output function, we have the type of topology put forward by Minsky and Papert [54] for their perceptron. The multicube structure overcomes the restriction that single-cube sigma-pi units have, as the multicube is a linearly scalable unit. We may also generalize this methodology to store other variables (not just site values), as we have done in our work on the quantized adaptive critic [19] [21] to overcome general problems of an exponential increase of resources, which relate to the number of inputs to a system.

7.1   Memory requirements of single-cube sigma-pi units mapped to the ASP

The sigma-pi networks we use in the following experimental simulations are all fully connected feed-forward neural networks: an XOR network, a 4-2-4 encoder network, and a 8-3-8 encoder network (discussed in section 8). The memory requirements for these are presented in Table 2. (For simplicity we map each 8-tuple used in the 8-3-8 encoder network to two 64 APE segments.)

Table 2 first defines the type of network in the far left-hand column. Then the maximum tuple size for the given network is defined. This is followed by the total number of sigma-pi units required to implement the network and the number of APEs to store the n-tuples for a given network. This is followed by the total number of APEs per unit, which is the number of APEs to store the n-tuples for a given network plus four APEs for the sigma-pi's output function $f(S_\mu)$,

the delta changes $\Delta(S_\mu)$, and the output error per visible node $e_o(S_\mu)$, Y, $REFCol$, μ_{IN}, $TEMPRAND$, and $RANDNUMB$. The segment size for the previous column is then defined. This is followed by the total number of APEs required for the network. Finally, the total number of data bits for each network is defined. The table shows that as the n-tuple size increases, so does the memory requirement. Our basic rule is that one should utilize an n-tuple size of $n \le 8$; for larger inputs, use a multicube sigma-pi unit.

7.2   Memory requirements of the multicube sigma-pi units

We now describe the mapping requirements for multicube units on the ASP. In some artificial neural networks we require fully connected neural units. This is, of course, impossible with normal single-cube sigma-pi units as they are normally upper bounded at an 8-tuple size of 2^8, as larger numbers of input lines means the storage requirements become exponentially large. To overcome this, we utilized multicube sigma-pi units. We already discussed multicube topology; we now give an example of how to overcome the problem of large input retina size. This is best described by continuing from the example discussed in section 7. The n-tuple is required to have 25 input lines, which requires 2^{25} memory locations for the site values of the single-cube sigma-pi unit. However, if we configure a multicube sigma-pi unit to have five 5-tuple sub-cube units, the multicube then requires 5 times 2^5 locations to store its site values, which is less than that required by the 25-tuple single-cube sigma-pi unit.

Table 2. Memory requirements of test networks.

Network	Max n-tuple Size	Number of Sigma-pi Units in Network	Number of APEs to Store Max n-tuple	Total Number of APEs Per Unit	Segment Size	Total Number of APEs Per Network	Number of Data Bits to Store Network
2-2-1 XOR	$2^2 = 4$	3	1	5	8	24	1.5K bits
4-2-4 ENCODER	$2^4 = 16$	6	4	9	16	96	6.1K bits
8-3-8 ENCODER	$2^8 = 256$	11	64*	69	64	1408	90K bits

7.3 Training and mapping requirements of multicube sigma-pi units on the ASP

The multicube sigma-pi unit in Figure 10 differs from the single-cube sigma-pi unit, as it has multiple sub-cubes feeding a sigma (summation) unit. The multicube unit is trained [4] [14]–[15] [20]–[21] in the same manner as a single-cube sigma-pi unit, but the site values in each subcube to be updated are adapted utilizing the mean $S_{\overline{m}}$ of all the addressed site values in the subcubes. As a result, visible output multicube units are required to reduce their output error where

$$e_o = [Y_t - \sigma(S_{\overline{m}})]^2 \qquad (35)$$

given $S_{\overline{m}}$ is the mean site value of all the addressed sites in the subcubes. The A_{R-P} update rule used for the multicube unit j, given address μ, is then

$$\Delta S_\mu^j \big|_{s_{\overline{m}}} = \alpha[Y^j - \alpha(S_{\overline{m}})]$$
$$r + \alpha\lambda[1 - Y^j - \alpha(S_{\overline{m}})]\bar{r} \qquad (36)$$

where $S_{\overline{m}}$ is defined as

$$S_{\overline{m}} = \frac{1}{N_s} \sum_{q=1}^{q=N} S_\mu^k \qquad (37)$$

where the index q denotes the set of subcubes in the kth multicube in the network and N_s is the number of subcube units in the multicube unit (for example, $N_s = 5$ for the multicube described in section 7.2). Then the output of a multicube unit is

$$P(Y = 1) = f(S_{\overline{m}}) \qquad (38)$$

The multicube sigma-pi unit necessitates extra variables and algorithmic requirements when compared to the single-cube sigma-pi unit previously defined. Each virtual PE (substring) now becomes one of a number of subcubes that make up the multicube unit (see Figure 11).

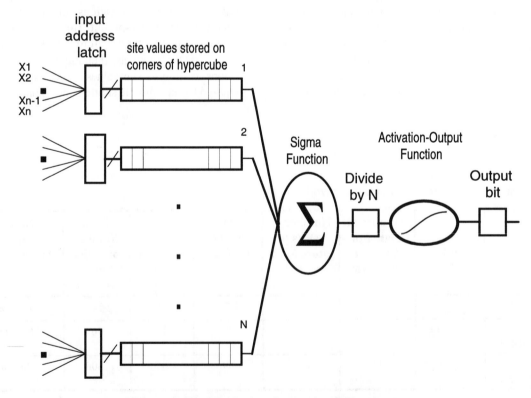

Figure 10. The Multicube sigma-pi unit structure.

342

Activity Bits						wf1				wf0			
a1	a2	a3	a4	a5	a6	bf7	bf6	bf5	bf4	bf3	bf2	bf1	bf0
						63...56	55...48	47...40	39...32	31...24	23...16	15...8	7...0
X	X	X	1	0	0	μ_0	S_{μ_0}	μ_l	S_{μ_l}	μ_m	S_{μ_m}	μ_n	S_{μ_n}
.	.	.	.	.	.	μ_1	S_{μ_1}	μ_{l+1}	$S_{\mu_{l+1}}$	μ_{m+1}	$S_{\mu_{m+1}}$	μ_{n+1}	$S_{\mu_{n+1}}$
.	.	.	.	.	.								
.	.	.	.	.	.	μ_{k-1}	$S_{\mu_{k-1}}$	μ_{l+k-1}	$S_{\mu_{l+k-1}}$	μ_{m+k-1}	$S_{\mu_{m+k-1}}$	μ_{n+k-1}	$S_{\mu_{n+k-1}}$
X	X	X	1	0	0	μ_k	S_{μ_k}	μ_{l+k}	$S_{\mu_{l+k}}$	μ_{m+k}	$S_{\mu_{m+k}}$	μ_{n+k}	$S_{\mu_{n+k}}$
X	X	X	0	1	0	Y	REFCol	μ_{IN}			TEMP RAND		RAND-NUMB
X	X	X	0	0	1	$e_o(S_{\overline{m}})$				$f(S_{\overline{m}})$			
X	X	X	0	1	1	VAR_MUL				MEAN_ACC			
X	X	X	1	0	1	$\Delta S_\mu \mid_{S_{\overline{m}}}$ $r=0$ and $y=0$				$\Delta S_\mu \mid_{S_{\overline{m}}}$ $r=0$ and $y=1$			
X	X	X	1	1	1	$\Delta S_\mu \mid_{S_{\overline{m}}}$ $r=1$ and $y=0$				$\Delta S_\mu \mid_{S_{\overline{m}}}$ $r=1$ and $y=1$			

Figure 11. Mapping a subcube of a multicube sigma-pi node and the A_{R-P} training regime to a ASP substack.

The multicube A_{R-P} training methodology requires the mean site value $S_{\overline{m}}$ to be computed. This means that the MPP system is required to sum all the addressed site values in the multicube units. This is carried out by the addition of "sets" of two subcube site values, which are added in parallel with other "sets" in the cube unit. If, for example, we had four subcube units in the multicube unit, labeled subcube unit one, subcube unit two, and so forth, the addressed site values of subcube units one and two are added at the same time as the addressed site values of subcube units three and four are added. Then the two sums from the previous additions are added to give the final summation value $\sum_{q=1}^{q=N} S_\mu$. These are accumulated in the MEAN_ACC variables in the substacks. This method takes $\log_2 N_s$ parallel addition operations and then multiplies by $1/N_s$ (that is, the VAR_MUL in the substacks) to obtain the mean of the addressed site value $S_{\overline{m}}$, which is finally stored in MEAN_ACC of each substack.

The memory requirements of the virtual PE string were extended to include a summation and a multiplier variable. The summation variable is required to accumulate the $\log_2 N_s$ additions. The mean $S_{\overline{m}}$ is the only operation that requires the neurocomputer system to perform a multiplication operation on the ASP. The mean site value $S_{\overline{m}}$ was also used to download the $f(S_{\overline{m}})$ and $\Delta S_\mu^j \mid S_{\overline{m}}$ values to the set of virtual PE's that make up the multicube. The training was then carried out in the same manner as described in section 6.2, except the delta change in the addressed site values are calculated using $S_{\mu_{(t)}}^j = S_{\mu_{(t-1)}}^j + \Delta S_{\mu_{(t)}}^j \mid S_{\overline{m}}$, with the delta change calculated utilizing the mean of the addressed site values $S_{\overline{m}}$ defined in Equation (36). The virtual PE mapping for a subcube unit in a multicube is depicted in Figure 11.

The layout of the substack for mapping a subcube of a multicube sigma-pi node and the A_{R-P} training regime to a ASP substack is similar to that of a single-cube unit in Figure 7.

8 Experimental work

The two network types in our experimental work are described below.

8.1 The XOR network

The XOR net is made up of two input units that simply distribute the input signals to the hidden layer. The next layer contains two hidden units, each taking their inputs from both input units. The output unit is a single visible unit taking its inputs from both hidden units.

The XOR network has to solve the $X \rightarrow Y$ input-output coding problem, where the input training set is defined as $X_1, X_2 \in \{00, 01, 10, 11\}$ and the target output set is defined as $Y \in \{0, 1, 1, 0\}$.

8.2   The V-H-V encoder network

The V-H-V encoders that we use for our simulations derive from Hinton and colleagues' research [46] [47] into the Boltzmann machine. This type of encoder is a simple abstraction of the recurring task of communicating information among various components of a parallel network. We used the 8-3-8 encoder (see Figure 12), the 4-2-4 encoder, and the XOR net to benchmark the ASP.

The encoders are made up of two groups of visible units, designated $v1$ and $v2$, representing the two systems that communicate their states. The $v1$ units are passive, used only to communicate their inputs to the next layer of the encoder. Each group has V units. In the simple formulation we consider here, $v1$ and $v2$ are not directly connected but are connected to a group of

H hidden units (that is, a single group of hidden units, designated h), with $H < V$, so h may act as a limited capacity channel through which information about $v1$ must be transmitted with optimal coding.

Since all simulations begin with all site values $\sigma(S_\mu) = 0.5$ or $S_{\mu_q} = 0$, giving $P(Y = 1_\mu) = 0.5$, that is, 50 percent probability of the output Y obtaining a value "1". In other words, no prior information has been bestowed on the network. Finding a solution to such a problem requires that the two visible groups come to agree on the meaning of a set of codes without any prior conventions for communicating through h.

9   Experimental results

Our research involved several structures, and the metric we used to show how the ASP performs was interconnections per second (IPS) [1]. The experimental results are presented in Table 3. We utilized an $S_\mu \in \{-10, \dots, 10\}$ and an ASP VASP-64/simulator clock rate of 20 MHz.

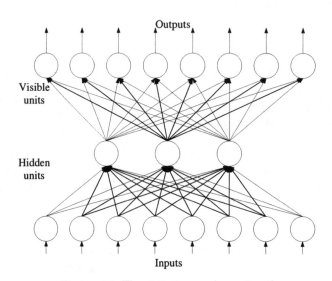

Figure 12. The 8-3-8 encoder network.

Table 3. Experimental results.

Network	Million IPS (Stage 1 Mapping)	Million IPS (Stage 2 Mapping)
2-2-1 XOR	$0.1\big|_{1\,NET}, 0.4\big\|_{4\,NETs}$	$0.2\big|_{1\,NET}, 0.8\big\|_{4\,NETs}$
4-2-4 Encoder	$0.25\big|_{1\,NET}, 1.0\big\|_{4\,NETs}$	$0.5\big|_{1\,NET}, 2.0\big\|_{4\,NETs}$
8-3-8 Encoder	$0.8\big|_{1\,NET}, 6.2\big\|_{8\,NETs}$	$1.6\big|_{1\,NET}, 12.4\big\|_{4\,NETs}$

The first column of Table 3 defines the network's structure. The second column presents the results for the given net in the first column using Stage 1 mapping. The first of the two figures in this column is for a single network with one input vector, and the second figure is for 4 or 8 networks with 4 or 8 input vectors presented in parallel, one per network. The third column presents results for the given network in the first column using Stage 2 mapping, and the second figure is for 4 or 8 networks with 4 or 8 input vectors presented in parallel, one per network. We utilized data-parallel methodology (see results for 4 and 8 nets), which is similar to batch-mode processing to simultaneously implement multiple instantiations of a single neural network on a parallel processor. This type of mapping has been used to increase the throughput rates of neural networks by other researchers, such as Singer [1].

The figures in Table 3 are only for the FF phase. When we implement the training phase with downloading of the deltas in the FF phase, it takes twice as much time to perform the FF and training phases when compared to the FF phase. This is twice as fast as that required by Singer [1] for the forward and backward passes required for a back propagation of error training regime. The third, data-parallel methodology [1] means that N_T copies of the net are made in the ASP. Then each net is given a different input vector and all the ΔS_μ^j (for a given node j and a set input address μ) are added to get the overall delta changes, as is done with batched back propagation of error. This increases the learning speed of the neural system by approximately N_T.

10   Concluding remarks

Our research methodologies enabled us to investigate the viability of mapping a neurocomputational system to an MPP system and the possible implications of the mapping on the algorithmic requirements of the machine. The ASP requires efficient mapping of a neural structure to the MPP machine, utilizing its functionality and communication facilities to the fullest extent. The research makes optimal use of the Associative String Processor's associative matching capabilities. We have also overcome, by utilizing lookup tables, one of the problems inherent in most neural networks—very serious overheads relating to complex and time-consuming mathematical function calculations that are normally calculated during the feedforward and training phases of these neural systems.

This research enables sigma-pi structures to be efficiently trained and mapped onto the ASP. Our methodology of constrained lookup tables means that we can precalculate the sigma-pi's output function $f(S_\mu)$, the delta changes ΔS_μ^j, and the output error per visible node $e_o(S_\mu)$. This means that computationally intensive mathematical functions, such as the sigmoidal function (Equation (16)), are precalculated. Previous work using the ASP to implement the back propagation of error training [58] has had to utilize an approximated sigmoid, using piecewise linear functions. Our research enables these structures to be implemented using the associative nature of the ASP, and the sigma-pi model may be viewed as an associative automaton with bounded site values that aid the high-speed training of a neural system by means of lookup tables for most mathematical computations. Due to the functionality of sigma-pi units, we are not carrying out the more normal $\sum x_i\, w_{ij}$ calculations that are used by semilinear units, which require us to perform n multiply operations (where n is the number of inputs to node j.) and then sum all the products. These are time-consuming tasks, hence the computational requirements of sigma-pi units are less than semilinear.

References

[1] A. Singer, "Exploiting the Inherent Parallelism of Artificial Neural Networks to Achieve 1300 Million Interconnections Per Second," *Proc. INNC,* 1990, pp. 656–660.

[2] R. Neville and J. Stonham, "Adaptive Reward-Penalty for Sigma-pi Networks," *The Int'l J. Neural, Parallel and Scientific Computation,* Vol. 2, No. 2, June 1994, pp. 141–164.

[3] R. Neville and J. Stonham, "Generalisation in Sigma-pi Networks," *Connection Science: J. Neural Computing, Artificial Intelligence and Cognitive Research,* Issue 7, No. 1, Mar. 1995.

[4] K. Gurney, "Training Nets of Hardware Realisable Sigma-pi Units," *Neural Networks,* Vol. 5, 1992a, pp. 289-303.

[5] R.M. Lea, "WASP: A WSI Associative String Processor," *J. VLSI Signal Processing,* Vol. 2, No. 4, May 1991, pp. 271–285.

[6] A. Krikelis, "Computer Vision Applications with the Associative String Processor," *J. Parallel and Distributed Computing,* Vol. 13, 1991, pp. 170–184.

[7] H. Provost, M. Mur, and B. Thooris, "A Real Time Environment for the Associative String Processor in Second Level Trigger Applications," *Proc. "REAL TIME 91,"* 1991.

[8] I. Aleksander and T.J. Stonham, "Guide to Pattern Recognition Using Random-Access Memories," *Com-

puters and Digital Techniques, Vol. 2, No. 1, Feb. 1979, pp. 29–40.

[9] I. Aleksander, W.V. Thomas, and P.A. Bowden, "WISARD, A Radical Step Forward in Image Recognition," *Sensor Rev.*, Vol. 4, No. 3, 1984, pp. 120–124.

[10] I. Aleksander, *Neural Computing Architectures: The Design of Brain-Like Machines,* I. Aleksander, ed., North Oxford Academic Publishers Ltd.

[11] I. Aleksander, "Weightless Neural Tools: Towards Cognitive Macrostructures," *CAIP Neural Network Workshop*, 1990.

[12] B.A. Wilkie, "A Stand-Alone, High Resolution, Adaptive Pattern Recognition System, doctoral thesis, PhD Thesis W499, Dept. of Electrical Eng., Brunel Univ., Middlesex, UK, 1983.

[13] W-K. Kan and I. Aleksander, "A Probabilistic Logic Neuron network for Associative Learning," *Proc. IEEE Int'l Conf. Neural Networks*, Vol. II, IEEE Press, Piscataway, N.J., 1987, pp. II.541–II.548.

[14] K. Gurney, "Learning in Nets of Structured Hypercubes," PhD thesis, Dept. of Electrical Eng., Brunel Univ., Middlesex, UK, available as Tech. Memo CN/R/144, 1989.

[15] K. Gurney, "Weighted Nodes and RAM-Nets: A Unified Approach," *J. Intelligent Systems*, Vol. 2, No. 1–4, 1992, pp. 155–185.

[16] K. Gurney, "Training Nets of Stochastic Units using System Identification," *Neural Networks*, Vol. 6, No. 1, 1993, pp. 133–145.

[17] R. Neville, "Investigate and Evaluate the Design of Probabilistic Nodes for Boolean N-Cube Networks," master's thesis, Dept. of Electrical Eng., Brunel Univ., UK, 1990.

[18] R. Neville and T. Stonham, "Adaptive Reward-Penalty for Probabilistic Logic Nodes*," Proc. Int'l Conf. Artificial Neural Networks,* 1992.

[19] R. Neville and T. Stonham, "Adaptive Critic for Probabilistic Logic Nets," *Proc. World Congress on Neural Networks*, 1993, pp. III.389–III.392.

[20] R. Neville and J. Stonham, "Augmentation of Generalisation of Probabilistic Logic Nets," *Proc. World Congress on Neural Networks*, WCNN-93, 1993, pp. IV.198–IV.201.

[21] R. Neville, "Augmentation of Sigma-pi Structures and Learning Regimes," PhD thesis, Dept. of Electrical Eng., Brunel Univ., Middlesex, UK, 1993, copies available from the author.

[22] R. Neville and J. Stonham, "Unbounded Reinforcement for the Associative Reward-Penalty Algorithm," *Proc. World Congress on Neural Networks*, WCNN-94, 1994, pp. III.637–III.640.

[23] R. Neville and J. Stonham, "A Comparison Study of Unbounded and Real-valued Reinforcement Associative Reward-Penalty Algorithms," *Proc. Int'l Conf. Artificial Neural Networks*, ICANN-94, 1994, pp. 651–654.

[24] C.E. Myers, "Learning with Delayed Reinforcement in an Exploratory Probabilistic Logic Neural Network," unpublished doctoral thesis, Dept. of Electrical Eng., Imperial College of Science, Univ. of London, 1990.

[25] C. Myers, "Output Functions for Probabilistic Logic Nodes," *Proc. 1st IEE Int'l Artificial Neural Networks*, 1989.

[26] T. Clarkson, D. Gorse, and J. Taylor, "Hardware Realisable Models of Neural Processing," *Proc. IEEE Int'l Conf. Artificial Neural Networks*, 1989, pp. 242–246.

[27] T. Clarkson et al., "Learning Probabilistic RAM nets using VLSI Structures," *IEEE Trans. Computers*, Vol. 41, No. 12, Dec. 1992, pp. 1,552–1,561.

[28] T. Clarkson et al., "Generalization in Probabilistic RAM Nets," *IEEE Trans. Neural Networks*, Vol. 4, No. 2, Mar. 1993, pp. 360–363.

[29] T. Clarkson, C.K. Ng, and Y. Guan, "The pRAM: An Adaptive VLSI Chip," *IEEE Trans. Neural Networks*, Vol. 4, No. 3, May 1993, pp. 408–412.

[30] D. Gorse and J. Taylor, "Reinforcement training strategies for probabilistic RAMs," *Theoretical Aspects of Neurocomputing: Selected Papers from Proc. Symp. Neural Networks and Neurocomputing, NEURONET '90*, 1990, pp. 180–184.

[31] D. Gorse and J. Taylor, "Training Strategies for Probabilistic RAMs," in *Parallel Processing in Neural Systems and Computers*, North-Holland, Amsterdam, 1990, pp. 161–164.

[32] D. Gorse and J. Taylor, "A Continuous Input RAM-Based Stochastic Neural Mode," *Neural Networks*, Vol. 4, No. 5, 1991, pp. 657–665.

[33] Y. Guan et al., "Noisy Reinforcement Training for pRAM Nets," *Neural Networks*, Vol. 7, No. 3, May 1994, pp. 523–538.

[34] W. Penny, K. Gurney, and T. Stonham, "Reward-Penalty Training for Logical Neural Networks," *Proc. Int'l Conf. Artificial Intelligence, Applications and Neural Networks*, 1990, pp. 26–29.

[35] T. Hui, P. Bolouri, and K. Gurney, "VLSI Implementation of Digital Neural Network with Reward-Penalty Learning," *Proc. 3rd Int'l Workshop on VLSI for Neural Networks and Artificial Intelligence*, Oxford University, UK, 1992.

[36] T. Hui, K. Gurney, and P. Bolouri, "A Cascadable 2048-neuron VLSI Artificial Neural Network with On-Board Learning," *Proc. Int'l Conf. Artificial Neural Networks*, 1992.

[37] T.K. Hui, "Device Specification of a Stochastic RAM-Based Artificial Neural Network Chip," MSc dissertation, Dept. of Electrical Eng., Univ. of Hertfordshire, UK, 1991.

[38] T. Hui, et al., "Design of a VLSI-based Artificial Neural Network System," *IEE Colloquium on the Eurochip Project*, London, 1991.

[39] T. Hui, K. Gurney, and P. Bolouri, "A Cascadable 2048-Neuron VLSI Artificial Neural Network with On-Board Learning," *Proc. Int'l Conf. Artificial Neural Networks*, Brighton, UK, 1992.

[40] P. Morgan, "Design of a Digital, RAM-based Artificial Neural Network," BEng dissertation, Dept. of Electrical Eng., Univ. of Hertfordshire, UK, 1992.

[41] M. Robinson, "Architecture Analysis of a Digital Neural Network," BEng dissertation, Dept. of Electrical Eng., Univ. of Hertfordshire, UK, 1992.

[42] B. Bolouri and P. Morgan, "A Family of VLSI Neural Processors for Real-Time Applications," *IEE Colloquium on: Hardware implementation of Neural Networks and Fuzzy Logic*, London, 1994.

[43] H. Bolouri, M. Ohlenroth, and T. Sheen, "Intelligent Adaptive Control Using Hierarchical Neural Network Ensembles," *IEE Colloquium on: Neural Networks for Control*, London, 1994.

[44] W.W. Bledsoe and I. Browning, "Pattern Recognition and Reading Machines," *Proc. Eastern Joint Computer Conf.*, 1959, pp. 225–232.

[45] W.W. Bledsoe and C.L. Blisson, "Improved Memory Matrices for the n-tuple Pattern Recognition Method," *IRE Trans. Electronic Computers*, ED11, 1962, pp. 4,141–415.

[46] G. Hinton, D. Ackley, and T. Sejnowski, "A Learning Algorithm for Boltzmann Machines," *Cognitive Science*, Vol. 9, 1985, pp. 147–169.

[47] G. Hinton, T. Sejnowski, and D. Ackley, "Boltzmann Machines: Constraint Satisfaction Networks that Learn," Tech. Report CMU-CS-84-119, Carnegie Mellon Univ., Pittsburgh, 1984.

[48] A. Barto and M. Jordan, "Gradient Following without Back-Propagation in Layered Networks," *Proc. Int'l Conf. Neural Networks*, IEEE Press, Piscataway, N.J., 1987, pp. II.629–II.636.

[49] V. Gullapalli, "A Stochastic Algorithm for Learning Real-Valued Functions Via Reinforcement Feedback," Tech. Report 88-91, Dept. of Computer and Information Sciences, COINS, Univ. of Massachusetts, Amherst, 1988.

[50] E. Thorndike, "Animal Intelligence," *Hafner*, Darien, Conn., 1911.

[51] R. Williams, "Reinforcement Learning in Connectionist Networks: A Mathematical Analysis," Tech. Report ICS Report 8605, Cognitive Science, Univ. of California, San Diego, 1986.

[52] R. Williams, "A Class of Gradient-estimation Algorithms for Reinforcement Learning in Neural Networks," *Proc. Int'l Conf. Neural Networks*, Vol. II, IEEE Press, Piscataway, N.J., 1987, pp. II.601–II.608.

[53] R. Williams, "Reinforcement–Learning Connectionist Systems," Tech. Report NU-CCS-87-3, College of Computer Science, Northeastern Univ., Boston, 1987.

[54] M. Minsky and S. Papert, *Perceptrons: An Introduction to Computational Geometry*, MIT Press, Cambridge, Mass., 1969.

[55] B. Widrow and M. Hoff, "Adaptive Switching Circuits," *IRE Western Electric Show and Convention Record*, Part 4, 1960, pp. 96–104.

[56] D. Rumelhart, J. McClelland, and the PDP Research Group, *Parallel Distributed Processing*, MIT Press, Cambridge, Mass., 1986.

[57] D.A. Malluhi, M.A. Bayoumi, and T.R.N. Rao, "A Parallel Algorithm for Neural Computing," *Proc. World Congress on Neural Networks*, 1994.

[58] A. Krikelis, and M. Grozinger, "Implementing Neural Networks with the Associative String Processor," *Proc. Int'l Workshop on VLSI for Artificial Intelligence and Neural Networks*, Oxford Univ., UK, 1990.

[59] R.S. Neville, R. Glover, and T.J. Stonham, "Evaluation of Training Sigma-pi Networks on a Massively Parallel Processor," *Proc. World Congress on Neural Networks*, 1995.

[60] R. Neville, R.J. Glover, and J. Stonham, "Evaluation of Training & Mapping Sigma-pi Networks to a Massively Parallel Processor," *IEEE ICNN'95, Proc. Int'l Conf. Neural Networks*, IEEE Press, Piscataway, N.J., 1995, pp. 1,042–1,047.

[61] R. Neville and J. Stonham, "Adaptive Critic for Sigma-Pi Networks," *INNS: Int'l Neural Networks J.*, 1996.

About the Authors

Anargyros Krikelis is the chief scientist, a member of the management council, and one of the founding members of Aspex Microsystems and is responsible for applications development and system specification and implementation. His research interests are associative massively parallel computer architectures, applications of massively parallel computation, programming methods and tools for parallel architectures, parallelizing compilers, and neural computation.

Krikelis received a Diploma of Electrical Engineering and Electronics from University of Patras (Greece) and MSc and PhD degrees from the Department of Electrical Engineering and Electronics of Brunel University, United Kingdom. He is the author of over 35 contributions to international conferences, journals, and books. He was the guest editor for a special issue on neural computing on massively parallel processors in the *Journal of Parallel and Distributed Computing*, March 1992. He is a member of the IEEE Computer Society.

Charles C. Weems directs the Parallel Image-Understanding Architectures research group at the University of Massachusetts, where he is an associate professor. His research interests include associative processing and architectures, parallel architectures to support low-, intermediate-, and high-level computer vision, benchmarks for vision, heterogeneous parallel architectures, heterogeneous parallel programming languages, architectural issues and hardware support for hard real-time systems, theory of parallel algorithms and architectures, and parallel vision algorithms.

Weems received BS and MA degrees in computer science from Oregon State University in 1977 and 1979, respectively, and a PhD degree in computer science from the University of Massachusetts at Amherst in 1984. He has authored numerous technical articles and coauthored three widely used introductory computer science texts. Weems is a member of the IEEE, the IEEE Computer Society, ACM, and the IAPR Technical Committee on special-purpose architectures.

IEEE Computer Society Publications

The world-renowned Computer Society publishes, promotes, and distributes a wide variety of authoritative computer science and engineering texts. These books are available in two formats: 100 percent original material by authors preeminent in their field who focus on relevant topics and cutting-edge research, and reprint collections consisting of carefully selected groups of previously published papers with accompanying original introductory and explanatory text.

Submission of proposals: For guidelines and information on Computer Society books, send e-mail to cs.books@computer.org or write to the Acquisitions Editor, IEEE Computer Society, P.O. Box 3014, 10662 Los Vaqueros Circle, Los Alamitos, CA 90720-1314. Telephone +1 714-821-8380. FAX +1 714-761-1784.

IEEE Computer Society Proceedings

The Computer Society also produces and actively promotes the proceedings of more than 130 acclaimed international conferences each year in multimedia formats that include hard and softcover books, CD-ROMs, videos, and on-line publications.

For information on Computer Society proceedings, send e-mail to cs.books@computer.org or write to Proceedings, IEEE Computer Society, P.O. Box 3014, 10662 Los Vaqueros Circle, Los Alamitos, CA 90720-1314. Telephone +1 714-821-8380. FAX +1 714-761-1784.

Additional information regarding the Computer Society, conferences and proceedings, CD-ROMs, videos, and books can also be accessed from our web site at http://computer.org/cspress

4/15/97